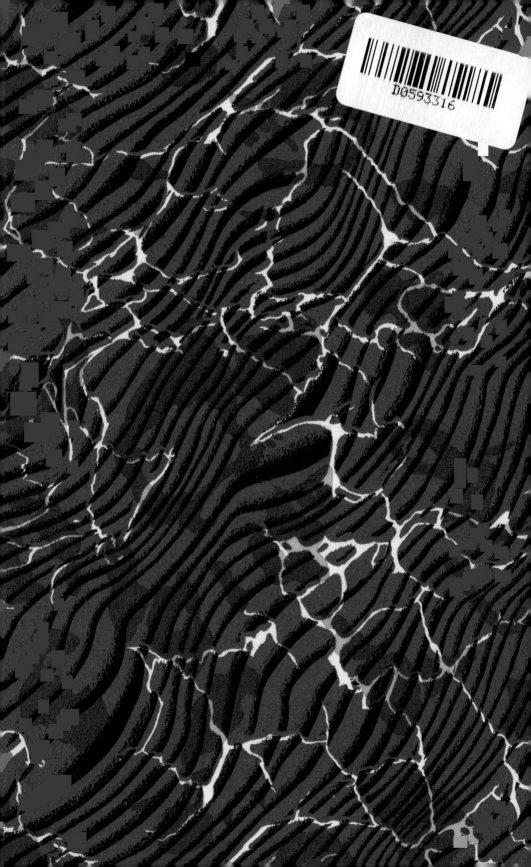

CLASSICS Appreciation SOCIETY

CRIME AND PUNISHMENT
by Fyodor Dostoevski

THE DIARY OF SAMUEL PEPYS

THE CONFESSIONS OF SAINT AUGUSTINE

PARADISE LOST
by John Milton

and

A Passion in the Desert
BY HONORÉ DE BALZAC

AARON BURR'S
*Letter Challenging Alexander
Hamilton to a Duel*

JAMES OTIS
Argues Against the Writs of Assistance

CLASSICS Appreciation SOCIETY
CONDENSATIONS

CONTENTS

Each Home Course Appreciation precedes its work.
ILLUSTRATED BY WILLIAM SHARP

CONTENTS

CRIME AND PUNISHMENT

by
Fyodor Dostoevski

TRANSLATED BY
Constance Garnett

A CONDENSATION

NOTE: *The editor's summaries of various omitted passages*
appear italicized and in brackets throughout the text.

The Main Characters

RODION RASKOLNIKOV, *familiarly known as Rodya, an ex-student.*

PULCHERIA RASKOLNIKOV, *his mother.*

DOUNIA RASKOLNIKOV, *his sister.*

SEMYON MARMELADOV, *an ex-clerk.*

KATERINA MARMELADOV, *his wife.*

SONIA MARMELADOV, *their daughter.*

PYOTR LUZHIN, *a middle-aged lawyer, engaged to Dounia.*

RAZUMIHIN, *a friend of Raskolnikov.*

SVIDRIGAILOV, *a landlord.*

ZAMETOV
ILYA PETROVITCH } *police officers.*
PORFIRY PETROVITCH

ALYONA IVANOVNA, *an old pawnbroker woman.*

LIZAVETA, *her sister.*

HOME COURSE APPRECIATION

O N A GLOOMY DECEMBER DAY in the year 1849, fifteen political prisoners were dragged from the imperial dungeons into the frosty air of Semenov Square in St. Petersburg. Their hands were tied behind them and white, shroudlike garments were pulled over their heads. After the prisoners were fastened to heavy posts, extreme unction was administered by a priest. The firing squad marched out and the death sentence was read aloud. The commands were shouted: "Ready! Aim!"—and then, at the last conceivable second, a carefully planted messenger burst upon the scene, waving an official pardon. By the "mercy" of the Czar, the death sentence had been commuted to exile in Siberia.

One prisoner went mad as soon as the bandage was taken from his eyes. But another lived to become one of Russia's greatest novelists. He was Fyodor Dostoevski, twenty-eight when he stood bareheaded and trembling in Semenov Square. Seventeen years later he was to write *Crime and Punishment,* one of the world's most famous novels.

What made the mock-execution even more ghastly for Dostoevski was that he was completely innocent of the dark crimes charged against him. From the first, he had been nervous and moody, a complete misfit in the profession which had been selected for him (he was educated to be a military engineer) and a social misfit as well. His physical inheritance was bad, too. His mother had died of consumption, his father was an alcoholic and he himself was afflicted by epilepsy.

The years of imprisonment and enforced military service in Siberia cut deeply into Dostoevski's consciousness. They accentuated his naturally dark view of life and provided many rich and terrible themes for his later writing. Foremost among them was guilt—guilt arising from a shameful, nameless crime, guilt from a sin so vague that it could be atoned for only by a lifetime of suffering. Dostoevski is a poet of the inarticulate, the downtrodden, the anguished and the ecstatically religious. His art is the art of nightmare.

CHILDHOOD EXPERIENCES OF DOSTOEVSKI

Dostoevski's career is exciting simply in the telling. He was born in 1821, Fyodor Mikhailovitch, the second son of an army doctor with a small practice and great pretensions to gentility. In 1830 his father bought an estate in the country, not far from Moscow. There he intended to set himself up as a squire and a man of property; and there quite by accident young Dostoevski had an experience that profoundly influenced his future attitudes and beliefs.

Walking in the woods one day, he heard the terrifying cry "Wolf!" He shrieked and ran as fast as he could to a nearby field where a peasant was plowing. All his life Dostoevski was to remember how the peasant, a thickset, stolid man of fifty or so, soothed him and with an earth-stained finger softly touched the boy's twitching lips. "Come, come, there," he said with a soft smile. "Christ be with you, little one! Cross yourself! There is no wolf." Many years later when he was imprisoned in Siberia with the very dregs of Russia, Dostoevski remembered this scene from his childhood and was able to love and understand even his sodden cellmates, for the sake of the peasant Marey.

Dostoevski's father, unlike his son, was that type of hard-fisted yet weak-willed manager whom the peasants hated. He drank uncontrollably and was cruel when drunk. One day when he stopped on a ride over the estate to rebuke some of his workers, the peasants banded together and beat him to death with their shovels. The murder was quickly hushed up, but Dostoevski learned of it and it troubled him greatly.

AN ARMY ENGINEER AND, SUDDENLY, A NOVELIST

THE BUSINESS OF LIFE AND SCHOOLING went badly for the young Dostoevski. His mother died during his early adolescence and the family fortunes were guided for a while by rough and unsympathetic uncles. The family's decision to enroll him in a course in army engineering proves clearly that Fyodor was never understood by them. He hated the army and all forms of mass discipline; he passed his

Fyodor Dostoevski,
1821–1881.

examinations only by cramming, and forgot at once everything he had crammed. When he finally presented a design as his final graduation project, the judges noted with some amazement that he had laid out an elaborate fortress without providing any windows or doors. He received his commission anyhow.

The writing of fiction was from the beginning Fyodor's natural talent. And before he had a story published or had any assured income, he resigned the commission which had cost him five long years of meaningless toil, in the hope of finishing a novel and establishing himself. Fortune was with him. One spring evening in 1845, the manuscript found its way to the desk of a young poet and editor, Alexey Nekrasov. Nekrasov stayed up all night reading *Poor Folk,* and at four o'clock in the morning, he rushed to the young author's apartment to proclaim his genius. Within a few days, Nekrasov's praise was echoed by V. G. Belinsky, an impeccable critic and the leader of a liberal intellectual circle.

DOSTOEVSKI'S FIRST NOVELS

The success of *Poor Folk* made Dostoevski famous but it did not make him rich. The Russian publishing industry was in its infancy, the reading public was small, and royalties were carelessly administered. And so Dostoevski had to mortgage himself by accepting payments in advance for pieces he had not yet written. In feverish haste he dashed off a short novel entitled *The Double*. But then his vein ran dry. He dabbled unsuccessfully in journalism and cheap pulp stories and joined the Petrashevski group to discuss political reforms. The meetings of this group led to his arrest in 1849.

In neither of his first two novels did Dostoevski find an adequate form for his themes. *Poor Folk* concerns a downtrodden copying clerk who writes long-winded, self-pitying letters to a sad young lady. Dostoevski was interested in the twistings and turnings of his hero's mind—a striking departure from previous Russian fiction. But the letter-form of the book is so undramatic and the characters so colorless that the story carries little impact for the modern reader.

Dostoevski's second novel, *The Double,* was a bolder but less successful effort. This time a humble clerk is tormented by the desire for glory and public esteem. But after being rejected, he comes upon a man who resembles him in every way, who has even the same name, yet who can achieve all the brilliant successes of which the clerk only dreams. Eventually the double usurps the victim's whole existence and drives him insane. The clerk and his double are mechanical expressions of Dostoevski's impulse to concern himself with split personalities. The story is too long in the telling and is marred by unskilled mixing of hallucination with reality, but Dostoevski had laid hold of a powerful new theme. Though he handled it poorly on this first attempt, it would recur in his finest novels, molded by the hand of a master.

A LIFE OF SORROW AND DISORDER

FOR MANY MEN, THE EXPERIENCE OF SIBERIA would have been utterly crushing. They would have returned bitter and rebellious. But Dostoevski, who had gone away a liberal, returned a thoroughgoing conservative. He wrote one completely objective book about Siberia, *The House of the Dead* (1858), which was the most popular of his works throughout his life. Dostoevski took his outrageous punishment as if he thought he had actually been guilty of some crime against the Little White Father, Czar Nicholas. Perhaps in some remote corner of his mind he felt that his wishes for reform might actually have concealed revolutionary designs. In any event, he assumed a terrible burden of guilt.

"He pulled the ax out, swung it with both arms . . . and . . . brought the blunt side down on her head."

Psychologists who have studied his life have thought it no accident that his epileptic seizures began to recur with special frequency immediately after his return from Siberia. Often they occurred directly after some reminder of death, such as passing a coffin in the street or hearing of the death of Belinsky, who had been like a father to him.

For a time, however, Dostoevski was entirely preoccupied in the struggle to make a living with his pen for the people dependent on him. He had returned from Siberia with a wife who was slowly dying of tuberculosis. When his brother Mikhail died in 1864, he assumed responsibility for his brother's widow and children. He founded a magazine, which flourished for several months as he wrote almost every issue singlehandedly. But finally, burdened with debts, he discontinued the review.

Overwhelmed by his responsibilities, Dostoevski went abroad in 1863 with a beautiful girl named Polina Suslova, who loved him yet repeatedly betrayed him. Perhaps it was because of her that he lost the last of his money on the gambling tables at Baden-Baden. He borrowed and reborrowed; on one occasion he signed a contract with an unscrupulous publisher to produce a novel by a specific date. If he failed to do so, the publisher would acquire, free of royalties, everything that Dostoevski might write for the next nine years! That novel, called *The Gambler,* was turned out in just twenty-six days.

Yet working under these pressures, Dostoevski somehow managed to produce two magnificent novels. The first was a somewhat untidy but ingenious exploration of a perverse and defeated personality, which appeared under the title of *Letters from the Underworld* in 1864. The second was *Crime and Punishment* in 1866. The early themes of his writing recur in these stories, but they are broadened, strengthened and dramatized by the power of a brooding imagination.

With the creation of *Crime and Punishment,* Dostoevski's life gradually became easier. In 1867 after his wife died, he married his secretary, Anna Grigorevna. A woman of strong character and good sense, she successfully mothered him, pacified his creditors and provided him with a peaceful family life. Thereafter he wrote unceasingly those huge rhapsodic novels that have so often been compared to the last acts of a vast tragedy: *The Idiot* (1869), *The Possessed* (1871), *A Raw Youth* (1875) and *The Brothers Karamazov* (1881). He had just completed this last novel when he died of a consumptive hemorrhage in January 1881. By this time, he was already famous throughout the world and his funeral occasioned a stirring public ovation.

"We will go to suffer together, and together we will bear our
  cross!"

A NOVELIST HAUNTED BY HIS OWN CREATION

THE STORY OF HOW "CRIME AND PUNISHMENT" was written is a saga of wretchedness. During the latter months of 1865, Dostoevski, a recent widower, was torn between two unhappy love affairs; he was lonely, miserably poor and debt-ridden, racked by frequent epileptic seizures and recurrent fever. He sold his books, pawned his clothes, squeezed from his friends every ruble he could beg or borrow. But day and night, with every ounce of flagging energy, he forced himself to write. A story is told that a servant was assigned to sit up with Dostoevski at night in the event of a fit. One day the fellow refused to do so any more on the grounds that Dostoevski had murder on his mind and talked of nothing else all night long.

Originally the book was conceived as a short novel on the horrors of drink, a topic worked into the completed novel in the form of the story of the Marmeladov family. But as soon as Raskolnikov entered the author's mind, the basic character of the story shifted. It became truly a story of murder and remorse, of crime and punishment. Dostoevski started to write it in the form of a confession made by the murderer; next he cast it as a diary kept by the murderer in the days just after his crime. But when these forms cramped his style, he did not hesitate to cast his work ruthlessly aside and start over again. Forgotten was the pressure to finish the novel, no matter in what form. When it started to live its own life, everything had to give way before it. Dostoevski wrote it in installments, with the printers waiting almost at his shoulder to snatch fresh sheets away to the presses, and creditors and dependents making chaos of the few hours he could snatch from his drudgery.

The novel, told in the third person, focuses upon the complex, divided figure of the ex-student Raskolnikov. He is a figure with a long literary history, this elegant, poverty-stricken intellectual. In the world of literature, he belongs with that class of angry, hope-haunted young men who are ambitious yet spiritual, who scorn the world yet long to be accepted by it. He is like a romantic figure out of Byron or Stendhal or Schiller. His soul is the center of the novel, and its most perplexing problem.

THE CROOKED CORRIDORS OF RASKOLNIKOV'S HEART

WHY DID RASKOLNIKOV COMMIT THE GRUESOME MURDERS of the old pawnbroker woman and her sister Lizaveta? Far from a lack of motives, the question confronts us with an excess of them. Many readers have thought it helped their understanding of the novel to call Raskolnikov mad; but certainly this was far from Dostoevski's intent. His hero is undoubtedly morbid, but the theory of madness is, at best, a last resort, because it reduces the whole novel to a clinical study instead of a dramatically moving work of art. One thing is clear: Raskolnikov's motives are extremely complex—and contradictory.

In the first place, he evidently intends to do good with the money he gets by the murders. His family is impoverished because he has contributed nothing to their support. His sister is about to marry the despicable Luzhin for money; his mother is in despair, and he, before his career is even launched, seems stranded for lack of rubles. Should he do "a very little evil" in order that a great deal of good might come of it? We cannot doubt that there is a great deal of benevolence in Raskolnikov's soul. We see that he gives freely of his meager funds to aid the Marmeladovs; he is indignant over his sister Dounia's plan to marry Luzhin; and he is deeply sympathetic with the wretched Sonia. Furthermore, we note that he does not use the money which he gains by his crime to alleviate his own misery.

Another side of his character is revealed in his division of mankind into slaves and masters. The slaves are servile, vulgar souls who reproduce their kind and yet have no other real purpose in the world. The masters, however, like Napoleon, have great ends to attain and often must destroy the slaves to achieve them. Raskolnikov naturally considers himself a master. He has been infected with rationalist, nihilist ideas from the west. His crime is scorn of humanity, the urge to live his life rationally and mechanically in defiance of human brotherhood. He would like to be a superman, such as Napoleon was and such as the German philosopher Nietzsche wanted men to be. He is "young, abstract and therefore cruel."

A MAN DIVIDED AGAINST HIMSELF

THUS CHRISTIAN CHARITY AND RATIONAL CRUELTY form the two halves of Raskolnikov. But under his own searching analysis and that of Porfiry, the police inspector, one part is destroyed and the personality is made whole. Raskolnikov decides for himself that he is no Napoleon; he is merely an "aesthetic louse." He tells Sonia that he killed simply to see if he could get away with it.

Then what motive impelled him? No one motive is singled out. Actually Raskolnikov probably murdered the women for all of them:

"Porfiry Petrovitch screwed up his eyes . . . a good-humored,
crafty look passed over his face."

to prove his theories, to gain a little money, to prove he had the courage to commit the crime and the cleverness to avoid the punishment.

Strangely, Dostoevski seems to have shared some of Raskolnikov's tortured sentiments. In his notebooks, beside the passage where Raskolnikov delves deeply into the heart of darkness where man blasphemes against humanity itself, Dostoevski wrote: "Devil take it! He is partly right!"

Raskolnikov, even in his blackest mood, *is* partly right in that he seems to be striving for righteousness; it is the means he uses to gain his ends that shock and perturb us. There is something Nazi-like in his disregard for human lives. But once Raskolnikov's deeply grounded religious faith begins working, the rebel wonders if he ever had a cause. It is then we begin to see the full extent of Raskolnikov's double personality: he is a Christian beneath his veneer of scientific rationalism and he is a profound moralist in spite of his sins.

Crime and Punishment is a detective story in the classic sense, but it is different from the ordinary "whodunit" in that the criminal is his own investigator. The police never have any evidence on which to convict him unless he gives it to them. But through those twisting monologues that distinguish the novel, Raskolnikov becomes his own investigator, judge and executioner.

MEMBERS OF THE SUPPORTING CAST

Of the other characters, Porfiry, the inspector, is especially effective. He overflows with humor, teases and insinuates, and acts more like a father confessor than a traditional sleuth. He delivers one great message of the novel when he says to Raskolnikov, "I regard you as one of those men who would stand and smile at their torturer while he cuts their entrails out, if only they have found faith or God. Find it and you will live. . . . Suffering, too, is a good thing. Suffer!"

Sonia the prostitute, though she often seems an abstraction of meekness, also helps Raskolnikov find himself. Her rather exaggerated patience and submission become more understandable when her religious zeal is fired later in the novel and she kindles the murderer with a shame for his crime.

Dounia and Razumihin bring the sunshine of normality to a world of midnight shadows. Yet their chatter recedes when Raskolnikov appears; the price they pay for being well adjusted is to lack perception. Svidrigailov is impressive as a reckless sensualist but his suicide shows that he too was sicker mentally than anyone had imagined. The lawyer Luzhin is especially contemptible because his schemings, unlike the hero's, are too clever to be punished by any man-made laws.

THE ART OF WAKING NIGHTMARE

DOSTOEVSKI'S GENIUS IS NOT PRIMARILY NARRATIVE; his art is one of character portrayal, motivation and analysis. As a record of what happens during thirty days following a murder, *Crime and Punishment* is bound to seem distorted. Characters appear and disappear before the feverish eyes of the hero, and when he is not aware of them, we have not the faintest idea what they are doing. Melodrama is evoked, as when Dounia shoots at Svidrigailov from six paces, and misses. Coincidences are overstrained: people turn up just when they are needed to take part in a scene; they overhear important pieces of conversation; they never have any conflicting business or social obligations outside the analysis of Raskolnikov's uneasy conscience. As a picture of outside reality, *Crime and Punishment* would never have become a classic.

The novel is great because it tells of a great adventure in the human heart, a terrible and wonderful experience of the power of evil and the glory of redemption. Many a hack writer has told a neater story or constructed a better-organized sequence of incidents. We may not think it artistic to introduce a major character like Marmeladov, give him one long speech and a bit of action, and then kill him off. But for Dostoevski, Marmeladov is an incident in Raskolnikov's nightmare, which has no fixed and orderly structure. Things stream together in Raskolnikov's disordered brain; reality blurs with fantasy. Svidrigailov's remark that Raskolnikov needs some fresh air is echoed, without any explanation, by Porfiry. After Porfiry asks Raskolnikov if he believes that Lazarus really rose from the dead, Sonia is made to read the story of Lazarus aloud.

These threads and wisps of coincidence have nothing to do with the "real" world as the unimaginative person sees it. But Dostoevski had his own inner eye for a kind of reality which lay deeper than appearances. "I have my own special view on reality in art," he wrote to a friend. "What the majority call almost fantastic and exceptional sometimes signifies for me the very essence of reality."

Crime and Punishment is a fantasia, but a fantasia more real than the world of statistics and social averages. It is a rhapsody on the tremendous themes of guilt and redemption, and one of the most powerful works of fiction ever written.

PART ONE

ON AN EXCEPTIONALLY hot evening early in July a young man came out of the garret in which he lodged and walked slowly, as though in hesitation, towards a bridge.

He had successfully avoided meeting his landlady on the staircase. His garret was under the roof of a high, five-storied house and was more like a cupboard than a room. The landlady who provided him with garret, dinners, and attendance, lived on the floor below, and every time he went out he was obliged to pass her kitchen, the door of which invariably stood open. And each time he passed, the young man had a sick, frightened feeling, which made him scowl and feel ashamed. He was hopelessly in debt to his landlady, and was afraid of meeting her.

This was not because he was cowardly and abject, quite the contrary; but for some time past he had been in an overstrained irritable condition, verging on hypochondria. He had become so completely absorbed in himself, and isolated from his fellows that he dreaded meeting not only his landlady but any one at all. He was crushed by poverty, but the anxieties of his position had of late ceased to weigh upon him. He had given up attending to matters of practical importance; he had lost all desire to do so. Nothing that any landlady could do had a real terror for him. But to be stopped on the stairs, to be forced to listen to her trivial, irrelevant gossip, to pestering demands for payment, threats and complaints, and to rack his brains for excuses, to prevaricate, to lie—no, rather than that, he would creep down the stairs like a cat and slip out unseen.

This evening, however, on coming out into the street, he became acutely aware of his fears.

"I want to attempt a thing *like that* and am frightened by these trifles," he thought, with an odd smile. "Hm . . . yes, all is in a man's hands and he lets it all slip from cowardice; that's an axiom. It would be interesting to know what it is men are most afraid of. Taking a new step, uttering a new word is what they fear most. . . . But I am talking too much. It's because I chatter that I do nothing. Or perhaps it is that I chatter because I do nothing. I've learned to chatter this last month, lying for days together in my den thinking . . . of Jack the Giant-killer. Why am I going there now? Am I capable of *that?* Is *that* serious? It is not serious at all. It's simply a fantasy to amuse myself; a plaything! Yes, maybe it is a plaything."

The heat in the street was terrible: and the airlessness, the bustle and the plaster, scaffolding, bricks, and dust all about him, and that special St. Petersburg * stench, so familiar to all who are unable to get out of town in summer—all worked painfully upon the young man's already overwrought nerves. The insufferable stench from the alehouses, which are particularly numerous in that part of the town, and the drunken men whom he met continually, although it was a working day, completed the revolting misery of the picture. An expression of the profoundest disgust gleamed for a moment in the young man's refined face. He was, by the way, exceptionally handsome, above the average in height, slim, well-built, with beautiful dark eyes and dark-brown hair. Soon he sank into deep thought, or more accurately speaking into a complete blankness of mind; he walked along not observing what was about him and not caring to observe it. From time to time, he would mutter something, from the habit of talking to himself, to which he had just confessed. At these moments he would become conscious that his ideas were sometimes in a tangle and that he was very weak; for two days he had scarcely tasted food.

He was so badly dressed that even a man accustomed to shabbiness would have been ashamed to be seen in the street in such rags. In that quarter of the town, however, scarcely any shortcoming in dress would have created surprise. Owing to the proximity of the Hay Market, the number of establishments of bad character, the preponderance of the trading and working class population crowded in these

* Now Leningrad

streets and alleys in the heart of Petersburg, types so various were to be seen in the streets that no figure, however queer, would have caused surprise. But there was such accumulated bitterness and contempt in the young man's heart, that, in spite of all the fastidiousness of youth, he minded his rags least of all in the street. It was a different matter when he met with acquaintances or with former fellow students, whom, indeed, he disliked meeting at any time. And yet when a drunken man who, for some unknown reason, was being taken somewhere in a huge wagon dragged by a heavy dray horse, suddenly shouted at him as he drove past: "Hey there, German hatter!" bawling at the top of his voice and pointing at him—the young man stopped suddenly and clutched tremulously at his hat. It was a tall round hat of good style, but completely worn out, rusty with age, all torn and bespattered, brimless and bent on one side in a most unseemly fashion. Not shame, however, but quite another feeling akin to terror had overtaken him.

"I knew it," he muttered in confusion, "I thought so! That's the worst of all! Why, a stupid thing like this, the most trivial detail might spoil the whole plan. Yes, my hat is too noticeable. . . . It looks absurd and that makes it noticeable. . . . With my rags I ought to wear a cap, any sort of old pancake, but not this grotesque thing. Nobody wears such a hat, it would be noticed a mile off, it would be remembered. . . . What matters is that people would remember it, and that would give them a clue. For this business one should be as little conspicuous as possible. . . . Trifles, trifles are what matter! Why, it's just such trifles that always ruin everything. . . ."

He had not far to go; he knew indeed how many steps it was from the gate of his lodging house: exactly seven hundred and thirty. He had counted them once when he had been lost in dreams. At the time he had put no faith in those dreams and was only tantalizing himself by their hideous but daring recklessness. Now, a month later, he had begun to look upon them differently, and, in spite of the monologues in which he jeered at his own impotence and indecision, he had involuntarily come to regard this "hideous" dream as an exploit to be attempted, although he still did not realize this himself. He was positively going now for a "rehearsal" of his project, and at every step his excitement grew more and more violent.

With a sinking heart and a nervous tremor, he went up to a huge house which on one side looked onto the canal, and on the other into the street. This house was let out in tiny tenements and was inhabited

5

by working people of all kinds—tailors, locksmiths, cooks, Germans of sorts, girls picking up a living as best they could, petty clerks, and so on. There was a continual coming and going through the two gates and in the two courtyards of the house. Three or four door-keepers were employed on the building. The young man was very glad to meet none of them, and at once slipped unnoticed through the door on the right, and up the staircase. It was a back staircase, dark and narrow, but he was familiar with it already, and knew his way, and he liked all these surroundings: in such darkness even the most inquisitive eyes were not to be dreaded.

"If I am so scared now, what would it be if it somehow came to pass that I were really going to do it?" he could not help asking himself as he reached the fourth story. There his progress was barred by some porters who were engaged in moving furniture out of a flat. He knew that the flat had been occupied by a German clerk in the civil service and his family. This German was moving out then, and so the fourth floor on this staircase would be untenanted except by the old woman. "That's a good thing anyway," he thought to himself, as he rang the bell of the old woman's flat. The bell gave a faint tinkle as though it were made of tin and not of copper. The little flats in such houses always have bells that ring like that. He had forgotten the note of that bell, and now its peculiar tinkle seemed to remind him of something and to bring it clearly before him. . . . He started, his nerves were terribly overstrained by now. In a little while, the door was opened a tiny crack: the old woman eyed her visitor with evident distrust through the crack and nothing could be seen but her little eyes glittering in the darkness. But, seeing a number of people on the landing, she grew bolder and opened the door wide. The young man stepped into the dark entry, which was partitioned off from the tiny kitchen. The old woman stood facing him in silence and looking inquiringly at him. She was a diminutive, withered old woman of sixty, with sharp malignant eyes and a sharp little nose. Her colorless, somewhat grizzled hair was thickly smeared with oil and she wore no kerchief over it. Round her thin long neck, which looked like a hen's leg, was knotted some sort of flannel rag, and, in spite of the heat, there hung flapping on her shoulders a mangy fur cape, yellow with age. The old woman coughed and groaned at every instant. The young man must have looked at her with a rather peculiar expression, for a gleam of mistrust came into her eyes again.

"Raskolnikov, a student, I came here a month ago," the young man made haste to mutter, with a half bow, remembering that he ought to be more polite.

"I remember, my good sir, I remember quite well your coming here," the old woman said distinctly, still keeping her inquiring eyes on his face.

"And here . . . I am again on the same errand," Raskolnikov continued, a little disconcerted and surprised at the old woman's mistrust. "Perhaps she is always like that though, only I did not notice it the other time," he thought with an uneasy feeling.

The old woman paused, as though hesitating; then stepped on one side, and pointing to the door of the room, she said, letting her visitor pass in front of her, "Step in, my good sir."

The little room into which the young man walked, with yellow paper on the walls, geraniums and muslin curtains in the windows, was brightly lighted up at that moment by the setting sun.

"So the sun will shine like this *then* too!" flashed as it were by chance through Raskolnikov's mind, and with a rapid glance he scanned everything in the room, trying as far as possible to notice and remember its arrangement. But there was nothing special in the room. The furniture, all very old and of yellow wood, consisted of a sofa with a huge bent wooden back, an oval table in front of the sofa, a dressing table with a looking-glass fixed on it between the windows, chairs along the walls, and two or three halfpenny prints in yellow frames, representing German damsels with birds in their hands —that was all. In the corner a light was burning before a small icon. Everything was very clean; the floor and the furniture were brightly polished; everything shone.

"Her sister Lizaveta's work," thought the young man. There was not a speck of dust to be seen in the whole flat.

"It's in the houses of spiteful old widows that one finds such cleanliness," Raskolnikov thought again, and he stole a curious glance at the cotton curtain over the door leading into another tiny room, in which stood the old woman's bed and chest of drawers and into which he had never looked before. These two rooms made up the whole flat.

"What do you want?" the old woman said severely, coming into the room and, as before, standing in front of him so as to look him straight in the face.

"I've brought something to pawn here," and he drew out of his pocket an old-fashioned flat silver watch, on the back of which was engraved a globe; the chain was of steel.

7

"But the time is up for your last pledge. The month was up the day before yesterday."

"I will bring you the interest for another month; wait a little."

"But that's for me to do as I please, my good sir, to wait or to sell your pledge at once."

"How much will you give me for the watch, Alyona Ivanovna?"

"You come with such trifles, my good sir, it's scarcely worth anything. I gave you two rubles last time for your ring and one could buy it quite new at a jeweler's for a ruble and a half."

"Give me four rubles for it. I shall redeem it. It was my father's. I shall be getting some money soon."

"A ruble and a half, and interest in advance, if you like!"

"A ruble and a half!" cried the young man.

"Please yourself." The old woman handed him back the watch. The young man took it, and was so angry that he was on the point of going away; but checked himself at once, remembering that there was nowhere else he could go, and that he had had another object also in coming.

"Hand it over," he said roughly.

The old woman fumbled in her pocket for her keys and disappeared behind the curtain into the other room. The young man, left standing alone in the middle of the room, listened inquisitively, thinking. He could hear her unlocking the chest of drawers.

"It must be the top drawer," he reflected. "So she carries the keys in a pocket on the right. All in one bunch on a steel ring. . . . And there's one key there, three times as big as all the others, with deep notches; that can't be the key of the chest of drawers . . . then there must be some other chest or strongbox . . . that's worth knowing. Strongboxes always have keys like that . . . but how degrading it all is."

The old woman came back.

"Here, sir: as we say ten kopecks for a ruble a month, so I must take fifteen kopecks from a ruble and a half for the month in advance. But for the two rubles I lent you before, you owe me now twenty kopecks on the same reckoning in advance. That makes thirty-five kopecks altogether. So I must give you a ruble and fifteen kopecks for the watch. Here it is."

"What! only a ruble and fifteen kopecks now!"

"Just so."

The young man did not dispute it and took the money. He looked

8

at the old woman, and was in no hurry to get away, as though there was still something he wanted to say or to do, but he did not himself quite know what.

"I may be bringing you something else in a day or two, Alyona Ivanovna—a valuable thing—silver—a cigarette box, as soon as I get it back from a friend . . ." he broke off in confusion.

"Well, we will talk about it then, sir."

"Good-by. Are you always at home alone, your sister is not here with you?" he asked her as casually as possible as he went out into the passage.

"What business is she of yours, my good sir?"

"Oh, nothing particular. I simply asked. You are too quick. . . . Good day, Alyona Ivanovna."

Raskolnikov went out in complete confusion. This confusion became more and more intense. As he went down the stairs, he even stopped short two or three times, as though suddenly struck by some thought. When he was in the street he cried out, "Oh, God, how loathsome it all is! and can I, can I possibly. . . . No, it's nonsense, it's rubbish!" he added resolutely. "And how could such an atrocious thing come into my head? What filthy things my heart is capable of. Yes, filthy above all, disgusting, loathsome, loathsome! . . . and for a whole month I've been . . ." But no words, no exclamations, could express his agitation. The feeling of intense repulsion which had begun to oppress and torture his heart while he was on his way to the old woman had by now reached such a pitch and had taken such a definite form that he did not know what to do with himself to escape from his wretchedness. He walked along the pavement like a drunken man, regardless of the passers-by, jostling against them, and only came to his senses when he was in the next street. Looking around, he noticed that he was standing close to a tavern which was entered by steps leading from the pavement to the basement. At that instant two drunken men came out of the door, and abusing and supporting one another, they mounted the steps. Without stopping to think, Raskolnikov went down the steps at once. Till that moment he had never been in a tavern, but now he felt giddy and was tormented by a burning thirst. He longed for a drink of cold beer, and attributed his sudden weakness to the want of food. He sat down at a sticky little table in a dark and dirty corner, ordered some beer and eagerly drank off the first glassful. At once he felt easier and his thoughts became clear.

"All that's nonsense," he said hopefully, "and there is nothing in it to worry about! It's simply physical derangement. Just a glass of beer, a piece of dry bread—and in one moment the brain is stronger, the mind is clearer and the will is firm! Phew, how utterly petty it all is!"

*   *   *

THERE ARE chance meetings with strangers that interest us from the first moment, before a word is spoken. Such was the impression made on Raskolnikov by the person sitting a little distance from him, who looked like a retired clerk. The young man often recalled this impression afterward, and even ascribed it to presentiment. He looked repeatedly at the clerk, partly no doubt because the latter was staring persistently at him, obviously anxious to enter into conversation. At the other persons in the room, including the tavernkeeper, the clerk looked as though he were used to their company and weary of it, showing a shade of condescending contempt for them as persons of station and culture inferior to his own, with whom it would be useless for him to converse. He was a man over fifty, bald and grizzled, of medium height and stoutly built. His face, bloated from continual drinking, was of a yellow, even greenish, tinge, with swollen eyelids out of which keen reddish eyes gleamed like little chinks. But there was something very strange in him: there was a light in his eyes as though of intense feeling—perhaps there were even thought and intelligence, but at the same time there was a gleam of something like madness. He was wearing an old and hopelessly ragged black dress coat, with all its buttons missing except one, and that one he had buttoned, evidently clinging to this last trace of respectability. A crumpled shirt front covered with spots and stains protruded from his canvas waistcoat. Like a clerk, he wore no beard, nor mustache, but had been so long unshaven that his chin looked like a stiff grayish brush; there was something respectable and like an official about his manner too. But he was restless; he ruffled up his hair and from time to time let his head drop into his hands dejectedly resting his ragged elbows on the stained and sticky table. At last he looked straight at Raskolnikov, and said loudly and resolutely:

"May I venture, honored sir, to engage you in polite conversation? Forasmuch as, though your exterior would not command respect, my

10

experience admonishes me that you are a man of education and not accustomed to drinking. I have always respected education when in conjunction with genuine sentiments, and I am besides a titular counselor in rank. Marmeladov—such is my name; titular counselor. I make bold to inquire—have you been in the service?"

"No, I am studying," answered the young man somewhat surprised at the grandiloquent style of the speaker and also at being so directly addressed. In spite of the momentary desire he had just been feeling for company of any sort, on being actually spoken to he felt immediately his habitual irritable and uneasy aversion for any stranger who approached or attempted to approach him.

"A student then, or formerly a student," cried the clerk. "Just what I thought! I'm a man of experience, immense experience, sir," and he tapped his forehead with his fingers in self-approval. "You've been a student or have attended some learned institution! . . . But allow me. . . ." He got up, staggered, took up his jug and glass, and sat down beside the young man, facing him a little sideways. He was drunk, but spoke fluently and boldly, only occasionally losing the thread of his sentences and drawling his words. He pounced upon Raskolnikov as greedily as though he too had not spoken to a soul for a month.

"Honored sir," he began almost with solemnity, "poverty is not a vice, that's a true saying. Yet I know too that drunkenness is not a virtue, and that that's even truer. But beggary, honored sir, beggary is a vice. In poverty you may still retain your innate nobility of soul, but in beggary—never—no one. For beggary a man is not chased out of human society with a stick, he is swept out with a broom, so as to make it as humiliating as possible; and quite right too, forasmuch as in beggary I am ready to be the first to humiliate myself. Hence the alehouse! Honored sir, a month ago Mr. Lebeziatnikov gave my wife a beating, and my wife is a very different matter from me! Do you understand? Allow me to ask you another question out of simple curiosity: have you ever spent a night on a hay barge on the River Neva?"

"No, I have not done so," answered Raskolnikov. "What do you mean?"

"Well, I've just come from one and it's the fifth night I've slept so. . . ." He filled his glass, emptied it and paused. Bits of hay were in fact clinging to his clothes and sticking to his hair. It seemed quite probable that he had not undressed or washed for the last five days.

His hands, particularly, were filthy. They were fat and red, with black nails.

His conversation seemed to excite a general though languid interest. The boys at the counter fell to sniggering. The innkeeper came down from the upper room, apparently on purpose to listen to the "funny fellow" and sat down at a little distance, yawning lazily but with dignity. Evidently Marmeladov was a familiar figure here, and he had most likely acquired his weakness for high-flown speeches from the habit of frequently entering into conversation with strangers of all sorts in the tavern. This habit develops into a necessity in some drunkards, and especially in those who are looked after sharply and kept in order at home. Hence in the company of other drinkers they try to justify themselves and even if possible obtain consideration.

"Funny fellow!" pronounced the innkeeper. "And why don't you work, why aren't you at your duty if you are in the service?"

"Why am I not at my duty, honored sir?" Marmeladov went on, addressing himself exclusively to Raskolnikov, as though it were he who had put that question to him. "Why am I not at my duty? Does not my heart ache to think what a useless worm I am? A month ago when Mr. Lebeziatnikov beat my wife with his own hands and I lay drunk, didn't I suffer? Excuse me, young man, has it ever happened to you . . . hm . . . well, to petition hopelessly for a loan?"

"Yes, it has. But what do you mean by hopelessly?"

"Hopelessly in the fullest sense, when you know beforehand that you will get nothing by it. You know, for instance, beforehand with positive certainty that this man, this most reputable and exemplary citizen, will on no consideration give you money; and indeed I ask you, why should he? For he knows of course that I shan't pay it back. From compassion? But Mr. Lebeziatnikov, who keeps up with modern ideas, explained the other day that compassion is forbidden nowadays by science itself and that that's what is done now in England, where there is political economy. Why, I ask you, should he give it to me? And yet though I know beforehand that he won't, I set off to him and . . ."

"Why do you go?" put in Raskolnikov.

"Well, when one has no one, nowhere else one can go! For every man must have somewhere to go, since there are times when one absolutely must go somewhere! When my own daughter first went out with a yellow ticket,* then I had to go . . . (for my daughter has a

* Given to prostitutes and criminals

12

yellow passport),″ he added in parenthesis, looking with a certain uneasiness at the young man. "No matter, sir, no matter!″ he went on hurriedly and with apparent composure when both the boys at the counter guffawed and even the innkeeper smiled. "No matter. I am not confounded by the wagging of their heads; for everyone knows everything about it already and all that is secret is made open. I accept it all, not with contempt, but with humility. So be it! So be it! 'Behold the man!' Excuse me, young man, can you . . . no, to put it more strongly and more distinctly . . . not *can* you but *dare* you, looking upon me, assert that I am not a pig?″

The young man did not answer a word.

"Well,″ the orator began again stolidly and with even increased dignity, after waiting for the laughter in the room to subside, "well, so be it, I am a pig, but she is a lady! I have the semblance of a beast, but Katerina Marmeladov, my spouse, is a person of education and an officer's daughter. Granted, granted, I am a scoundrel, but she is a woman of noble heart, full of sentiments, refined by education. And yet . . . oh, if only she felt for me! Honored sir, honored sir, you know every man ought to have at least one place where people feel for him! But Katerina, though she is magnanimous, is unjust. . . . And yet, although I realize that when she pulls my hair she only does it out of pity—for I repeat without being ashamed, she pulls my hair, young man,″ he declared with redoubled dignity, hearing the sniggering again—"but, my God, if she would but once. . . . But no, no! It's all in vain and it's no use talking! No use talking! For more than once, my wish came true and more than once she has felt for me but . . . such is my fate and I am a beast by nature!″

"Rather!″ assented the innkeeper, yawning. Marmeladov struck his fist resolutely on the table.

"Such is my fate! Do you know, sir, do you know, I have sold her very stockings for drink? Not her shoes—that would be more or less in the order of things, but her stockings, her stockings I have sold for drink! Her mohair shawl I sold for drink, a present to her long ago, her own property, not mine; and we live in a cold room and she caught cold this winter and has begun coughing and spitting blood too. We have three little children and Katerina is at work from morning till night; she is scrubbing and cleaning and washing the children, for she's been used to cleanliness from a child. But her chest is weak and she has a tendency to consumption and I feel it! Do you suppose I don't feel it? And the more I drink the more I feel it. That's why I drink too. I try to find sympathy and feeling in drink. . . . I drink so that I may suffer twice as much!" And as though in despair he laid his head down on the table.

"Young man," he went on, raising his head again, "in your face I seem to read some trouble of mind. When you came in I read it, and that was why I addressed you at once. For in unfolding to you the story of my life, I do not wish to make myself a laughingstock before these idle listeners, who indeed know all about it already, but I am looking for a man of feeling and education. Know then that my wife was educated in a high-class school for the daughters of noblemen, and on leaving she danced the shawl dance before the governor and other personages for which she was presented with a gold medal and a certificate of merit. The medal . . . well, the medal of course was sold—long ago, hm . . . but the certificate of merit is still in her trunk and not long ago she showed it to our landlady. And although she is most continually on bad terms with the landlady, yet she wanted to tell someone or other of her past honors and of the happy days that are gone. I don't condemn her for it. I don't blame her, for the one thing left her is recollection of the past, and all the rest is dust and ashes. Yes, yes, she is a lady of spirit, proud and determined. She scrubs the floors herself and has nothing but black bread to eat, but won't allow herself to be treated with disrespect. That's why she would not overlook Mr. Lebeziatnikov's rudeness to her and so when he gave her a beating for it, she took to her bed more from the hurt to her feelings than from the blows.

"She was a widow when I married her, with three children, one smaller than the other. She married her first husband, an infantry officer, for love, and ran away with him from her father's house. She was exceedingly fond of her husband; but he gave way to cards, got into trouble and with that he died. He used to beat her at the end and although she paid him back (of which I have authentic documentary evidence) to this day she speaks of him with tears and she throws him up to me; and I am glad, I am glad that, though only in imagination, she should think of herself as having once been happy. . . . And she was left at his death with three children in a wild and remote district where I happened to be at the time; and she was left in such hopeless poverty that, although I have seen many ups and downs of all sorts, I don't feel equal to describing it even. Her relations had all thrown her off. And she was proud, too, excessively proud. . . . And then, honored sir, and then, I, being at the time a widower, with a

14

daughter of fourteen left me by my first wife, offered her my hand, for I could not bear the sight of such suffering. You can judge the extremity of her calamities, that she, a woman of education and culture and distinguished family should have consented to be my wife. But she did! Weeping and sobbing and wringing her hands, she married me! For she had nowhere to turn! Do you understand, sir, do you understand what it means when you have absolutely nowhere to turn? No, that you don't understand yet. . . .

"And for a whole year, I performed my duties conscientiously and faithfully, and did not touch this" (he tapped the jug with his finger) "for I have feelings. But even so, I could not please her; and then I lost my place too, and that through no fault of mine but through changes in the office; and then I did touch it! . . . It will soon be a year and a half since we found ourselves at last after many wanderings and numerous calamities in this magnificent capital, adorned with innumerable monuments. Here too I obtained a situation. . . . I obtained it and I lost it again. Do you understand? This time it was through my own fault I lost it: for my weakness had come out. . . . We have now only part of a room; and what we live upon and what we pay our rent with, I could not say. There are a lot of people living there besides ourselves. Dirt and disorder, a perfect Bedlam . . . hm . . . yes . . . and meanwhile my daughter by my first wife has grown up; and what my daughter has had to put up with from her stepmother while she was growing up, I won't speak of. For though Katerina is full of generous feelings, she is a spirited lady, irritable and short-tempered. . . . Yes. But it's no use going over that!

"Sonia, as you may well fancy, has had no education. I did make an effort four years ago to give her a course of geography and universal history, but as I was not very well up in those subjects myself and we had no suitable books, and what books we had . . . hm . . . anyway, we have not even those now, so all our instruction came to an end. . . . And there are the little ones hungry. . . . And Katerina walking up and down and wringing her hands, her cheeks flushed red, as they always are in that disease: 'Here you live with us,' says she, 'you eat and drink and are kept warm and you do nothing to help.' And much she gets to eat and drink when there is not a crust for the little ones for three days! I was lying at the time . . . well, what of it? I was lying drunk and I heard my Sonia speaking (she is a gentle creature with a soft little voice . . . fair hair and such a pale, thin little face). She said: 'Katerina, am I really to do a thing like that?' And a woman of evil character and very well-known to the police had two or three times tried to get at her through the landlady. 'And why not?' said Katerina with a jeer, 'Are you something mighty precious to be so careful of?' But don't blame her, don't blame her, honored sir, don't blame her! She was not herself when she spoke, but driven to distraction by her illness and the crying of the hungry children; and it was said more to wound her than anything else. . . . For that's Katerina's character, and when children cry, even from hunger, she falls to beating them at once. At six o'clock I saw Sonia get up, put on her kerchief and her cape and go out of the room. And about nine o'clock she came back. She walked straight up to Katerina and she laid thirty rubles on the table before her in silence. She did not utter a word, she did not even look at her, she simply picked up our big green *drap de dames* shawl (we have a shawl, made of *drap de dames*), put it over her head and face and lay down on the bed with her face to the wall; only her little shoulders and her body kept shuddering. . . . And I went on lying there, just as before. . . . And then I saw, young man, I saw Katerina in the same silence go up to Sonia's little bed; she was on her knees all the evening kissing Sonia's feet and would not get up and then they both fell asleep in each other's arms . . . together, together . . . yes . . . and I . . . lay drunk."

Marmeladov stopped short, as though his voice had failed him. Then he hurriedly filled his glass, drank and cleared his throat.

"Since then, sir," he went on after a brief pause, "since then, owing to an unfortunate occurrence and through information given by evil-intentioned persons—in all of which that evil procuress took a leading part on the pretext that she had been treated with want of respect—since then my daughter Sonia has been forced to take a yellow ticket, and owing to that she is unable to go on living with us. For our landlady would not hear of it . . . and so that's how it happened. And Sonia comes to us now, mostly after dark; she comforts Katerina and gives her all she can. . . . She has a bed with a tailor and his family. She lodges with them. They all live in one room, but Sonia has her own, partitioned off. . . . Hm . . . yes . . . very poor people and all with cleft palates . . . yes.

"Then I got up in the morning and put on my rags, lifted up my hands to heaven and set off to my former employer. His excellency is a man of God. He is wax . . . wax before the face of the Lord; even as wax melteth! . . . His eyes were dim when he heard my story. 'Marmeladov, once already you have deceived my expectations . . . I'll take you once more on my own responsibility'—that's what he said. 'Remember,' he said, 'and now you can go.' I kissed the dust at his feet—in thought only, for in reality he would not have allowed me to do it, being a statesman and a man of modern and enlightened ideas. I returned home and when I announced that I'd been taken back into the service and should receive a salary, heavens, what a to-do there was!

"That was five weeks ago, sir. Yes. . . . As soon as Katerina and Sonia heard of it, mercy on us, it was as though I stepped into the kingdom of heaven. It used to be nothing but abuse. Now they were walking on tiptoe, hushing the children. 'Your father is tired from his work at the office; he is resting, shh!' They made me coffee before I went to work and boiled cream for me! They began to get real cream for me; do you hear that? And how they managed to get together the money for a decent outfit—eleven rubles, fifty kopecks—I can't guess. Boots, cotton shirt-fronts—a most magnificent uniform, they got up all in splendid style, for eleven rubles and a half. The first morning I came back from the office, I found Katerina had cooked two courses for dinner—soup and salt meat with horse-radish—which we had never dreamed of till then. She had not any dresses . . . none at all, but she got herself up as though she were going on a visit; and not that she'd anything to do it with. She smartened herself up with nothing at all, she'd done her hair nicely, put on a clean collar of some sort, cuffs, and there she was, quite a different person. She was younger and better looking. Sonia, my little darling, had helped with money. 'For the time,' she said, 'it won't do for me to come and see you too often. After dark maybe when no one can see.' Do you hear, do you hear? I lay down for a nap after dinner and what do you think? Though Katerina had quarrelled to the last degree with our landlady only a week before, she could not resist asking her in to coffee. For two hours they were sitting, whispering together. 'My husband is in the service again, now, and receiving a salary,' says she, 'and he went himself to his excellency and his excellency himself came out to him, made all the others wait and led him by the hand before everybody into his study. "To be sure," says he, "Semyon Marmeladov, remembering your past services," says he, "and in spite of your propensity to that foolish weakness, since you promise now and since moreover we've got on badly without you, I rely now on your word as a gentleman."'

"And all that, let me tell you, she has simply made up for herself, and not simply out of wantonness, for the sake of bragging; no, she believes it all herself, she amuses herself with her own fancies, upon my word she does! And I don't blame her for it, no, I don't blame her! . . . Six days ago when I brought her my first earnings in full— twenty-three rubles, forty kopecks altogether—she called me her poppet: 'poppet,' said she, 'my little poppet.' And when we were by ourselves, you understand? You would not think me a beauty, you would not think much of me as a husband, would you? . . . Well, she pinched my cheek. 'My little poppet,' said she."

Marmeladov broke off, tried to smile, but suddenly his chin began to twitch. He controlled himself however. The tavern, the degraded appearance of the man, the five nights in the hay barge, and the pot of spirits, and yet his poignant love for his wife and children bewildered his listener. Raskolnikov listened intently but with a sick sensation. He felt vexed that he had come here.

"Honored sir, honored sir," cried Marmeladov recovering himself —"Oh, sir, perhaps all this seems a laughing matter to you, as it does to others, and perhaps I am only worrying you with the stupidity of all the trivial details of my home life, but it is not a laughing matter to me. For I can feel it all. . . . And the whole of that heavenly day of my life and the whole of that evening I passed in fleeting dreams of how I would arrange it all, and how I would dress all the children and how I should give her rest and how I should rescue my own daughter from dishonor and restore her to the bosom of her family. . . . And a great deal more. . . .

"Well, then, sir," (Marmeladov suddenly gave a sort of start, raised his head and gazed intently at his listener) "well, on the very next day after all those dreams—that is to say, exactly five days ago in the evening—by a cunning trick, like a thief in the night, I stole from my wife the key of her box, took out what was left of my earnings (how much it was I have forgotten) and now look at me, all of you! It's the fifth day since I left home and they are looking for me there and it's the end of my employment and my uniform is lying in a tavern on the Egyptian Bridge. I exchanged it for the garments I have on . . . and it's the end of everything!"

Marmeladov struck his forehead with his fist, clenched his teeth, closed his eyes, and leaned heavily with his elbow on the table. But a minute later his face suddenly changed and with a certain assumed slyness and affectation of bravado, he glanced at Raskolnikov, laughed and said, "This morning I went to see Sonia. I went to ask her for a pick-me-up! He-he-he!"

"You don't say she gave it to you?" cried one of the newcomers; he shouted the words and went off into a guffaw.

"This very quart was bought with her money," Marmeladov declared, addressing himself exclusively to Raskolnikov. "Thirty kopecks she gave me with her own hands, her last, all she had, as I saw. . . . She said nothing, she only looked at me without a word. . . . Not on earth, but up yonder . . . they grieve over men, they weep, but they don't blame them, they don't blame them! But it hurts more, it hurts more when they don't blame! Thirty kopecks yes! And maybe she needs them now, eh? What do you think, my dear sir? And here I, her own father, here I took thirty kopecks of that money for a drink! And I am drinking it! And I have already drunk it! Come, who will have pity on a man like me, eh? Are you sorry for me, sir, or not? Tell me, sir, are you sorry or not? He-he-he!"

He would have filled his glass, but there was no drink left. The pot was empty.

"What are you to be pitied for?" shouted the tavernkeeper who was again near them.

Shouts of laughter and even oaths followed. The laughter and the oaths came from those who were listening and also from those who had heard nothing but were simply looking at the figure of the discharged government clerk.

"To be pitied! Why am I to be pitied?" Marmeladov suddenly declaimed, standing up with his arm outstretched, as though he had been only waiting for that question.

"Why am I to be pitied, you say? Yes! there's nothing to pity me for! I ought to be crucified, crucified on a cross, not pitied! Crucify me, oh judge, crucify me but pity me! And then I will go by myself to be crucified, for it's not merry-making I seek but tears and tribulation! . . . Do you suppose, you who sell, that this pint of yours has been sweet to me? It was tribulation I sought at the bottom of it, tears and tribulation, and I have found it, and I have tasted it; but He will pity us Who has had pity on all men, Who has understood all men and all things. He is the One. He too is the judge. He will come in that day and He will ask: 'Where is the daughter who gave herself for her cross, consumptive stepmother and for the little children of another? Where is the daughter who had pity upon the filthy drunkard, her earthly father, undismayed by his beastliness?' And He will say, 'Come to me! I have already forgiven thee once. . . . I have forgiven thee once. . . . Thy sins which are many are forgiven thee for thou hast loved much. . . .' And he will forgive my Sonia, He will forgive, I know it . . . I felt it in my heart when I was with her just now! And He will judge and will forgive all, the good and the evil, the wise and the meek. . . . And when He has done with all of them, then He will summon us. 'You too come forth,' He will say, 'Come forth ye drunkards, come forth, ye weak ones, come forth, ye children of shame!' And we shall all come forth, without shame and shall stand before him. And He will say unto us, 'Ye are swine, made in the Image of the Beast and with his mark; but come ye also!' And the wise ones and those of understanding will say, 'Oh Lord, why dost Thou receive these men?' And He will say, 'This is why I receive them, oh ye wise, this is why I receive them, oh ye of understanding, that not one of them believed himself to be worthy of this.' And He will hold out His hands to us and we shall fall down before Him . . . and we shall weep . . . and we shall understand all things! Then we shall understand all! . . . and all will understand. Katerina . . . even she will understand. . . . Lord, Thy kingdom come!"

And he sank down on the bench exhausted, and helpless, looking at no one, apparently oblivious of his surroundings and plunged in deep thought. His words had created a certain impression; there was a moment of silence; but soon laughter and oaths were heard again.

"That's his notion!"

"Talked himself silly!"

"A fine clerk he is!"

And so on, and so on.

"Let us go, sir," said Marmeladov all at once, raising his head and addressing Raskolnikov. "Come along with me . . . I'm going to Katerina—time I did."

Raskolnikov had for some time been wanting to go and he had meant to help him. Marmeladov was much unsteadier on his legs than in his speech and leaned heavily on the young man. They had two or three hundred paces to go. The drunken man was more and more overcome by dismay and confusion as they drew nearer the house.

"It's not Katerina I am afraid of now," he muttered in agitation, "and that she will begin pulling my hair. What does my hair matter! Bother my hair! That's what I say! Indeed it will be better if she does begin pulling it, that's not what I am afraid of . . . it's her eyes I am afraid of . . . yes, her eyes . . . the red on her cheeks, too,

20

frightens me . . . and her breathing too. . . . Have you noticed how people in that disease breathe . . . when they are excited? I am frightened of the children's crying, too. . . . For if Sonia has not taken them food . . . I don't know what's happened! I don't know! But blows I am not afraid of. . . . Know, sir, that such blows are not a pain to me, but even an enjoyment. In fact I can't get on without it. . . . It's better so. Let her strike me, it relieves her heart . . . it's better so . . . There is the house. Lead the way!"

They went in from the yard and up to the fourth story. The staircase got darker and darker as they went up. It was nearly eleven o'clock and although in summer in Petersburg there is no real night, yet it was quite dark at the top of the stairs.

A grimy little door at the very top of the stairs stood ajar. A very poor-looking room about ten paces long was lighted up by a candle-end; the whole of it was visible from the entrance. It was all in disorder, littered up with rags of all sorts, especially children's garments. Across the farthest corner was stretched a ragged sheet. Behind it probably was the bed. There was nothing in the room except two chairs and a sofa covered with American leather, full of holes, before which stood an old kitchen-table, unpainted and uncovered. At the edge of the table stood a smoldering tallow-candle in an iron candlestick. It appeared that the family had a room to themselves, not part of a room, but their room was practically a passage. The door leading to the other rooms, or rather cupboards, into which the flat was divided stood half open, and there was shouting, uproar and laughter within. People seemed to be playing cards and drinking tea there. Words of the most unceremonious kind flew out from time to time.

Raskolnikov recognized Katerina at once. She was a rather tall, slim and graceful woman, terribly emaciated, with magnificent dark-brown hair and with a hectic flush in her cheeks. She was pacing up and down in her little room, pressing her hands against her chest; her lips were parched and her breathing came in nervous broken gasps. Her eyes glittered as in fever and looked about with a harsh immovable stare. And that consumptive and excited face with the last flickering light of the candle-end playing upon it made a sickening impression. She seemed to Raskolnikov about thirty years old and was certainly a strange wife for Marmeladov.

She had not heard them and did not notice them coming in. She seemed to be lost in thought, hearing and seeing nothing. The room was close, but she had not opened the window; a stench rose from

21

the staircase, but the door to the stairs was not closed. From the inner rooms clouds of tobacco smoke floated in; she kept coughing, but did not close the door. The youngest child, a girl of six, was asleep, sitting curled up on the floor with her head on the sofa. A boy, a year older, stood crying and shaking in the corner; probably he had just had a beating. Beside him stood a girl nine years old, tall and thin, wearing a thin and ragged chemise with an ancient cashmere robe flung over her bare shoulders, long outgrown and barely reaching her knees. Her arm, as thin as a stick, was around her brother's neck. She was trying to comfort him, whispering something to him, and doing all she could to keep him from whimpering again. At the same time her large dark eyes, which looked larger still from the thinness of her frightened face, were watching her mother with alarm. Marmeladov did not enter the door, but dropped on his knees in the very doorway, pushing Raskolnikov in front of him. The woman, seeing a stranger, stopped indifferently opposite him, coming to herself for a moment and apparently wondering what he had come for. But evidently she decided that he was going into the next room, as he had to pass through hers to get there. Taking no further notice of him, she walked toward the outer door to close it and uttered a sudden scream on seeing her husband on his knees in the doorway.

"Ah!" she cried out in a frenzy, "he has come back! The criminal! the monster! . . . And where is the money? What's in your pocket? Show me! And your clothes are all different! Where are your clothes? Where is the money? Speak!"

And she fell to searching him. Marmeladov submissively and obediently held up both arms to facilitate the search. Not a penny was there.

"Where is the money?" she cried. "Mercy on us, can he have drunk it all? There were twelve silver rubles left in the chest!" In a fury she seized him by the hair and dragged him into the room. Marmeladov helped her efforts by meekly crawling along on his knees.

"And this is a consolation to me! This does not hurt me, but is a positive con-so-la-tion, ho-no-red sir," he called out, shaken to and fro by his hair and even once striking the ground with his forehead. The child asleep on the floor woke up and began to cry. The boy in the corner, losing all control, began trembling and screaming and rushed to his sister in violent terror, almost in a fit. The eldest girl was shaking like a leaf.

22

"He's drunk it! he's drunk it all," the poor woman screamed in despair, "and his clothes are gone! And they are hungry, hungry!" Wringing her hands, she pointed to the children. "Oh, accursed life! And you, are you not ashamed?" she said pouncing all at once upon Raskolnikov. "Have you been drinking with him? You have been drinking with him, too! Go away!"

The young man was hastening away without uttering a word. The inner door was thrown wide open and inquisitive faces were peering in at it. Coarse laughing faces with pipes and cigarettes and heads wearing caps thrust themselves in at the doorway. Further on could be seen figures in dressing gowns flung open, in costumes of unseemly scantiness, some of them with cards in their hands. They were particularly diverted when Marmeladov, dragged about by his hair, shouted that it was a consolation to him. They even began to come into the room. At last a sinister shrill outcry was heard: this came from the landlady herself pushing her way among them and trying to restore order after her own fashion and to frighten the poor woman by ordering her with coarse abuse to clear out of the room the next day.

As he went out, Raskolnikov had time to put his hand into his pocket, to snatch up the coppers he had received in exchange for his ruble in the tavern and to lay them unnoticed on the window. Afterwards on the stairs, he changed his mind and would have gone back.

"What a stupid thing I've done," he thought to himself. "They have Sonia to look after them and I want the money myself." But reflecting that it would be impossible to take it back now and that in any case he would not have taken it, he dismissed it with a wave of his hand and turned back to his lodging. . . . "Hm! And maybe Sonia herself will be bankrupt today, for there is always a risk, hunting big game . . . digging for gold . . . then they would all be without a crust tomorrow except for my money. Hurrah for Sonia! What a mine they've dug there! And they're making the most of it! Yes, they are making the most of it! They've wept over it and grown used to it. Man grows used to everything, the scoundrel!

"And what if I am wrong?" he cried suddenly after a moment's thought. "What if man is not really a scoundrel, man in general, I mean, the whole race of mankind? Then all the rest is prejudice, simply artificial terrors and there are no barriers and it's all as it should be."

23

[*The next morning Raskolnikov received a letter from his mother, Pulcheria Alexandrovna, in which she told what had happened to his sister, Dounia.*

After taking household service in the home of a man named Svidrigailov, Dounia discovered that her master was an unscrupulous man who made immoral proposals behind his wife's back. When his wife overheard her husband soliciting Dounia, she dismissed her at once amid much open scandal. But when the scandal was at its height, Mr. Svidrigailov produced a letter of Dounia's, which set her conduct in its true, perfectly innocent light; whatever blame there was, Svidrigailov assumed himself. Attracted by this commotion and, apparently, by the character of Dounia, a middle-aged lawyer named Pyotr Luzhin made the acquaintance of the family. He asked for Dounia's hand and was accepted. Pulcheria concluded with the news that both she and Dounia were leaving for St. Petersburg in a week.

Although the letter from his mother painted Dounia's marriage in glowing terms, Raskolnikov was deeply suspicious. Several casual phrases seemed to indicate Dounia was sacrificing herself to Luzhin in order to help him. Full of anger, Raskolnikov set out to visit his friend Razumihin. On the way he stopped in at a tavern for a glass of vodka which made him very sleepy. Nervous and exhausted, he lay down on the grass in a park and fell fast asleep.]

IN A MORBID condition of the brain, dreams often have a singular actuality, vividness, and extraordinary semblance of reality. At times monstrous images are created, but the setting and the whole picture are so truthlike and filled with details so delicate, so unexpectedly, but so artistically consistent, that the dreamer, were he an artist, could never have invented them in the waking state. Such sick dreams always remain long in the memory and make a powerful impression on the overwrought and deranged nervous system.

Raskolnikov had a fearful dream. He dreamed he was back in his childhood in the little town of his birth. He was a child about seven years old, walking into the country with his father on the evening of a holiday. It was a gray and heavy day, the country was exactly as he remembered it; indeed he recalled it far more vividly in his dream than he had done in memory. The little town stood on a level flat as bare as the hand, not even a willow near it; only in the far distance, a wood lay, a dark blur on the very edge of the horizon. A few paces beyond the last market garden stood a tavern, a big tavern which had always aroused in him a feeling of aversion, even of fear, when he walked by it with his father. There was always a crowd there, always shouting, laughter and abuse, hideous hoarse singing and often fighting. Drunken and horrible-looking figures were hanging about the tavern. He used to cling close to his father, trembling all over when he met them. . . . And now he dreamed that he was walking with his father past the tavern on the way to the graveyard; he was holding his father's hand and looking with dread at the tavern. A peculiar circumstance attracted his attention: there seemed to be some kind of festivity going on; there were crowds of gaily dressed townspeople, peasant women, their husbands and riffraff of all sorts, all singing, and all more or less drunk. Near the entrance of the tavern stood a cart. It was one of those big carts usually drawn by heavy cart horses and laden with casks of wine or other heavy goods. He always liked looking at those great cart horses, with their long manes, thick legs and slow even pace, drawing along a perfect mountain with no appearance of effort, as though it were easier going with a load than without it. But now, strange to say, in the shafts of such a cart he saw a thin little sorrel beast, one of those peasants' nags which he had often seen straining their utmost under a heavy load of wood or hay, especially when the wheels were stuck in the mud or in a rut. And the peasants would beat them so cruelly, sometimes even about the nose and eyes, and he felt so sorry, so sorry for them that he almost cried, and his mother always used to take him away from the window. All of a sudden there was a great uproar of shouting, singing and the balalaika, and from the tavern a number of big and very drunken peasants came out, wearing red and blue shirts and coats thrown over their shoulders.

"Get in, get in!" shouted one of them, a young thick-necked peasant with a fleshy face red as a carrot. "I'll take you all, get in!"

But at once there was an outbreak of laughter and exclamations in the crowd.

"Take us all with a beast like that!"

"Why, Mikolka, are you crazy to put a nag like that in such a cart?"

"And this mare is twenty if she is a day, mates!"

"Get in, I'll take you all," Mikolka shouted again, leaping first into the cart, seizing the reins and standing straight up in front. "The bay has gone with Marvey," he shouted from the cart, "and this brute, mates, is just breaking my heart. I feel as if I could kill her. She's just eating her head off. Get in, I tell you! I'll make her gallop! She'll gallop!" And he picked up the whip, preparing himself with relish to flog the little mare.

"Get in! Come along!" The crowd laughed. "D'you hear, she'll gallop!"

"Gallop indeed! She has not had a gallop in her for the last ten years!"

"She'll jog along!"

"Don't you mind her, mates, bring a whip each of you, get ready!"

"All right! Give it to her!"

They all clambered into Mikolka's cart, laughing and making jokes. Six men got in and there was still room for more. They hauled in a fat, rosy-cheeked woman. She was dressed in red cotton, in a pointed, beaded headdress and thick leather shoes; she was cracking nuts and laughing. The crowd around them was laughing too and indeed, how could they help laughing? That wretched nag was to drag the whole cartload of them at a gallop! Two young fellows in the cart were just getting whips ready to help Mikolka. With the cry of "Now!" the mare tugged with all her might, but far from galloping, could scarcely move forward; she struggled with her legs, gasping and shrinking from the blows of the three whips which were showered upon her like hail. The laughter in the cart and in the crowd was redoubled, but Mikolka flew into a rage and furiously thrashed the mare, as though he supposed she really could gallop.

"Let me get in, too, mates," shouted a young man in the crowd whose appetite was aroused.

"Get in, everybody get in," cried Mikolka, "she will draw you all. I'll beat her to death!" And he thrashed and thrashed at the mare with fury.

"Father, Father," Raskolnikov cried, "Father, what are they doing? Father, they are beating the poor horse!"

"Come along, come along!" said his father. "They are drunken and foolish, they are in fun; come away, don't look!" and he tried to draw him away, but Raskolnikov tore himself away from his hand, and with horror, ran to the horse. The poor beast was in a bad way. She was gasping, standing still, then tugging again and almost falling.

"Beat her to death," cried Mikolka, "it's come to that. I'll do for her!"

26

"What are you about, are you a Christian, you devil?" shouted an old man in the crowd.

"Did any one ever see the like? A wretched nag like that pulling such a cartload," said another.

"You'll kill her," shouted the third.

"Don't meddle! It's my property. I'll do what I choose. Get in, more of you! Get in, all of you! I will have her go at a gallop!"

All at once the mare, roused by the shower of blows, began feebly kicking. Even the old man could not help smiling. To think of a wretched little beast like that trying to kick!

Two lads in the crowd snatched up whips and ran to the mare to beat her about the ribs. One ran to each side.

"Hit her in the face, in the eyes, in the eyes," cried Mikolka.

"Give us a song, mates," shouted someone in the cart and everyone in the cart joined in a riotous song, jingling a tambourine and whistling. The woman went on cracking nuts and laughing.

Raskolnikov ran beside the mare, ran in front of her, saw her being whipped across the eyes, right in the eyes! He was crying, he felt choking, his tears were streaming. One of the men gave him a cut with the whip across the face, but he did not feel it. Wringing his hands and screaming, he rushed up to the gray-headed old man with the gray beard, who was shaking his head in disapproval. One woman seized him by the hand and would have taken him away, but he tore himself from her and ran back to the mare. She was almost at the last gasp, but began kicking once more.

"I'll teach you to kick," Mikolka shouted ferociously. He threw down the whip, bent forward and picked up from the bottom of the cart a long, thick shaft; he took hold of one end with both hands and with an effort brandished it over the mare.

"He'll crush her," was shouted around him. "He'll kill her!"

"It's my property," shouted Mikolka and brought the shaft down with a swinging blow. There was the sound of a heavy thud.

"Thrash her, thrash her! Why have you stopped?" shouted voices in the crowd.

Mikolka swung the shaft a second time and it fell a second time on the spine of the luckless mare. She sank back on her haunches, but lurched forward and tugged forward with all her force, tugged first on one side and then on the other, trying to move the cart. But the six whips were attacking her in all directions, and the shaft was raised again and fell upon her a third time, then a fourth, with heavy measured blows. Mikolka was in a fury that he could not kill her at one blow.

"She's a tough one," was shouted in the crowd.

"She'll fall in a minute, mates. There will soon be an end of her," said an admiring spectator in the crowd.

"Fetch an ax to her! Finish her off," shouted a third.

"I'll show you! Stand off," Mikolka screamed frantically; he threw down the shaft, stooped down in the cart and picked up an iron crowbar. "Look out," he shouted, and with all his might he dealt a stunning blow at the poor mare. The blow fell; the mare staggered, sank back, tried to pull, but the bar fell again with a swinging blow on her back and she fell on the ground like a log.

"Finish her off," shouted Mikolka and he leaped out of the cart. Several young men, also flushed with drink, seized anything they could come across—whips, sticks, poles—and ran to the dying mare. Mikolka stood on one side and began dealing random blows with the crowbar. The mare stretched out her head, drew a long breath and died.

"You butchered her," some one shouted in the crowd.

"Why wouldn't she gallop then?"

"My property!" shouted Mikolka, with bloodshot eyes, brandishing the bar in his hands. He stood as though regretting that he had nothing more to beat.

"No mistake about it, you are not a Christian," many voices were shouting in the crowd.

The poor boy Raskolnikov made his way screaming through the crowd to the sorrel nag, put his arms around her head and kissed it, kissed the eyes and kissed the lips. . . . Then he jumped up and flew in a frenzy toward Mikolka. At that instant his father who had been running after him, snatched him up and carried him out of the crowd.

"Come along, come! Let us go home," he said to him.

"Father! Why did they . . . kill . . . the poor horse?" he sobbed, but his voice broke and the words came in shrieks from his panting chest.

"They are drunk. . . . They are brutal . . . it's not our business!" said his father. He put his arms around his father but he felt choked, choked. He tried to draw a breath, to cry out—and woke up.

He woke up, gasping for breath, his hair soaked with perspiration, and stood up in terror.

"Thank God, that was only a dream," he said, sitting down under a tree and drawing deep breaths. "But what is it? Is it some fever coming on? Such a hideous dream!"

[*The dream reminded Raskolnikov of his plan to kill the old pawnbroker, Alyona, and filled him with horror; yet, on crossing the Hay Market, he overheard her sister Lizaveta making an appointment for the next evening at seven. He knew, therefore, that his victim would be alone at that hour.*

The next day, Raskolnikov rose from a troubled sleep, stole an ax from the porter's room of his lodging and at ten minutes past seven was climbing the stairs of Alyona's apartment house.]

Here was the fourth story, here was the door, here was the flat opposite, the empty one. The flat underneath was apparently empty also; the visiting card nailed on the door had been torn off—they had gone away! Raskolnikov was out of breath. For one instant the thought floated through his mind "Shall I go back?" But he made no answer and began listening at the old woman's door: a dead silence. Then he listened again on the staircase, listened long and intently . . . then looked about him for the last time, pulled himself together, drew himself up, and once more tried the ax in the noose. "Am I very pale?" he wondered. "Am I not evidently agitated? She is mistrustful. . . . Had I better wait a little longer . . . till my heart leaves off thumping?"

But his heart did not leave off. On the contrary, as though to spite him, it throbbed more and more violently. He could stand it no longer, he slowly put out his hand to the bell and rang. Half a minute later he rang again, more loudly.

No answer. To go on ringing was useless and out of place. The old woman was, of course, at home, but she was suspicious and alone. He had some knowledge of her habits . . . and once more he put his ear to the door. Either his senses were peculiarly keen (which it is difficult to suppose), or the sound was really very distinct. Anyway, he suddenly heard something like the cautious touch of a hand on the lock and the rustle of a skirt at the very door. Some one was standing stealthily close to the lock and, just as he was doing on the outside, was secretly listening within, and seemed to have her ear to the door. . . . He moved a little on purpose and muttered something aloud that he might not have the appearance of hiding, then rang a third

29

time, but quietly, soberly and without impatience. Recalling it afterwards, that moment stood out in his mind vividly, distinctly, for ever; he could not make out how he had had such cunning, for his mind was, as it were, clouded at moments and he was almost unconscious of his body. . . . An instant later he heard the latch being unfastened.

THE DOOR WAS opened a tiny crack, and again two sharp and suspicious eyes stared at him out of the darkness. Then Raskolnikov lost his head and nearly made a great mistake.

Fearing the old woman would be frightened by being alone, and knowing that the sight of him would not disarm her suspicions, he took hold of the door and drew it towards him to prevent the old woman from attempting to shut it again. Seeing this, she did not pull the door back, but neither did she let go of the handle so that he almost dragged her out with it to the stairs. Then he advanced straight upon her. She stepped back in alarm, tried to say something, but seemed unable to speak and stared with open eyes at him.

"Good evening, Alyona Ivanovna," he began, trying to speak easily; but his voice would not obey him; it broke and shook. "I have come . . . I have brought something . . . but we'd better come in . . . to the light. . . ."

And leaving her, he passed straight into the room uninvited. The old woman ran after him; her tongue was unloosed.

"Good heavens! What is it? Who is it? What do you want?"

"Why, Alyona, you know me . . . Raskolnikov . . . here, I brought you the pledge I promised the other day . . ." and he held out the pledge.

The old woman glanced for a moment at the pledge, but at once stared into the eyes of her uninvited visitor. She looked intently, maliciously and mistrustfully. A minute passed; he even fancied something like a sneer in her eyes, as though she had already guessed everything. He felt that he was losing his head, that he was almost frightened, so frightened that if she were to look like that and not say a word for another half minute, he thought he would have run away from her.

"Why do you look at me as though you did not know me?" he said suddenly, also with malice. "Take it if you like; if not, I'll go elsewhere. I am in a hurry."

He had not even thought of saying this, but it was suddenly said of itself. The old woman recovered herself, and her visitor's resolute tone evidently restored her confidence.

"But why, my good sir, all of a sudden. . . . What is it?" she asked, looking at the pledge.

"The silver cigarette case; I spoke of it last time, you know."

She held out her hand, saying, "But how pale you are, to be sure . . . and are your hands trembling too? Have you been bathing, or what?"

"Fever," he answered abruptly. "You can't help getting pale . . . if you've nothing to eat," he added, with difficulty articulating the words.

His strength was failing him again. But his answer sounded like the truth; the old woman took the pledge.

"What is it?" she asked once more, scanning Raskolnikov intently and weighing the pledge in her hand.

"A thing . . . cigarette case. . . . Silver. . . . Look at it."

"It does not seem somehow like silver. How you have wrapped it up!"

Trying to untie the string and turning to the window, to the light (all her windows were shut, in spite of the stifling heat), she left him altogether for some seconds and stood with her back to him. He unbuttoned his coat and freed the ax from the noose, but did not yet take it out, simply holding it in his right hand under the coat. His hands were fearfully weak; he felt them every moment growing more numb and more wooden. He was afraid he would let the ax slip and fall. . . . A sudden giddiness came over him.

"But what have you tied it up like this for?" the old woman cried with vexation and moved towards him.

He had not a minute more to lose. He pulled the ax out, swung it with both arms, scarcely conscious of himself, and almost without effort, almost mechanically, brought the blunt side down on her head. He seemed not to use his own strength in this. But as soon as he had once brought the ax down, his strength returned to him.

The old woman was always bareheaded. Her thin, light hair, streaked with grey, thickly smeared with grease, was plaited in a rat's tail and fastened by a broken horn comb which stood out on the nape of her neck. As she was so short, the blow fell on the very top of her skull. She cried out, but very faintly, and suddenly sank all of a heap on the floor, raising her hands to her head. In one hand she still

31

held "the pledge." Then he dealt her another and another blow with the blunt side and on the same spot. The blood gushed as from an overturned glass, the body fell back. He stepped back, let it fall and at once bent over her face; she was dead. Her eyes seemed to be starting out of their sockets, the brow and the whole face were drawn and contorted convulsively.

He laid the ax on the floor near the dead body and felt at once in her pocket (trying to avoid the streaming body)—the same right-hand pocket from which she had taken the key on his last visit. He was in full possession of his faculties, free from confusion or giddiness, but his hands were still trembling. He remembered afterwards that he had been particularly collected and careful, trying all the time not to get smeared with blood. . . . He pulled out the keys at once; they were all, as before, in one bunch on a steel ring. He ran at once into the bedroom with them.

It was a very small room with a whole shrine of holy images. Against the other wall stood a big bed, very clean and covered with a silk patchwork quilt. Against a third wall was a chest of drawers. Strange to say, as soon as he began to fit the keys into the chest, as soon as he heard their jingling, a convulsive shudder passed over him. He suddenly felt tempted again to give it all up and go away. But that was only for an instant; it was too late to go back. He positively smiled at himself, when suddenly another terrifying idea occurred to his mind. He suddenly fancied that the old woman might be still alive and might recover her senses. Leaving the keys in the chest, he ran back to the body, snatched up the ax and lifted it once more over the old woman, but did not bring it down. There was no doubt that she was dead. Bending down and examining her again more closely, he saw clearly that the skull was broken and even battered in on one side. He was about to feel it with his finger, but drew back his hand and indeed it was evident without that. Meanwhile there was a perfect pool of blood.

All at once he noticed a string on her neck; he tugged at it, but the string was strong and did not snap and besides, it was soaked with blood. He tried to pull it out from the front of the dress, but something held it and prevented its coming. In his impatience he raised the ax again to cut the string from above, but did not dare, and with difficulty, smearing his hand and the ax in the blood, after two minutes' hurried effort, he cut the string and took it off without touching the body with the ax; he was not mistaken—it was a purse. On the

32

string were two crosses, one of Cyprus wood and one of copper, and an image in silver filigree, and with them a small greasy chamois leather purse with a steel rim and ring. The purse was stuffed very full; Raskolnikov thrust it into his pocket without looking at it, flung the crosses onto the old woman's body and rushed back into the bedroom, this time taking the ax with him.

He was in terrible haste; he snatched the keys and began trying them again. But he was unsuccessful. They would not fit into the locks. It was not so much that his hands were shaking, but that he kept making mistakes; though he saw, for instance, that a key was not the right one and would not fit, still he tried to put it in. Suddenly he realized that the big key with the deep notches, which was hanging there with the small keys could not possibly belong to the chest of drawers (on his last visit this had struck him), but to some strongbox, and that everything perhaps was hidden in that box. He left the chest of drawers and at once felt under the bedstead, knowing that old women usually keep boxes under their beds. And so it was; there was a good-sized box under the bed, at least a yard in length, with an arched lid covered with red leather and studded with steel nails. The notched key fitted at once and unlocked it. At the top, under a white sheet, was a coat of red brocade lined with hareskin; under it was a silk dress, then a shawl and it seemed as though there was nothing below but clothes. The first thing he did was to wipe his bloodstained hands on the red brocade. "It's red, and on red, blood will be less noticeable," the thought passed through his mind; then he suddenly came to himself. "Good God, am I going out of my senses?" he thought with terror.

But no sooner did he touch the clothes than a gold watch slipped from under the fur coat. He made haste to turn them all over. There turned out to be various articles made of gold among the clothes— probably all pledges, unredeemed or waiting to be redeemed—brace- lets, chains, earrings, pins and such things. Some were in cases, others simply wrapped in newspaper, carefully and exactly folded and tied round with tape. Without any delay, he began filling up the pockets of his trousers and overcoat, without examining or undoing the parcels and cases; but he did not have time to take many. . . .

He suddenly heard steps in the room where the old woman lay. He stopped short and was still as death. But all was quiet. All at once he heard distinctly a faint cry, as though some one had uttered a low broken moan. Then again dead silence for a minute or two. He sat

33

squatting on his heels by the box and waited, holding his breath. Suddenly he jumped up, seized the ax and ran out of the bedroom.

In the middle of the room stood Lizaveta with a big bundle in her arms. She was gazing in stupefaction at her murdered sister, white as a sheet and seeming not to have the strength to cry out. Seeing him run out of the bedroom, she began quivering all over, like a leaf; a shudder ran down her face; she lifted her hand, opened her mouth, but still did not scream. She began slowly backing away from him into the corner, staring intently, persistently at him, but still uttered no sound, as though she could not get breath to scream. He rushed at her with the ax; her mouth twitched piteously, as babies' mouths, when they begin to be frightened. And this hapless Lizaveta was so simple and had been so thoroughly crushed and scared that she did not even raise a hand to guard her face, though that was the most necessary and natural action at the moment, for the ax was raised over her face. She only put up her empty left hand, but not to her face, slowly holding it out before her as though motioning him away. The ax fell with the sharp edge just on the skull and split at one blow all the top of the head. She fell heavily at once. Raskolnikov completely lost his head, snatched up her bundle, dropped it again and ran into the entry.

Fear gained more and more mastery over him, especially after this second, quite unexpected murder. He longed to run away from the place as fast as possible. And if at that moment he had been capable of seeing and reasoning more correctly, if he had been able to realize all the difficulties of his position, the hopelessness, the hideousness and the absurdity of it, if he could have understood how many obstacles and, perhaps, crimes he had still to overcome or to commit, to get out of that place and to make his way home, it is very possible that he would have flung up everything and would have gone to give himself up—not from fear, but from simple horror and loathing of what he had done. The feeling of loathing especially surged up within him and grew stronger every minute. He would not now have gone to the box or even into the room for anything in the world.

But a sort of blankness, even dreaminess, had begun by degrees to take possession of him; at moments he forgot himself, or rather, forgot what was of importance and caught at trifles. Glancing, however, into the kitchen and seeing a bucket half full of water on a bench, he thought of washing his hands and the ax. His hands were sticky with blood. He dropped the ax with the blade into the water, snatched a piece of soap that lay in a broken saucer on the window and began washing his hands in the bucket. When they were clean, he took out the ax, washed the blade and spent about three minutes washing the wood where there were spots of blood, rubbing them with soap. Then he wiped it all with some linen that was hanging to dry on a line in the kitchen and then he was a long while attentively examining the ax at the window. There was no trace left on it; only the wood was still damp. He carefully hung the ax in the noose under his coat. Then as far as was possible, in the dim light in the kitchen, he looked over his overcoat, his trousers and his boots. At the first glance there seemed to be nothing but stains on the boots. He wetted the rag and rubbed the boots. But he knew he was not looking thoroughly, that there might be something quite noticeable that he was overlooking. He stood in the middle of the room, lost in thought. Dark agonizing ideas rose in his mind—the idea that he was mad and that at that moment he was incapable of reasoning, of protecting himself, that he ought perhaps to be doing something utterly different from what he was now doing. "Good God!" he muttered "I must fly, fly," and he rushed into the entry. But here a shock of terror awaited him such as he had never known before.

He stood and gazed and could not believe his eyes: the door, the outer door from the stairs, at which he had not long before waited and rung, was standing unfastened and at least six inches open. No lock, no bolt, all that time, all that time! The old woman had not shut it after him, perhaps as a precaution. But, good God! Why, he had seen Lizaveta afterwards! And how could he, how could he have failed to reflect that she must have come in somehow! She could not have come through the wall!

He dashed to the door and fastened the latch.

"But no, the wrong thing again. I must get away, get away. . . ."

He unfastened the latch, opened the door and began listening on the staircase.

He listened a long time. Somewhere far away, it might be in the gateway, two voices were loudly and shrilly shouting, quarrelling and scolding. "What are they about?" He waited patiently. At last all was still, as though suddenly cut off; they had separated. He was meaning to go out, but suddenly, on the floor below, a door was noisily opened and someone began going downstairs humming a tune. "How is it they all make such a noise!" flashed through his mind. Once more he closed the door and waited. At last all was still, not a soul stirring. He was just taking a step towards the stairs when he heard fresh footsteps.

35

The steps sounded very far off, at the very bottom of the stairs, but he remembered quite clearly and distinctly that from the first sound he began for some reason to suspect that this was someone coming *there,* to the fourth floor, to the old woman. Why? Were the sounds somehow peculiar, significant? The steps were heavy, even and un-hurried. Now *he* had passed the first floor, now he was mounting higher, it was growing more and more distinct! He could hear his heavy breathing. And now the third story had been reached. Coming here! And it seemed to him all at once that he was turned to stone, that it was like a dream in which one is being pursued, nearly caught and will be killed, and is rooted to the spot and cannot even move one's arms.

At last when the unknown was mounting to the fourth floor, he suddenly started, and succeeded in slipping neatly and quickly back into the flat and closing the door behind him. Then he took the hook and softly, noiselessly, fixed it in the catch. Instinct helped him. When he had done this, he crouched holding his breath by the door. The unknown visitor was by now also at the door. They were now stand-ing opposite each other as he had just before been standing with the old woman when the door divided them and he was listening.

The visitor panted several times. "He must be a big, fat man," thought Raskolnikov, squeezing the ax in his hand. It seemed like a dream indeed. The visitor took hold of the bell and rang loudly.

As soon as the tin bell tinkled, Raskolnikov seemed to be aware of something moving in the room. For some seconds he listened quite seriously. The unknown rang again, waited and suddenly tugged violently and impatiently at the handle of the door. Raskolnikov gazed in horror at the hook shaking in its fastening, and in blank terror expected every minute that the fastening would be pulled out. It certainly did seem possible, so violently was he shaking it. He was tempted to hold the fastening, but *he* might be aware of it. A giddiness came over him again. "I shall fall down!" flashed through his mind, but the unknown began to speak and he recovered himself at once.

"What's up? Are they asleep or murdered? D-damn them!" he bawled in a thick voice, "Hey, Alyona, old witch! Lizaveta, hey, my beauty! open the door! Oh, damn them! Are they asleep or what?"

And again, enraged, he tugged with all his might a dozen times at the bell. He must certainly be a man of authority and an intimate acquaintance.

At this moment light hurried steps were heard not far off, on the stairs. Some one else was approaching. Raskolnikov had not heard them at first.

"You don't say there's no one at home," the newcomer cried in a cheerful, ringing voice, addressing the first visitor, who still went on pulling the bell. "Good evening, my friend."

"From his voice he must be quite young," thought Raskolnikov.

"Who the devil can tell? I've almost broken the lock," answered the other. "But how do you come to know me?"

"Why! The day before yesterday I beat you three times running at billiards."

"Oh!"

"So they are not at home? That's queer. It's awfully stupid though. Where could the old woman have gone? I've come on business."

"Yes; and I have business with her, too."

"Well, what can we do? Go back, I suppose. Ah! Ah! And I was hoping to get some money!" cried the young man.

"We must give it up, of course, but what did she fix this time for? The old witch fixed the time for me to come herself. It's out of my way. And where the devil she can have got to, I can't make out. She sits here from year's end to year's end, the old hag; her legs are bad and yet here all of a sudden she is out for a walk!"

"Hadn't we better ask the porter?"

"What?"

"Where she's gone and when she'll be back."

"Hm. . . . Damn it all! . . . We might ask. . . . But you know she never does go anywhere."

And he once more tugged at the door handle.

"Damn it all. There's nothing to be done, we must go!"

"Stay!" cried the young man suddenly. "Do you see how the door shakes if you pull it?"

"Well?"

"That shows it's not locked, but fastened with the hook! Do you hear how the hook clanks?"

"Well?"

"Why, don't you see? That proves that one of them is at home. If they were all out, they would have locked the door from outside with the key and not with the hook from inside. There, do you hear how the hook is clanking? To fasten the hook on the inside they must be at home, don't you see? So there they are sitting inside and don't open the door!"

37

"Well! And so they must be!" cried the older man, astonished. "What are they about in there!" And he began furiously shaking the door.

"Stay!" cried the young man again. "Don't pull at it! There must be something wrong. . . . Here, you've been ringing and pulling at the door and still they don't open! So either they've both fainted or . . ."

"What?"

"I tell you what. Let's go and fetch the porter, let him wake them up."

"All right."

Both were going down.

"Stay. You stop here while I run down for the porter."

"What for?"

"Well, you'd better."

"All right."

"I'm studying the law, you see! It's evident, e-vi-dent there's something wrong here!" the young man cried hotly, and he ran downstairs.

The other man remained. Once more he softly touched the bell which gave one tinkle, then gently, as though reflecting and looking about him, began touching the door-handle, pulling it and letting it go to make sure once more that it was only fastened by the hook. Then puffing and panting he bent down and began looking at the keyhole; but the key was in the lock on the inside and so nothing could be seen.

Raskolnikov stood keeping tight hold of the ax. He was in a sort of delirium. He was even making ready to fight if they should come in. While they were knocking and talking together, the idea several times occurred to him to end it all at once and shout to them through the door. Now and then he was tempted to swear at them, to jeer at them, while they could not open the door! "Only make haste!" was the thought that flashed through his mind.

"But what the devil is he about? . . ." Time was passing, one minute, and another—no one came. The man who was waiting began to be restless.

"What the devil?" he cried suddenly and in impatience deserting his sentry duty, he, too, went down, hurrying and thumping with his heavy boots on the stairs. The steps died away.

"Good heavens! What am I to do?"

Raskolnikov unfastened the hook, opened the door—there was no sound. Abruptly, without any thought at all, he went out, closing the door as thoroughly as he could, and went downstairs.

He had gone down three flights when he suddenly heard a loud noise below—where could he go? There was nowhere to hide. He turned back to the flat.

"Hey there! Catch the brute!"

Somebody dashed out of a flat below, shouting, and rather fell than ran down the stairs, bawling at the top of his voice.

"Blast him! Blast him! Blast him!"

The shout ended in a shriek; the last sounds came from the yard; all was still. But at the same instant several men talking loud and fast began noisily mounting the stairs. There were three or four of them. He distinguished the ringing voice of the young man. "They!"

Filled with despair he went straight to meet them, feeling "come what must!" If they stopped him—all was lost; if they let him pass—all was lost too; they would remember him. They were approaching; they were only a flight from him—and suddenly deliverance! A few steps from him on the right, there was an empty flat with the door wide open, the flat on the second floor where the painters had been at work, and which, as though for his benefit, they had just left. It was they, no doubt, who had just run down, shouting. The floor had only just been painted; in the middle of the room stood a pail and a broken pot with paint and brushes. In one instant he had whisked in at the open door and hidden behind the wall and only in the nick of time; they had already reached the landing. Then they turned and went on up to the fourth floor, talking loudly. He waited, went out on tiptoe and ran down the stairs.

No one was on the stairs, nor in the gateway. He passed quickly through the gateway and turned to the left in the street.

He knew, he knew perfectly well that at that moment they were at the flat, that they were greatly astonished at finding it unlocked, as the door had just been fastened, that by now they were looking at the bodies, that before another minute had passed they would guess and completely realize that the murderer had just been there, and had succeeded in hiding somewhere, slipping by them and escaping. They would guess most likely that he had been in the empty flat while they were going upstairs. And meanwhile he dared not quicken his pace much, though the next turning was still nearly a hundred yards away. "Should he slip through some gateway and wait somewhere in an unknown street? No, hopeless! Should he fling away the ax? Should he take a cab? Hopeless, hopeless!"

At last he reached the turning. He turned down it more dead than alive. Here he was halfway to safety; it was less risky because there was a great crowd of people and he was lost in it like a grain of sand. But all he had suffered had so weakened him that he could scarcely move. Perspiration ran down him in drops, his neck was all wet. "My word, he has been going it!" someone shouted at him when he came out on the canal bank.

He was only dimly conscious of himself now, and the farther he went the worse it was. He remembered however that on coming out onto the canal bank, he was alarmed at finding few people there and so he was more conspicuous; he had thought of turning back. Though he was almost falling from fatigue, he went a long way around so as to get home from quite a different direction.

He was not fully conscious when he passed through the gateway of his house! He was already on the staircase before he recollected the ax. And yet he had a very grave problem before him, to put it back and to escape observation as far as possible in doing so. He was of course incapable of reflecting that it might perhaps be far better not to restore the ax at all, but to drop it later on in somebody's yard. But it all happened fortunately, the door of the porter's room was closed but not locked, so that it seemed most likely that the porter was at home. But he had so completely lost all power of reflection that he walked straight to the door and opened it. If the porter had asked him, "What do you want?" he would perhaps have simply handed him the ax. But again the porter was not at home and he succeeded in putting the ax back under the bench and even covering it with the chunk of wood as before. He met no one, not a soul, afterward on the way to his room; the landlady's door was shut. When he was in his room, he flung himself on the sofa just as he was—he did not sleep, but sank into blank forgetfulness. If anyone had come into his room then, he would have jumped up at once and screamed. Scraps and shreds of thoughts were simply swarming in his brain, but he could not catch at one, he could not rest on one, in spite of all his efforts. . . .

PART TWO

[*Hours later Raskolnikov woke from his daze and in a frenzy began to stuff his loot into a hole in the wall, but he fell asleep before he could hide his bloodstained clothing. Toward noon the next day he was awakened by a summons to report at the police station—about an I.O.U. that was due; he was dismissed after signing a promise to pay it. While at the station, he learned that the two men at the door were being held for the murders. He hurried home, took the loot from its hiding place and buried it under a heavy stone in a deserted courtyard. He then called on his friend Razumihin, but refused to help him do some translating. He wandered the streets for hours and finally returned home, desperately ill.]*

HE WAS NOT completely unconscious, however, all the time he was ill; he was in a feverish state, sometimes delirious, sometimes half conscious. He remembered a great deal afterwards. Sometimes it seemed as though there were a number of people round him; they wanted to take him away somewhere, there was a great deal of squabbling and discussing about him. Then he would be alone in the room; they had all gone away afraid of him and only now and then they opened the door a crack to look at him; they threatened him, plotted something together, laughed and mocked at him. He remembered Nastasya, the boardinghouse maid, often at his bedside; he distinguished another person, too, whom he seemed to know very well, though he could not remember who he was, and this fretted him, even made him cry. Sometimes he fancied he had been lying there a month; at other times it all seemed part of the same day. But of *that*—of *that* he had no recollection, and yet every minute he felt that he had forgotten something he ought to remember. He worried and tormented himself trying to remember, moaned, flew into a rage, or sank into awful, intolerable terror. Then he struggled to get up, would have run away, but someone always prevented him by force, and he sank back into impotence and forgetfulness. At last he returned to complete consciousness.

It happened at ten o'clock in the morning. On fine days the sun shone into the room at that hour, throwing a streak of light on the right wall and the corner near the door. Nastasya, the maid, was standing beside him with another person, a complete stranger, who was looking at him very inquisitively. He was a young man with a beard, wearing a full, short-waisted coat, and looked like a messenger. The landlady was peeping in at the half-opened door. Raskolnikov sat up.

"Who is this, Nastasya?" he asked, pointing to the young man.

41

"I say, he's himself again!" she said.

"He is himself," echoed the man.

Concluding that he had returned to his senses, the landlady closed the door and disappeared. She was always shy and dreaded conversations or discussions. She was a woman of forty, not at all bad-looking, fat and buxom, with black eyes and eyebrows, good-natured from fatness and laziness, and absurdly bashful.

"Who . . . are you?" he went on, addressing the man. But at that moment the door was flung open, and, stooping a little, as he was so tall, his good friend Razumihin came in.

"What a cabin it is!" he cried. "I am always knocking my head. You call this a lodging! So you are conscious, brother? I've just heard the news."

"He has just come to," said Nastasya.

"Just come to," echoed the man again, with a smile.

"And who are you?" Razumihin asked, suddenly addressing him. "My name is Razumihin, a student and gentleman; and Raskolnikov here is my friend. And who are you?"

"I am the messenger from our office and I've come on business."

"Please sit down." Razumihin seated himself on the other side of the table. "It's a good thing you've come to, brother," he went on to Raskolnikov. "For the last four days you have scarcely eaten or drunk anything. We had to give you tea in spoonfuls. I brought Doctor Zossimov to see you twice. You remember Zossimov? He examined you carefully and said at once it was nothing serious—something seemed to have gone to your head. Some nervous nonsense, the result of bad feeding; he says you have not had enough beer and radish, but it's nothing much; it will pass and you will be all right. Zossimov is a first-rate doctor! He is making quite a name. Come, I won't keep you," he said, addressing the man again. "Will you explain what you want? You must know, Rodya, this is the second time they have sent from the office; but it was another man last time, and I talked to him. Who was it who came before?"

"That was the day before yesterday, I venture to say, if you please, sir. That was an agent who is in our office, too."

"He was more intelligent than you, don't you think so?"

"Yes, indeed, sir, he is of more weight than I am."

"Quite so; go on."

"At your mamma's request, a remittance is sent to you from our office," the man began, addressing Raskolnikov. "If you are in an

42

intelligible condition, I've thirty-five rubles to remit to you, received from an agent at your mamma's request as on previous occasions. Do you remember, sir?"

"Yes, I remember . . ." Raskolnikov said dreamily.

"You hear! He remembers!" cried Razumihin. "He is in 'an intelligible condition'! And I see you are an intelligent man too. Well, it's always pleasant to hear words of wisdom."

"And at the request of your mamma, we have instructions to hand you these thirty-five rubles in the hope of better to come."

"That 'hoping for better to come' is the best thing you've said, though 'your mamma' is not bad either. Come then, what do you say? Is he fully conscious, eh?"

"That's all right. If only he can sign this little paper."

"He can scrawl his name. Have you got the book?"

"Yes, here's the book."

"Give it to me. Here, Rodya, sit up. I'll hold you. Take the pen and scribble 'Raskolnikov' for him. For just now, brother, money is sweeter to us than treacle."

"I don't want it," said Raskolnikov, pushing away the pen.

"Not want it?"

"I won't sign it."

"How the devil can you do without signing it?"

"I don't want . . . the money."

"Don't want the money! Come, brother, that's nonsense, I bear witness. Don't trouble, please, it's only that he is on his travels again. But that's pretty common with him at all times though. . . . You are a man of judgment and we will take him in hand, that is, more simply, take his hand and he will sign it. Here."

"But I can come another time."

"No, no. Why should we trouble you? You are a man of judgment. . . . Now, Rodya, don't keep your visitor, you see he is waiting," and he made ready to hold Raskolnikov's hand in earnest.

"Stop, I'll do it alone," said the latter, taking the pen and signing his name.

The messenger took out the money and went away.

"Bravo! And now, brother, are you hungry?"

*　　*　　*

"Did I say anything in delirium?"

"I should think so! You were beside yourself."

"What did I rave about?"

"What next? What did you rave about? What people rave about.
. . . Well, brother, now I must not lose time. To work." Razumihin
got up from the table and took up his cap.

"What did I rave about?"

"How he keeps on! Are you afraid of having let out some secret?
Don't worry yourself; you said nothing about a countess. But you said
a lot about a bulldog, and about earrings and chains, and about Kres-
tovsky Island, and some porter, and Fomitch and Petrovitch, the
police inspectors. And another thing that was of special interest to you
was your own sock. You whined, 'Give me my sock.' Inspector
Zametov hunted all about your room for your socks, and with his own
scented, ring-bedecked fingers he gave you the rag. And only then
were you comforted, and for the next twenty-four hours you held the
wretched thing in your hand; we could not get it from you. It is most
likely somewhere under your quilt at this moment. And then you
asked so piteously for fringe for your trousers. We tried to find out
what sort of fringe, but we could not make it out. Now to business!
Here are thirty-five rubles; I take ten of them, and shall give you an
account of them in an hour or two. I will let Doctor Zossimov know at
the same time, though he ought to have been here long ago, for it is
nearly twelve. And you, Nastasya, look in pretty often while I am
away, to see whether he wants a drink or anything else. Good-by!"

Nastasya opened the door and stood listening as he went out, but
could not resist running downstairs after him. She was very eager to
hear what he would say to the landlady. She was evidently quite fas-
cinated by Razumihin.

No sooner had she left the room than the sick man flung off the
bedclothes and leaped out of bed like a madman. With burning,
switching impatience he had waited for them to be gone so that he
might set to work. But to what work? Now, as though to spite him, it
eluded him.

"Good God, only tell me one thing: do they know of it yet or not?
What if they know it and are only pretending, mocking me while I am
laid up, and then they will come in and tell me that it's been discovered long ago and that they have only . . . What am I to do now?
That's what I've forgotten, as though on purpose; forgotten it all at
once. I remembered a minute ago."

He stood in the middle of the room and gazed in miserable bewilderment about him; he walked to the door, opened it, listened; but that

was not what he wanted. Suddenly, as though recalling something, he rushed to the corner where there was a hole under the paper, began examining it, put his hand into the hole, fumbled—but that was not it. He went to the stove, opened it and began rummaging in the ashes; the frayed edges of his trousers and the rags cut off his pockets were lying there just as he had thrown them. No one had looked, then! Then he remembered, the sock about which Razumihin had just been telling him. Yes, there it lay on the sofa under the quilt, but it was so covered with dust and grime that Inspector Zametov could not have seen anything on it.

"Bah, Zametov! The police office! And why am I sent for to the police office? Where's the notice? Bah! I am mixing it up; that was then. I looked at my sock then, too, but now . . . now I have been ill. But what did Zametov come for? Why did Razumihin bring him?" he muttered, helplessly sitting on the sofa again. "What does it mean? Am I still in delirium, or is it real? I believe it is real. . . . Ah, I remember, I must escape! Make haste to escape. Yes, I must, I must escape! Yes . . . but where? And where are my clothes? I've no boots. They've taken them away! They've hidden them! I understand! Ah, here is my coat—they passed that over! And here is money on the table, thank God! And here's the I.O.U. . . . I'll take the money and go and take another lodging. They won't find me! . . . Yes, but the address bureau? They'll find me, Razumihin will find me. Better escape altogether . . . far away . . . to America, and let them do their worst! And take the I.O.U. . . . it would be of use there. . . . What else shall I take? They think I am ill! They don't know that I can walk, ha-ha-ha! I could see by their eyes that they know all about it! If only I could get downstairs! And what if they have set a watch there—policemen! What's this tea? Ah, and here is beer left, half a bottle, cold!"

He snatched up the bottle, which still contained a glassful of beer, and gulped it down with relish, as though quenching a flame in his breast. But in another minute the beer had gone to his head, and a faint and even pleasant shiver ran down his spine. He lay down and pulled the quilt over him. His sick and incoherent thoughts grew more and more disconnected, and soon a light, pleasant drowsiness came upon him. With a sense of comfort he nestled his head in the pillow, wrapped more closely about him the soft, wadded quilt which had replaced the old, ragged greatcoat, sighed softly and sank into a deep, sound, refreshing sleep.

He woke up, hearing someone come in. He opened his eyes and saw Razumihin standing in the doorway, uncertain whether to come in or not. Raskolnikov sat up quickly on the sofa and gazed at him, as though trying to recall something.

"Ah, you are not asleep! Here I am! Nastasya, bring in the parcel!" Razumihin shouted down the stairs. "You shall have the account directly."

"What time is it?" asked Raskolnikov, looking round uneasily.

"Yes, you had a fine sleep, brother, it's almost evening, it will be six o'clock directly. You have slept more than six hours."

"Good heavens! Have I?"

"And why not? It will do you good. What's the hurry? A tryst, is it? We've all time before us. I've been waiting for the last three hours for you; I've been up twice and found you asleep. I've called on Zossimov twice; not at home, only fancy! But no matter, he will turn up. And I've been out on my own business, too. You know I've been moving today, moving with my uncle. I have an uncle living with me now. But that's no matter, to business. Give me the parcel, Nastasya. We will open it directly. And how do you feel now, brother?"

"I am quite well, I am not ill. Razumihin, have you been here long?"

"I tell you I've been waiting for the last three hours."

"No, before."

"How do you mean?"

"How long have you been coming here?"

"Why I told you all about it this morning. Don't you remember?"

Raskolnikov pondered. The morning seemed like a dream to him. He could not remember alone, and looked inquiringly at Razumihin.

"Hm!" said the latter, "he has forgotten. I fancied then that you were not quite yourself. Now you are better for your sleep. . . . You really look much better. First rate! Well, to business. Look here, my dear boy."

He began untying the bundle, which evidently interested him.

"Believe me, brother, this is something specially near my heart. For we must make a man of you. Let's begin from the top. Do you see this cap?" he said, taking out of the bundle a fairly good, though cheap, and ordinary cap. "Let me try it on."

"Presently, afterwards," said Raskolnikov, waving it off pettishly.

"Come, Rodya, my boy, don't oppose it, afterwards will be too late; and I shan't sleep all night, for I bought it by guess, without

46

measure. Just right!" he cried triumphantly, fitting it on, "just your size! A proper head-covering is the first thing in dress and a recommendation in its own way. Well, now let us pass to these breeches," and he exhibited to Raskolnikov a pair of light, summer trousers of gray woolen material. "No holes, no spots, and quite respectable, although a little worn; and a waistcoat to match, quite in the fashion. And its being worn really is an improvement, it's softer, smoother. . . . You see, Rodya, to my thinking, the great thing for getting on in the world is always to keep to the seasons; if you don't insist on having asparagus in January, you keep your money in your purse! and it's the same with this purchase. It's summer now, so I've been buying summer things—warmer materials will be wanted for autumn, so you will have to throw these away in any case . . . especially as they will be done for by then from their own lack of coherence if not your higher standard of luxury. Come, price them! What do you say? Two rubles twenty-five kopecks! And remember the condition: if you wear these out, you will have another suit for nothing! They only do business on that system at the stores I buy in. Now for the boots. What do you say? You see that they are a bit worn, but they'll last a couple of months, for it's foreign work and foreign leather; the secretary of the English Embassy sold them last week—he had only worn them six days, but he was very short of cash. Price—a ruble and a half. A bargain?"

"But perhaps they won't fit," observed Nastasya.

"Not fit? Just look!" and he pulled out of his pocket Raskolnikov's old, broken boot, stiffly coated with dry mud. "I did not go empty-handed—they took the size from this monster. We all did our best. And as to your linen, your landlady has seen to that. Here, to begin with are three shirts, hempen but with a fashionable front. . . . And so, Rodya, you are set up with a complete new outfit, for your overcoat is all right, and even has a style of its own. That comes from getting one's clothes from a store like Sharmer's! As for your socks and other things, I leave them to you; we've twenty-five rubles left. And now, brother, let me change your linen, for I daresay you will throw off your illness with your shirt."

"Let me be! I don't want to!" Raskolnikov waved him off. He had listened with disgust to Razumihin's efforts to be playful about his purchases.

"Come, brother, don't tell me I've been trudging around for nothing," Razumihin insisted. "Nastasya, don't be bashful, but help me—

that's it," and in spite of Raskolnikov's resistance he changed his linen. The latter sank back on the pillows and for a minute or two said nothing.

"It will be long before I get rid of them," he thought. "What money was all that bought with?" he asked at last, gazing at the wall.

"Money? Why, your own, what the messenger brought from your mother. Have you forgotten that, too?"

"I remember now," said Raskolnikov after a long, sullen silence. Razumihin looked at him, frowning and uneasy.

The door opened and a tall, stout man whose appearance seemed familiar to Raskolnikov came in.

"Zossimov! At last!" cried Razumihin, delighted.

[*Zossimov and Razumihin, discussing the murder, said that the first two suspects had been released and now a house painter had been arrested: he had sold a pair of gold earrings that had been pawned with the old woman. He pled innocence, saying that he had found the earrings behind the door of the flat in which he and his fellow painter had been working. His guilt was hotly debated across Raskolnikov's sickbed, when the door opened and a stranger entered.*]

THIS WAS A gentleman no longer young, of a stiff and portly appearance, and a cautious and sour countenance. He began by stopping short in the doorway, staring about him with offensive and undisguised astonishment, as though asking himself what sort of place he had come to. Mistrustfully and with an affectation of being alarmed and almost affronted, he scanned Raskolnikov's low and narrow "cabin." With the same amazement he stared at Raskolnikov, who lay undressed, disheveled, unwashed, on his miserable dirty sofa, looking fixedly at him. Then with the same deliberation he scrutinized the uncouth, unkempt figure and unshaven face of Razumihin, who looked him boldly and inquiringly in the face without rising from his seat. A constrained silence lasted for a couple of minutes, and then, as might be expected, some shifting took place. Reflecting, probably from certain fairly unmistakable signs, that he would get nothing in this "cabin" by attempting to overawe them, the gentleman softened somewhat, and civilly, though with some severity, emphasizing every syllable of his question, addressed Zossimov:

"Mr. Rodion Raskolnikov, a student, or formerly a student?"

Zossimov made a slight movement, and would have answered had not Razumihin anticipated him.

"Here he is lying on the sofa! What do you want?"

This familiar "what do you want" seemed to cut the ground from under the feet of the pompous gentleman. He was turning to Razumihin, but checked himself in time and turned to Zossimov again.

"This is Raskolnikov," mumbled Zossimov, nodding towards him. Then he gave a prolonged yawn, opening his mouth as wide as possible. Then he lazily put his hand into his waistcoat pocket, pulled out a huge gold watch in a round hunter's case, opened it, looked at it and as slowly and lazily proceeded to put it back.

Raskolnikov himself lay without speaking, on his back, gazing persistently, though without understanding, at the stranger. When Zossimov said "This is Raskolnikov," he jumped up quickly, sat on the sofa and with an almost defiant, but weak and breaking, voice articulated:

"Yes, I am Raskolnikov! What do you want?"

The visitor scrutinized him and pronounced impressively:

"I am Pyotr Luzhin. I believe I have reason to hope that my name is not wholly unknown to you?"

But Raskolnikov, who had expected something quite different, gazed blankly and dreamily at him, making no reply, as though he heard the name of Pyotr Luzhin for the first time.

"Is it possible that you can up to the present have received no information?" asked Luzhin, somewhat disconcerted.

In reply Raskolnikov sank languidly back on the pillow, put his hands behind his head and gazed at the ceiling. A look of dismay came into Luzhin's face. Zossimov and Razumihin stared at him more inquisitively than ever, and at last he showed unmistakable signs of embarrassment.

"I had presumed and calculated," he faltered, "that a letter posted more than ten days, if not a fortnight ago . . ."

"I say, why are you standing in the doorway?" Razumihin interrupted suddenly. "If you've something to say, sit down. Nastasya and you are so crowded. Nastasya, make room. Here's a chair, thread your way in!"

He moved his chair back from the table, made a little space between the table and his knees, and waited in a rather cramped position for the visitor to "thread his way in." The minute was so chosen that it was impossible to refuse, and the visitor squeezed his way through, hurrying and stumbling. Reaching the chair, he sat down, looking suspiciously at Razumihin.

"No need to be nervous," the latter blurted out. "Rodya has been ill for the last five days and delirious for three, but now he is recovering and has got an appetite. This is his doctor, who has just had a look at him. I am a comrade of Rodya's, like him, formerly a student, and now I am nursing him; so don't you take any notice of us, but go on with your business."

"Thank you. But shall I not disturb the invalid by my presence and conversation?" Pyotr asked of Zossimov.

"N-no," mumbled Zossimov; "you may amuse him." He yawned again.

"He has been conscious a long time, since the morning," went on Razumihin, whose familiarity seemed so much like unaffected good nature that Pyotr began to be more cheerful, partly, perhaps, because this shabby and impudent person had introduced himself as a student.

"Your mamma," began Luzhin.

"Hm!" Razumihin cleared his throat loudly. Luzhin looked at him inquiringly.

"That's all right, go on."

Luzhin shrugged his shoulders.

"Your mamma had commenced a letter to you while I was sojourning in her neighborhood. On my arrival here I purposely allowed a few days to elapse before coming to see you, in order that I might be fully assured that you were in full possession of the tidings; but now, to my astonishment . . ."

"I know, I know!" Raskolnikov cried suddenly with impatient vexation. "So you are the fiancé? * I know, and that's enough!"

There was no doubt about Luzhin's being offended this time, but he said nothing. He made a violent effort to understand what it all meant. There was a moment's silence.

Meanwhile Raskolnikov, who had turned a little towards him when he answered, began suddenly staring at him again with marked curiosity, as though he had not had a good look at him yet, or as though something new had struck him; he rose from his pillow on purpose to stare at him. . . . Pyotr Luzhin had taken up the role of fiancé. All his clothes were fresh from the tailor's and were all right, except for being too new and too distinctly appropriate. Even the

* Of Dounia, Raskolnikov's sister

50

stylish new round hat had the same significance. Pyotr treated it too respectfully and held it too carefully in his hands. The exquisite pair of lavender gloves told the same tale, if only from the fact of his not wearing them, but carrying them in his hand for show. Light and youthful colors predominated in his attire. He wore a charming summer jacket of a fawn shade, light thin trousers, a waistcoat of the same, new and fine linen, a cravat of the lightest cambric with pink stripes on it, and the best of it was, this all suited Pyotr Luzhin. His very fresh and even handsome face looked younger than his forty-five years at all times. His dark, muttonchop whiskers made an agreeable setting on both sides, growing thickly about his shining, clean-shaven chin. Even his hair, touched here and there with gray, though it had been combed and curled at a hairdresser's, did not give him a stupid appearance, as curled hair usually does, by inevitably suggesting a German on his wedding day. If there really was something unpleasing and repulsive in his rather good-looking and imposing countenance, it was due to quite other causes. After scanning Mr. Luzhin unceremoniously, Raskolnikov smiled malignantly, sank back on the pillow and stared at the ceiling as before.

But Mr. Luzhin hardened his heart and seemed to determine to take no notice of their oddities.

"I feel the greatest regret at finding you in this situation," he began, again breaking the silence with an effort. "If I had been aware of your illness I should have come earlier. But you know what business is. I have, too, a very important legal affair in the Senate, not to mention other preoccupations which you may well conjecture. I am expecting your mamma and sister any minute."

Raskolnikov made a movement and seemed about to speak; his face showed some excitement. Pyotr Tuzhin paused, waited, but as nothing followed, he went on:

"Any minute. I have found a lodging for them on their arrival."

"Where?" asked Raskolnikov weakly.

"Very near here, in Bakaleyev's house."

"There are two storys of rooms, let by a merchant; I've been there," put in Razumihin.

"Yes, rooms . . ."

"A disgusting place—filthy, stinking and, what's more, of doubtful character. Things have happened there, and there are all sorts of queer people living there. And I went there about a scandalous business. It's cheap, though . . ."

51

"I could not, of course, find out so much about it, for I am a stranger in Petersburg myself," Pyotr replied huffily. "However, the two rooms are exceedingly clean, and as it is for so short a time . . . I have already take a permanent, that is, our future flat," he said, addressing Raskolnikov, "and I am having it done up. And meanwhile I am myself cramped for room in a lodging with my friend Andrey Lebeziatnikov; it was he who told me of this house, too . . ."

"Lebeziatnikov?" said Raskolnikov slowly, as if recalling something.

"Yes, Andrey Lebeziatnikov, a clerk in the Ministry. Do you know him?"

"Yes . . . no," Raskolnikov answered.

"Excuse me, I fancied so from your inquiry. I was once his guardian. . . . A very nice young man and advanced. I like to meet young people: one learns new things from them." Luzhin looked round hopefully at them all.

"How do you mean?" asked Razumihin.

"In the most serious and essential matters," Luzhin replied, as though delighted at the question. "You see, it's ten years since I visited Petersburg. All the novelties, reforms, ideas have reached us in the provinces, but to see it all more clearly one must be in Petersburg. And it's my notion that you observe and learn most by watching the younger generation. And I confess I am delighted . . ."

"At what?"

"Your question is a wide one. I may be mistaken, but I fancy I find clearer views, more, so to say, criticism, more practicality . . ."

"That's true," Zossimov let drop.

"Nonsense! There's no practicality." Razumihin flew at him. "Practicality is a difficult thing to find; it does not drop down from heaven. And for the last two hundred years we have been divorced from all practical life. Ideas, if you like, are fermenting," he said to Luzhin, "and desire for good exists, though it's in a childish form, and honesty you may find, although there are crowds of brigands. Anyway, there's no practicality. Practicality goes well shod."

"I don't agree with you," Luzhin replied, with evident enjoyment. "Of course, people do get carried away and make mistakes, but one must have indulgence; those mistakes are merely evidence of enthusiasm for the cause and of abnormal external environment. If little has been done, the time has been but short; of means I will not speak. It's my personal view, if you care to know, that something has been accomplished already. New valuable ideas, new valuable works are circulating in the place of our old dreamy and romantic authors. Literature is taking a maturer form, many injurious prejudices have been rooted up and turned into ridicule. . . . In a word, we have cut ourselves off irrevocably from the past, and that, to my thinking, is a great thing . . ."

"He's learned it by heart to show off!" Raskolnikov pronounced suddenly.

"What?" asked Luzhin, not catching his words; but he received no reply.

"That's all true," Zossimov hastened to interpose.

"Isn't it so?" Luzhin went on, glancing affably at Zossimov. "You must admit," he went on, addressing Razumihin with a shade of triumph and superciliousness—he almost added "young man"—"that there is an advance, or, as they say now, progress in the name of science and economic truth . . ."

"A commonplace."

"No, not a commonplace! Hitherto, for instance, if I were told, 'love thy neighbor,' what came of it?" Luzhin went on, perhaps with excessive haste. "It came to my tearing my coat in half to share with my neighbor and we both were left half naked. As a Russian proverb has it, 'catch several hares and you won't catch one.' Science now tells us, love yourself before all men, for everything in the world rests on self-interest. You love yourself and manage your own affairs properly and your coat remains whole. Economic truth adds that the better private affairs are organized in society—the more whole coats, so to say—the firmer are its foundations and the better is the common welfare organized too. Therefore, in acquiring wealth solely and exclusively for myself, I am acquiring so to speak, for all, and helping to bring to pass my neighbor's getting a little more than a torn coat; and that not from private, personal liberality, but as a consequence of the general advance. The idea is simple, but unhappily it has been a long time reaching us, being hindered by idealism and sentimentality. And yet it would seem to want very little wit to perceive it . . ."

"Excuse me, I've very little wit myself," Razumihin cut in sharply, "and so let us drop it. I began this discussion with an object, but I've grown so sick during the last three years of this chattering to amuse oneself, of this incessant flow of commonplaces, always the same, that, by Jove, I blush even when other people talk like that. You are in a hurry, no doubt, to exhibit your acquirements; and I don't blame you, that's quite pardonable. I only wanted to find out what sort of man you are, for so many unscrupulous people have got hold of the progressive cause of late and have so distorted in their own interests everything they touched, that the whole cause has been dragged in the mire. That's enough!"

"Excuse me, sir," said Luzhin, affronted, and speaking with excessive dignity. "Do you mean to suggest so unceremoniously that I too . . ."

"Oh, my dear sir . . . how could I? . . . Come, that's enough," Razumihin concluded, and he turned abruptly to Zossimov to continue their previous conversation.

Pyotr Luzhin had the good sense to accept the disavowal. He made up his mind to take leave in another minute or two.

"I trust our acquaintance," he said, addressing Raskolnikov, "may, upon your recovery and in view of the circumstances of which you are aware, become closer. . . . Above all, I hope for your return to health. . . ."

Raskolnikov did not even turn his head. Pyotr Luzhin began getting up from his chair.

"One of her customers must have killed her," Zossimov declared positively.

"Not a doubt of it," replied Razumihin. "Inspector Petrovitch doesn't give his opinion, but is examining all who have left pledges with her there."

"Examining them?" Raskolnikov asked aloud.

"Yes. What then?"

"Nothing."

"How does he get hold of them?" asked Zossimov.

"His suspects have given the names of some of them, other names are on the wrappers of the pledges and some have come forward by themselves."

"It must have been a cunning and practiced ruffian! The boldness of it! The coolness!"

"That's just what it wasn't!" interposed Razumihin. "That's what throws you all off the scent. But I maintain that he is not cunning, nor practiced, and probably this was his first crime! The supposition that it was a calculated crime and a cunning criminal doesn't work. Suppose him to have been inexperienced, and it's clear that it was only a chance that saved him—and chance may do anything. Why, he did not foresee obstacles, perhaps! And how did he set to work? He took

54

jewels worth ten or twenty rubles, stuffing his pockets with them, ransacked the old woman's trunk, her rags—and they found fifteen hundred rubles, besides notes, in a box in the top drawer of the chest! He did not know how to rob; he could only murder. It was his first crime, I assure you, his first crime; he lost his head. And he got off more by luck than good counsel!"

"You are talking of the murder of the old pawnbroker, I believe?" Pyotr Luzhin put in, addressing Zossimov. He was standing, hat and gloves in hand, but before departing he felt disposed to throw off a few more intellectual phrases. He was evidently anxious to make a favorable impression and his vanity overcame his prudence.

"Yes. You've heard of it?"

"Oh, yes, being in the neighborhood."

"Do you know the details?"

"I can't say that; but another circumstance interests me in the case —the whole question, so to say. Not to speak of the fact that crime has been greatly on the increase among the lower classes during the last five years, not to speak of the cases of robbery and arson everywhere, what strikes me as the strangest thing is that in the higher classes, too, crime is increasing proportionately. In one place one hears of a student's robbing the mail on the highway; in another place people of good social position forge false banknotes; in Moscow of late a whole gang has been captured who used to forge lottery tickets, and one of the ringleaders was a lecturer in universal history; then our secretary abroad was murdered from some obscure motive of gain. . . . And if this old woman, the pawnbroker, has been murdered by someone of a higher class in society—for peasants don't pawn gold trinkets—how are we to explain this demoralization of the civilized part of our society?"

"There are many economic changes," put in Zossimov.

"But why do you worry about it?" Raskolnikov interposed suddenly. "It's in accordance with your theory!"

"In accordance with my theory?" cried Luzhin.

"Why, carry out logically the theory you were advocating and it follows that people may be killed . . ."

"Upon my word!" cried Luzhin.

"No, that's not so," put in Zossimov.

Raskolnikov lay with a white face and twitching upper lip, breathing painfully.

"There's a measure in all things," Luzhin went on superciliously.

"Economic ideas are not an incitement to murder, and one has but to suppose . . ."

"And is it true," Raskolnikov interposed once more suddenly, again in a voice quivering with fury and delight in insulting him, "is it true that you told your fiancée . . . within an hour of her acceptance, that what pleased you most . . . was that she was a beggar . . . because it was better to raise a wife from poverty, so that you may have complete control over her, and reproach her with your being her benefactor?"

"Upon my word," Luzhin cried wrathfully and irritably, crimson with confusion, "to distort my words in this way! Excuse me, allow me to assure you that the report which has reached you, or rather let me say, has been conveyed to you, has no foundation in truth, and I . . . suspect who . . . in a word . . . this arrow . . . in a word, your mamma . . . She seemed to me in other things, with all her excellent qualities, of a somewhat high-flown and romantic way of thinking. . . . But I was a thousand miles from supposing that she would misunderstand and misrepresent things in so fanciful a way. . . . And indeed . . . indeed . . ."

"I tell you what," cried Raskolnikov, raising himself on his pillow and fixing his piercing, glittering eyes upon him, "I tell you what."

"What?" Luzhin stood still, waiting with a defiant and offended face. Silence lasted for some seconds.

"Why, if ever again . . . you dare to mention a single word . . . about my mother . . . I shall send you flying downstairs!"

"What's the matter with you?" cried Razumihin.

"So that's how it is?" Luzhin turned pale and bit his lip. "Let me tell you, sir," he began deliberately, doing his utmost to restrain himself but breathing hard, "at the first moment I saw you you were ill-disposed to me, but I remained here on purpose to find out more. I could forgive a great deal in a sick man and a relative, but you . . . never after this. . . ."

"I am not ill," cried Raskolnikov.

"So much the worse. . . ."

"Go to hell!"

But Luzhin was already leaving without finishing his speech, squeezing between the table and the chair; Razumihin got up this time to let him pass. Without glancing at anyone, and not even nodding to Zossimov, who had for some time been making signs to him to let the sick man alone, he went out, lifting his hat to the level of his shoulder to avoid crushing it as he stooped to go out of the door. And even the curve of his spine was expressive of the horrible insult he had received.

"How could you—how could you!" Razumihin said, shaking his head in perplexity.

"Let me alone—let me alone all of you!" Raskolnikov cried in a frenzy. "Will you ever leave off tormenting me? I am not afraid of you! I am not afraid of anyone, anyone now! Get away from me! I want to be alone, alone, alone!"

"Come along," said Zossimov, nodding to Razumihin.

"But we can't leave him like this!"

"Come along," Zossimov repeated insistently, and he went out. Razumihin thought a minute and ran to overtake him.

[*Raskolnikov dressed himself in the clothes Razumihin had bought and sneaked out of the house, determined that everything would be changed somehow. He went to a restaurant where he met Zametov, the police officer. They discussed the murder and crime in general; Raskolnikov outlined how he would perform certain crimes and then, in a burst of hysteria, actually suggested that he had murdered the pawnbroker. Zametov refused to believe him. On leaving, Raskolnikov met Razumihin, whom he insulted, and walked on to a bridge where he saw a woman intent on committing suicide. Deciding that this way out was loathsome, he then set out for the police station.*]

To reach the police office he had to go straight forward and take the second turning to the left. It was only a few paces away. But at the first turning he stopped and, after a minute's thought, turned into a side street and went two streets out of his way, possibly without any object, or possibly to delay a minute and gain time. He walked, looking at the ground; suddenly someone seemed to whisper in his ear; he lifted his head and saw that he was standing at the very gate of *the* house. He had not passed it, he had not been near it since *that* evening.

An overwhelming, unaccountable prompting drew him on. He went to the house, passed through the gateway, then into the first entrance on the right, and began mounting the familiar staircase to the fourth story. The narrow, steep staircase was very dark. He stopped at each landing and looked around him with curiosity; on the first landing the framework of the window had been taken out. "That wasn't so then," he thought. Here was the flat on the second story where the painters had been working. "It's shut up and the door newly painted. So it's for rent." Then the third story and the fourth. "Here!" He was perplexed to find the door of the flat wide open. There were men there, he could hear voices; he had not expected that. After brief hesitation he mounted the last stairs and went into the flat. It, too, was being done up; there were workmen in it. This seemed to amaze him; he somehow fancied that he would find everything as he left it, even perhaps the corpses in the same places on the floor. And now, bare walls, no furniture; it seemed strange. He walked to the window and sat down on the window sill. There were two workmen, both young fellows, but one much younger than the other. They were papering the walls with a new white paper covered with lilac flowers, instead of the old, dirty, yellow one. Raskolnikov for some reason felt horribly annoyed by this. He looked at the new paper with dislike, as though he felt sorry to have it all so changed. The workmen had obviously stayed beyond their time and now they were hurriedly rolling up their paper and getting ready to go home. . . .

Raskolnikov got up and walked into the other room where the strongbox, the bed, and the chest of drawers had been; the room seemed to him very tiny without furniture in it. The paper was the same; the paper in the corner showed where the case of icons had stood. He looked at it and went to the window. The elder workman looked at him askance.

"What do you want?" he asked suddenly.

Instead of answering Raskolnikov went into the passage and pulled the bell. The same bell, the same cracked note. He rang it a second and a third time; he listened and remembered. The hideous and agonizingly fearful sensation he had felt then began to come back more and more vividly. He shuddered at every ring and it gave him more and more satisfaction.

"Well, what do you want? Who are you?" the workman shouted, going out to him. Raskolnikov went inside again.

"I want to take a flat," he said. "I am looking around."

"It's not the time to look at rooms at night; and you ought to come up with the porter."

"The floors have been washed, will they be painted?" Raskolnikov went on. "Is there no blood?"

"What blood?"

58

"Why, the old woman and her sister were murdered here. There was a perfect pool there."

"But who are you?" the workman cried, uneasy.

"Who am I?"

"Yes."

"You want to know? Come to the police station. I'll tell you."

The workmen looked at him in amazement.

"It's time for us to go; we are late. Come along. We must lock up," said the elder workman.

"Very well, come along," said Raskolnikov indifferently, and going out first, he went slowly downstairs. "Hey, porter," he cried in the gateway.

At the entrance several people were standing, staring at the passers-by; the two porters, a peasant woman, a man in a long coat and a few others. Raskolnikov went straight over to them.

"What do you want?" asked one of the porters.

"Have you been to the police office?"

"I've just been there. What do you want?"

"Is it open?"

"Of course."

"Is the assistant there?"

"He was there for a time. What do you want?"

Raskolnikov made no reply, but stood beside them lost in thought.

"He's been to look at the flat," said the elder workman, coming forward.

"Which flat?"

"Where we work. 'Why have you washed away the blood?' says he. 'There has been a murder here,' says he, 'and I've come to take it.' And he began ringing the bell, all but broke it. 'Come to the police station,' says he. 'I'll tell you everything there.' He wouldn't leave us."

The porter looked at Raskolnikov, frowning and perplexed.

"Who are you?" he shouted as impressively as he could.

"I am Rodion Raskolnikov, formerly a student. I live not far from here." Raskolnikov said this in a lazy, dreamy voice, not turning around, but looking intently into the darkening street.

"Why have you been to the flat?"

"To look at it."

"What is there to look at?"

"Take him straight to the police station," the man in the long coat jerked in abruptly.

Raskolnikov looked intently at him over his shoulder and said in the same slow, lazy tone: "Come along."

"Yes, take him," the man went on more confidently. "Why was he going into *that?* What's in his mind, eh?"

"He's not drunk, but God knows what's the matter with him," muttered the workman.

"But what do you want?" the porter shouted again, beginning to get angry in earnest. "Why are you hanging about?"

"You shirk from the police station then?" said Raskolnikov jeeringly.

"How shirk from it? Why are you hanging about?"

"He's a rogue!" shouted the peasant woman.

"Why waste time talking to him?" cried the other porter, a huge peasant in a full open coat and with keys on his belt. "Get along! He is a rogue and no mistake. Get along!"

And seizing Raskolnikov by the shoulder he flung him into the street. Raskolnikov lurched forward, but recovered his footing, looked at the spectators in silence and walked away.

"Strange man!" observed the workman.

"There are strange folks about nowadays," said the woman.

"You should have taken him to the police station all the same," said the man in the long coat.

"Better have nothing to do with him," decided the big porter. "A regular rogue! Just what he wants, you may be sure, but once you take him up, you won't get rid of him. . . . We know the sort!"

"Shall I go there or not?" thought Raskolnikov, standing in the middle of the thoroughfare at the crossroads, and he looked about him, as though expecting from someone a decisive word. But no sound came. All was dead and silent like the stones on which he walked, dead to him, to him alone. . . . All at once at the end of the street, two hundred yards away, in the gathering dusk he saw a crowd and heard talk and shouts. In the middle of the crowd stood a carriage. . . . A light gleamed in the middle of the street. "What is it?" Raskolnikov turned to the right and went up to the crowd. He seemed to clutch at everything and smiled coldly when he recognized it, for he had fully made up his mind to go to the police station and knew that it would all soon be over.

[*The carriage had run over a drunkard. Raskolnikov identified him as Marmeladov and directed the police to the man's lodging, where*

Marmeladov died. Raskolnikov gave the widow, Katerina, twenty rubles and left quickly. He met Razumihin at a drinking party and the two arrived at Raskolnikov's room to find his mother, Pulcheria, and sister, Dounia, waiting.]

PART THREE

[*Raskolnikov told his sister that he would disown her if she married Luzhin. Razumihin declared that Raskolnikov was delirious and promised to spend the night with him after escorting the ladies to their lodging.*]

"Ah, I see you think I am in such a condition!" Razumihin broke in upon Pulcheria's thoughts, guessing them, as he strolled along the pavement with huge steps, so that the two ladies could hardly keep up with him—a fact he did not observe, however. "Nonsense! That is . . . I am drunk like a fool, but that's not it; I am not drunk from wine. It's seeing you that has turned my head. . . . But don't mind me! Don't take any notice: I am talking nonsense, I am not worthy of you . . . I am utterly unworthy of you! The minute I've taken you home, I'll pour a couple of pailfuls of water over my head in the gutter here, and then I shall be all right. . . . If only you knew how I love you both! Don't laugh, and don't be angry! You may be angry with anyone, but not with me! I am his friend, and therefore I am your friend, too. I want to be . . . I had a presentiment. . . . Last year there was a moment . . . though it wasn't a presentiment really, for you seem to have fallen from heaven. And I expect I shan't sleep all night . . . Doctor Zossimov was afraid a little time ago that your son would go mad . . . that's why he mustn't be irritated."

"What do you say?" cried the mother.

"Did the doctor really say that?" asked Dounia, alarmed.

"Yes, but it's not so, not a bit of it. He gave him some medicine . . . a powder . . . I saw it . . . and then your coming here. . . . Ah! It would have been better if you had come tomorrow. It's a good thing we went away. And in an hour Zossimov himself will report to you about everything. He is not drunk! And I shan't be drunk. . . . But what made me get so tight? Because they got me into an argu-

61

ment, damn them! I've sworn never to argue! They talk such trash! I almost came to blows! I've left my uncle to preside. Would you be- lieve, they insist on complete absence of individualism and that's just what they relish! Not to be themselves, to be as unlike themselves as they can. That's what they regard as the highest point of progress. If only their nonsense were their own, but as it is. . . ."

"Listen," Pulcheria interrupted timidly, but it only added fuel to the flames.

"What do you think?" shouted Razumihin, louder than ever, "you think I am attacking them for talking nonsense? Not a bit! I like them to talk nonsense. That's man's one privilege over all creation. Through error you come to the truth! I am a man because I err! You never reach any truth without making fourteen mistakes and very likely a hundred and fourteen. And a fine thing, too, in its way; but we can't even make mistakes on our own account! Talk nonsense, but talk your own nonsense, and I'll kiss you for it. To go wrong in one's own way is better than to go right in someone else's. In the first case you are a man; in the second you're no better than a bird. Truth won't escape you, but life can be cramped. There have been examples. And what are we doing now? In science, development, thought, invention, ideals, aims, liberalism, judgment, experience and everything, every- thing, everything, we are still in the preparatory class at school. We prefer to live on other people's ideas. It's what we are used to! Am I right, am I right?" cried Razumihin, pressing and shaking the two ladies' hands.

"Oh, mercy, I do not know," cried poor Pulcheria.

"Yes, yes . . . though I don't agree with you in everything," added Dounia earnestly and at once uttered a cry, for he squeezed her hand so painfully.

"Yes, you say yes . . . well after that you . . . you . . ." he cried in a transport, "you are a fount of goodness, purity, sense . . . and perfection. Give me your hand . . . you give me yours, too! I want to kiss your hands here at once, on my knees . . ." and he fell on his knees on the pavement, fortunately at that time deserted.

"Leave off, I entreat you! What are you doing?" Pulcheria cried, greatly distressed.

"Get up, get up!" said Dounia laughing, though she, too, was upset.

"Not for anything till you let me kiss your hands! That's it! Enough! I get up and we'll go on! I am a luckless fool, I am unworthy of you and drunk . . . and I am ashamed. . . . I am not worthy to love you, but to do homage to you is the duty of every man who is not a perfect beast! And I've done homage. . . . Here are your lodgings, and for that alone Rodya was right in driving your Pyotr Luzhin away. . . . How dare he! how dare he put you in such lodgings! It's a scandal! Do you know the sort of people they take in here? And you his betrothed! You are his betrothed? Yes! Well, then, I'll tell you, your fiancé is a scoundrel."

"Excuse me, Mr. Razumihin, you are forgetting . . ." Pulcheria was beginning.

"Yes, yes, you are right. I did forget myself. I am ashamed of it," Razumihin made haste to apologize. "But . . . but you can't be angry with me for speaking so! For I speak sincerely and not because . . . hm, hm! That would be disgraceful; in fact, not because I'm in . . . hm! Well, anyway I won't say why. I daren't. . . . But we all saw today when he came in that that man is not of our sort. Not because he had his hair curled at the barber's, not because he was in such a hurry to show his wit, but because he is a spy, a speculator, because he is a skinflint and a buffoon. That's evident. Do you think him clever? No, he is a fool, a fool. And is he a match for you? Good heavens! Do you see, ladies?" He stopped suddenly on the way up-stairs to their rooms. "Though all my friends there are drunk, yet they are all honest, and though we do talk a lot of trash, and I do, too, yet we shall talk our way to the truth at last, for we are on the right path, while Pyotr Luzhin . . . is not on the right path. Though I've been calling them all sorts of names just now, I do respect them all . . . though I don't respect Officer Zametov, I like him, for he is a puppy, and that bullock Zossimov, because he is an honest man and knows his work. But enough. It's all said and forgiven. Is it forgiven? Well, then, let's go on. I know this corridor. I've been here. There was a scandal here at room number three. . . . Where are you here? Which number? eight? Well, lock yourselves in for the night, then. Don't let anybody in. In a quarter of an hour I'll come back with news, and half an hour later I'll bring Zossimov, you'll see! Good-by! I'll run!"

"Good heavens, Dounia, what is going to happen?" said Pulcheria, addressing her daughter with anxiety and dismay.

"Don't worry yourself, Mother," said Dounia, taking off her hat and cape. "God has sent this gentleman to our aid, though he has come from a drinking party. We can depend on him, I assure you. And all that he has done for Rodya. . . ."

"Ah. Dounia, goodness knows whether he will come! How could I bring myself to leave Rodya? . . . And how different, how different I had fancied our meeting! How sullen he was, as though not pleased to see us. . . ."

Tears came into her eyes.

"No, it's not that, Mother. You didn't see. You were crying all the time. He is quite weakened by serious illness—that's the reason."

"Ah, that illness! What will happen, what will happen? And how he talked to you, Dounia!" said the mother, looking timidly at her daughter, trying to read her thoughts and already half consoled by Dounia's standing up for her brother, which meant that she had already forgiven him. "I am sure he will think better of it tomorrow," she added, probing her daughter further.

"And I am sure that he will say the same tomorrow . . . about that," Dounia said finally. And, of course, there was no going beyond that, for this was a point which Pulcheria was afraid to discuss. Dounia went up and kissed her mother. The latter warmly embraced her without speaking. Then she sat down to wait anxiously for Razumihin's return, timidly watching her daughter, who walked up and down the room with her arms folded, lost in thought. This walking up and down when she was thinking was a habit of Dounia's and the mother was always afraid to break in on her daughter's mood at such moments.

Razumihin, of course, was ridiculous in his sudden drunken infatuation for Raskolnikov's sister. Yet apart from his eccentric condition, many people would have thought it justified if they had seen Dounia, especially at that moment when she was walking to and fro with folded arms, pensive and melancholy. Dounia Raskolnikov was remarkably good-looking; she was tall, strikingly well-proportioned, strong and self-reliant—the latter quality was apparent in every gesture, though it did not in the least detract from the grace and softness of her movements. In her face she resembled her brother, but she might be described as really beautiful. Her hair was dark brown, a little lighter than her brother's; there was a proud light in her almost black eyes and yet at times a look of extraordinary kindness. She was pale, but it was a healthy pallor; her face was radiant with freshness and vigor. Her mouth was rather small; the full red lower lip projected a little as did her chin; it was the only irregularity in her beautiful face, but it gave it a peculiarly individual and almost haughty expression. Her face was always more serious and thoughtful than gay; but how well smiles, how well youthful, lighthearted, irresponsible laughter suited her face! It was natural enough that a warm, open, simplehearted, honest giant like Razumihin, who had never seen anyone like her and was not quite sober at the time, should lose his head immediately. Besides, as chance would have it, he saw Dounia for the first time transfigured by her love for her brother and her joy at meeting him. Afterwards he saw her lower lip quiver with indignation at her brother's insolent, cruel and ungrateful words—and Razumihin's fate was sealed.

[*Next morning, Razumihin called on the ladies. After some discussion of Raskolnikov's condition, they showed him a note they had received from Luzhin. Dated the previous evening, it read:*]

"DEAR MADAM, Pulcheria Raskolnikov, I have the honor to inform you that owing to unforeseen obstacles I was rendered unable to meet you at the railway station; I sent a very competent person with the same object in view. I likewise shall be deprived of the honor of an interview with you tomorrow morning by business in the Senate that does not admit of delay, and also that I may not intrude on your family circle while you are meeting your son, and Dounia her brother. I shall have the honor of visiting you and paying you my respects at your lodgings not later than tomorrow evening at eight o'clock precisely, and herewith I venture to present my earnest and, I may add, imperative request that Rodion may not be present at our interview —as he offered me a gross and unprecedented affront on the occasion of my visit to him in his illness yesterday, and, moreover, since I desire from you personally an indispensable and circumstantial explanation upon a certain point, in regard to which I wish to learn your own interpretation. I have the honor to inform you, in anticipation, that if, in spite of my request, I meet Rodion, I shall be compelled to withdraw immediately and then you have only yourself to blame. I write on the assumption that Rodion who appeared so ill at my visit, suddenly recovered two hours later and so, being able to leave the house, may visit you also. I was confirmed in that belief by the testimony of my own eyes in the lodging of a drunken man who was run over and has since died, to whose daughter, a young woman of notorious behavior, he gave twenty-five rubles on the pretext of the funeral, which gravely surprised me knowing what pains you were at to raise that sum. Herewith expressing my special respect to your estimable daughter, Dounia, I beg you to accept the respectful homage of

Your humble servant,

P. LUZHIN."

"What am I to do now?" began Pulcheria, almost weeping. "How can I ask Rodya not to come? Yesterday he insisted so earnestly on our refusing Pyotr Luzhin and now we are ordered not to receive Rodya! He will come on purpose if he knows, and . . . what will happen then?"

"Act on Dounia's decision," Razumihin answered calmly at once.

"Oh, dear me! She says . . . goodness knows what she says. She doesn't explain her object! She says that it would be best not that it would be best, but that it's absolutely necessary that Rodya should make a point of being here at eight o'clock and that they must meet. . . . I didn't want even to show him the letter, but to prevent him from coming by some stratagem with your help . . . because he is so irritable. . . . Besides I don't understand about that drunkard who died and that daughter, and how he could have given the daughter all the money . . . which . . ."

"Which cost you such sacrifice, Mother," put in Dounia.

"He was not himself yesterday," Razumihin said thoughtfully. "If you only knew what he was up to in a restaurant yesterday, though there was sense in it too. . . . Hm! He did say something, as we were going home yesterday evening, about a dead man and a girl, but I didn't understand a word. . . . But last night, I myself . . ."

"The best thing, Mother, will be for us to go to him ourselves and there I assure you we shall see at once what's to be done. Besides, it's getting late—good heavens, it's past ten," she cried, looking at a splendid gold enameled watch which hung around her neck on a thin Venetian chain, and looked entirely out of keeping with the rest of her dress. "A present from her fiancé," thought Razumihin.

"We must start, Dounia, we must start," her mother cried in a flutter. "He will be thinking we are still angry after yesterday, from our coming so late. Merciful heavens!"

While she said this, she was hurriedly putting on her hat and mantle; Dounia, too, put on her things. Her gloves, as Razumihin noticed, were not merely shabby but had holes in them, and yet this evident poverty gave the two ladies an air of special dignity, which is always found in people who know how to wear poor clothes. Razumihin looked reverently at Dounia and felt proud of escorting her. "The queen who mended her stockings in prison," he thought, "must have looked then every inch a queen and even more a queen than at sumptuous banquets and receptions."

"My God," exclaimed Pulcheria, "little did I think that I should ever fear seeing my son, my darling, darling Rodya! I am afraid, my friend," she added, glancing at Razumihin timidly.

"Don't be afraid, Mother," said Dounia, kissing her. "Better have faith in him."

"Oh, dear! I have faith in him, but I haven't slept all night," exclaimed the poor woman.

[*Raskolnikov, visited by his mother, sister, and Razumihin, seemed much better physically, but he was gloomy and abstract, and although he showed remarkable control, every word seemed to require effort. The visit went awkwardly and finally Raskolnikov broke out in an angry tirade against Dounia's proposed marriage to Luzhin.*]

". . . You cannot respect Luzhin. I have seen him and talked with him. So you are selling yourself for money, and so in any case you are acting basely, and I am glad at least that you can blush for it."

"It is not true. I am not lying," cried Dounia, losing her composure. "I would not marry him if I were not convinced that he thinks highly of me. I would not marry him if I were not firmly convinced that I can respect him. Fortunately, I can have convincing proof of it this very day . . . and such a marriage is not a vileness, as you say! And even if you were right, if I really had determined on a vile action, is it not merciless on your part to speak to me like that? Why do you demand of me a heroism that perhaps you have not either? It is despotism; it is tyranny. If I ruin anyone, it is only myself. . . . I am not committing a murder. Why do you look at me like that? Why are you so pale? Rodya, darling, what's the matter?"

"Good heavens! You have made him faint," cried Pulcheria.

"No, no, nonsense! It's nothing. A little giddiness—not fainting. You have fainting on the brain. H'm, yes, what was I saying? Oh, yes. In what way will you get convincing proof today that you can respect him, and that he . . . esteems you, as you said. I think you said today?"

"Mother, show Rodya the letter," said Dounia.

With trembling hands, Pulcheria gave him the letter. He took it with great interest, but, before opening it, he suddenly looked with a sort of wonder at Dounia.

"It is strange," he said, slowly, as though struck by a new idea. "What am I making such a fuss for? What is it all about? Marry whom you like!"

He said this as though to himself, but said it aloud, and looked for some time at his sister, as though puzzled. He opened the letter at last, still with the same look of strange wonder on his face. Then, slowly and attentively, he began reading, and read it through twice. Pulcheria showed marked anxiety, and all indeed expected something.

"What surprises me," he began, after a short pause, handing the letter to his mother, but not addressing anyone in particular, "is that he is a business man, a lawyer, and his conversation is pretentious indeed, and yet he writes such an uneducated letter."

They all started. They had expected something quite different.

"But they all write like that, you know," Razumihin observed abruptly.

"Have you read it?"

"Yes."

"We showed him, Rodya. We . . . consulted him just now," Pulcheria began, embarrassed.

"That's just the jargon of the courts," Razumihin put in. "Legal documents are written like that to this day."

"Legal? Yes, it's just legal—business language—not so very un-educated, and not quite educated—business language!"

"Pyotr makes no secret of the fact that he had a cheap education. He is proud indeed of having made his own way," Dounia observed, somewhat offended by her brother's tone.

"Well, if he's proud of it, he has reason, I don't deny it. You seem to be offended, Sister, at my making only such a frivolous criticism of the letter, and to think that I speak of such trifling matters on purpose to annoy you. It is quite the contrary; an observation apropos of the style occurred to me that is by no means irrelevant as things stand. There is one expression, 'blame yourselves' put in very significantly and plainly, and there is besides a threat that he will go away at once if I am present. That threat to go away is equivalent to a threat to abandon you both if you are disobedient, and to abandon you now after summoning you to Petersburg. Well, what do you think? Can one resent such an expression from Luzhin, as we should if he" (he pointed to Razumihin) "had written it, or Zossimov, or one of us?"

"N-no," answered Dounia, with more animation. "I saw clearly that it was too naively expressed, and that perhaps he simply has no skill in writing . . . that is a true criticism, Brother. I did not expect, indeed . . ."

"It is expressed in legal style, and sounds coarser than perhaps he intended. But I must disillusion you a little. There is one expression in the letter, one slander about me, and rather a contemptible one. I gave the money last night to the widow, a woman in consumption, crushed with trouble, and not 'on the pretext of the funeral,' but simply to pay for the funeral, and not to the daughter—a young woman, as he writes, of notorious behavior (whom I saw last night for the first time in my life)—but to the widow. In all this I see a too hasty desire to slander me and to raise dissension between us. It is expressed again in legal jargon, that is to say, with a too obvious display of the aim, and with a very naive eagerness. He is a man of intelligence, but to act sensibly, intelligence is not enough. It all shows the man and . . . I don't think he has a great esteem for you. I tell you this simply to warn you, because I sincerely wish for your good. . . ."

Dounia did not reply. Her resolution had been taken. She was only awaiting the evening.

"Then what is your decision, Rodya?" asked Pulcheria, who was more uneasy than ever at the sudden, new businesslike tone of his talk.

"What decision?"

"You see Pyotr writes that you are not to be with us this evening, and that he will go away if you come. So will you . . . come?"

"That, of course, is not for me to decide, but for you first, if you are not offended by such a request; and secondly, by Dounia, if she, too, is not offended. I will do what you think best," he added drily.

"Dounia has already decided, and I fully agree with her," Pulcheria hastened to declare.

"I decided to ask you, Rodya, to urge you not to fail to be with us at this interview," said Dounia. "Will you come?"

"Yes."

"I will ask you, too, to be with us at eight o'clock," she said, addressing Razumihin. "Mother, I am inviting him, too."

"Quite right, Dounia. Well, since you have decided," added Pulcheria, "so be it. I shall feel easier myself. I do not like concealment and deception. Better let us have the whole truth. . . . Pyotr may be angry or not, now!"

At that moment the door was softly opened, and a young girl walked into the room, looking timidly about her. Everyone turned towards her with surprise and curiosity. At first sight, Raskolnikov did not recognize her. It was Sonia Marmeladov. He had seen her yesterday for the first time, but at such a moment, in such surroundings and in such a dress, that his memory retained a very different image of her. Now she was a modestly and poorly dressed young girl, very young, indeed almost like a child, with a modest and refined manner, with a candid but somewhat frightened-looking face. She was wearing a very plain indoor dress, and had on a shabby old-fashioned hat, but she still carried a parasol. Unexpectedly finding the room full of people, she was not so much embarrassed as completely overwhelmed with shyness, like a little child. She was even about to retreat.

"Oh . . . it's you!" said Raskolnikov, extremely astonished, and he, too, was confused. He at once recollected that his mother and sister knew through Luzhin's letter of "some young woman of notorious behavior." He had only just been protesting against Luzhin's calumny and declaring that he had seen the girl last night for the first time, and suddenly she had walked in. He remembered, too, that he had not protested against the expression "of notorious behavior." All this passed vaguely and fleetingly through his brain, but looking at her more intently, he saw that the humiliated creature was so humiliated that he felt suddenly sorry for her. When she made a movement to retreat in terror, it sent a pang to his heart.

"I did not expect you," he said, hurriedly, with a look that made her stop. "Please sit down. You come, no doubt, from Katerina Marmeladov. Allow me—not there. Sit here. . . ."

At Sonia's entrance, Razumihin, who had been sitting on one of Raskolnikov's three chairs, close to the door, got up to allow her to enter. Raskolnikov had at first shown her the place on the sofa where Zossimov had been sitting, but feeling that the sofa which served him as a bed, was too *familiar* a place, he hurriedly motioned her to Razumihin's chair.

"You sit here," he said to Razumihin, putting him on the sofa.

Sonia sat down, almost shaking with terror, and looked timidly at the two ladies. It was evidently almost inconceivable to her that she could sit down beside them. At the thought of it, she was so frightened that she hurriedly got up again, and in utter confusion addressed Raskolnikov.

"I . . . I . . . have come for one minute. Forgive me for disturbing you," she began falteringly. "I come from my mother and she had no one to send. Katerina told me to beg you . . . to be at the service . . . in the morning . . . and then . . . to us . . . to her . . . to do her the honor . . . she told me to beg you . . ." Sonia stammered and ceased speaking.

"I will try, certainly, most certainly," answered Raskolnikov. He, too, stood up, and he, too, faltered and could not finish his sentence. "Please sit down," he said, suddenly. "I want to talk to you. You are perhaps in a hurry, but please, be so kind, spare me two minutes," and he drew up a chair for her.

Sonia sat down again, and again timidly she took a hurried, frightened look at the two ladies, and dropped her eyes. Raskolnikov's pale face flushed; a shudder passed over him; his eyes glowed.

"Mother," he said, firmly and insistently, "this is Miss Sonia Marmeladov, the daughter of that unfortunate Mr. Marmeladov who was run over yesterday before my eyes and of whom I was just telling you."

Pulcheria glanced at Sonia, and slightly screwed up her eyes. In spite of her embarrassment before Rodya's urgent and challenging look, she could not deny herself that satisfaction. Dounia gazed gravely and intently into the poor girl's face, and scrutinized her with perplexity. Sonia, hearing herself introduced, tried to raise her eyes again, but was more embarrassed than ever.

"I wanted to ask you," said Raskolnikov, hastily, "how things were arranged yesterday. You were not worried by the police, for instance?"

"No, that was all right . . . it was too evident, the cause of death . . . they did not worry us . . . only the lodgers are angry."

"Why?"

"At the body's remaining so long. You see it is hot now. So that, today, they will carry it to the cemetery, into the chapel, until tomorrow. At first Katerina was unwilling, but now she sees herself that it's necessary. . . ."

"Today, then?"

"She begs you to do us the honor to be in the church tomorrow for the service, and then to be present at the funeral lunch."

"She is giving a funeral lunch?"

"Yes . . . just a little. . . . She told me to thank you very much for helping us yesterday. But for you, we should have had nothing for the funeral."

All at once her lips and chin began trembling, but, with an effort, she controlled herself, looking down again.

During the conversation, Raskolnikov watched her carefully. She had a thin, very thin, pale little face, rather irregular and angular, with a sharp little nose and chin. She could not have been called pretty, but her blue eyes were so clear, and when they lighted up, there was such a kindliness and simplicity in her expression that one could not help being attracted. Her face and her whole figure indeed had another peculiar characteristic. In spite of her eighteen years, she looked almost a little girl—almost a child. And in some of her gestures, this childishness seemed almost absurd.

"But has Katerina been able to manage with such small means? Does she even mean to have a funeral lunch?" Raskolnikov asked, persistently keeping up the conversation.

"The coffin will be plain, of course . . . and everything will be plain, so it won't cost much. Katerina and I have reckoned it all out, so that there will be enough left . . . and Katerina was very anxious it should be so. You know one can't . . . it's a comfort to her . . . she is like that, you know. . . ."

"I understand, I understand . . . of course . . . why do you look at my room like that? My mother has just said it is like a tomb."

"You gave us everything yesterday," Sonia said suddenly in reply, in a loud rapid whisper; and again she looked down in confusion. Her lips and chin were trembling once more. She had been struck at once by Raskolnikov's poor surroundings, and now these words broke out spontaneously. A silence followed. There was a light in Dounia's eyes, and even Pulcheria looked kindly at Sonia.

"Rodya," she said, getting up, "we shall have dinner together, of course. Come, Dounia. . . . And you, Rodya, had better go for a little walk, and then rest and lie down before you come to see us. . . . I am afraid we have exhausted you. . . ."

"Yes, yes, I'll come," he answered, getting up fussily. "But I have something to see to."

72

"But surely you will have dinner together?" cried Razumihin, looking in surprise at Raskolnikov. "What do you mean?"

"Yes, yes, I am coming . . . of course, of course! And you stay a minute. You do not want him just now, do you, Mother? Or perhaps I am taking him from you?"

"Oh, no, no. And will you, Razumihin, do us the favor of dining with us?"

"Please do," added Dounia.

Razumihin bowed, positively radiant. For one moment, they were all strangely embarrassed.

"Good-by, Rodya, that is—till we meet. I do not like saying good-by. Good-by, Nastasya. Ah, I have said good-by again."

Pulcheria meant to greet Sonia, too; but it somehow failed to come off, and she went in a flutter out of the room.

But Dounia seemed to await her turn, and following her mother out, gave Sonia an attentive, courteous bow. Sonia, in confusion, gave a hurried, frightened curtsy. There was a look of poignant discomfort in her face, as though Dounia's courtesy and attention were oppressive and painful to her.

"Dounia, good-by," called Raskolnikov, in the passage. "Give me your hand."

"Why, I did give it to you. Have you forgotten?" said Dounia, turning warmly and awkwardly to him.

"Never mind, give it to me again." And he squeezed her fingers warmly.

Dounia smiled, flushed, pulled her hand away, and went off quite happy.

"Come, that's capital," he said to Sonia, going back and looking brightly at her. "God give peace to the dead; the living have still to live. That is right, isn't it?"

Sonia looked surprised at the sudden brightness of his face. He looked at her for some moments in silence. The whole history of the dead father floated before his memory in those moments. . . .

[*Raskolnikov told Razumihin that he wanted to inform the police that he had pawned certain things with the murdered pawnbroker. Razumihin suggested that they go to Officer Porfiry. The two men and Sonia left together; as they parted, Raskolnikov told Sonia he would come to see her. On her way home, Sonia was followed by*

*an unknown gentleman, well-dressed, rather tall and thickset, about
fifty. He told her, as he turned into the apartment next to hers, that
he had arrived in Petersburg only two days before.*

*At Porfiry's, Raskolnikov and Razumihin found Inspector
Zametov. In the course of discussion, mention was made of an
essay Raskolnikov had written some time before that, unknown to
him, had been published about two months ago. The article analyzed the psychology of a criminal before and after a crime; it
maintained that there were certain extraordinary people who had
a perfect right to commit crimes, who were not bound by ordinary
rules of law.]*

R ASKOLNIKOV SMILED. He saw the point at once and knew where
they wanted to drive him. He decided to take up the challenge.
"That wasn't quite my contention," he began simply and modestly.
"Yet I admit that you have stated it almost correctly; perhaps, if you
like, perfectly so." (It almost gave him pleasure to admit this.) "The
only difference is that I don't contend that extraordinary people are
always bound to commit breaches of morals, as you call it. In fact, I
doubt whether such an argument could be published. I simply hinted
that an 'extraordinary' man has the right . . . that is, not an official
right, but an inner right to decide in his own conscience to overstep
. . . certain obstacles, and only in case it is essential for the practical fulfillment of his idea—sometimes, perhaps, of benefit to the whole
of humanity. You say that my article isn't definite; I am ready to make
it as clear as I can. Perhaps I am right in thinking you want me to.
Very well. I maintain that if the discoveries of Kepler and Newton
could not have been made known except by sacrificing the lives of
one, a dozen, a hundred, or more men, Newton would have had the
right, would indeed have been in duty bound . . . to *eliminate* the
dozen or the hundred men for the sake of making his discoveries
known to the whole of humanity. But it does not follow that Newton
had a right to murder people right and left and to steal every day in
the market. Then, I remember, I maintain in my article that all . . .
well, legislators and leaders of men, such as Lycurgus, Solon, Mohammed, Napoleon, and so on, were all without exception criminals,
from the very fact that, making a new law, they transgressed the ancient one handed down from their ancestors and held sacred by the
people; and they did not stop short at bloodshed either, if that blood-

shed—often of innocent persons fighting bravely in defense of ancient law—were of use to their cause. It's remarkable, in fact, that the majority, indeed, of these benefactors and leaders of humanity were guilty of terrible carnage. In short, I maintain that all great men or even men a little out of the common—that is to say capable of giving some new word—must, from their very nature, be criminals—more or less, of course. Otherwise it's hard for them to get out of the common rut; and to remain in the common rut is what they can't submit to, from their very nature again, and to my mind they ought not, indeed, to submit to it.

"You see that there is nothing particularly new in all that. The same thing has been printed and read a thousand times before. As for my division of people into ordinary and extraordinary, I acknowledge that it's somewhat arbitrary, but I don't insist upon exact numbers. I only believe in my leading idea that men are *in general* divided by a law of nature into two categories, inferior (ordinary)—that is, so to say, material that serves only to reproduce its kind; and men who have the gift or the talent to utter *a new word*. There are, of course, innumerable subdivisions, but the distinguishing features of both categories are fairly well marked. The first category, generally speaking, are men conservative in temperament and law-abiding; they live under control and love to be controlled. To my thinking it is their duty to be controlled, because that's their vocation, and there is nothing humiliating in it for them. The second category all transgress the law; they are destroyers or disposed to destruction according to their capacities. The crimes of these men are of course relative and varied; for the most part they seek in very varied ways the destruction of the present for the sake of the better. But if such a one is forced for the sake of his idea to step over a corpse or wade through blood, he can, I maintain, find within himself, in his conscience, a sanction for wading through blood. That depends on the idea and its dimensions —note that! It's only in that sense I speak of their right to crime in my article (you remember it began with the legal question). There's no need for such anxiety, however; the masses will scarcely ever admit this right; they punish them or hang them (more or less), and in doing so, fulfill quite justly their conservative vocation. But the same masses set these criminals on a pedestal in the next generation and worship them (more or less). The first category is always the man of the present; the second the man of the future. The first preserve the world and people it; the second move the world and lead it to its goal.

75

Each class has an equal right to exist. In fact, all have equal rights with me—and *vive la guerre éternelle* *—till the New Jerusalem, of course!"

"Then you believe in the New Jerusalem, do you?" asked Porfiry Petrovitch.

"I do," Raskolnikov answered firmly; as he said these words and as during the whole preceding tirade he kept his eyes on one spot on the carpet.

"And . . . and do you believe in God? Excuse my curiosity."

"I do," repeated Raskolnikov, raising his eyes to Porfiry.

"And . . . do you believe in Lazarus' rising from the dead?"

"I . . . I do. Why do you ask all this?"

"You believe it literally?"

"Literally."

"You don't say so. . . . I asked from curiosity. Excuse me. But let us go back to the question; they are not always executed. Some, on the contrary—"

"Triumph in their lifetime? Oh, yes, some attain their ends in this life, and then—"

"They begin executing other people?"

"If it's necessary; indeed, for the most part they do. Your remark is very witty."

"Thank you. But tell me this: how do you distinguish those extraordinary people from the ordinary ones? Are there signs at their birth? I feel there ought to be more exactitude, more external definition. Excuse the natural anxiety of a practical law-abiding citizen, but couldn't they adopt a special uniform, for instance, couldn't they wear something, be branded in some way? For you know if confusion arises and a member of one category imagines that he belongs to the other, begins to 'eliminate obstacles,' as you so happily expressed it, then—"

"Oh, that very often happens! That remark is wittier than the other."

"Thank you."

"No reason to; but take note that the mistake can only arise in the first category, that is among the ordinary people (as I perhaps unfortunately called them). In spite of their predisposition to obedience very many of them, through a playfulness of nature, sometimes vouchsafed even to the cow, like to imagine themselves advanced people, 'destroyers,' and to push themselves into the 'new movement,'

* Long live the eternal war

and this quite sincerely. Meanwhile the really *new* people are very often unobserved by them, or even despised as reactionaries of groveling tendencies. But I don't think there is any considerable danger here, and you really need not be uneasy for they never go very far. Of course, they might have a thrashing sometimes for letting their fancy run away with them and to teach them their place, but no more; in fact, even this isn't necessary as they castigate themselves, for they are very conscientious: some perform this service for one another and others chastise themselves with their own hands. . . . They will impose various public acts of penitence upon themselves with a beautiful and edifying effect; in fact you've nothing to be uneasy about. . . . It's a law of nature. . . ."

"Why, are you both joking?" Razumihin cried out. "There you sit, making fun of one another. Are you serious, Rodya?"

Raskolnikov raised his pale and almost mournful face and made no reply. And the unconcealed, persistent, nervous, and *discourteous* sarcasm of Porfiry seemed strange to Razumihin beside that quiet and mournful face.

"Well, brother, if you are really serious. . . . You are right, of course, in saying that it's not new, that it's like what we've read and heard a thousand times already; but what is really *original* in all this, and is exclusively your own—to my horror—is that you sanction bloodshed in the name of *conscience,* and, excuse my saying so, with such fanaticism. . . . That, I take it, is the point of your article. But that sanction of bloodshed by *conscience* is to my mind . . . more terrible than the official, legal sanction of bloodshed. . . ."

"You are quite right. It is more terrible," Porfiry agreed.

"Yes, you must have exaggerated! There is some mistake. I shall read it. You can't think that! I shall read it."

"All *that* is not in the article; there's only a hint of it," said Raskolnikov.

"Yes, yes." Porfiry couldn't sit still. "Your attitude to crime is pretty clear to me now, but . . . excuse me for my impertinence (I am really ashamed to be worrying you like this), you see, you've removed my anxiety as to the two grades' getting mixed, but . . . there are various practical possibilities that make me uneasy! What if some man or youth imagines that he is a Lycurgus or Mohammed—a future one, of course—and suppose he begins to remove all obstacles. . . . He has some great enterprise before him and needs money for it . . . and tries to get it. Do you see?"

Inspector Zametov gave a sudden guffaw in his corner. Raskolnikov did not even raise his eyes to him.

"I must admit," he went on calmly, "that such cases certainly must arise. The vain and foolish are particularly apt to fall into that snare; young people especially."

"Yes, you see. Well then?"

"What then?" Raskolnikov smiled in reply; "that's not my fault. So it is and so it always will be. He said just now" (he nodded at Razumihin) "that I sanction bloodshed. Society is too well protected by prisons, banishment, criminal investigators, penal servitude. There's no need to be uneasy. You have but to catch the thief."

"And what if we do catch him?" asked Porfiry.

"Then he gets what he deserves."

"You are certainly logical. But what of his conscience?"

"Why do you care about that?"

"Simply from humanity."

"If he has a conscience he will suffer for his mistake. That will be his punishment—as well as the prison."

"But the real geniuses," asked Razumihin frowning, "those who have the right to murder? Oughtn't they to suffer at all even for the blood they've shed?"

"Why the word *ought*? It's not a matter of permission or prohibition. He will suffer if he is sorry for his victim. Pain and suffering are always inevitable for a large intelligence and a deep heart. The really great men must, I think, have great sadness on earth," he added dreamily, not in the tone of the conversation.

He raised his eyes, looked earnestly at them all, smiled and took his cap. He was too quiet by comparison with his manner at his entrance, and he felt this. Everyone got up.

[*Zametov wondered whether it was not some "future Napoleon" who had killed the old pawnbroker; Porfiry questioned Raskolnikov about the painters, but Raskolnikov gave the "correct" answer. Raskolnikov and Razumihin left, the one terrified, the other indignant at the officers' suspicions. Raskolnikov hurried home to inspect the hole in which he had hidden the loot; somewhat reassured at finding nothing, he left the house, only to find a stranger inquiring about him. He followed the stranger who finally addressed only one word to him: "Murderer." Raskolnikov returned to his room where he fell into a tormented sleep from which he awoke*

to find seated at his table the stranger who had followed Sonia.
He introduced himself as Arkady Svidrigailov, Dounia's former
employer who had created the scandal by his attentions when
Dounia worked as a maid in his house.]

PART FOUR

[*To atone for all past unpleasantness and to prevent her marrying*
Luzhin, Svidrigailov offered to make Dounia a present of 10,000
rubles. He also added that his late wife had left Dounia 3,000
rubles which she would receive within two or three weeks. He left
as Razumihin arrived to accompany Raskolnikov to the evening
meeting with Luzhin.]

I N THE CORRIDOR they came upon Luzhin; he had arrived punctually
at eight, and was looking for the number, so that all three went in
together without greeting or looking at one another. The young men
walked in first, while Pyotr Luzhin, for good manners, lingered a little
in the passage, taking off his coat. Pulcheria came forward at once to
greet him in the doorway while Dounia was welcoming her brother.
Pyotr walked in and quite amiably, though with redoubled dignity,
bowed to the ladies. He looked, however, as though he were a little
put out and could not yet recover himself. Pulcheria, who seemed
also a little embarrassed, hastened to make them all sit down at the
round table where a samovar * was boiling. Dounia and Luzhin were
facing one another on opposite sides of the table. Razumihin and
Raskolnikov were facing Pulcheria; Razumihin was next to Luzhin
and Raskolnikov was beside his sister.

A moment's silence followed. Pyotr Luzhin deliberately drew out
a cambric handkerchief reeking of scent and blew his nose with an
air of a benevolent man who felt himself slighted and was firmly resolved to insist on an explanation. In the passage the idea had occurred to him to keep on his overcoat and walk away, and so give the
two ladies a sharp and emphatic lesson and make them feel the
gravity of the position. But he could not bring himself to do this. Be-
* Russian urn for making tea

sides, he could not endure uncertainty and he wanted an explanation: if his request had been so openly disobeyed, there was something behind it and in that case it was better to find it out beforehand; it rested with him to punish them and there would always be time for that.

"I trust you had a favorable journey," he inquired officially of Pulcheria.

"Oh, very, Pyotr."

"I am gratified to hear it. And Dounia is not over-fatigued either?"

"I am young and strong. I don't get tired. But it was a great strain for Mother," answered Dounia.

"That's unavoidable; our national railways are of terrible length. 'Mother Russia,' as they say, is a vast country. . . . In spite of all my desire to do so, I was unable to meet you yesterday. But I trust all passed off without inconvenience?"

"Oh, no, Pyotr, it was all terribly disheartening," Pulcheria hastened to declare with peculiar intonation, "and if our friend Razumihin had not been sent to us, I really believe by God Himself, we should have been utterly lost. Here he is! Mr. Razumihin," she added, introducing him to Luzhin.

"I had the pleasure . . . yesterday," muttered Luzhin with a hostile glance sidelong at Razumihin; then he scowled and was silent.

Pyotr Luzhin belonged to that class of persons, on the surface very polite in society, who make a great point of punctiliousness, but who, as soon as they are crossed in anything, are completely disconcerted and become more like sacks of flour than elegant and lively men of society. Again all was silent; Raskolnikov was obstinately mute; Dounia was unwilling to open the conversation too soon. Razumihin had nothing to say, so Pulcheria was anxious again.

"Mr. Svidrigailov's wife is dead. Have you heard?" she began, having recourse to her leading item of conversation.

"To be sure, I heard so. I was immediately informed, and I have come to make you acquainted with the fact that Arkady Svidrigailov set off in haste for Petersburg immediately after his wife's funeral. So at least I have excellent authority for believing."

"To Petersburg? Here?" Dounia asked in alarm and looked at her mother.

"Yes, indeed, and doubtless not without some design, having in view the rapidity of his departure and all the circumstances preceding it."

"Good heavens! won't he leave Dounia in peace even here?" cried Pulcheria.

"I imagine that neither you nor Dounia has any grounds for uneasiness unless, of course, you are yourselves desirous of getting into communication with him. For my part, I am on my guard and am now discovering where he is lodging. . . ."

"Pyotr, I beg you," said Dounia, "say no more of Mr. Svidrigailov. It makes me miserable."

"He has just been to see me," said Raskolnikov, breaking his silence for the first time.

There were exclamations from all, and they all turned to him. Even Pyotr Luzhin was roused.

"An hour and a half ago, he came in when I was asleep, waked me and introduced himself," Raskolnikov continued. "He was fairly cheerful and at ease and quite hopes that we shall become friends. He is particularly anxious, Dounia, for an interview with you, for which he asked me to assist. He has a proposition to make to you and he told me about it. He told me, too, that a week before her death his wife left you three thousand rubles in her will, Dounia, and that you can receive the money very shortly."

"Thank God!" cried Pulcheria, crossing herself. "Pray for her soul, Dounia!"

"It's a fact!" broke from Luzhin.

"Tell us, what more?" Dounia urged Raskolnikov.

"Then he said that he wasn't rich and all the estate was left to his children who are now with an aunt; then that he was staying somewhere not far from me, but where, I don't know. I didn't ask. . . ."

"But what, what does he want to propose to Dounia?" cried Pulcheria in a fright. "Did he tell you?"

"Yes."

"What was it?"

"I'll tell you afterwards."

Raskolnikov ceased speaking and turned his attention to his tea. Pyotr looked at his watch.

"I am compelled to keep a business engagement, and so I shall not be in your way," he added with an air of some pique, and he began getting up.

"Don't go, Pyotr," said Dounia, "you intended to spend the evening. Besides, you wrote yourself that you wanted to have an explanation with Mother."

"Precisely so, Dounia," Pyotr Luzhin answered impressively, sitting down again, and putting down his hat. "I certainly desired an explanation from you and your honored mother upon a very important point indeed. But as your brother cannot speak openly in my presence to some proposals of Mr. Svidrigailov, I too do not desire and am not able to speak openly . . . in the presence of others . . . of certain matters of the greatest gravity. Moreover, my most weighty and urgent request has been disregarded. . . ."

Assuming an aggrieved air, Luzhin relapsed into dignified silence.

"Your request that my brother should not be present at our meeting was disregarded solely at my instance," said Dounia. "You wrote that you had been insulted by my brother; I think that this must be explained at once, and you must be reconciled. And if Rodya really has insulted you, then he *should* and *will* apologize."

Pyotr Luzhin took a stronger line.

"There are insults, Dounia, which no good will can make us forget. There is a line in everything which it is dangerous to overstep; and when it has been overstepped, there is no return."

"That wasn't what I was speaking of exactly, Pyotr," Dounia interrupted, with some impatience. "Please understand that our whole future depends now on whether all this is explained and set right as soon as possible. I tell you frankly at the start that I cannot look at it in any other light, and if you have the least regard for me, all this business must be ended today, however hard that may be. I repeat that if my brother is to blame, he will ask your forgiveness."

"I am surprised at your putting the question like that," said Luzhin, getting more and more irritated. "Esteeming, and so to say, adoring you, I may at the same time, very well indeed, be able to dislike some member of your family. Though I lay claim to the happiness of your hand, I cannot accept duties incompatible with—"

"Ah, don't be so ready to take offense, Pyotr," Dounia interrupted with feeling, "and be the sensible and generous man I have always considered, and wish to consider, you to be. I've given you a great promise. I am your betrothed. Trust me in this matter and, believe me, I shall be capable of judging impartially. My assuming the part of judge is as much a surprise for my brother as for you. When I insisted on his coming to our interview today after your letter, I told him nothing of what I meant to do. Understand that if you are not reconciled I must choose between you—it must be either you or he.

82

That is how the question rests on your side and on his. I don't want to be mistaken in my choice, and I must not be. For your sake I must break off with my brother; for my brother's sake I must break off with you. I can find out for certain now whether he is a brother to me, and I want to know it; and of you, whether I am dear to you, whether you esteem me, whether you are the husband for me."

"My dear Dounia," Luzhin declared huffily, "your words are of too much consequence to me; I will say more: they are offensive in view of the position I have the honor to occupy in relation to you. To say nothing of your strange and offensive setting me on a level with an impertinent boy, you admit the possibility of breaking your promise to me. You say 'you or he,' showing thereby of how little consequence I am in your eyes. . . . I cannot let this pass considering the relationship and . . . the obligations existing between us."

"What!" cried Dounia, flushing. "I set your interest beside all that has hitherto been most precious in my life, what has made up the *whole* of my life, and here you are offended at my making too *little* account of you."

Raskolnikov smiled sarcastically; Razumihin fidgeted, but Pyotr Luzhin did not accept the reproof; on the contrary, at every word he became more persistent and irritable, as though he relished it.

"Love for the future partner of your life, for your husband, ought to outweigh your love for your brother," he pronounced sententiously, "and in any case I cannot be put on the same level. . . . Although I said so emphatically that I would not speak openly in your brother's presence, nevertheless, I intend now to ask your honored mother for a necessary explanation on a point of great importance closely affecting my dignity. Your son," he said turning to Pulcheria, "yesterday in the presence of Mr. Razsudkin . . . or . . . I think that's it? Excuse me. I have forgotten your surname. . . ." (he bowed politely to Razumihin) "insulted me by misrepresenting the idea I expressed to you in a private conversation, drinking coffee—that is, that marriage with a poor girl who has had experience of trouble is more advantageous from the conjugal point of view than with one who has lived in luxury, since it is more profitable for the moral character. Your son intentionally exaggerated the significance of my words and made them ridiculous, accusing me of malicious intentions, and, as far as I could see, relied upon your correspondence with him. I shall consider myself happy, Pulcheria Raskolnikov, if it is possible for you to convince me of an opposite conclusion, and thereby considerately re-assure me. Kindly let me know in what terms precisely you repeated my words in your letter to your son Rodion."

"I don't remember," faltered Pulcheria. "I repeated them as I understood them. I don't know how Rodya repeated them to you. Perhaps he exaggerated."

"He could not have exaggerated them, except at your instigation."

"Pyotr Luzhin," Pulcheria declared with dignity, "the proof that Dounia and I did not take your words in a very bad sense is the fact that we are here."

"Good, Mother," said Dounia approvingly.

"Then this is my fault again," said Luzhin, aggrieved.

"Well, Mr. Luzhin, you keep blaming Rodion, but you yourself have just written what was false about him," Pulcheria added, gaining courage.

"I don't remember writing anything false."

"You wrote," Raskolnikov said sharply, not turning to Luzhin, "that I gave money yesterday not to the widow of the man who was killed, as was the fact, but to his daughter (whom I had never seen till yesterday). You wrote this to make dissension between me and my family, and for that object added coarse expressions about the conduct of a girl whom you don't know. All that is mean slander."

"Excuse me, sir," said Luzhin, quivering with fury. "I enlarged upon your qualities and conduct in my letter solely in response to your sister's and mother's inquiries as to how I found you and what impression you made on me. As for what you've alluded to in my letter, be so good as to point out one word of falsehood. Show, that is, that you didn't throw away your money, and that there are not worthless persons in that family, however unfortunate."

"To my thinking, you with all your virtues are not worth the little finger of that unfortunate girl at whom you throw stones."

"Would you go so far then as to let her associate with your mother and sister?"

"I have done so already, if you care to know. I made her sit down today with Mother and Dounia."

"Rodya!" cried Pulcheria. Dounia crimsoned; Razumihin knitted his brows. Luzhin smiled with lofty sarcasm.

"You may see for yourself, my dear Dounia," he said, "whether it is possible for us to agree. I hope now that this question is at an end, once and for all. I will withdraw so that I may not hinder the pleasures of family intimacy, and the discussion of secrets." He got up from his chair and took his hat. "But in withdrawing, I venture to request that for the future I may be spared similar meetings, and, so to say, compromises. I appeal particularly to you, my dear Mrs. Raskolnikov, on this subject—the more since my letter was addressed to you and to no one else."

Pulcheria was a little offended.

"You seem to think we are completely under your authority, Pyotr Luzhin. Dounia has told you the reason your desire was disregarded, she had the best intentions. And indeed you write as though you were laying commands upon me. Are we to consider every desire of yours as a command? Let me tell you on the contrary that you ought to show particular delicacy and consideration for us now, because we have thrown up everything, and have come here relying on you, and so we are in any case in a sense in your hands."

"That is not quite true, my dear Pulcheria. Especially at the present moment when the news has come of the Svidrigailov legacy, which seems indeed very apropos, judging from the new tone you take to me," he added sarcastically.

"Judging from that remark, we may certainly presume that you were reckoning on our helplessness," Dounia observed irritably.

"But now in any case I cannot reckon on it, and I particularly desire not to hinder your discussion of the secret proposals of Arkady Svidrigailov, which he has entrusted to your brother and which have, I perceive, a great and possibly a very agreeable interest for you."

"Good heavens!" cried Pulcheria.

Razumihin could not sit still on his chair.

"Aren't you ashamed now, sister?" asked Raskolnikov.

"I am ashamed, Rodya," said Dounia. "Pyotr Luzhin, go away," she said to him, white with anger.

Pyotr Luzhin had apparently not at all expected such a conclusion. He had too much confidence in himself, in his power and in the helplessness of his victims. He could not believe it even now. He turned pale, and his lips quivered.

"Dounia, if I go out of this door now after such a dismissal then, you may count on it, I will never come back. Consider what you are doing. My word is not to be shaken."

"What insolence!" cried Dounia, springing up from her seat. "I don't want you to come back again."

"What! So that's how it stands!" cried Luzhin, utterly unable to the last moment to believe in the rupture and so completely thrown out of his reckoning now. "So that's how it stands! But do you know, Dounia, that I might protest?"

"What right have you to speak to her like that?" Pulcheria intervened hotly. "And what can you protest about? What rights have you? Am I to give my Dounia to a man like you? Go away, leave us altogether! We are to blame for having agreed to a wrong action, and I above all. . . ."

"But you have bound me, Pulcheria," Luzhin stormed in a frenzy, "by your promise, and now you deny it and . . . besides . . . I have been led on account of that into expenses. . . ."

This last complaint was so characteristic of Pyotr Luzhin that Raskolnikov, pale with anger and with the effort of restraining it, could not help breaking into laughter. But Pulcheria was furious.

"Expenses? What expenses? Are you speaking of our trunk? But the conductor brought it for nothing for you! Mercy on us that we have bound you! What are you thinking about, Pyotr Luzhin? It was you who bound us, hand and foot, not we!"

"Enough, Mother. No more, please," Dounia implored. "Pyotr Luzhin, do be kind and go!"

"I am going, but one last word," he said, quite unable to control himself. "Your mamma seems to have entirely forgotten that I made up my mind to take you, so to speak, after the gossip of the town had spread all over the district in regard to your reputation. Disregarding public opinion for your sake and reinstating your reputation, I certainly might very well count on a fitting return, and might indeed look for gratitude on your part. And my eyes have only now been opened! I see myself that I may have acted very, very recklessly in disregarding the universal verdict. . . ."

"Does the fellow want his head smashed?" cried Razumihin, jumping up.

"You are a mean and spiteful man!" cried Dounia.

"Not a word! Not a movement!" cried Raskolnikov, holding Razumihin back; then going close up to Luzhin, "Kindly leave the room!" he said quietly and distinctly, "and not a word more or . . ."

Pyotr Luzhin gazed at him for some seconds with a pale face that worked with anger; then he turned, went out, and rarely has any man carried away in his heart such vindictive hatred as he felt against Raskolnikov. Him, and him alone, he blamed for everything. It is

86

noteworthy that as he went downstairs he still imagined that his case was perhaps not utterly lost, and that, so far as the ladies were concerned, all might "very well indeed" be set right again.

[*The bitter Luzhin was determined to crush the "conceited milksop" who had caused his downfall, while the Raskolnikov family rejoiced at being free. Raskolnikov's report of his conversation with Svidrigailov was greeted with suspicions of some terrible plot. Razumihin saw only the brighter side and soon involved them in a plan to start a publishing house. The scheme was just taking shape when Raskolnikov announced that he had to leave them forever; offering no word of explanation, he departed, committing his mother and sister to the care of Razumihin. He went directly to Sonia's house where he began to torment her with her horrible position and that of her family.*]

"Katerina, your mother, is in consumption, rapid consumption; she will soon die," said Raskolnikov.

"Oh, no, no, no!" Sonia unconsciously clutched both his hands, as though imploring that she should not.

"But it will be better if she does die."

"No, not better, not at all better!" Sonia unconsciously repeated in dismay.

"And the children? What can you do except take them to live with you?"

"Oh, I don't know," cried Sonia, almost in despair, and she put her hands to her head.

It was evident that that idea had very often occurred to her before and he had only roused it again.

"And what if even now while Katerina is alive, you should get ill and are taken to the hospital, what will happen then?" he persisted pitilessly.

"How can you? That cannot be!"

And Sonia's face worked with awful terror.

"Cannot be?" Raskolnikov went on with a harsh smile. "You are not insured against it, are you? What will happen to them then? They will be in the street, all of them. She will cough and beg and knock her head against some wall, as she did today, and the children will cry. . . . Then she will fall down, be taken to the police station and to the hospital. She will die, and the children . . ."

87

"Oh, no. . . . God will not let it be!" broke at last from Sonia's overburdened bosom.

She listened, looking imploringly at him, clasping her hands in dumb entreaty, as though it all depended upon him.

Raskolnikov got up and began to walk about the room. A minute passed. Sonia was standing with her hands and her head hanging in terrible dejection.

"And can't you save? Put by for a rainy day?" he asked, stopping suddenly before her.

"No," whispered Sonia.

"Of course not. Have you tried?" he added almost ironically.

"Yes."

"And it didn't come off! Of course not! No need to ask."

And again he paced the room. Another minute passed.

"You don't get money every day?"

Sonia was more confused than ever and color rushed into her face again.

"No," she whispered with a painful effort.

"It will be the same with your sister, no doubt," he said suddenly.

"No, no! It can't be, no!" Sonia cried aloud in desperation, as though she had been stabbed. "God would not allow anything so awful!"

"He lets others come to it."

"No, no! God will protect her, God!" she repeated.

"But, perhaps, there is no God at all," Raskolnikov answered with a sort of malignance, as he laughed and looked at her.

Sonia's face suddenly changed; a tremor passed over it. She looked at him with unutterable reproach, tried to say something, but could not speak and broke into bitter, bitter sobs, hiding her face in her hands.

"You say your mother's mind is unbalanced; your own mind is unbalanced," he said after a brief silence.

Five minutes passed. He still paced up and down the room in silence, not looking at her. At last he went up to her; his eyes glittered. He put his two hands on her shoulders and looked straight into her tearful face. His eyes were hard, feverish and piercing, his lips were twitching. All at once he bent down quickly and dropping to the ground, kissed her foot. Sonia drew back from him as from a madman. And certainly he looked like a madman.

"What are you doing to me?" she muttered, turning pale, and a sudden anguish clutched at her heart.

He stood up at once.

"I did not bow down to you. I bowed down to all the suffering of humanity," he said wildly and walked away to the window. "Listen," he added, turning to her a minute later. "I said just now to an insolent man that he was not worth your little finger . . . and that I did my sister honor making her sit beside you."

"Oh, you said that to them! And in her presence?" cried Sonia, frightened. "Sit down with me! An honor! Why, I'm . . . dishonorable. . . . Ah, why did you say that?"

"It was not because of your dishonor and your sin I said that of you, but because of your great suffering. But you are a great sinner, that's true," he added almost solemnly, "and your worst sin is that you have destroyed and betrayed yourself *for nothing*. Isn't that fearful? Isn't it fearful that you are living in this filth which you loathe so, and at the same time you know yourself (you've only to open your eyes) that you are not helping anyone by it, not saving anyone from anything! Tell me," he went on almost in a frenzy, "how this shame and degradation can exist in you side by side with other, opposite, holy feelings? It would be better, a thousand times better and wiser, to leap into the water and end it all!"

"But what would become of them?" Sonia asked faintly, gazing at him with eyes of anguish, but not seeming surprised at his suggestion.

Raskolnikov looked strangely at her. He read it all in her face; so she must have had that thought already, perhaps many times, and earnestly she had thought out in her despair how to end it and so earnestly that now she scarcely wondered at his suggestion. She had not even noticed the cruelty of his words. (The significance of his reproaches and his peculiar attitude to her shame she had, of course, not noticed either, and that, too, was clear to him.) But he saw how monstrously the thought of her disgraceful, shameful position was torturing her and had long tortured her. "What, what," he thought, "could have hindered her from putting an end to it?" Only then he realized what those poor little orphan children and that pitiful half-crazy mother, knocking her head against the wall in her consumption, meant for Sonia. . . .

What held her up—surely not depravity? All that infamy had obviously only touched her mechanically, not one drop of real depravity had penetrated to her heart; he saw that. He saw through her as she stood before him. . . .

"There are three ways before her," he thought, "the canal, the madhouse, or . . . at last to sink into depravity which obscures the mind and turns the heart to stone."

The last idea was the most revolting, but he was a skeptic; he was young, abstract and therefore cruel, and so he could not help believing that the last end was the most likely. . . .

"So you pray to God a great deal, Sonia?" he asked her.

Sonia did not speak; he stood beside her waiting for an answer.

"What should I be without God?" she whispered rapidly, forcibly, glancing at him with suddenly flashing eyes and squeezing his hand.

"Ah, so that is it!" he thought.

"And what does God do for you?" he asked, probing her further.

Sonia was silent a long while, as though she could not answer. Her weak chest kept heaving with emotion.

"Be silent! Don't ask! You don't deserve!" she cried suddenly, looking sternly and wrathfully at him.

"That's it, that's it," he repeated to himself.

"He does everything," she whispered quickly, looking down again.

"That's the way out! That's the explanation," he decided, scrutinizing her with eager curiosity, with a new, strange, almost morbid feeling. He gazed at that pale, thin, irregular, angular little face, those soft blue eyes, which could flash with such fire, such stern energy, that little body still shaking with indignation and anger—and it all seemed to him more and more strange, almost impossible. "She is a religious maniac!" he repeated to himself.

There was a book lying on the chest of drawers. He had noticed it every time he paced up and down the room. Now he took it up and looked at it. It was the New Testament in the Russian translation. It was bound in leather, old and worn.

"Where did you get that?" he called to her across the room.

She was still standing in the same place, three steps from the table.

"It was brought to me," she answered, a bit unwillingly, not looking at him.

"Who brought it?"

"Lizaveta. I asked her for it."

"Lizaveta! Strange!" he thought.

Everything about Sonia seemed to him strange and more wonder-

90

ful every moment. He carried the book to the candle and began to turn over the pages.

"Where is the story of Lazarus?" he asked suddenly.

Sonia looked obstinately at the ground and would not answer. She was standing sideways to the table.

"Where is the raising of Lazarus? Find it for me, Sonia."

She stole a glance at him.

"You are not looking in the right place. . . . It's in the fourth gospel," she whispered sternly, without looking at him.

"Find it and read it to me," he said. He sat down with his elbow on the table, leaned his head on his hand and looked away sullenly, prepared to listen.

"In three weeks' time they'll welcome me in the madhouse! I shall be there if I am not in a worse place," he muttered to himself.

Sonia heard Raskolnikov's request distrustfully and moved hesitatingly to the table. She took the book however.

"Haven't you read it?" she asked, looking up at him across the table.

Her voice became sterner and sterner.

"Long ago. . . . when I was at school. Read!"

"And haven't you heard it in church?"

"I . . . haven't been. Do you go often?"

"N-no," whispered Sonia.

Raskolnikov smiled.

"I understand. . . . And you won't go to your father's funeral tomorrow?"

"Yes, I shall. I was at church last week, too. . . . I had a requiem service."

"For whom?"

"For Lizaveta. She was killed with an ax."

His nerves were more and more strained. His head began to go around.

"Were you friends with Lizaveta?"

"Yes. . . . She was good . . . she used to come . . . not often . . . she couldn't. We used to read together and . . . talk. She will see God."

The last phrase sounded strange in his ears. And here was something new again: the mysterious meetings with Lizaveta and both of them—religious maniacs.

91

"I shall be a religious maniac myself soon! It's infectious!" he thought. "Read!" he cried irritably and insistently.

Sonia still hesitated. Her heart was throbbing. She hardly dared to read to him. He looked almost with exasperation at the "unhappy lunatic."

"What for? You don't believe. . . ." she whispered softly, breathlessly.

"Read! I want you to," he persisted. "You used to read to Lizaveta."

Sonia opened the book and found the place. Her hands were shaking; her voice failed her. Twice she tried to begin and could not bring out the first syllable.

"Now a certain man was sick named Lazarus of Bethany. . . ." she forced herself at last to read, but at the third word her voice broke like an overstrained string. There was a catch in her breath.

Raskolnikov saw in part why Sonia could not bring herself to read to him and the more he saw this, the more roughly and irritably he insisted on her doing so. He understood only too well how painful it was for her to betray and unveil all that was her *own*. He understood that these feelings really were her *secret treasure,* which she had kept perhaps for years, perhaps from childhood, while she lived with an unhappy father and a distracted stepmother crazed by grief, in the midst of starving children and unseemly abuse and reproaches. But at the same time he knew now and knew for certain that, although it filled her with dread and suffering, yet she had a tormenting desire to read and to read to *him* that he might hear it, and to read *now* whatever might come of it! . . . He read this in her eyes, he could see it in her intense emotion. She mastered herself, controlled the spasm in her throat and went on reading the eleventh chapter of St. John. She went on to the nineteenth verse:

"And many of the Jews came to Martha and Mary to comfort them concerning their brother.

"Then Martha as soon as she heard that Jesus was coming went and met Him: but Mary sat still in the house.

"Then said Martha unto Jesus, Lord, if Thou hadst been here, my brother had not died.

"But I know that even now whatsoever Thou wilt ask God, God will give it Thee. . . ."

Then she stopped again with a shamefaced feeling that her voice would quiver and break again.

92

"Jesus said unto her, thy brother shall rise again.

"Martha said unto Him, I know that he shall rise again in the resurrection, at the last day.

"Jesus said unto her, I am the resurrection and the life: he that believeth in Me though he were dead, yet shall he live.

"And whosoever liveth and believeth in Me shall never die. Believest thou this?

"She said unto Him . . ."

(And drawing a painful breath, Sonia read distinctly and forcibly as though she were making a public confession of faith.)

"Yea, Lord: I believe that Thou art the Christ, the Son of God Which should come into the world."

She stopped and looked up quickly at him, but controlling herself went on reading. Raskolnikov sat without moving, his elbows on the table and his eyes turned away. She read to the thirty-second verse.

"Then when Mary was come where Jesus was and saw Him, she fell down at His feet, saying unto Him, Lord if Thou hadst been here, my brother had not died.

"When Jesus therefore saw her weeping, and the Jews also weeping which came with her, He groaned in the spirit and was troubled,

"And said, Where have ye laid him? They said unto Him, Lord, come and see.

"Jesus wept.

"Then said the Jews, behold how He loved him!

"And some of them said, could not this Man which opened the eyes of the blind, have caused that even this man should not have died?"

Raskolnikov turned and looked at her with emotion. Yes, he had known it! She was trembling in a real physical fever. He had expected it. She was getting near the story of the greatest miracle and a feeling of immense triumph came over her. Her voice rang out like a bell; triumph and joy gave it power. The lines danced before her eyes, but she knew what she was reading by heart. At the last verse "Could not this Man which opened the eyes of the blind . . ." dropping her voice, she passionately reproduced the doubt, the reproach and censure of the blind disbelieving Jews, who in another moment would fall at His feet as though struck by thunder, sobbing and believing. . . . "And *he, he* too, is blinded and unbelieving; he, too, will hear; he, too, will believe; yes, yes! At once, now," was what she was dreaming, and she was quivering with happy anticipation.

93

"Jesus therefore again groaning in Himself cometh to the grave. It was a cave, and a stone lay upon it.

"Jesus said, Take ye away the stone. Martha, the sister of him that was dead, saith unto Him, Lord by this time he stinketh: for he hath been dead four days."

She laid emphasis on the word *four*.

"Jesus saith unto her, Said I not unto thee that if thou wouldest believe, thou shouldest see the glory of God?

"Then they took away the stone from the place where the dead was laid. And Jesus lifted up His eyes and said, Father, I thank Thee that Thou hast heard Me.

"And I knew that Thou hearest Me always; but because of the people which stand by I said it, that they may believe that Thou hast sent Me.

"And when He thus had spoken, He cried with a loud voice, Lazarus, come forth.

"And he that was dead came forth."

(She read loudly, cold and trembling with ecstasy, as though she were seeing it before her eyes.)

"Bound hand and foot with graveclothes; and his face was bound about with a napkin. Jesus saith unto them, Loose him and let him go.

"Then many of the Jews which came to Mary and had seen the things which Jesus did believed on Him."

She could read no more, closed the book and got up from her chair quickly.

"That is all about the raising of Lazarus," she whispered severely and abruptly; and turning away, she stood motionless, not daring to raise her eyes to him. She still trembled feverishly. The candle-end was flickering out in the battered candlestick, dimly lighting up in the poverty-stricken room the murderer and the harlot who had so strangely been reading together the eternal book. Five minutes or more passed.

"I came to speak of something," Raskolnikov said aloud, frowning. He got up and went to Sonia. She lifted her eyes to him in silence. His face was particularly stern and there was a sort of savage determination in it.

"I have abandoned my family today," he said. "My mother and sister. I am not going to see them. I've broken with them completely."

"What for?" asked Sonia, amazed. Her recent meeting with his

94

mother and sister had left a great impression which she could not analyze. She heard his news almost with horror.

"I have only you now," he added. "Let us go together. . . . I've come to you; we are both accursed; let us go our way together!"

His eyes glittered "as though he were mad," Sonia thought, in her turn.

"Go where?" she asked in alarm and she involuntarily stepped back.

"How do I know? I only know it's the same road. I know that and nothing more. It's the same goal!"

She looked at him and understood nothing. She knew only that he was terribly, infinitely unhappy.

"Not one of them will understand, if you tell them, but I have understood. I need you. That is why I have come to you."

"I don't understand," whispered Sonia.

"You'll understand later. Haven't you done the same? You too have transgressed . . . have had the strength to transgress. You have laid hands on yourself; you have destroyed a life . . . *your own* . . . it's all the same! You might have lived in spirit and understanding, but you'll end in the Hay Market. . . . You won't be able to stand it, and if you remain alone you'll go out of your mind like me. You are like a mad creature already. So we must go together on the same road! Let us go!"

"What for? What's all this for?" said Sonia, strangely and violently agitated by his words.

"What for? Because you can't remain like this, that's why! You must look things straight in the face at last and not weep like a child and cry that God won't allow it. What will happen if you should really be taken to the hospital tomorrow? Katerina is mad and in consumption; she'll soon die; and the children? Do you mean to tell me they won't come to grief? Haven't you seen children here at the street corners sent out by their mothers to beg? I've found out where those mothers live and in what surroundings. Children can't remain children there! At seven the child is vicious and a thief. Yet children, you know, are the image of Christ: 'theirs is the kingdom of Heaven.' He bade us honor and love them; they are the humanity of the future. . . ."

"What's to be done, what's to be done?" repeated Sonia, weeping hysterically and wringing her hands.

95

"What's to be done? Break what must be broken, once for all, that's all, and take the suffering on oneself. What? You don't understand? You'll understand later. . . . Freedom and power, and above all, power! Over all trembling creation and all the antheap! . . . That's the goal, remember that! That's my farewell message. Perhaps it's the last time I shall speak to you. If I don't come tomorrow, you'll hear of it all, and then remember these words. And some day later on in years to come you'll understand perhaps what they meant. If I come tomorrow, I'll tell you who killed Lizaveta. . . . Good-by."

Sonia started with terror.

"Why, do you know who killed her?" she asked, chilled with horror, looking wildly at him.

"I know and will tell . . . you, only you. I have chosen you. I'm not coming to you to ask forgiveness, but simply to tell you. I chose you long ago to hear this, when your father talked of you and when Lizaveta was alive, I thought of it. Good-by, don't shake hands. Tomorrow!"

He went out. Sonia gazed at him as at a madman. But she herself was like one insane and felt it. Her head was going around.

"Good heavens, how does he know who killed Lizaveta? What did *those* words mean? It's awful!" But at the same time *the idea* did not enter her head, not for a moment! "Oh, he must be terribly unhappy! . . . He has abandoned his mother and sister. . . . What for? What has happened? And what had he in his mind? What did he say to her? He had kissed her foot and said . . . said (yes, he had said it clearly) that he could not live without her. . . . Oh, merciful heavens!"

Sonia spent the whole night feverish and delirious. She jumped up from time to time, wept and wrung her hands, then sank again into feverish sleep and dreamed of her sister and mother and Lizaveta, of reading the gospel and of him . . . him with pale face, with burning eyes . . . kissing her feet, weeping.

On the other side of the door on the right, which divided Sonia's room from another flat, was a room which had long stood empty. A card was fixed on the gate and a notice stuck in the windows over the canal advertising it to let. Sonia had long been accustomed to the room's being uninhabited. But all that time Mr. Svidrigailov had been standing, listening at the door of the empty room. When Raskolnikov went out, he stood still a moment, went on tiptoe to his own room which adjoined the empty one, brought a chair and noiselessly carried it to the door that led to Sonia's room. The conversation had struck him as interesting and remarkable, and he had greatly enjoyed it—so much that he brought a chair so that he might not in the future, tomorrow for instance, have to endure the inconvenience of standing a whole hour, but might listen in comfort.

WHEN NEXT MORNING at eleven o'clock punctually Raskolnikov went into the department of the investigation of criminal cases and sent his name in to Porfiry Petrovitch, he was surprised at being kept waiting so long: it was at least ten minutes before he was summoned. He had expected that they would pounce upon him. But he stood in the waiting room, and people who apparently had nothing to do with him were continually passing to and fro before him. In the next room which looked like an office, several clerks were sitting writing and obviously they had no notion who or what Raskolnikov might be. . . .

Finally his name was called and he found Porfiry Petrovitch alone in his study. His study was a room neither large nor small, furnished with a large writing table, that stood before a sofa upholstered in checked material, a bureau, a bookcase in the corner and several chairs—all government furniture, of polished yellow wood. In the farther wall there was a closed door; beyond it there were, no doubt, other rooms. On Raskolnikov's entrance, Porfiry Petrovitch had at once closed the door by which he had come in and they remained alone. He met his visitor with an apparently genial and good-tempered air, and it was only after a few minutes that Raskolnikov saw signs of a certain awkwardness in him, as though he had been thrown out of his reckoning or caught in something very secret.

"Ah, my dear fellow! Here you are . . . in our domain," began Porfiry, holding out both hands to him. "Come, sit down, old man . . . or perhaps you don't like to be called 'my dear fellow' and 'old man'—*tout court?* Please don't think it too familiar. . . . Here, on the sofa."

Raskolnikov sat down, keeping his eyes fixed on him. "In our domain," the apologies for familiarity, the French phrase *tout court,* were all characteristic signs.

"He held out both hands to me, but he did not give me one—he drew it back in time," thought Raskolnikov suspiciously. Both were watching each other, but when their eyes met, quick as lightning they looked away.

"I brought you this paper . . . about the watch. Here it is. Is it all right or shall I copy it again?"

"What? A paper? Yes, yes, don't be uneasy, it's all right," Porfiry Petrovitch said as though in haste, and after he had said it he took the paper and looked at it. "Yes, it's all right. Nothing more is needed," he declared with the same rapidity and he laid the paper on the table.

A minute later when he was talking of something else, he took it from the table and put it on his bureau.

"I believe you said yesterday you would like to question me . . . formally . . . about my acquaintance with the murdered woman?" Raskolnikov was beginning again.

"Yes, yes, yes! There's no hurry, there's no hurry," muttered Porfiry Petrovitch, moving to and fro about the table without any apparent aim, making dashes toward the window, the bureau and the table, at one moment avoiding Raskolnikov's suspicious glance, then again standing still and looking him straight in the face.

His fat round little figure looked very strange, like a ball rolling from one side to the other and bounding back.

"We've plenty of time. Do you smoke? Have you your own? Here, a cigarette!" he went on, offering his visitor a cigarette. "You know I am receiving you here, but my own quarters are through there, you know, my government quarters. But I am living outside for the time. I had to have some repairs done here. It's almost finished now. . . . Government quarters, you know, are a capital thing. Eh, what do you think?"

"Yes, a capital thing," answered Raskolnikov, looking at him almost ironically.

"A capital thing, a capital thing," repeated Porfiry Petrovitch, as though he had just thought of something quite different. "Yes, a capital thing," he almost shouted at last, suddenly staring at Raskolnikov and stopping short two steps from him.

This stupid repetition was too incongruous with the serious, brooding and enigmatic glance he turned upon his visitor.

This stirred Raskolnikov's spleen more than ever and he could not resist an ironical and rather incautious challenge.

"Tell me, please," he asked suddenly, looking almost insolently at him and taking a kind of pleasure in his own insolence. "I believe it's a sort of legal rule, a sort of legal tradition—for all investigating lawyers—to begin their attack from afar with a trivial or at least an irrelevant subject so as to encourage, or rather, to divert the man they are cross-examining, to disarm his caution and then all at once to give him an unexpected knockdown blow with some fatal question. Isn't that so? It's a sacred tradition, mentioned, I fancy, in all the manuals of the art?"

"Yes, yes. . . . Why? Do you imagine that was why I spoke about government quarters . . . eh?"

And as he said this, Porfiry Petrovitch screwed up his eyes and winked; a good-humored, crafty look passed over his face. The wrinkles on his forehead were smoothed out, his eyes contracted, his features broadened and he suddenly went off into a nervous prolonged laugh, shaking all over and looking Raskolnikov straight in the face. The latter forced himself to laugh too, but when Porfiry, seeing that he was laughing, broke into such a guffaw that he turned almost crimson, Raskolnikov's repulsion overcame all precaution; he left off laughing, scowled and stared with hatred at Porfiry, keeping his eyes fixed on him while his intentionally prolonged laughter lasted. There was lack of precaution on both sides, however, for Porfiry Petrovitch seemed to be laughing in his visitor's face and to be very little disturbed at the annoyance with which the visitor received it. The latter fact was very significant in Raskolnikov's eyes: he saw that Porfiry Petrovitch had not been embarrassed just before either, but that he, Raskolnikov, had perhaps fallen into a trap; that there must be something, some motive here unknown to him; that, perhaps, everything was in readiness and in another moment would break upon him. . . .

He went straight to the point at once, rose from his seat and took his cap.

"Porfiry Petrovitch," he began resolutely, though with considerable irritation, "yesterday you expressed a desire that I should come to you for some inquiries." He laid special stress on the word "inquiries." "I have come and, if you have anything to ask me, ask it, and if not, allow me to withdraw. I have no time to spare. . . . I have to be at the funeral of that man who was run over, of whom you . . . know also," he added, feeling angry at once at having made this addition and more irritated at his anger. "I am sick of it all, do you hear, and have long been. It's partly what made me ill. In short," he shouted, feeling that the phrase about his illness was still more out of place, "in short, kindly examine me or let me go at once. And if you must examine me, do so in the proper form! I will not allow you to do so otherwise, and so meanwhile, good-by, as we have evidently nothing to keep us now."

"Good heavens! What do you mean? What shall I question you about?" cackled Porfiry Petrovitch with a change of tone, instantly leaving off laughing. "Please don't disturb yourself." He began fidgeting from place to place and fussily making Raskolnikov sit down. "There's no hurry, there's no hurry. It's all nonsense. Oh, no, I'm very glad you've come to see me at last . . . I look upon you simply as a visitor. And as for my confounded laughter, please excuse it, Rodion Raskolnikov. Rodion Raskolnikov? That *is* your name? . . . It's my nerves. You tickled me so with your witty observation; I assure you, sometimes I shake with laughter like an indiarubber ball for half an hour at a time. . . . I'm often afraid of an attack of paralysis. Do sit down. Please do, or I shall think you are angry. . . ."

Raskolnikov did not speak; he listened, watching him, still frowning angrily. He did sit down, but still held his cap.

"I must tell you one thing about myself, my dear Rodion," Porfiry continued, moving about the room and again avoiding his visitor's eyes. "You see, I'm a bachelor, a man of no consequence and not used to society; besides, I have nothing before me. I'm set, I'm running to seed and . . . and have you noticed, Rodion Raskolnikov, that in our Petersburg circles, if two clever men meet who are not intimate, but respect each other, like you and me, it takes them half an hour before they can find a subject for conversation—they are dumb, they sit opposite each other and feel awkward. Everyone has subjects of conversation, ladies for instance . . . people in high society always have their subjects of conversation, *c'est de rigueur,** but people of the middle sort like us, thinking people that is, are always tongue-tied and awkward. What is the reason for it? Whether it is the lack of public interest or whether it is that we are so honest we don't want to deceive one another, I don't know. What do you think? Do put down your cap; it looks as if you were just going; it makes me uncomfortable . . . I am so delighted. . . ."

Raskolnikov put down his cap and continued listening in silence with a serious frowning face to the vague and empty chatter of Porfiry Petrovitch. "Does he really want to distract my attention with his silly babble?"

"You are certainly quite right about it," Porfiry began gaily, looking with extraordinary simplicity at Raskolnikov (which startled him and instantly put him on his guard), "certainly quite right in laughing so

* One must, to be polite.

100

wittily at our legal forms, he-he! Some of these elaborate psychological methods are exceedingly ridiculous and perhaps useless if one adheres too closely to the forms. Yes . . . I am talking of forms again. Well, if I recognize, or more strictly speaking, if I suspect someone or other to be a criminal in any case entrusted to me . . . you're reading for the law, of course, Mr. Raskolnikov?"

"Yes, I was. . . ."

"Well, then, it is a precedent for you for the future—though don't suppose I should venture to instruct you after the articles you publish about crime! No, I simply make bold to state it by way of fact, if I took this man or that for a criminal, why, I ask, should I worry him prematurely, even though I had evidence against him? In one case I may be bound, for instance, to arrest a man at once, but another may be in quite a different position, you know, so why shouldn't I let him walk about the town a bit, he-he-he! But I see you don't quite understand, so I'll give you a clearer example. If I put him in prison too soon, I may very likely give him, so to speak, moral support, he-he! You're laughing?"

Raskolnikov had no idea of laughing. He was sitting with compressed lips, his feverish eyes fixed on Porfiry Petrovitch's.

"Yet that is the case, with some types especially, for men are so different. You say evidence. Well, there may be evidence. But evidence, you know, can generally be taken two ways. . . . And if I shut him up too soon—even though I might be convinced *he* was the man, I should very likely be depriving myself of the means of getting further evidence against him. And how? By giving him, so to speak, a definite position, I shall put him out of suspense and set his mind at rest so that he will retreat into his shell. They say that at Sevastopol, the clever people were in a terrible fright that the enemy would attack openly and take Sevastopol at once. But when they saw that the enemy preferred a regular siege, they were delighted, I am told, and reassured, for the thing would drag on for two months at least. You're laughing. You don't believe me again? Of course, you're right, too. You're right, you're right. These are all special cases, I admit. But you must observe this, my dear Raskolnikov, the general case, the case for which all legal forms and rules are intended, for which they are calculated and laid down in books, does not exist at all, for the reason that every case, every crime for instance, so soon as it actually occurs, at once becomes a thoroughly special case and sometimes a case unlike any that's gone before. Very comic cases of that sort sometimes occur. If

I leave one man quite alone, if I don't touch him and don't worry him, but let him know or at least suspect every moment that I know all about it and am watching him day and night, and if he is in continual suspicion and terror, he'll be bound to lose his head. He'll come of himself, or maybe do something which will make it as plain as twice two are four—it's delightful. It may be so with a simple peasant, but with one of our sort, an intelligent man cultivated on a certain side, it's a dead certainty. For, my dear fellow, it's a very important matter to know on what side a man is cultivated. And then there are nerves, there are nerves! You have overlooked them! Why, they are all sick, nervous and irritable! . . . And then how they all suffer from spleen! That I assure you is a regular gold mine for us. And it's no anxiety to me, his running about the town free! Let him, let him walk about for a bit! I know well enough that I've caught him and that he won't escape me. . . . It's not merely that he has nowhere to run to, he is *psychologically* unable to escape me, he-he! What an expression! Through a law of nature he can't escape me if he had anywhere to go. Have you seen a butterfly around a candle? That's how he will keep circling and circling around me. Freedom will lose its attractions. He'll begin to brood; he'll weave a tangle around himself; he'll worry himself to death! What's more, he will provide me with a mathematical proof— if I only give him a long enough interval. . . . And he'll keep circling around me, getting nearer and nearer and then—flop! He'll fly straight into my mouth and I'll swallow him, and that will be very amusing, he-he-he! You don't believe me?"

Raskolnikov made no reply; he sat pale and motionless, still gazing with the same intensity into Porfiry's face.

"It's a lesson," he thought, turning cold. "This is beyond the cat playing with a mouse, like yesterday. He can't be showing off his power with no motive . . . prompting me; he is far too clever for that. . . . He must have another object. What is it? It's all nonsense, my friend; you are pretending—to scare me! You've no proofs and the man I saw had no real existence. You simply want to make me lose my head, to work me up beforehand and so to crush me. But you are wrong! You won't do it! But why give me such a hint? Is he reckoning on my shattered nerves? No, my friend, you are wrong! You won't do it even though you have some trap for me . . . let us see what you have in store for me."

And he braced himself to face a terrible and unknown ordeal. At times he longed to fall on Porfiry and strangle him. This anger was what he dreaded from the beginning. He felt that his parched lips were flecked with foam; his heart was throbbing. But he was still determined not to speak till the right moment. He realized that this was the best policy in his position, because instead of saying too much he would be irritating his enemy by his silence and provoking him into speaking too freely. Anyhow, this was what he hoped for.

"No, I see you don't believe me. You think I am playing a harmless joke on you," Porfiry began again, getting more and more lively, chuckling at every instant and again pacing around the room. . . . Well, I'll tell you the whole truth, my dear fellow, about this *special case*. I mean: actual fact and a man's temperament, my dear sir, are weighty matters and it's astonishing how they sometimes deceive the sharpest calculation! . . . Well, to proceed, wit, in my opinion, is a splendid thing. It is, so to say, an adornment of nature and a consolation of life, and what tricks it can play! So that it sometimes is hard for a poor examining lawyer to know where he is, especially when he's liable to be carried away by his own fancy too, for you know he is a man after all. But the poor fellow is saved by the criminal's temperament; worse luck for him! But young people carried away by their own wit don't think of that 'when they overstep all obstacles' as you wittily and cleverly expressed it yesterday. He will lie—that is, the man who is a *special case,* the incognito—and he will lie well, in the cleverest fashion; you might think he would triumph and enjoy the fruits of his wit, but at the most interesting, the most flagrant moment he will faint. Of course there may be illness and a stuffy room as well, but anyway! Anyway he's given us the idea! He lied incomparably, but he didn't reckon on his temperament. That's what betrays him! Another time he will be carried away by his playful wit into making fun of the man who suspects him. He will turn pale, as it were, on purpose to mislead, but his paleness will be *too natural,* too much like the real thing. Again he has given us an idea! Though his questioner may be deceived at first, he will think differently next day if he is not a fool, and, of course, it is like that at every step! He puts himself forward where he is not wanted, speaks continually when he ought to keep silent, brings in all sorts of allegorical allusions, he-he! Comes and asks: why didn't you take me long ago? He-he-he! And that can happen, you know, with the cleverest man—the psychologist, the literary man. The temperament reflects everything like a mirror! Gaze into it and admire what you see! But why are you so pale, Mr. Raskolnikov? Is the room stuffy? Shall I open the window?"

"Oh, don't trouble, please," cried Raskolnikov and he suddenly broke into a laugh. "Please don't trouble."

Porfiry stood facing him, paused a moment and suddenly he too laughed. Raskolnikov got up from the sofa, abruptly checking his hysterical laughter.

"Porfiry Petrovitch," he began, speaking loudly and distinctly, though his legs trembled and he could scarcely stand. "I see clearly at last that you actually suspect me of murdering that old woman and her sister Lizaveta. Let me tell you for my part that I am sick of this. If you find that you have a right to prosecute me legally, to arrest me, then prosecute me, arrest me. But I will not let myself be jeered at to my face and worried. . . ."

His lips trembled, his eyes glowed with fury and he could not restrain his voice.

"I won't allow it!" he shouted, bringing his fist down on the table. "Do you hear that, Porfiry Petrovitch? I won't allow it."

"Good heavens! What does it mean?" cried Porfiry Petrovitch, apparently quite frightened. "Rodion Raskolnikov, my dear fellow, what is the matter with you?"

"I won't allow it," Raskolnikov shouted again.

"Hush, my dear man! They'll hear and come in. Just think—what could we say to them?" Porfiry Petrovitch whispered in horror, bringing his face close to Raskolnikov's.

"I won't allow it, I won't allow it," Raskolnikov repeated mechanically, but he too spoke in a sudden whisper.

Porfiry turned quickly and ran to open the window.

"Some fresh air! And you must have some water, my dear fellow. You're ill!" He was running to the door to call for some when he found a decanter of water in the corner. "Come, drink a little," he whispered, rushing up to him with the decanter. "It will be sure to do you good."

Porfiry Petrovitch's alarm and sympathy were so natural that Raskolnikov was silent and began looking at him with wild curiosity. He did not take the water, however.

"Rodion Raskolnikov, my dear fellow, you'll drive yourself out of your mind, I assure you, ach, ach! Have some water; do drink a little."

He forced him to take the glass. Raskolnikov raised it mechanically to his lips, but set it on the table again with disgust.

*　　*　　*

Raskolnikov looked haughtily and contemptuously at him.

"Briefly," he said loudly and imperiously, rising to his feet and in so doing, pushing Porfiry back a little, "briefly, I want to know, do you acknowledge me perfectly free from suspicion or not? Tell me, Porfiry Petrovitch; tell me once for all and make haste!"

"What a business I'm having with you!" cried Porfiry with a perfectly good-humored, sly and composed face. "And why do you want to know, why do you want to know so much, since they haven't begun to worry you? Why, you are like a child asking for matches! And why are you so uneasy? Why do you force yourself upon us, eh? He-he-he!"

"I repeat," Raskolnikov cried furiously, "that I can't put up with it!"

"With what? Uncertainty?" interrupted Porfiry.

"Don't jeer at me! I won't have it! I tell you I won't have it. I can't and I won't, do you hear, do you hear?" he shouted, bringing his fist down on the table again.

"Hush! Hush! They'll overhear! I warn you seriously; take care of yourself. I am not joking," Porfiry whispered, but this time there was not the look of old-womanish good-nature and alarm in his face. Now he was peremptory, stern, frowning and for once laying aside all mystification.

But this was only for an instant. Raskolnikov, bewildered, suddenly fell into actual frenzy, but, strange to say, he again obeyed the command to speak quietly, though he was in a perfect paroxysm of fury.

"I will not allow myself to be tortured," he whispered, instantly recognizing with hatred that he could not help obeying the command and driven to even greater fury by the thought. "Arrest me, search me, but kindly act in due form and don't play with me! Don't dare!"

"Don't worry about the form," Porfiry interrupted with the same sly smile, as it were, gloating with enjoyment over Raskolnikov. "I invited you to see me quite in a friendly way."

"I don't want your friendship and I spit on it! Do you hear? And, here, I take my cap and go. What will you say now if you mean to arrest me?"

He took up his cap and went to the door.

"And won't you see my little surprise?" chuckled Porfiry, again taking him by the arm and stopping him at the door.

He seemed to become more playful and good-humored—a thing which maddened Raskolnikov.

"What surprise?" he asked, standing still and looking at Porfiry in alarm.

"My little surprise; it's sitting there behind the door, he-he-he!" He pointed to the locked door. "I locked him in so that he should not escape. . . ."

"You are lying! Call the clerks! You knew I was ill and tried to work me into a frenzy to make me betray myself; that was your object! Produce your facts! I understand it all. You've no evidence; you have only wretched rubbishy suspicions like Zametov's! You knew my character, you wanted to drive me to fury and then to knock me down with priests and deputies. . . . Are you waiting for them? What are you waiting for? Where are they? Produce them!"

"Why deputies, my good man? What things people will imagine! And to do so would not be acting in form as you say; you don't know the business, my dear fellow. . . . And there's no escaping form, as you see," Porfiry muttered, listening at the door through which a noise could be heard.

"Ah, they're coming," cried Raskolnikov. "You've sent for them! You expected them! Well, produce them all: your deputies, your witnesses, what you like! . . . I am ready!"

But at this moment a strange incident occurred, something so unexpected that neither Raskolnikov nor Porfiry Petrovitch could have looked for such a conclusion to their interview.

WHEN HE REMEMBERED the scene afterwards, this is how Raskolnikov saw it.

The noise behind the door increased, and suddenly the door was opened a little.

"What is it?" cried Porfiry Petrovitch, annoyed. "Why, I gave orders . . ."

For an instant there was no answer, but it was evident that there were several persons at the door, and that they were apparently pushing somebody back.

"What is it?" Porfiry Petrovitch repeated, uneasily.

"The prisoner Nikolay has been brought," someone answered.

"He is not wanted! Take him away! Let him wait! What's he doing here? How irregular!" cried Porfiry, rushing to the door.

"But he . . ." began the same voice, and suddenly ceased.

106

Two seconds, not more, were spent in actual struggle; then someone gave a violent shove, and then a man, very pale, strode into the room.

This man's appearance was at first sight very strange. He stared straight before him, as though seeing nothing. There was a determined gleam in his eyes; at the same time there was a deathly pallor in his face, as though he were being led to the scaffold. His white lips were faintly twitching.

He was dressed like a house painter and was of medium height, very young, slim, his hair cut in a round crop, with thin spare features. The man whom he had thrust back followed him into the room and succeeded in seizing him by the shoulder; he was a warder; but Nikolay pulled his arm away.

Several persons crowded inquisitively into the doorway. Some of them tried to get in. All this took place almost instantaneously.

"Go away, it's too soon! Wait till you are sent for! . . . Why have you brought him so soon?" Porfiry Petrovitch muttered, extremely annoyed and, as it were, thrown out of his reckoning.

But Nikolay suddenly knelt down.

"What's the matter?" cried Porfiry, surprised.

"I am guilty! Mine is the sin! I am the murderer," Nikolay articulated suddenly, rather breathless, but speaking fairly loudly.

For ten seconds there was silence as though all had been struck dumb; even the warder stepped back, mechanically retreated to the door and stood immovable.

"What is it?" cried Porfiry Petrovitch, recovering from his momentary stupefaction.

"I . . . am the murderer," repeated Nikolay, after a brief pause.

"What . . . you . . . what . . . whom did you kill?" Porfiry Petrovitch was obviously bewildered.

Nikolay again was silent for a moment.

"Alyona Ivanovna and her sister Lizaveta Ivanovna, I . . . killed . . . with an ax. Darkness came over me," he added suddenly, and was again silent.

He still remained on his knees. Porfiry Petrovitch stood for some moments as though meditating, but suddenly roused himself and waved back the uninvited spectators. They instantly vanished and closed the door. Then he looked towards Raskolnikov, who was standing in the corner, staring wildly at Nikolay, and moved towards him, but stopped short, looked from Nikolay to Raskolnikov and then

107

again at Nikolay, and seeming unable to restrain himself, darted at the latter.

"You're in too great a hurry," he shouted at him, almost angrily. . . ."Did you do it alone?"

"Yes, alone. The other painter is not guilty and had no share in it."

"Don't be in a hurry about him! A-ach! How was it you ran downstairs like that at the time? The porters met you both!"

"It was to put them off the scent. . . . I ran after him," Nikolay replied hurriedly, as though he had prepared the answer.

"I knew it!" cried Porfiry, with vexation. "It's not his own tale he is telling," he muttered as though to himself, and suddenly his eyes rested on Raskolnikov again.

He was apparently so taken up with Nikolay that for a moment he had forgotten Raskolnikov. He was a little taken aback.

"My dear Raskolnikov, excuse me!" He flew up to him. "This won't do; I'm afraid you must go . . . it's no good your staying . . . I will . . . you see, what a surprise! . . . Good-by!"

And taking him by the arm, he showed him to the door.

"I suppose you didn't expect it?" said Raskolnikov who, though he had not yet fully grasped the situation, had regained his courage.

"You did not expect it either, my friend. See how your hand is trembling! He-he!"

"You're trembling, too, Porfiry Petrovitch!"

"Yes, I am; I didn't expect it."

They were already at the door; Porfiry was impatient for Raskolnikov to be gone.

"And your little surprise—aren't you going to show it to me?" Raskolnikov said, sarcastically.

"Why, his teeth are chattering as he asks, he-he! You are an ironical person! Come, till we meet again!"

"I believe we can say *good-by!*"

"That's in God's hands," muttered Porfiry, with an unnatural smile.

[*In his own room Raskolnikov was again confronted by the anonymous man who had accused him of being a murderer. He had come this time to apologize for his accusation; he was the surprise Porfiry had intended for Raskolnikov, but after Nikolay's confession, he too was sent away. The man apologized and departed, leaving Raskolnikov more firmly resolved to resist the temptation to confess.*]

PART FIVE

[*Luzhin's wounded vanity was increasing; he called Sonia to his room and gave her ten rubles for her distressed family, then appeared at the funeral party and accused her of stealing a hundred-ruble-note from him. The note was found in her pocket, but the plot failed when Luzhin's roommate appeared and testified that he had seen Luzhin himself slip the note into Sonia's pocket. Luzhin left in disgrace after Raskolnikov disclosed that this had been Luzhin's attempt to discredit him and to win back Dounia.*

The disturbance was too much for the landlady and she packed the widow and her poor children out into the street. Raskolnikov followed Sonia to her lodgings, determined to confess his guilt to her.]

"Listen, Sonia." He suddenly smiled, a pale helpless smile for two seconds. "You remember what I meant to tell you yesterday?"

Sonia waited uneasily.

"I said as I went away that perhaps I was saying good-by forever, but that if I came today I would tell you who . . . who killed Lizaveta."

She began trembling all over.

"Well, here I've come to tell you."

"Then you really meant it yesterday?" she whispered with difficulty. "How do you know?" she asked quickly, as though suddenly regaining her reason.

Sonia's face grew paler and paler, and she breathed painfully.

"I know."

She paused a minute.

"Have they found him?" she asked timidly.

"No."

"Then how do you know about *it?*" she asked again, hardly audibly and again after a minute's pause.

He turned to her and looked very intently at her.

"Guess," he said, with the same distorted helpless smile.

A shudder passed over her.

"But you . . . why do you frighten me like this?" she said, smiling like a child.

109

"I must be a great friend of *his* . . . since I know," Raskolnikov went on, still gazing into her face, as though he could not turn his eyes away. "He . . . did not mean to kill that Lizaveta . . . he . . . killed her accidentally. . . . He meant to kill the old woman when she was alone and he went there . . . and then Lizaveta came in . . . he killed her too."

Another awful moment passed. Both still gazed at each other.

"You can't guess, then?" he asked suddenly, feeling as though he were flinging himself down from a steeple.

"N-no . . ." whispered Sonia.

"Take a good look."

As soon as he had said this again, the same familiar sensation froze his heart. He looked at her and all at once seemed to see in her face the face of Lizaveta. He remembered clearly the expression in Lizaveta's face, when he approached her with the ax and she stepped back to the wall, putting out her hand, with childish terror in her face, looking as little children do when they begin to be frightened of something, looking intently and uneasily at what frightens them, shrinking back and holding out their little hands on the point of crying. Almost the same thing happened now to Sonia. With the same helplessness and the same terror, she looked at him for a while and, suddenly putting out her left hand, pressed her fingers faintly against his breast and slowly began to get up from the bed, moving farther from him and keeping her eyes fixed even more immovably on him. Her terror infected him. The same fear showed itself on his face. In the same way he stared at her and almost with the same *childish* smile.

"Have you guessed?" he whispered at last.

"Good God!" broke in an awful wail from her bosom.

She sank helplessly onto the bed with her face in the pillows, but a moment later she got up, moved quickly to him, seized both his hands and, gripping them tight in her thin fingers, began looking into his face again with the same intent stare. In this last desperate look she tried to look into him and catch some last hope. But there was no hope; there was no doubt remaining; it was all true! Later on, indeed, when she recalled that moment, she thought it strange and wondered why she had seen at once that there was no doubt. She could not have said, for instance, that she had foreseen something of the sort—and yet now, as soon as he told her, she suddenly fancied that she had really foreseen this very thing.

110

"Stop, Sonia, enough! don't torture me," he begged her miserably.

It was not at all, not at all like this he had thought of telling her, but this is how it happened.

She jumped up, seeming not to know what she was doing, and, wringing her hands, walked into the middle of the room, but quickly went back and sat down again beside him, her shoulder almost touching his. All of a sudden she started as though she had been stabbed, uttered a cry and fell on her knees before him, she did not know why.

"What have you done—what have you done to yourself!" she said in despair, and, jumping up, she flung herself on his neck, threw her arms around him, and held him tight.

Raskolnikov drew back and looked at her with a mournful smile.

"You are a strange girl, Sonia—you kiss me and hug me when I tell you about that. . . . You don't think what you are doing."

"There is no one—no one in the whole world now so unhappy as you!" she cried in a frenzy, not hearing what he said, and she suddenly broke into violent hysterical weeping.

A feeling long unfamiliar to him flooded his heart and softened it at once. He did not struggle against it. Two tears started into his eyes and hung on his eyelashes.

"Then you won't leave me, Sonia?" he said, looking at her almost with hope.

"No, no, never, nowhere!" cried Sonia. "I will follow you, I will follow you everywhere. Oh, my God! Oh, how miserable I am! . . . Why, why didn't I know you before! Why didn't you come before? Oh, dear!"

"Here I have come."

"Yes, now! What's to be done now! . . . Together, together!" she repeated almost unconsciously, and she hugged him again. "I'll follow you to Siberia!"

He recoiled at this, and the same hostile, almost haughty smile came to his lips.

"Perhaps I don't want to go to Siberia yet, Sonia," he said.

Sonia looked at him quickly.

Again after her first passionate, agonizing sympathy for the unhappy man, the terrible idea of the murder overwhelmed her. In his changed tone she seemed to hear the murderer speaking. She looked at him bewildered. She knew nothing as yet: why, how, with what object it had been done. Now all these questions rushed at once into

111

her mind. And again she could not believe it: "He, he is a murderer! Could it be true?"

"What's the meaning of it? Where am I?" she said in complete bewilderment, as though still unable to recover herself. "How could you, you, a man like you. . . . How could you bring yourself to it? . . . What does it mean?"

"Oh, well—to plunder. Leave off, Sonia," he answered wearily, almost with vexation.

Sonia stood as though struck dumb, but suddenly she cried:

"You were hungry! It was . . . to help your mother? Yes?"

"No, Sonia, no," he muttered, turning away and hanging his head. "I was not so hungry. . . . I certainly did want to help my mother, but . . . that's not the real thing either. . . . Don't torture me, Sonia."

Sonia clasped her hands.

"Could it, could it all be true? Good God, what a truth! Who could believe it? And how could you give away your last coin and yet rob and murder! Ah," she cried suddenly, "that money you gave Katerina . . . that money. . . . Can that money—"

"No, Sonia," he broke in hurriedly, "that money was not it. Don't worry yourself! That money my mother sent me and it came when I was ill, the day I gave it to you. . . . Razumihin saw it . . . he received it for me. . . . That money was mine—my own."

Sonia listened to him in bewilderment and did her utmost to comprehend.

"And *that* money. . . . I don't even know really whether there was any money," he added softly, as though reflecting. "I took a purse off her neck, made of chamois leather . . . a purse stuffed full of something . . . but I didn't look in it; I suppose I hadn't time. . . . And the things—chains and trinkets—I buried under a stone with the purse next morning in a yard."

Sonia strained every nerve to listen.

"Then why . . . why? You said you did it to rob, but you took nothing?" she asked quickly, catching at a straw.

"I don't know. . . . I haven't yet decided whether to take that money or not," he said, musing again; and, seeming to wake up with a start, he gave a brief ironical smile. "Ach, what silly stuff I am talking, eh?"

The thought flashed through Sonia's mind: wasn't he mad? But she

112

dismissed it at once. "No, it was something else." She could make nothing of it, nothing.

"Do you know, Sonia," he said suddenly with conviction, "let me tell you: if I'd simply killed because I was hungry," laying stress on every word and looking enigmatically but sincerely at her, "I should be *happy* now. You must believe that! What would it matter to you?" he cried a moment later with a sort of despair. "What would it matter to you if I were to confess that I did wrong! What do you gain by such a stupid triumph over me? Ah, Sonia, was it for that I've come to you today?"

Again Sonia tried to say something, but did not speak.

"I asked you to go with me yesterday because you are all I have left."

"Go where?" asked Sonia timidly.

"Not to steal and not to murder; don't be anxious," he smiled bitterly. "We are so different. . . . And you know, Sonia, it's only now, only this moment that I understand *where* I asked you to go with me yesterday! Yesterday when I said it, I did not know where. I asked you for one thing; I came to you for one thing—not to leave me. You won't leave me, Sonia?"

She squeezed his hand.

"And why, why did I tell her? Why did I let her know?" he cried a minute later in despair, looking with infinite anguish at her. "Here you expect an explanation from me, Sonia; you are sitting and waiting for it. I see that. But what can I tell you? You won't understand and will only suffer misery . . . on my account! Well, you are crying and embracing me again. Why do you do it? Because I couldn't bear my burden and have come to throw it on another, you must now suffer too and I shall feel better! And can you love such a mean wretch?"

"But aren't you suffering too?" cried Sonia.

Again a wave of the same feeling surged into his heart, and again for an instant softened it.

"Sonia, I have a bad heart; take note of that. It may explain a great deal. I have come because I am bad. There are men who wouldn't have come. But I am a coward and . . . a mean wretch. But . . . never mind! That's not the point. I must speak now, but I don't know how to begin."

He paused and sank into thought.

113

"Ach, we are so different," he cried again. "We are not alike. And why, why did I come? I shall never forgive myself that."

"No, no, it was a good thing you came," cried Sonia. "It's better I should know, far better!"

He looked at her with anguish.

"What if it were really that?" he said, as though reaching a conclusion. "Yes, that's what it was! I wanted to become a Napoleon; that is why I killed her. . . . Do you understand now?"

"N-no," Sonia whispered naively and timidly. "Only speak, speak! I shall understand, I shall understand *in myself!*" she kept begging him.

"You'll understand? Very well; we shall see!" He paused and was for some time lost in meditation.

"It was like this: I asked myself one day this question—what if Napoleon, for instance, had happened to be in my place, and if he had not had Toulon nor Egypt nor the passage of Mont Blanc to begin his career with, but instead of all those picturesque and monumental things, there had simply been some ridiculous old hag, a pawnbroker, who had to be murdered to get money from her trunk (for his career, you understand). Well, would he have brought himself to that, if there had been no other means? Wouldn't he have felt a pang at its being so far from monumental and . . . and sinful, too?"

"You had better tell me straight out . . . without examples," she begged, still more timidly and scarcely audibly.

He turned to her, looked sadly at her and took her hands.

"You are right again, Sonia. Of course that's all nonsense; it's almost all talk! You see, you know that my mother has scarcely anything; my sister happened to have a good education and was condemned to drudge as a governess. All their hopes were centered on me. I was a student, but I couldn't keep myself at the university and was forced for a time to leave it. Even if I had lingered on like that, in ten or twelve years I might (with luck) hope to be some sort of teacher or clerk with a salary of a thousand rubles" (he repeated it as though it were a lesson) "and by that time my mother would be worn out with grief and anxiety and I could not succeed in keeping her in comfort while my sister . . . well, my sister might well have fared worse! . . . So I resolved to gain possession of the old woman's money and to use it for my first years without worrying my mother, to keep myself at the university and for a little while after leaving it—and to do this all on a broad, thorough scale so as to build

114

up a completely new career and enter upon a new life of independence. . . . Well . . . that's all. . . . Well, of course, in killing the old woman I did wrong. . . . Well, that's enough."

He struggled to the end of his speech in exhaustion and let his head sink.

"Oh, that's not it, that's not it," Sonia cried in distress. "How could one . . . no, that's not right, not right."

"You see yourself that it's not right. But I've spoken truly; it's the truth."

"As though that could be the truth! Good God!"

"I've only killed a louse, Sonia, a useless, loathsome, harmful creature."

"A human being—a louse!"

"I too know it wasn't a louse," he answered, looking strangely at her. "But I am talking nonsense, Sonia," he added. "I've been talking nonsense a long time. . . . That's not it; you are right there. There were quite, quite other causes for it! I haven't talked to anyone for so long, Sonia. . . . My head aches dreadfully now."

His eyes shone with feverish brilliance. He was almost delirious; an uneasy smile strayed on his lips. His terrible exhaustion could be seen through his excitement. Sonia saw how he was suffering. She too was growing dizzy. And he talked so strangely; it seemed somehow comprehensible, but yet. . . . "But how, how! Good God!" And she wrung her hands in despair.

"No, Sonia, that's not it," he began again suddenly, raising his head, as though a new and sudden train of thought had struck and roused him—"that's not it! Better . . . imagine—yes, it's certainly better—imagine that I am vain, envious, malicious, base, vindictive and . . . well, perhaps with a tendency to insanity. Let's have it all out at once! They've talked of madness already, I noticed. . . .

"I divined, Sonia," he went on eagerly, "that power is only vouchsafed to the man who dares to stoop and pick it up. There is only one thing, one thing needful: one has only to dare! Then for the first time in my life an idea took shape in my mind which no one had ever thought of before me, no one! I saw clear as daylight how strange it is that not a single person living in this mad world has had the daring to go straight for it all and send it flying to the devil! I . . . I wanted *to have the daring* . . . and I killed her. I only wanted to have the daring, Sonia! That was the whole cause of it!"

"Oh hush, hush," cried Sonia, clasping her hands. "You turned

115

away from God and God has smitten you, has given you over to the devil!"

"Then, Sonia, when I used to lie there in the dark and all this became clear to me, was it a temptation of the devil, eh?"

"Hush, don't laugh, blasphemer! You don't understand, you don't understand! Oh God! He won't understand!"

"Hush, Sonia! I am not laughing. I know myself that it was the devil leading me. Hush, Sonia, hush!" he repeated with gloomy insistence. "I know it all, I have thought it all over and over and whispered it all over to myself, lying there in the dark. . . . I've argued it all over with myself, every point of it, and I know it all, all! . . . I want to prove one thing only, that the devil led me on then and he has shown me since that I had not the right to take that path, because I am just such a louse as all the rest. He was mocking me and here I've come to you now! Welcome your guest! If I were not a louse, should I have come to you? Listen: when I went then to the old woman's I only went to *try*. . . . You may be sure of that!"

"And you murdered her!"

"But how did I murder her? Is that how men do murders? Do men go to commit a murder as I went then? I will tell you some day how I went! Did I murder the old woman? I murdered myself, not her! I crushed myself once for all, forever. . . . But it was the devil that killed that old woman, not I. Enough, enough, Sonia, enough! Let me be!" he cried in a sudden spasm of agony. "Let me be!"

He leaned his elbows on his knees and squeezed his head in his hands as in a vise.

"What suffering!" A wail of anguish broke from Sonia.

"Well, what am I to do now?" he asked, suddenly raising his head and looking at her with a face hideously distorted by despair.

"What are you to do?" she cried, jumping up, and her eyes that had been full of tears suddenly began to shine. "Stand up!" She seized him by the shoulder; he got up, looking at her almost bewildered. "Go at once, this very minute, stand at the crossroads, bow down, first kiss the earth which you have defiled and then bow down to all the world and say to all men aloud, 'I am a murderer!' Then God will send you life again. Will you go, will you go?" she asked him, trembling all over, snatching his two hands, squeezing them tight in hers and gazing at him with eyes full of fire.

He was amazed at her sudden ecstasy. "Don't be a child, Sonia," he said softly. "What wrong have I done them? Why should I go to them? What should I say to them? That's only a phantom. . . .

116

They destroy men by millions themselves and look on it as a virtue. They are knaves and scoundrels, Sonia! I am not going to them. And what should I say to them—that I murdered her, but did not dare to take the money and hid it under a stone?" he added with a bitter smile. "Why, they would laugh at me, and would call me a fool for not getting it. A coward and a fool! They wouldn't understand and they don't deserve to understand. Why should I go to them? I won't. Don't be a child, Sonia. . . ."

"It will be too much for you to bear, too much!" she repeated, holding out her hands in despairing supplication.

"Perhaps I've been unfair to myself," he observed gloomily, pondering. "Perhaps after all I am a man and not a louse and I've been in too great a hurry to condemn myself. I'll make another fight for it."

A haughty smile appeared on his lips.

"What a burden to bear! And your whole life, your whole life!"

"I shall get used to it," he said grimly and thoughtfully. "Listen," he began a minute later, "stop crying; it's time to talk of the facts: I've come to tell you that the police are after me, on my track. . . ."

"Ach!" Sonia cried in terror.

"Well, why do you cry out? You want me to go to Siberia and now you are frightened? But let me tell you: I shall not give myself up. I shall make a struggle for it and they won't do anything to me. They've no real evidence. Yesterday I was in great danger and believed I was lost; but today things are going better. All the facts they know can be explained two ways: that's to say I can turn their accusations to my credit. Do you understand? And I shall, for I've learned my lesson. But they will certainly arrest me. If it had not been for something that happened, they would have done so today for certain; perhaps even now they will arrest me today. . . . But that's no matter, Sonia; they'll let me out again . . . for there isn't any real proof against me, and there won't be. I give you my word for it. And they can't convict a man on what they have against me. Enough. . . . I only tell you that you may know. . . . I will try to manage somehow to put it to my mother and sister so that they won't be frightened. . . . My sister's future is secure now, I believe . . . and my mother's must be too. . . . Well, that's all. Be careful, though. Will you come and see me in prison when I am there?"

"Oh, I will, I will."

They sat side by side, both mournful and dejected, as though they had been cast up by the tempest alone on some deserted shore. He looked at Sonia and felt how great was her love for him, and strange to say, he felt it suddenly burdensome and painful to be so loved. Yes, it was a strange and awful sensation! On his way to see Sonia he had felt that all his hopes rested on her; he expected to be rid of at least part of his suffering and now when all her heart turned towards him, he suddenly felt that he was immeasurably unhappier than before.

"Sonia," he said, "you'd better not come and see me when I am in prison."

Sonia did not answer; she was crying. Several minutes passed.

"Have you a cross on you?" she asked, as though suddenly thinking of it.

He did not at first understand the question.

"No, of course not. Here; take this one of cypress wood. I have another, a copper one that belonged to Lizaveta. I changed with Lizaveta: she gave me her cross and I gave her my little icon. I will wear Lizaveta's now and give you this. Take it . . . it's mine! It's mine, you know," she begged him. "We will go to suffer together, and together we will bear our cross!"

"Give it to me," said Raskolnikov.

He did not want to hurt her feelings. But immediately he drew back the hand he held out for the cross.

"Not now, Sonia. Better later," he added to comfort her.

"Yes, yes, better," she repeated with conviction. "When you go to meet your suffering, then put it on. You will come to me; I'll put it on you; we will pray and go together."

[*Dispossessed and now obviously deranged, Sonia's mother took her children into the streets to sing and dance for pennies; she collapsed there and was brought to Sonia's room to die. Svidrigailov suddenly appeared, drew Raskolnikov aside and told him that he would give Sonia and the children the 10,000 rubles he had offered Dounia. He also let Raskolnikov know that he had heard his confession to Sonia.*]

PART SIX

[*The mysterious behavior of Svidrigailov caused Raskolnikov to undergo a period of profound uneasiness. He decided, finally, to have it out with him, but as he opened the door to his room he stumbled on Porfiry, the police inspector.*]

"AH THESE CIGARETTES!" Porfiry Petrovitch ejaculated at last, having lighted one. "They are pernicious, positively pernicious, and yet I can't give them up! I cough, I begin to have tickling in my throat and a difficulty in breathing. You know I am a coward, I went lately to my doctor; he always gives at least half an hour to each patient. He positively laughed when he looked at me; he sounded me: 'Tobacco's bad for you,' he said. 'Your lungs are affected.' But how am I to give it up? What is there to take its place? I don't drink; that's one mischief—he-he-he—that I don't do. Everything is relative, Rodion Raskolnikov; everything is relative!"

"Why, he's playing his professional tricks again," Raskolnikov thought with disgust. All the circumstances of their last interview suddenly came back to him, and he felt a rush of the feeling that had come upon him then.

"I came to see you the day before yesterday, in the evening; you didn't know?" Porfiry Petrovitch went on, looking around the room. "I came into this very room. I was passing by, just as I did today, and I thought I'd return your call. I walked in, since your door was wide open. I looked around, waited and went out without leaving my name with your servant. Don't you lock your door?"

Raskolnikov's face grew more and more gloomy. Porfiry seemed to guess his state of mind.

"I've come to have it out with you, Rodion Raskolnikov, my dear fellow! I owe you an explanation and must give it to you," he continued with a slight smile, just patting Raskolnikov's knee.

But almost at the same instant a serious and careworn look came into his face; to his surprise, Raskolnikov saw a touch of sadness in it. He had never seen and never suspected such an expression in his face.

"A strange scene passed between us last time we met, Rodion Raskolnikov. Our first interview, too, was a strange one; but then . . . and one thing after another! This is the point: I have perhaps acted unfairly to you; I feel it. Do you remember how we parted? Your nerves were unhinged and your knees were shaking and so were mine. And, you know, our behavior was unseemly, even ungentlemanly. And yet we are gentlemen—above all, in any case, gentlemen; that must be understood. Do you remember what we came to? . . . It was quite indecorous."

"What is he up to, what does he take me for?" Raskolnikov asked

119

himself in amazement, raising his head and looking with open eyes at Porfiry.

"I've decided openness is better between us," Porfiry Petrovitch went on, turning his head away and dropping his eyes, as though unwilling to disconcert his former victim and as though disdaining his former wiles. "Yes, such suspicions and such scenes cannot continue for long. Nikolay put a stop to it, or I don't know what we might not have come to. . . . You are nervously irritable, Rodion Raskolnikov, by temperament; it's out of proportion with other qualities of your heart and character, which I flatter myself I have to some extent divined. Of course I did reflect even then that it does not always happen that a man gets up and blurts out his whole story. It does happen sometimes, if you make a man lose all patience, though even then it's rare. I was capable of realizing that. If I only had a fact, I thought, the least little fact to go upon, something I could lay hold of, something tangible, not merely psychological. For if a man is guilty, you must be able to get something substantial out of him; one may reckon upon most surprising results indeed. I was reckoning on your temperament, Rodion Raskolnikov, on your temperament above all things! I had great hopes of you at that time."

"But what are you driving at now?" Raskolnikov muttered at last, asking the question without thinking.

"What is he talking about?" he wondered distractedly. "Does he really take me to be innocent?"

"What am I driving at? I've come to explain myself. I consider it my duty, so to speak. I want to make clear to you how the whole business, the whole misunderstanding arose. I've caused you a great deal of suffering, Rodion Raskolnikov. I am not a monster. I understand what it must mean for a man who has been unfortunate, but who is proud, imperious and above all impatient, to have to bear such treatment! I regard you in any case as a man of noble character and not without elements of magnanimity, though I don't agree with all your convictions. I wanted to tell you this first, frankly and quite sincerely, for above all I don't want to deceive you. When I made your acquaintance, I felt attracted by you. Perhaps you will laugh at my saying so. You have a right to. I know you disliked me from the first and indeed you've no reason to like me. You may think what you like, but I desire now to do all I can to efface that impression and to show that I am a man of heart and conscience. I speak sincerely."

Porfiry Petrovitch made a dignified pause. Raskolnikov felt a rush

120

of renewed alarm. The thought that Porfiry believed him to be innocent began to make him uneasy.

"It's scarcely necessary to go over everything in detail," Porfiry Petrovitch went on. "Indeed I could scarcely attempt it. To begin with, there were rumors. Through whom, how, and when those rumors came to me . . . and how they affected you, I need not go into. My suspicions were aroused by a complete accident which might just as easily not have happened. What was it? Hm! I believe there is no need to go into that either. Those rumors and that accident led to one idea in my mind. I admit it openly—for one may as well make a clean breast of it—I was the first to pitch on you. The old woman's notes on the pledges and the rest of it—that all came to nothing. Yours was one of a hundred. I happened, too, to hear of the scene at the office from a man who described it capitally, unconsciously reproducing the scene with great vividness. It was just one thing after another, my dear fellow!

"How could I avoid being brought to certain ideas? From a hundred rabbits you can't make a horse; a hundred suspicions don't make a proof, as the English proverb says, but that's only from the rational point of view—you can't help being partial, for after all, a lawyer is only human. I thought, too, of your article in that journal; do you remember? On your first visit we talked of it. I jeered at you at the time, but that was only to lead you on. I repeat, Rodion Raskolnikov, you are ill and impatient. That you were bold, headstrong, in earnest and . . . had felt a great deal I recognized long before. I too have felt the same, so that your article seemed familiar to me. It was conceived on sleepless nights, with a throbbing heart, in ecstasy and suppressed enthusiasm. And that proud suppressed enthusiasm in young people is dangerous! I jeered at you then, but let me tell you that, as a literary amateur, I am awfully fond of such first essays, full of the heat of youth. There is a mistiness and a chord vibrating in the mist. Your article is absurd and fantastic, but there's a transparent sincerity, a youthful incorruptible pride and the daring of despair in it. It's a gloomy article, but that's what's fine in it. I read your article and put it aside, thinking as I did so 'that man won't go the common way.' Well, I ask you, after that as a preliminary, how could I help being carried away by what followed? . . .

"Do you suppose I didn't come to search your room all this time? I did, I did, he-he! I was here even when you were lying ill in bed; not officially, not in my own person, but I was here. Your room was searched to the last thread at the first suspicion; but, I thought to my-self, now that man will come, will come of himself and quickly, too; if he's guilty, he's sure to come. Another man wouldn't but he will. And you remember how Mr. Razumihin began discussing the subject with you? We arranged that to excite you; we purposely spread rumors so that he might discuss the case with you, and Razumihin is not a man to restrain his indignation. Mr. Zametov was tremendously struck by your anger and your open daring. Think of blurting out in a restaurant 'I killed her!' It was too daring, too reckless. I thought so myself: if he is guilty he will be a formidable opponent. That was what I thought at the time. I was expecting you. But you simply bowled Zametov over and . . . well, you see, it all lies in this—that this damnable psychology can be taken two ways! Well, I kept ex-pecting you, and so it was: you came! My heart was fairly throbbing. Ach!

"Now, why need you have come? Your laughter too as you came in; do you remember? I saw it all plain as daylight, but if I hadn't ex-pected you so specially, I should not have noticed anything in your laughter. You see what influence a mood has! Mr. Razumihin then —ah, that stone, that stone under which the things were hidden! I seem to see it somewhere in a kitchen garden. It was in a kitchen garden, you told Zametov and afterwards you repeated that in my of-fice? And when we began picking your article to pieces, how you explained it! One could take every word of yours in two senses, as though there were another meaning hidden. . . .

"And so, Rodion Raskolnikov, can you wonder that I played such pranks on you? And what made you come at that very minute? Some-one seemed to have sent you, by Jove! And if Nikolay had not parted us . . . and do you remember Nikolay at the time? Do you remem-ber him clearly? It was a thunderbolt, a regular thunderbolt! And how I met him! I didn't believe in the thunderbolt, not for a minute. You could see it for yourself; and how could I? Even afterwards, when you had gone and he began making very, very plausible answers on certain points so that I was surprised at him myself, even then I didn't believe his story! You see what it is to be as firm as a rock! No, thought I. What has Nikolay got to do with it!"

"Razumihin told me just now that you think Nikolay guilty and had assured him of it. . . ."

His voice failed him, and he broke off. He had been listening in indescribable agitation, as this man who had seen through and through him went back upon himself. He was afraid of believing it and did not believe it. In those still ambiguous words he kept eagerly looking for something more definite and conclusive.

"Mr. Razumihin!" cried Porfiry Petrovitch, seeming glad of a question from Raskolnikov, who had till then been silent. "He-he-he! But I had to put Mr. Razumihin off; two is company, three is none. Mr. Razumihin is not the right man; besides, he is an outsider. He came running to me with a pale face. . . . But never mind him; why bring him in? To return to Nikolay: would you like to know what sort of a type he is; how I understand him, that is? To begin with, he is still a child and not exactly a coward, but something by way of an artist. Really, don't laugh at my describing him so. He is innocent and responsive to influence. He has a heart and is a fantastic fellow. He sings and dances; he tells stories, they say, so that people come from other villages to hear him. He attends school too, and laughs till he cries if you hold up a finger to him; he will drink himself senseless— not as a regular vice, but at times when people treat him, like a child. And he stole too, without knowing it himself, for 'How can it be stealing, if one picks it up?' he asked himself. And do you know he was for two years in his village under the spiritual guidance of a certain elder? I learned all this from Nikolay and from his fellow villagers. And what's more, he wanted to run into the wilderness! He was full of fervor, prayed at night, read the old books, 'the true' ones, and read himself crazy.

"Petersburg had a great effect upon him, especially the women and the wine. He responds to everything and he forgot the elder and all that. I learned that an artist here took a fancy to him and used to go and see him; and now this business came upon him.

"Well, he was frightened. He tried to hang himself! He ran away! How can one get over the idea the people have of Russian legal proceedings! The very word 'trial' frightens some of them. Whose fault is it? We shall see what the new juries will do. God grant they do good! Well, in prison, it seems, he remembered the venerable elder; the Bible, too, made its appearance again. Do you know, Rodion Raskolnikov, the force of the word 'suffering' among some of these people? It's not a question of suffering for someone's benefit, but simply, 'one must suffer.' If they suffer at the hands of the authorities, so much the better.

"So I suspect now that Nikolay wants to take his suffering or something of the sort. I know it for certain from facts. Only he doesn't

123

know that I know. . . . No, Rodion Raskolnikov, Nikolay doesn't come in! This is a fantastic, gloomy business, a modern case, an incident of today when the heart of man is troubled, when the phrase is quoted that blood 'renews,' when comfort is preached as the aim of life. Here we have bookish dreams, a heart unhinged by theories. Here we see resolution in the first stage, but resolution of a special kind: he resolved to do it like jumping over a precipice or from a bell tower and his legs shook as he went to the crime. He forgot to shut the door after him and he murdered two people for a theory. He committed the murder and couldn't take the money, and what he did manage to snatch up he hid under a stone. It wasn't enough for him to suffer agony behind the door while they battered at the door and rang the bell—no, he had to go to the empty lodging, half delirious, to recall the bell-ringing; he wanted to feel the cold shiver over again. . . . Well, that, we grant, was through illness, but consider this: he is a murderer, but looks upon himself as an honest man, despises others, poses as injured innocence. No, that's not the work of a Nikolay, my dear Rodion Raskolnikov!"

All that had been said before had sounded so like a recantation that these words were too great a shock. Raskolnikov shuddered as though he had been stabbed.

"Then . . . who then . . . is the murderer?" he asked in a breathless voice, unable to restrain himself.

Porfiry Petrovitch sank back in his chair, as though he were amazed at the question.

"Who is the murderer?" he repeated, as though unable to believe his ears. "Why *you,* Rodion Raskolnikov! You are the murderer," he added almost in a whisper, in a voice of genuine conviction.

Raskolnikov leaped from the sofa, stood up for a few seconds and sat down again without uttering a word. His face twitched convulsively.

"Your lip is twitching just as it did before," Porfiry Petrovitch observed almost sympathetically. "You've been misunderstanding me, I think, Rodion Raskolnikov," he added after a brief pause. "That's why you are so surprised. I came on purpose to tell you everything and deal openly with you."

"It was not I who murdered her," Raskolnikov whispered like a frightened child caught in the act.

"No, it was you, you Rodion Raskolnikov, and no one else," Porfiry whispered sternly, with conviction.

124

They were both silent and the silence lasted strangely long—about ten minutes. Raskolnikov put his elbow on the table and passed his fingers through his hair. Porfiry Petrovitch sat quietly waiting. Suddenly Raskolnikov looked scornfully at Porfiry.

"You are at your old tricks again, Porfiry Petrovitch! Your old method again. I wonder you don't get sick of it!"

"Oh, stop that. What does that matter now? It would be a different matter if there were witnesses present, but we are whispering alone. You see yourself that I have not come to chase and capture you like a hare. Whether you confess it or not is nothing to me now; for myself, I am convinced without it. . . ."

Raskolnikov thought a minute.

"Listen, Porfiry Petrovitch. You have already said you have nothing but psychology to go on. Well, what if you are mistaken yourself, now?"

"No, Rodion Raskolnikov, I am not mistaken. I have a little fact even now; providence sent it to me."

"What little fact?"

"I won't tell you what, Rodion Raskolnikov. And in any case, I haven't the right to put it off any longer. I must arrest you. So think it over: it makes no difference to me *now* and so I speak only for your sake. Believe me, it will be better."

Raskolnikov smiled malignantly.

"That's not simply ridiculous, it's positively shameless. Why, even if I were guilty, which I don't admit, what reason should I have to confess, when you tell me yourself that I shall be in greater safety in prison?"

"Ah, Rodion Raskolnikov, don't put too much faith in words; perhaps prison will not be altogether a restful place. That's only theory and my theory, and what authority am I for you? Perhaps even now I am hiding something from you? I can't lay bare everything, he-he! And how can you ask what advantage? Don't you know how it would lessen your sentence? You would be confessing at a moment when another man has taken the crime on himself and so has muddled the whole case. Consider that! I swear before God that I will so arrange that your confession shall come as a complete surprise. We will make a clean sweep of all these psychological points, of all suspicion against you, so that your crime will appear to have been something like an aberration, for in truth it was an aberration. I am an honest man, my dear Raskolnikov, and will keep my word."

Raskolnikov maintained a mournful silence and let his head sink dejectedly. He pondered a long while and at last smiled again, but his smile was sad and gentle.

"No!" he said, apparently abandoning all attempt to keep up appearances with Porfiry. "It's not worth it. I don't care about lessening the sentence!"

"That's just what I was afraid of!" Porfiry cried warmly and, as it seemed, involuntarily. "That's just what I feared—that you wouldn't care about the mitigation of sentence."

Raskolnikov looked sadly and expressively at him.

"Ah, don't disdain life!" Porfiry went on. "You have a great deal of it still before you. How can you say you don't want a mitigation of sentence? You are an impatient fellow!"

"A great deal of what lies before me?"

"Of life. What sort of prophet are you? Do you know much about it? Seek and ye shall find. This may be God's means for bringing you to Him. And it's not forever, the bondage. . . ."

"The time will be shortened," laughed Raskolnikov.

"Why? Is it the bourgeois disgrace you are afraid of? It may be that you are afraid of it without knowing it, because you are young! But anyway *you* shouldn't be afraid of giving yourself up and confessing."

"Ach, hang it!" Raskolnikov whispered with loathing and contempt, as though he did not want to speak aloud.

He got up again as though he meant to go away, but sat down again in evident despair.

"Hang it, if you like! You've lost faith and you think that I am grossly flattering you; but how long has your life been? How much do you understand? You made up a theory and then were ashamed that it broke down and turned out to be not at all original! It turned out something base, that's true, but you are not hopelessly base. By no means so base! At least you didn't deceive yourself for long; you went straight to the furthest point at one bound. How do I regard you? I regard you as one of those men who would stand and smile at their torturer while he cuts their entrails out, if only they have found faith or God. Find it and you will live. You have long needed a change of air. Suffering, too, is a good thing. Suffer! Maybe Nikolay is right in wanting to suffer. I know you don't believe in it—but don't be overwise; fling yourself straight into life, without deliberation; don't be afraid—the flood will bear you to the bank and set you safe on your feet again. What bank? How can I tell? I only believe that you have long life before you. I know that you take all my words now for a set speech prepared beforehand, but maybe you will remember them after. They may be of use some time. That's why I speak. It's as well that you only killed the old woman. If you'd invented another theory you might perhaps have done something a thousand times more hideous. You ought to thank God, perhaps. How do you know? Perhaps God is saving you for something. But keep a good heart and have less fear! Are you afraid of the great expiation before you? No, it would be shameful to be afraid of it. Since you have taken such a step, you must harden your heart. There is justice in it. You must fulfill the demands of justice. I know that you don't believe it, but indeed, life will bring you through. You will live it down in time. What you need now is fresh air, fresh air, fresh air!"

Raskolnikov positively started.

"But who are you? what prophet are you? From the height of what majestic calm do you proclaim these words of wisdom?"

"Who am I? I am a man with nothing to hope for, that's all. A man perhaps of feeling and sympathy, maybe of some knowledge too, but my day is over. But you are a different matter; there is life waiting for you. Though, who knows? Maybe your life, too, will pass off in smoke and come to nothing. Come! What does it matter that you will pass into another class of men? It's not comfort you regret with your heart! What of it that perhaps no one will see you for so long? It's not time, but yourself that will decide that. Be the sun and all will see you. The sun has before all to be the sun. Why are you smiling again? At my being such a Schiller? I bet you're imagining that I am trying to get around you by flattery. Well, perhaps I am, he-he-he! Perhaps you'd better not believe my word; perhaps you'd better never believe it altogether—I'm made that way, I confess it. But let me add: you can judge for yourself, I think, how far I am a base sort of man and how far I am honest."

"When do you mean to arrest me?"

"Well, I can let you walk about another day or two. Think it over, my dear fellow, and pray to God. It's more in your interest, believe me."

"And what if I run away?" asked Raskolnikov with a strange smile.

"No, you won't run away. A peasant would run away, a fashionable dissenter would run away, the flunkey of another man's thought, for you've only to show him the end of your little finger and he'll be ready to believe in anything for the rest of his life. But you've ceased to believe in your theory already; what will you run away with? And what would you do in hiding? It would be hateful and difficult for you, and what you need more than anything in life is a definite position, an atmosphere to suit you. And what sort of atmosphere would you have? If you ran away, you'd come back to yourself. *You can't get on without us.* And if I put you in prison—say you've been there a month, or two, or three—remember my word, you'll confess by yourself and perhaps to your own surprise. You won't know an hour beforehand that you are coming with a confession. I am convinced that you will decide 'to take your suffering.' You don't believe my words now, but you'll come to it by yourself. For suffering, Rodion Raskolnikov, is a great thing. Never mind my having grown fat. I know all the same. Don't laugh at it; there's an idea in suffering; Nikolay is right. No, you won't run away, Rodion Raskolnikov."

Raskolnikov got up and took his cap. Porfiry Petrovitch also rose.

"Are you going for a walk? The evening will be fine, if only we don't have a storm. Though it would be a good thing to freshen the air."

He too took his cap.

"Porfiry Petrovitch, please don't take up the notion that I have confessed to you today," Raskolnikov pronounced with sullen insistence. "You're a strange man and I have listened to you from simple curiosity. But I have admitted nothing. Remember that!"

"Oh, I know that. I'll remember. Look at him! He's trembling! Don't be uneasy, my dear fellow. Have it your own way. Walk about a bit; you won't be able to walk too far. If anything happens, I have one request to make of you," he added, dropping his voice. "It's an awkward one, but important. If anything were to happen (though indeed I don't believe in it and think you quite incapable of it), yet in case you were taken during these forty or fifty hours with the notion of putting an end to the business in some other way, in some fantastic fashion—laying hands on yourself—(it's an absurd proposition, but you must forgive me for it) do leave a brief but precise note, only two lines and mention the stone. It will be more generous. Come! Till we meet! Good thoughts and sound decisions to you!"

Porfiry went out, stooping and avoiding looking at Raskolnikov. The latter went to the window and waited with impatience till he calculated that Porfiry had reached the street; and then he moved away. He too went hurriedly out of the room.

[*Raskolnikov next carried out the plan that Porfiry had interrupted —his interview with Svidrigailov. Finding him tipsy in a tavern, Raskolnikov endured a long monologue which convinced him that Svidrigailov would probably use his knowledge of the murders to force Dounia to marry him. Worried that Dounia might accept this proposal in order to protect him, Raskolnikov crossed a bridge, without noticing that as Dounia appeared on one end, Svidrigailov appeared on the other.*]

HE SEEMED TO BE approaching cautiously. He did not go on to the bridge, but stood aside on the pavement, doing all he could to avoid Raskolnikov's seeing him. He had observed Dounia for some time and had been making signs to her. She fancied he was signalling to beg her not to speak to her brother, but to come to him.

That was what Dounia did. She stole by her brother and went up to Svidrigailov.

"Let us make haste away," Svidrigailov whispered to her, "I don't want Rodion to know of our meeting. I must tell you I've been sitting with him in the restaurant close by, where he looked me up and I had great difficulty in getting rid of him. He has somehow heard of my letter to you and suspects something. It wasn't you who told him, of course, but if not you, who then?"

"Well, we've turned the corner now," Dounia interrupted, "and my brother won't see us. I have to tell you that I am going no further with you. Speak to me here. You can tell it all in the street."

"In the first place, I can't say it in the street; secondly, you must hear Sonia Marmeladov too; and, thirdly, I will show you some papers. . . . Oh well, if you won't agree to come with me, I shall refuse to give any explanation and go away at once. But I beg you not to forget that a very curious secret of your beloved brother's is entirely in my keeping."

Dounia stood still, hesitating, and looked at Svidrigailov with searching eyes.

"What are you afraid of?" he observed quietly. "The town is not the country. And even in the country you did me more harm than I did you."

"Have you prepared Sonia?"

"No, I have not said a word to her and am not quite certain whether she is at home now. But most likely she is. She has buried her mother today: she is not likely to go visiting on such a day. For

129

the time I don't want to speak to anyone about it and I half regret having spoken to you. The slightest indiscretion is as bad as betrayal in a thing like this. I live there in that house we are coming to. That's the porter of our house—he knows me very well; you see, he's bowing; he sees I'm coming with a lady and no doubt he has noticed your face already and you will be glad of that if you are afraid of me and suspicious. Excuse my putting things so coarsely. I haven't a flat to myself; Sonia's room is next to mine—she lodges in the next flat. The whole floor is let out in lodgings. Why are you frightened like a child? Am I really so terrible?"

Svidrigailov's lips were twisted in a condescending smile; but he was in no smiling mood. His heart was throbbing and he could scarcely breathe. He spoke rather loud to cover his growing excitement. But Dounia did not notice this peculiar excitement; she was so irritated by his remark that she was frightened of him like a child and he was so terrifying to her.

"Though I know that you are not a man . . . of honor, I am not in the least afraid of you. Lead the way," she said with apparent composure; but her face was very pale.

Svidrigailov stopped at Sonia's room.

"Allow me to inquire whether she is at home. . . . She is not. How unfortunate! But I know she may come quite soon. If she's gone out, it can only be to see a lady about the orphans. Their mother is dead. . . . I've been meddling and making arrangements for them. If she does not come back in ten minutes, I will send her to you, today if you like. This is my flat. These are my two rooms. My landlady has the next room. Now, look this way. I will show you my chief piece of evidence: this door from my bedroom leads into two perfectly empty rooms which are for rent. Here they are . . . you must look into them with some attention."

Svidrigailov occupied two fairly large furnished rooms. Dounia was looking about her mistrustfully, but saw nothing special in the furniture or position of the rooms. Yet there was something to observe: for instance, that Svidrigailov's flat was exactly between two sets of almost uninhabited apartments. His rooms were not entered directly from the passage, but through the landlady's two almost empty rooms. Unlocking a door leading out of his bedroom, Svidrigailov showed Dounia the two empty rooms that were for rent. Dounia stopped in the doorway, not knowing what she was called to look upon, but Svidrigailov hastened to explain.

"Look here, at this second large room. Notice that door; it's locked. By the door stands a chair, the only one in the two rooms. I brought it from my rooms so as to listen more conveniently. Just the other side of the door is Sonia's table; she sat there talking to your brother Rodion. And I sat here listening on two successive evenings, for two hours each time—and of course I was able to learn something. What do you think?"

"You listened?"

"Yes, I did. Now come back to my room; we can't sit down here."

He took Dounia back into his sitting room and offered her a chair. He sat down at the opposite side of the table, at least seven feet from her, but probably there was the same glow in his eyes which had once frightened Dounia so much. She shuddered and once more looked about her distrustfully. It was an involuntary gesture; she evidently did not wish to betray her uneasiness. But the secluded position of Svidrigailov's lodging had suddenly struck her. She wanted to ask whether his landlady at least were at home, but pride kept her from asking. Moreover, she had another trouble in her heart incomparably greater than fear for herself. She was in great distress.

"Here is your letter," she said, laying it on the table. "Can it be true what you write? You hint at a crime committed, you say, by my brother. You hint at it too clearly; you daren't deny it now. I must tell you that I'd heard of this stupid story before you wrote and don't believe a word of it. It's a disgusting and ridiculous suspicion. I know the story and why and how it was invented. You can have no proofs. You promised to prove it. Speak! But let me warn you that I don't believe you! I don't believe you!"

Dounia said this, speaking hurriedly, and for an instant the color rushed to her face.

"If you didn't believe it, how could you risk coming alone to my rooms? Why have you come? Simply from curiosity?"

"Don't torment me. Speak, speak!"

"There's no denying that you are a brave girl. Upon my word, I thought you would have asked Mr. Razumihin to escort you here. But he was not with you nor anywhere near. I was on the lookout. It's spirited of you; it proves you wanted to spare Rodion. But everything is divine in you. . . . About your brother, what am I to say to you? You've just seen him yourself. What did you think of him?"

"Surely that's not the only thing you are building on?"

"No, not on that, but on his own words. He came here on two successive evenings to see Sonia. I've shown you where they sat. He made a full confession to her. He is a murderer. He killed an old woman, a pawnbroker, with whom he had pawned things himself. He killed her sister too, a peddler woman called Lizaveta, who happened to come in while he was murdering her sister. He killed them with an ax he brought with him. He murdered them to rob them and he did rob them. He took money and various things. . . . He told all this, word for word, to Sonia, the only person who knows his secret. But she has had no share by word or deed in the murder; she was as horrified at it as you are now. Don't be anxious; she won't betray him."

"It cannot be," muttered Dounia, with white lips. She gasped for breath. "It cannot be. There was not the slightest cause, no sort of ground. . . . It's a lie, a lie! . . . What . . . were the causes?"

"It's a long story, my dear Dounia. Here's . . . how shall I tell you? A theory of a sort, the same one by which I, for instance, consider that a single misdeed is permissible if the principal aim is right: a solitary wrongdoing may bring hundreds of good deeds! It's galling too, of course, for a young man of gifts and overweening pride to know that if he had, for instance, a paltry three thousand, his whole career, his whole future would be differently shaped and yet not to have that three thousand! Add to that, nervous irritability from hunger, from lodging in a hole, from rags, from a vivid sense of the charm of his social position and his sister's and mother's position too. Above all, vanity, pride and vanity, though goodness knows he may have good qualities too. . . . I am not blaming him—please don't think it; besides, it's not my business. A special little theory came in too—a theory of a sort—dividing mankind, you see, into ordinary and superior persons: that is, persons to whom the law does not apply, owing to their superiority; those who make laws for the rest of mankind, that is. It's all right as a theory. Napoleon attracted him tremendously; what affected him was that a great many men of genius have not hesitated at wrongdoing, but have overstepped the law without thinking about it. He seems to have fancied that he was a genius too—that is, he was convinced of it for a time. He has suffered a great deal and is still suffering from the idea that he could make a theory, but was incapable of boldly overstepping the law, and so he is not a man of genius. And that's humiliating for a young man of any pride, in our day especially. . . . You are very pale, Dounia."

"I know his theory. I read that article of his about men to whom all is permitted. Razumihin brought it to me."

"Mr. Razumihin? Your brother's article? In a magazine? Is there such an article? I didn't know. It must be interesting. But where are you going, my dear Dounia?"

"I want to see Sonia," Dounia articulated faintly. "How do I go to her? She has come in, perhaps. I must see her at once. Perhaps she . . ."

Dounia could not finish. Her breath literally failed her.

"Sonia will not be back till night, at least I believe not. She was to have been back at once, but if not, then she will not be in till quite late."

"Ah, then you are lying! I see . . . you were lying . . . lying all the time. . . . I don't believe you! I don't believe you!" cried Dounia, completely losing her head.

Almost fainting, she sank onto a chair which Svidrigailov made haste to give her.

"Dounia, what is it? Control yourself! Here is some water. Drink a little. . . ."

He sprinkled some water over her. Dounia shuddered and came to herself.

"It has acted violently," Svidrigailov muttered to himself, frowning. "Dounia, calm yourself! Believe me, he has friends. We will save him. Would you like me to take him abroad? I have money; I can get a ticket in three days. And as for the murder, he will do all sorts of good deeds yet to atone for it. Calm yourself. He may become a great man yet. Well, how are you? How do you feel?"

"Cruel man! To be able to jeer at it! Let me go. . . ."

"Where are you going?"

"To him. Where is he? Do you know? Why is this door locked? We came in through that door and now it is locked. When did you manage to lock it?"

"We shouldn't be shouting all over the flat on such a subject. I am far from jeering; it's simply that I'm sick of talking like this. But how can you go in such a state? Do you want to betray him? You will drive him to fury, and he will give himself up. Let me tell you, he is already being watched; they are already on his track. You will simply be giving him away. Wait a little: I saw him and was talking to him just now. He can still be saved. Wait a bit; sit down; let us think it over together. I asked you to come in order to discuss it alone with you and to consider it thoroughly. But do sit down!"

"How can you save him? Can he really be saved?"

Dounia sat down. Svidrigailov sat down beside her.

"It all depends on you, on you, on you alone," he began with glowing eyes, almost in a whisper and hardly able to utter the words for emotion.

Dounia drew back from him in alarm. He too was trembling all over.

"You . . . one word from you, and he is saved. I . . . I'll save him. I have money and friends. I'll send him away at once. I'll get a passport, two passports, one for him and one for me. I have friends . . . capable people. . . . If you like, I'll take a passport for you . . . for your mother. . . . What do you want with Razumihin? I love you too. . . . I love you beyond everything. . . . Let me kiss the hem of your dress, let me, let me. . . . The very rustle of it is too much for me. Tell me 'do that,' and I'll do it. I'll do everything. I will do the impossible. What you believe, I will believe. I'll do anything—anything! Don't, don't look at me like that. Do you know that you are killing me? . . ."

He was almost beginning to rave. . . . Something seemed suddenly to go to his head. Dounia jumped up and rushed to the door.

"Open it! Open it!" she called, shaking the door. "Open it! Is there no one there?"

Svidrigailov got up and came to himself. His still trembling lips slowly broke into an angry mocking smile.

"There is no one at home," he said quietly and emphatically. "The landlady has gone out, and it's a waste of time to shout like that. You are only exciting yourself uselessly."

"Where is the key? Open the door at once, at once, you evil man!"

"I have lost the key and cannot find it."

"This is an outrage," cried Dounia, turning pale as death. She rushed to the farthest corner, where she made haste to barricade herself with a little table.

She did not scream, but she fixed her eyes on her tormentor and watched every movement he made.

Svidrigailov remained standing at the other end of the room facing her. He was positively composed, at least in appearance, but his face was pale as before. The mocking smile did not leave his face.

"You spoke of outrage just now, my dear Dounia. In that case you may be sure I've taken measures. Sonia is not at home. The closest neighbors are far away—there are five locked rooms between them and us. I am at least twice as strong as you are and I have nothing to

134

fear, besides. For you could not complain afterwards. You surely would not be willing actually to betray your brother? Besides, no one would believe you. How should a girl have come alone to visit a solitary man in his lodgings? So that even if you do sacrifice your brother, you could prove nothing. It is very difficult to prove an assault, Dounia."

"Scoundrel!" whispered Dounia indignantly.

"As you like; but observe I was only speaking by way of a general proposition. It's my personal conviction that you are perfectly right—violence is hateful. I only spoke to show you that you need have no remorse even if . . . you were willing to save your brother of your own accord, as I suggest to you. You would be simply submitting to circumstances, to violence, in fact, if we must use that word. Think about it. Your brother's and your mother's fate are in your hands. I will be your slave . . . all my life . . . I will wait here."

Svidrigailov sat down on the sofa about eight steps from Dounia. She had not the slightest doubt now of his unbending determination. Besides, she knew him. Suddenly she pulled out of her pocket a revolver, cocked it and laid it in her hand on the table. Svidrigailov jumped up.

"Aha! So that's it, is it?" he cried, surprised but smiling maliciously. "Well, that completely alters the aspect of affairs. You've made things wonderfully easier for me, dearest Dounia. But where did you get the revolver? Was it Mr. Razumihin's? Why, it's my revolver, an old friend! And how I've hunted for it! The shooting lessons I've given you in the country have not been thrown away."

"It's not your revolver, it belonged to your wife, whom you killed, wretch! There was nothing of yours in her house. I took it when I began to suspect what you were capable of. If you dare to advance one step, I swear I'll kill you." She was frantic.

"But your brother? I ask from curiosity," said Svidrigailov, still standing where he was.

"Inform, if you want to! Don't stir! Don't come nearer! I'll shoot! You poisoned your wife. I know; you are a murderer yourself!" She held the revolver ready.

"Are you so positive I poisoned her?"

"You did! You hinted it yourself! You talked to me of poison. . . . I know you went to get it. . . . You had it in readiness. . . . It was your doing. . . . It must have been your doing. . . . Scoundrel!"

"Even if that were true, it would have been for your sake . . . you would have been the cause."

"You are lying! I hated you always, always. . . ."

"Oho, my darling Dounia! You seem to have forgotten how you softened to me in the heat of propaganda. I saw it in your eyes. Do you remember that moonlight night when the nightingale was singing?"

"That's a lie!" There was a flash of fury in Dounia's eyes. "That's a lie and a libel!"

"A lie? Well, if you like, it's a lie. I made it up. Women ought not to be reminded of such things," he said, smiling. "I know you will shoot, you pretty wild creature. Well, shoot away!"

Dounia raised the revolver and, deadly pale, gazed at him, measuring the distance and awaiting the first movement on his part. Her lower lip was white and quivering and her big black eyes flashed like fire. He had never seen her so handsome. The fire glowing in her eyes at the moment she raised the revolver seemed to kindle him and there was a pang of anguish in his heart. He took a step forward and a shot rang out. The bullet grazed his hair and flew into the wall behind. He stood still and laughed softly.

"The wasp has stung me. She aimed straight at my head. What's this? Blood?" he pulled out his handkerchief to wipe the blood, which flowed in a thin stream down his right temple. The bullet seemed to have just grazed the skin.

Dounia lowered the revolver and looked at Svidrigailov, not so much in terror as in a sort of wild amazement. She seemed not to understand what she was doing and what was going on.

"Well, you missed! Fire again. I'll wait," said Svidrigailov softly, still smiling, but gloomily. "If you go on like that, I shall have time to seize you before you cock again."

Dounia started, quickly cocked the pistol and again raised it.

"Let me be," she cried in despair. "I swear I'll shoot again. I . . . I'll kill you."

"Well . . . at three paces you can hardly help it. But if you don't . . . then." His eyes flashed and he took two steps forward. Dounia pulled the trigger again: it did not fire.

"You haven't loaded it properly. Never mind; you have another charge there. Get it ready. I'll wait."

He stood facing her, two paces away, waiting and gazing at her with wild determination, with feverishly passionate, stubborn, set eyes.

136

Dounia saw that he would sooner die than let her go. "And . . . now, of course, she would kill him, at two paces!" he uttered.

Suddenly she flung away the revolver.

"She's dropped it!" said Svidrigailov with surprise, and he drew a deep breath. A weight seemed to have rolled from his heart—perhaps not only the fear of death; indeed he may scarcely have felt it at that moment. It was the deliverance from another feeling, darker and more bitter, which he could not himself have defined.

He went to Dounia and gently put his arm around her waist. She did not resist but, trembling like a leaf, looked at him with suppliant eyes. He tried to say something but his lips moved without being able to utter a sound.

"Let me go," Dounia implored. Svidrigailov shuddered. Her voice now was quite different.

"Then you don't love me?" he asked softly.

Dounia shook her head.

"And . . . and you can't? Never?" he whispered in despair.

"Never!"

There followed a moment of terrible, dumb struggle in the heart of Svidrigailov. He looked at her with an indescribable gaze. Suddenly he withdrew his arm, turned quickly to the window and stood facing it. Another moment passed.

"Here's the key."

He took it out of the left pocket of his coat and laid it on the table behind him, without turning or looking at Dounia.

"Take it! Make haste!"

He looked stubbornly out of the window. Dounia went up to the table to take the key.

"Make haste! Make haste!" repeated Svidrigailov, still without turning or moving. But there seemed a terrible significance in the tone of that "make haste."

Dounia understood it, snatched up the key, flew to the door, unlocked it quickly and rushed out of the room. A minute later, she ran out onto the canal bank.

Svidrigailov remained three minutes standing at the window. At last he slowly turned, looked about him and passed his hand over his forehead. A strange smile contorted his face—a pitiful, sad, weak smile, a smile of despair. The blood, which was already getting dry, smeared his hand. He looked angrily at it, then wetted a towel and washed his temple. The revolver which Dounia had flung away lay near the door

137

and suddenly caught his eye. He picked it up and examined it. It was a little pocket three-barrel revolver of old-fashioned construction. There were still two charges and one capsule left in it. It could be fired again. He thought a little, put the revolver in his pocket, took his hat and went out.

[*Svidrigailov spent the evening going from one low haunt to another, returning home finally to settle his affairs. He gave Sonia 3000 rubles and asked her to convey his greetings to Raskolnikov. He spent a nightmarish night in a decrepit hotel, went out into the street at dawn, and, declaring to an absolute stranger that he was going to America, shot himself. In the evening of the same day, Raskolnikov, who had been walking all night, went to say good-by to his mother. He found Dounia waiting for him in his room, said his good-by to her, and then went to see Sonia.*]

WHEN HE WENT into Sonia's room, it was already getting dark. All day Sonia had been waiting for him in terrible anxiety. Dounia had been waiting with her. She had come to her that morning, remembering Svidrigailov's words that Sonia knew. We will not describe the conversation and tears of the two girls, and how friendly they became. Dounia gained one comfort at least from that interview, that her brother would not be alone. He had gone to Sonia first with his confession; he had gone to her for human fellowship when he needed it; she would go with him wherever fate might send him. Dounia did not ask, but she knew it was so. She looked at Sonia almost with reverence and at first almost embarrassed her by it. Sonia was almost on the point of tears. She felt herself, on the contrary, hardly worthy to look at Dounia. Dounia's gracious image when she had bowed to her so attentively and respectfully at their first meeting in Raskolnikov's room had remained in her mind as one of the fairest visions of her life.

Dounia at last became impatient and, leaving Sonia, went to her brother's room to await him there; she kept thinking that he would come there first. When she had gone, Sonia began to be tortured by the dread of his committing suicide, and Dounia too feared it. But they had spent the day trying to persuade each other that that could not be, and both were less anxious while they were together. As soon as they parted, each thought of nothing else. Sonia remembered how

Svidrigailov had said to her the day before that Raskolnikov had two alternatives—Siberia or . . . Besides she knew his vanity, his pride and his lack of faith.

"Is it possible that he has nothing but cowardice and fear of death to make him live?" she thought at last in despair.

Meanwhile the sun was setting. Sonia was standing in dejection, looking intently out of the window, but from it she could see nothing but the unwhitewashed blank wall of the next house. At last when she began to feel sure of his death—he walked into the room.

She gave a cry of joy, but looking carefully into his face she turned pale.

"Yes," said Raskolnikov, smiling. "I have come for your cross, Sonia. It was you who told me to go to the crossroads; why is it you who are frightened now it's come to that?"

Sonia gazed at him, astonished. His tone seemed strange to her; a cold shiver ran over her, but in a moment she guessed that the tone and the words were a mask. He spoke to her looking away, as though to avoid meeting her eyes.

"You see, Sonia, I've decided that it will be better so. There is one fact. . . . But it's a long story and there's no need to discuss it. But do you know what angers me? It annoys me that all those stupid brutish faces will be gaping at me directly, pestering me with their stupid questions, which I shall have to answer. They'll point their fingers at me. . . . Tfoo! You know I am not going to Porfiry; I am sick of him. I'd rather go to my friend Ilya, the Explosive Lieutenant; how I shall surprise him! What a sensation I shall make! But I must be cooler; I've become too irritable of late. You know I was nearly shaking my fist at my sister just now, because she turned to take a last look at me. It's a brutal state to be in! Ah! What am I coming to? Well, where are the crosses?"

He seemed hardly to know what he was doing. He could not stay still or concentrate his attention on anything; his ideas seemed to gallop after one another; he talked incoherently; his hands trembled slightly.

Without a word, Sonia took out of the drawer two crosses, one of cypress wood and one of copper. She made the sign of the cross over herself and over him, and put the wooden cross on his neck.

"It's the symbol of my taking up the cross," he laughed. "As though I had not suffered much till now! The wooden cross—that is the peasant one; the copper one—that is Lizaveta's. Show me! So she had it on . . . at that moment? I remember two things like these too, a silver one and a little icon. I threw them back on the old woman's neck. Those would be appropriate now; really, those are what I ought to put on now. . . . But I am talking nonsense and forgetting what matters; I'm somehow forgetful. . . . You see I have come to warn you, Sonia, so that you might know . . . that's all— that's all I came for. But I thought I had more to say. You wanted me to go yourself. Well, now I am going to prison and you'll have your wish. Well, what are you crying for? You too? Don't! Leave off! Oh, how I hate it all!"

But his feeling was stirred; his heart ached as he looked at her. "Why is she grieving too?" he thought to himself. "What am I to her? Why does she weep? Why is she looking after me like my mother or Dounia? She'll be my nurse."

"Cross yourself; say at least one prayer," Sonia begged in a timid broken voice.

"Oh certainly, as much as you like! And sincerely, Sonia, sincerely. . . ."

But he wanted to say something quite different.

He crossed himself several times. Sonia took up her shawl and put it over her head. It was the green *drap de dames* shawl of which Marmeladov had spoken, "the family shawl." Raskolnikov thought of that looking at it, but he did not ask. He began to feel himself that he was certainly forgetting things and was disgustingly agitated. He was frightened at this. He was suddenly struck too by the thought that Sonia meant to go with him.

"What are you doing? Where are you going? Stay here, stay! I'll go alone," he cried in cowardly vexation, and almost resentful, he moved toward the door. "What's the use of going in procession!" he muttered going out.

Sonia remained standing in the middle of the room. He had not even said good-by to her; he had forgotten her. A poignant and rebellious doubt surged in his heart.

"Was it right, was it right, all this?" he thought again as he went down the stairs. "Couldn't he stop and retract it all . . . and not go?"

But still he went. He felt suddenly once for all that he mustn't ask himself questions. As he turned into the street he remembered that he had not said good-by to Sonia, that he had left her in the middle of the room in her green shawl, not daring to stir after he had shouted at her, and he stopped short for a moment. At the same instant, another thought dawned upon him, as though it had been lying in wait to strike him then.

"Why, with what object did I go to her just now? I told her—on business; on what business? I had no sort of business! To tell her I was *going;* but where was the need? Do I love her? No, no, I drove her away just now like a dog. Did I want her crosses? Oh, how low I've sunk! No, I wanted her tears; I wanted to see her terror, to see how her heart ached! I had to have something to cling to, something to delay me, some friendly face to see! And I dared to believe in myself, to dream of what I would do! I am a beggarly contemptible wretch, contemptible!"

He walked along the canal bank; he had not much farther to go. But on reaching the bridge he stopped and, turning out of his way along it, went to the Hay Market. . . .

He suddenly recalled Sonia's words, "Go to the crossroads, bow down to the people, kiss the earth, for you have sinned against it too; and say aloud to the whole world, 'I am a murderer.' " He trembled, remembering that. And the hopeless misery and anxiety of all that time, especially of the last hours, had weighed so heavily upon him that he positively clutched at the chance of this new unmixed, complete sensation. It came over him like a fit; it was like a single spark kindled in his soul and spreading fire through him. Everything in him softened at once and the tears started into his eyes. He fell to the earth on the spot. . . .

He knelt down in the middle of the square, bowed down to the earth and kissed that filthy earth with bliss and rapture. He got up and bowed down a second time.

"He's boozed," a youth near him observed.

There was a roar of laughter.

"He's going to Jerusalem, brothers, and saying good-by to his children and his country. He's bowing down to all the world and kissing the great city of St. Petersburg and its pavement," added a workman who was a little drunk.

"Quite a young man, too!" observed a third.

"And a gentleman," someone observed soberly.

"There's no knowing who's a gentleman and who isn't nowadays."

These exclamations and remarks checked Raskolnikov, and the words, "I am a murderer," which were perhaps on the point of dropping from his lips, died away. He bore these remarks quietly,

141

however, and without looking around, he turned down a street leading to the police office. He had a glimpse of something on the way which did not surprise him; he had felt that it must be so. The second time he bowed down in the Hay Market, he saw, standing fifty paces from him on the left, Sonia. She was hiding from him behind one of the wooden shanties in the market place. She had followed him then on his painful way! Raskolnikov at that moment felt and knew once for all that Sonia was with him forever and would follow him to the ends of the earth, wherever fate might take him. It wrung his heart . . . but he was just reaching the fatal place.

He went into the yard fairly resolutely. He had to mount to the third story. "I shall be some time going up," he thought. He felt as though the fateful moment was still far off, as though he had plenty of time left for consideration. . . .

Turning cold and hardly conscious, he opened the door of the office. There were very few people in it this time—only a house porter and a peasant. The doorkeeper did not even peep out from behind his screen. Raskolnikov walked into the next room. "Perhaps I still need not speak," passed through his mind. Some sort of clerk not wearing a uniform was settling himself at a bureau to write. In a corner another clerk was seating himself. Inspector Zametov was not there.

"No one in?" Raskolnikov asked, addressing the person at the bureau.

"Whom do you want?"

"A-ah! Not a sound was heard, not a sight was seen, but I scent the Russian . . . how does it go on in the fairy tale . . . I've forgotten! At your service!" a familiar voice cried suddenly.

Raskolnikov shuddered. The Explosive Lieutenant stood before him. He had just come in from the third room. "It is the hand of fate," thought Raskolnikov. "Why is he here?"

"You've come to see us? What about?" cried Ilya Petrovitch. He was obviously in an exceedingly good humor and perhaps a trifle exhilarated. "If it's on business, you are rather early. It's only a chance that I am here . . . however I'll do what I can. I must admit, I . . . what is it, what is it? Excuse me. . . ."

"Raskolnikov."

"Of course—Raskolnikov! You didn't imagine I'd forgotten? Don't think I am like that. . . . Yes, yes, of course. Raskolnikov! I made many inquiries about you. . . . It was explained to me after

142

your visit here that you were a literary man . . . and a learned one too. . . . Mercy on us! What literary or scientific man does not begin by some originality of conduct? . . . But I am forgetting to ask you: is there anything you want really? . . ."

"No, I only looked in . . . I came to ask . . . I thought that I should find Zametov here."

"Oh, yes! Of course, you've made friends; I heard. Well, no, Zametov is not here. Yes, we've lost Zametov. He's not been here since yesterday . . . He quarrelled with everyone on leaving . . . in the rudest way. He is a feather-headed youngster, that's all; one might have expected something from him, but you know what they are—our brilliant young men. He wanted to go in for some examination, but it's only to talk and boast about it; it will go no further than that. . . . Zametov will make a scandal in the French style in a house of bad reputation over a glass of champagne . . . that's all your Zametov is good for! While I'm perhaps, so to speak, burning with devotion and lofty feelings, and besides I have rank, consequence, a post! I am married and have children, I fulfill the duties of a man and a citizen, but who is he, may I ask? I appeal to you as a man ennobled by education. . . . Then these midwives, too, have become extraordinarily numerous."

Raskolnikov raised his eyebrows inquiringly. The words of Ilya Petrovitch, who had obviously been dining, were for the most part a stream of empty sounds for him. But some of them he understood. He looked at him inquiringly, not knowing how it would end.

"I mean those crop-headed wenches," the talkative Ilya Petrovitch continued. "Midwives is my name for them. I think it a very satisfactory one, ha-ha! They go to the Academy, study anatomy. If I fall ill, am I to send for a young lady to treat me? What do you say? Ha-ha!" Ilya Petrovitch laughed, quite pleased with his own wit. "It's an immoderate zeal for education, but once you're educated, that's enough. Why abuse it? Why insult honorable people, as that scoundrel Zametov does? Why did he insult me, I ask you? Look at these suicides, too; how common they are, you can't fancy! People spend their last halfpenny and kill themselves, boys and girls and old people. Only this morning we heard about a gentleman who had just come to town. I say, what was the name of that gentleman who shot himself?"

"Svidrigailov," someone answered from the other room with drowsy listlessness.

143

Raskolnikov started. "Svidrigailov! Svidrigailov has shot himself!" he cried.

"What? Do you know Svidrigailov?"

"Yes . . . I knew him. . . . He hadn't been here long."

"Yes, that's so. He had lost his wife, was a man of reckless habits and all of a sudden shot himself, and in such a shocking way. . . . He left in his notebook a few words: that he dies in full possession of his faculties and that no one is to blame for his death. He had money, they say. How did you come to know him?"

"I . . . was acquainted . . . my sister was governess in his family."

"Bah-bah-bah! Then no doubt you can tell us something about him. You had no suspicion?"

"I saw him yesterday while he . . . was drinking wine; I knew nothing."

Raskolnikov felt as though something had fallen on him and was stifling him.

"You've turned pale again. It's so stuffy here. . . ."

"Yes, I must go," muttered Raskolnikov. "Excuse my troubling you. . . ."

"Oh, not at all; as often as you like. It's a pleasure to see you and I am glad to say so."

Ilya Petrovitch held out his hand.

"I only wanted . . . I came to see Zametov."

"I understand, I understand, and it's a pleasure to see you."

"I . . . am very glad . . . good-by," Raskolnikov smiled.

He went out; he reeled, he was overtaken with giddiness and did not know what he was doing. He began going down the stairs, supporting himself with his right hand against the wall. He fancied that a porter pushed past him on his way upstairs to the police office, that a dog in the lower story kept up a shrill barking and that a woman flung a rolling pin at it and shouted. He went down and out into the yard. There, not far from the entrance, stood Sonia, pale and horror-stricken. She looked wildly at him. He stood still before her. There was a look of poignant agony, of despair, in her face. She clasped her hands. His lips worked in an ugly, meaningless smile. He stood still a minute, grinned and went back to the police office.

Ilya Petrovitch had sat down and was rummaging among some papers. Before him stood the same peasant who had pushed by on the stairs.

144

"Hello! Back again! have you left something behind? What's the matter?"

Raskolnikov, with white lips and staring eyes, came slowly nearer. He walked right to the table, leaned his hand on it, tried to say something, but could not; only incoherent sounds were audible.

"You are feeling ill. A chair! Here, sit down! Some water!"

Raskolnikov dropped onto a chair, but he kept his eyes fixed on the face of Ilya Petrovitch, which expressed unpleasant surprise. Both looked at each other for a minute and waited. Water was brought.

"It was I . . ." began Raskolnikov.

"Drink some water."

Raskolnikov refused the water with his hand, and softly and brokenly, but distinctly said:

"It was I who killed the old pawnbroker woman and her sister Lizaveta with an ax and robbed them."

Ilya Petrovitch opened his mouth. People ran up on all sides.

Raskolnikov repeated his statement.

Epilogue

[*Five months after his confession, Raskolnikov was sentenced to penal servitude in the second class for a term of only eight years— a sentence more merciful than could have been expected, because the criminal had not tried to justify himself.*

Sonia went with him to Siberia. "But that is the beginning of a new story," Dostoevski writes, "the story of the gradual renewal of a man, the story of his gradual regeneration, of his passing from one world into another, of his initiation into a new unknown life. That might be the subject of a new story, but our present story is ended."]

A PASSION
IN THE
DESERT

by

Honoré de Balzac

HOME COURSE APPRECIATION

ONORÉ DE BALZAC (1799–1850) is famous for the great series of panoramic novels in which he reproduced the vast
spectacle of French society. This long series of novels,
which he called *The Human Comedy,* undertakes nothing less than
to study men as they appeared to him on every level of society, under
every conceivable circumstance. Its author is known as a sharp-
sighted observer and an energetic writer of businesslike prose. He is
not usually considered a recorder of delicate sensibilities. Yet under
Balzac's rough and rather insensitive exterior dwelt a writer with the
feelings of a poet.

Balzac was to all appearances a bustling literary businessman with
a red face, a plump build and a loud voice. He was insatiable in his
appetite for pleasure and prestige; and he was prodigious in his ability
to dash off a novel in a few days' time. He loved social acceptance as
only a climber can love it, and he appreciated the full, rich spectacle
of urban life as only a provincial can appreciate it.

In *A Passion in the Desert,* Balzac shows himself in a different
light from that of the literary historian. Here his vast and crowded
canvas is contracted to portray a single man and a single beast. Instead of the crowded boulevards and theaters and cafés of Paris, we
see the barren wastes of the Sahara. In place of the artificial manners
and complex motives of civilization, the story concerns itself with the
simple responses of two creatures in the wild. A few things about the
style of the story betray its old-fashioned character. Some of the de-
scriptive prose sounds a little too lyrical to modern ears. And the

device of two narrators, an old soldier telling the story to the author, and the author repeating it to a lady, is clumsy.

The reader may well ask, on finishing the story, just what the point of it is. The word in the title that expresses the theme is "passion." We notice that in this bizarre relationship, the human being turns out to be more savage than the wild beast. A story that began with a few words about how hard it is to train wild animals has turned into something much bigger; it has become a prose poem of the tawny, barren Sahara and of the passions which, though they may unite, eventually divide men and animals. Balzac had come to feel, as he analyzed the emotions of human beings, that there was still something primitive and uncivilized in them. In *A Passion in the Desert* he reversed this observation, showing that there may be something almost human in the affections of a beast. The effect of the story, however, is not grotesque; at the end, the old soldier feels in all sincerity that when he lived with the panther in the desert, he was closer to the heart of things than he could ever be in civilization.

The focus of the story is that strange relationship brought about by the vast loneliness and emptiness of the desert. In describing that, Balzac showed us how it is possible for man to face the life force directly, to feel completely a part of God's creation. Yet though the old soldier experienced this wonder, he could not shake off the fears and distrusts born with him. And so, although the panther had no urge to kill him, the soldier could not fully forget his fears. The panther loved and trusted him—and she wasn't hungry.

Only after ingrained fear had impelled his knife hand did the soldier realize what he had done. He then regretted his act, but he also seemed relieved to be free of the suspenseful association on the desert. For all its beauty, the desert had terrified him. It was "everything, and nothing" . . . it was "God without mankind."

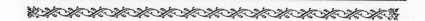

"THE WHOLE SHOW is dreadful," she cried, coming out of the menagerie of M. Martin. She had just been looking at that daring speculator "working with his hyena"—to speak in the style of the program.

"By what means," she continued, "can he have tamed these animals to such a point as to be certain of their affection for——"

"What seems to you a problem," said I, interrupting, "is really quite natural."

"Oh!" she cried, letting an incredulous smile wander over her lips.

"You think that beasts are wholly without passions?" I asked her. "Quite the reverse; we can communicate to them all the vices arising in our own state of civilization."

She looked at me with an air of astonishment.

"But," I continued, "the first time I saw M. Martin, I admit, like you, I did give vent to an exclamation of surprise. I found myself next to an old soldier with the right leg amputated, who had come in with me. His face had struck me. He had one of those heroic heads, stamped with the seal of warfare, and on which the battles of Napoleon are written. Besides, he had that frank, good-humored expression which always impresses me favorably. He was without doubt one of those troopers who are surprised at nothing, who find matter for laughter in the contortions of a dying comrade, who bury or plunder him quite light-heartedly, who stand intrepidly in the way of bullets; in fact, one of those men who waste no time in deliberation, and would not hesitate to make friends with the devil himself. After looking very attentively at the proprietor of the menagerie getting out of his box, my companion pursed up his lips with an air of mockery and contempt, with that peculiar and expressive twist which superior people assume to show they are not taken in. Then, when I was expatiating on the courage of M. Martin, he smiled, shook his head knowingly, and said, 'Well known.'

" 'How "well known"?' I said. 'If you would only explain me the mystery, I should be vastly obliged.'

"After a few minutes, during which we made acquaintance, we went to dine at the first *restaurateur's* whose shop caught our eye. At dessert a bottle of champagne completely refreshed and brightened up the memories of this odd old soldier. He told me his story, and I saw that he was right when he exclaimed, 'Well known.' "

When she got home, she teased me to that extent, was so charming, and made so many promises, that I consented to communicate to her the confidences of the old soldier. Next day she received the following episode of an epic which one might call "The French in Egypt."

During the expedition in Upper Egypt under General Desaix, a Provençal soldier fell into the hands of the Maugrabins, and was taken by these Arabs into the deserts beyond the falls of the Nile.

In order to place a sufficient distance between themselves and the French army, the Maugrabins made forced marches, and only halted when night was upon them. They camped round a well overshadowed by palm trees under which they had previously concealed a store of provisions. Not surmising that the notion of flight would occur to their prisoner, they contented themselves with binding his hands, and after eating a few dates, and giving provender to their horses, went to sleep.

When the brave Provençal saw that his enemies were no longer watching him, he made use of his teeth to steal a scimitar, fixed the blade between his knees, and cut the cords which prevented him using his hands; in a moment he was free. He at once seized a rifle and a dagger, then taking the precaution to provide himself with a sack of dried dates, oats, and powder and shot, and to fasten a scimitar to his waist, he leaped on to a horse, and spurred on vigorously in the direction where he thought to find the French army. So impatient was he to see a bivouac again that he pressed on the already tired courser at such speed that its flanks were lacerated with his spurs, and at last the poor animal died, leaving the Frenchman alone in the desert. After walking some time in the sand with all the courage of an escaped convict, the soldier was obliged to stop, as the day had already ended. In spite of the beauty of an Oriental sky at night, he felt he had not strength enough to go on. Fortunately he had been able to find a small hill, on the summit of which a few palm trees shot up into the air; it was their verdure seen from afar which had brought hope and consolation to his heart. His fatigue was so great that he lay down upon a rock of granite, capriciously cut out like a campbed; there he fell asleep without taking any precaution to defend himself while he slept. He had made the sacrifice of his life. His last thought was one of regret. He repented having left the Maugrabins, whose nomadic life seemed to smile upon him now that he was far from them and without help. He was awakened by the sun, whose pitiless rays fell with all their force on the granite and produced an intolerable heat—for he had had the stupidity to place himself inversely to the shadow thrown by the verdant majestic heads of the palm trees. He looked at the solitary trees and shuddered—they reminded him of the graceful shafts crowned with foliage which characterize the Saracen columns in the cathedral of Arles.

But when, after counting the palm trees, he cast his eyes around him, the most horrible despair was infused into his soul. Before him stretched an ocean without limit. The dark sand of the desert spread farther than eye could reach in every direction, and glittered like steel struck with bright light. It might have been a sea of looking glass, or lakes melted together in a mirror. A fiery vapor carried up in surging waves made a perpetual whirlwind over the quivering land. The sky was lit with an Oriental splendor of insupportable purity, leaving naught for the imagination to desire. Heaven and earth were on fire.

The silence was awful in its wild and terrible majesty. Infinity, immensity, closed in upon the soul from every side. Not a cloud in the sky, not a breath in the air, not a flaw on the bosom of the sand, ever moving in diminutive waves; the horizon ended as at sea on a clear day, with one line of light, definite as the cut of a sword.

The Provençal threw his arms round the trunk of one of the palm trees, as though it were the body of a friend, and then, in the shelter of the thin, straight shadow that the palm cast upon the granite, he wept. Then sitting down he remained as he was, contemplating with profound sadness the implacable scene, which was all he had to look upon. He cried aloud, to measure the solitude. His voice, lost in the hollows of the hill, sounded faintly, and aroused no echo—the echo was in his own heart. The Provençal was twenty-two years old; he loaded his carbine.

"There'll be time enough," he said to himself, laying on the ground the weapon which alone could bring him deliverance.

Viewing alternately the dark expanse of the desert and the blue expanse of the sky, the soldier dreamed of France—he smelled with delight the gutters of Paris—he remembered the towns through which he had passed, the faces of his comrades, the most minute details of his life. His Southern fancy soon showed him the stones of his beloved Provence, in the play of the heat which undulated above the wide expanse of the desert. Realizing the danger of this cruel mirage, he went down the opposite side of the hill to that by which he had come up the day before. Great was his joy in discovering a kind of grotto naturally cut into the immense granite rocks which formed the base of the knoll. The remains of a rug showed that this place of refuge had at one time been inhabited; at a short distance he saw some palm trees full of dates. Then the instinct which binds us to life awoke again in his heart. He hoped to live long enough to await the passing of some Maugrabins, or perhaps he might hear the sound of cannon; for at this time Bonaparte was traversing Egypt.

This thought gave him new life. The palm tree seemed to bend with the weight of the ripe fruit. He shook some of it down. When he tasted this unhoped-for manna, he felt sure that the palms had been cultivated by a former inhabitant—the savory, fresh meat of the dates were proof of the care of his predecessor. He passed suddenly from dark despair to an almost insane joy. He went up again to the top of the hill, and spent the rest of the day in cutting down one of the sterile palm trees, which the night before had served him for shelter. A vague memory made him think of the animals of the desert; and in case they might come to drink at the spring, visible from the base of the rocks but lost farther down, he resolved to guard himself from their visits by placing a barrier at the entrance of his hermitage.

In spite of his diligence, and the strength which the fear of being devoured asleep gave him, he was unable to cut the palm in pieces, though he succeeded in cutting it down. When, toward evening, this king of the desert fell, the noise of its crash resounded far and wide, like a sigh in the solitude; the soldier shuddered as though he had heard some voice predicting woe.

But like an heir who does not long bewail a deceased relative, he tore off from this beautiful tree the tall broad green leaves which are its poetic adornment, and used them to mend the mat on which he was to sleep.

Fatigued by the heat and his work, he fell asleep under the red ceiling of his wet cave.

In the middle of the night his sleep was troubled by an extraordinary noise; he sat up, and the deep silence around allowed him to distinguish the alternative accents of a respiration whose savage energy could not belong to a human creature.

A profound terror, increased still further by the darkness, the silence, and his waking images, froze his heart within him. He almost felt his hair stand on end, when by straining his eyes to their utmost he perceived through the shadow two faint yellow lights. At first he attributed these lights to the reflection of his own pupils, but soon the vivid brilliance of the night aided him gradually to distinguish the objects around him in the cave, and he beheld a huge animal lying but two steps from him. Was it a lion, a tiger, or a crocodile?

The Provençal was not sufficiently educated to know under what species his enemy ought to be classed; but his fright was all the greater, as his ignorance led him to imagine all terrors at once; he endured a cruel torture, noting every variation of the breathing close to him without daring to make the slightest movement. An odor, pungent like that of a fox, but more penetrating, more profound—so to speak—filled the cave, and when the Provençal became sensible of this, his terror reached its height, for he could no longer doubt the proximity of a terrible companion, whose royal dwelling served him for a shelter.

Presently the reflection of the moon descending on the horizon lit up the den, rendering gradually visible and resplendent the spotted skin of a panther.

This lion of Egypt slept, curled up like a big dog, the peaceful possessor of a sumptuous niche at the gate of an *hôtel;* its eyes opened for a moment and closed again; its face was turned towards the man. A thousand confused thoughts passed through the Frenchman's mind; first he thought of killing it with a bullet from his gun, but he saw there was not enough distance between them for him to take proper aim—the shot would miss the mark. And if it were to wake! the thought made his limbs rigid. He listened to his own heart beating in the midst of the silence, and cursed the too violent pulsations which the flow of blood brought on, fearing to disturb that sleep which allowed him time to think of some means of escape.

Twice he placed his hand on his scimitar, intending to cut off the head of his enemy; but the difficulty of cutting the stiff short hair compelled him to abandon this daring project. To miss would be to die for *certain,* he thought; he preferred the chances of fair fight, and made up his mind to wait till morning; the morning did not leave him long to wait.

He could now examine the panther at ease; its muzzle was smeared with blood.

"She's had a good dinner," he thought, without troubling himself as to whether her feast might have been on human flesh. "She won't be hungry when she gets up."

It was a female. The fur on her belly and flanks was glistening white; many small marks like velvet formed beautiful bracelets round her feet; her sinuous tail was also white, ending with black rings; the overpart of her dress, yellow like burnished gold, very lissome and soft, had the characteristic blotches in the form of rosettes, which distinguish the panther from every other feline species.

This tranquil and formidable hostess snored in an attitude as graceful as that of a cat lying on a cushion. Her bloodstained paws, nervous and well armed, were stretched out before her face, which rested upon them, and from which radiated her straight slender whiskers, like threads of silver.

If she had been like that in a cage, the Provençal would doubtless have admired the grace of the animal, and the vigorous contrasts of vivid color which gave her robe an imperial splendor; but just then his sight was troubled by her sinister appearance.

The presence of the panther, even asleep, could not fail to produce the effect which the magnetic eyes of the serpent are said to have on the nightingale.

For a moment the courage of the soldier began to fail before this danger, though no doubt it would have risen at the mouth of a cannon charged with shell. Nevertheless, a bold thought brought daylight to his soul and sealed up the source of the cold sweat which sprang forth on his brow. Like men driven to bay, who defy death and offer their body to the smiter, so he, seeing in this merely a tragic episode, resolved to play his part with honor to the last.

"The day before yesterday the Arabs would have killed me, perhaps," he said; so considering himself as good as dead already, he waited bravely, with excited curiosity, the awakening of his enemy.

When the sun appeared, the panther suddenly opened her eyes; then she put out her paws with energy, as if to stretch them and get rid of cramp. At last she yawned, showing the formidable apparatus of her teeth and pointed tongue, rough as a file.

She licked off the blood which stained her paws and muzzle, and scratched her head with reiterated gestures full of prettiness. "All right, make a little toilet," the Frenchman said to himself, beginning to recover his gaiety with his courage; "we'll say good morning to each other presently," and he seized the small, short dagger which he had taken from the Maugrabins.

At this moment the panther turned her head toward the man and looked at him fixedly without moving. The rigidity of her metallic eyes and their insupportable luster made him shudder, especially when the animal walked toward him. But he looked at her caressingly, staring into her eyes in order to magnetize her, and let her come quite close to him; then with a movement both gentle and amorous, as though he were caressing the most beautiful of women, he passed his hand over her whole body, from the head to the tail, scratching the flexible vertebrae which divided the panther's yellow back. The animal waved her tail voluptuously, and her eyes grew gentle; and when for the third time the Frenchman accomplished this interesting flattery, she gave forth one of those purrings by which cats express their pleasure; but this murmur issued from a throat so powerful and so deep, that it resounded through the cave like the vast vibrations of an organ in a church. The man, understanding the importance of his caresses, redoubled them in such a way as to surprise and stupefy his imperious courtesan. When he felt sure of having extinguished the ferocity of his capricious companion, whose hunger had so fortunately been satisfied the day before, he got up to go out of the cave; the panther let him go out, but when he had reached the summit of the hill she sprang with the lightness of a sparrow hopping from twig to twig, and rubbed herself against his legs, putting up her back after the manner of all the race of cats. Then regarding her guest with eyes whose glare had softened a little, she gave vent to that wild cry which naturalists compare to the grating of a saw.

"She is exacting," said the Frenchman, smiling.

He was bold enough to play with her ears; he caressed her belly and scratched her head as hard as he could. When he saw he was successful he tickled her skull with the point of his dagger, watching for the

155

moment to kill her, but the hardness of her bones made him tremble for his success.

The sultana of the desert showed herself gracious to her slave; she lifted her head, stretched out her neck, and manifested her delight by the tranquillity of her attitude. It suddenly occurred to the soldier that to kill this savage princess with one blow he must poniard her in the throat.

He raised the blade, when the panther, satisfied, no doubt, laid herself gracefully at his feet, and cast up at him glances in which, in spite of their natural fierceness, was mingled confusedly a kind of good will. The poor Provençal ate his dates, leaning against one of the palm trees, and casting his eyes alternately on the desert in quest of some liberator and on his terrible companion to watch her uncertain clemency.

The panther looked at the place where the date stones fell, and every time that he threw one down her eyes expressed an incredible mistrust.

She examined the man with an almost commercial prudence. However, this examination was favorable to him, for when he had finished his meager meal she licked his boots with her powerful rough tongue, brushing off with marvelous skill the dust gathered in the creases.

"Ah, but when she's really hungry!" thought the Frenchman. In spite of the shudder this thought caused him, the soldier began to measure curiously the proportions of the panther, certainly one of the most splendid specimens of its race. She was three feet high and four feet long without counting her tail; this powerful weapon, rounded like a cudgel, was nearly three feet long. The head, large as that of a lioness, was distinguished by a rare expression of refinement. The cold cruelty of a tiger was dominant, it was true, but there was also a vague resemblance to the face of a sensual woman. Indeed, the face of this solitary queen had something of the gaiety of a drunken Nero: she had satiated herself with blood, and she wanted to play.

The soldier tried if he might walk up and down, and the panther left him free, contenting herself with following him with her eyes, less like a faithful dog than a big Angora cat, observing everything, and every movement of her master.

When he looked round, he saw, by the spring, the remains of his horse; the panther had dragged the carcass all that way; about two-thirds of it had been devoured already. The sight reassured him.

It was easy to explain the panther's absence, and the respect she had had for him while he slept. The first piece of good luck emboldened him to tempt the future, and he conceived the wild hope of continuing on good terms with the panther during the entire day, neglecting no means of taming her and remaining in her good graces.

He returned to her, and had the unspeakable joy of seeing her wag her tail with an almost imperceptible movement at his approach. He sat down, then, without fear, by her side, and they began to play together; he took her paws and muzzle, pulled her ears, rolled her over on her back, stroked her warm, delicate flanks. She let him do whatever he liked, and when he began to stroke the hair on her feet she drew her claws in carefully.

The man, keeping the dagger in one hand, thought to plunge it into the belly of the too confiding panther, but he was afraid that he would be immediately strangled in her last convulsive struggle; besides, he felt in his heart a sort of remorse which bade him respect a creature that had done him no harm. He seemed to have found a friend, in a boundless desert; half unconsciously he thought of his first sweetheart, whom he had nicknamed "Mignonne" by way of contrast, because she was so atrociously jealous that all the time of their love he was in fear of the knife with which she had always threatened him.

This memory of his early days suggested to him the idea of making the young panther answer to this name, now that he began to admire with less terror her swiftness, suppleness, and softness. Toward the end of the day he had familiarized himself with his perilous position; he now almost liked the painfulness of it. At last his companion had got into the habit of looking up at him whenever he cried in a falsetto voice, "Mignonne."

At the setting of the sun Mignonne gave, several times running, a profound melancholy cry. "She's been well brought up," said the lighthearted soldier, "she says her prayers." But this mental joke only occurred to him when he noticed what a pacific attitude his companion remained in. "Come, *ma petite blonde,* I'll let you go to bed first," he said to her, counting on the activity of his own legs to run away as quickly as possible, directly she was asleep, and seek another shelter for the night.

The soldier awaited with impatience the hour of his flight, and when it had arrived he walked vigorously in the direction of the Nile;

but hardly had he made a quarter of a league in the sand when he heard the panther bounding after him, crying with that saw-like cry, more dreadful even than the sound of her leaping.

"Ah!" he said, "then she's taken a fancy to me; she has never met any one before, and it is really quite flattering to have her first love." That instant the man fell into one of those movable quicksands so terrible to travelers and from which it is impossible to save oneself. Feeling himself caught he gave a shriek of alarm; the panther seized him with her teeth by the collar, and, springing vigorously backwards, drew him as if by magic out of the whirling sand.

"Ah, Mignonne!" cried the soldier, caressing her enthusiastically, "we're bound together for life and death—but no jokes, mind!" and he retraced his steps.

From that time the desert seemed inhabited. It contained a being to whom the man could talk, and whose ferocity was rendered gentle by him, though he could not explain to himself the reason for their strange friendship. Great as was the soldier's desire to stay up on guard, he slept.

On awakening he could not find Mignonne; he mounted the hill, and in the distance saw her springing towards him after the habit of these animals, who cannot run on account of the extreme flexibility of the vertebral column. Mignonne arrived, her jaws covered with blood; she received the wonted caress of her companion, showing with much purring how happy it made her. Her eyes, full of languor, turned still more gently than the day before toward the Provençal, who talked to her as one would to a tame animal.

"Ah! mademoiselle, you are a nice girl, aren't you? Just look at that! so we like to be made much of, don't we? Aren't you ashamed of yourself? So you have been eating some Arab or other, have you? That doesn't matter. They're animals just the same as you are; but don't you take to eating Frenchmen, or I shan't like you any longer."

She played like a dog with its master, letting herself be rolled over, knocked about, and stroked, alternately; sometimes she herself would provoke the soldier, putting up her paw with a soliciting gesture.

Some days passed in this manner. This companionship permitted the Provençal to appreciate the sublime beauty of the desert; now that he had a living thing to think about, alternations of fear and quiet, and plenty to eat, his mind became filled with contrasts and his life began to be diversified.

Solitude revealed to him all her secrets, and enveloped him in her delights. He discovered in the rising and setting of the sun sights unknown to the world. He knew what it was to tremble when he heard over his head the hiss of a bird's wings, so rarely did they pass, or when he saw the clouds, changing and many-colored travelers, melt one into another. He studied in the nighttime the effect of the moon upon the ocean of sand, where the simoom made waves swift of movement and rapid in their change. He lived the life of the Eastern day, marveling at its wonderful pomp; then, after having reveled in the sight of a hurricane over the plain where the whirling sands made red, dry mists and death-bearing clouds, he would welcome the night with joy, for then fell the healthful freshness of the stars, and he listened to imaginary music in the skies. Then solitude taught him to unroll the treasures of dreams. He passed whole hours in remembering mere nothings, and comparing his present life with his past.

At last he grew passionately fond of the panther; for some sort of affection was a necessity.

Whether it was that his will powerfully projected had modified the character of his companion, or whether, because she found abundant food in her predatory excursions in the deserts, she respected the man's life, he began to fear her no longer, seeing her so well tamed.

He devoted the greater part of his time to sleep, but he was obliged to watch like a spider in its web that the moment of his deliverance might not escape him, if any one should pass the line marked by the horizon. He had sacrificed his shirt to make a flag with, which he hung at the top of a palm tree, whose foliage he had torn off. Taught by necessity, he found the means of keeping it spread out, by fastening it with little sticks; for the wind might not be blowing at the moment when the passing traveler was looking through the desert.

It was during the long hours, when he had abandoned hope, that he amused himself with the panther. He had come to learn the different inflections of her voice, the expressions of her eyes; he had studied the capricious patterns of all the rosettes which marked the gold of her robe. Mignonne was not angry even when he took hold of the tuft at the end of her tail to count the rings, those graceful ornaments which glittered in the sun like jewelry. It gave him pleasure to contemplate the supple, fine outlines of her form, the whiteness of her belly, the graceful pose of her head. But it was especially when she was playing that he felt most pleasure in looking at her; the agility and youthful lightness of her movements were a continual surprise to him; he wondered at the supple way the beast jumped and climbed, washed herself and arranged her fur, crouched down and prepared to spring. However rapid her spring might be, however slippery the stone she was on, she would always stop short at the word "Mignonne."

One day, in a bright midday sun, an enormous bird coursed through the air. The man left his panther to look at his new guest; but after waiting a moment the deserted sultana growled deeply.

"My goodness! I do believe she's jealous," he cried, seeing her eyes become hard again, "the soul of Virginie * has passed into her body, that's certain."

The eagle disappeared into the air, while the soldier admired the curved contour of the panther.

But there was such youth and grace in her form! she was beautiful as a woman! the blond fur of her robe mingled well with the delicate tints of faint white which marked her flanks.

The profuse light cast down by the sun made this living gold, these russet markings, to burn in a way to give them an indefinable attraction.

The man and the panther looked at one another with a look full of meaning; the coquette quivered when she felt her friend stroke her head; her eyes flashed like lightning—then she shut them tightly.

"She has a soul," he said, looking at the stillness of this queen of the sands, golden like them, white like them, solitary and burning like them.

"Well," she said, "I have read your plea in favor of beasts; but how did two so well adapted to understand each other end?"

"Ah, well! you see, they ended as all great passions do end—by a misunderstanding. From some reason *one* suspects the other of treason; they don't come to an explanation through pride, and quarrel and part from sheer obstinacy."

"Yet sometimes at the best moments a single word or a look is enough—but anyhow go on with your story."

"It's horribly difficult, but you will understand, after what the old villain told me over his champagne. He said—'I don't know if I hurt her, but she turned round, as if enraged, and with her sharp teeth caught hold of my leg—gently, I dare say; but I, thinking she would devour me, plunged my dagger into her throat. She rolled over, giving a cry that froze my heart; and I saw her dying, still looking at me without anger. I would have given all the world—my cross even,

* His old sweetheart

160

which I had not got then—to have brought her to life again. It was as though I had murdered a real person; and the soldiers who had seen my flag, and had come to my assistance, found me in tears.

" 'Well, sir,' he said, after a moment of silence, 'since then I have been in war in Germany, in Spain, in Russia, in France; I've certainly carried my carcass about a good deal, but never have I seen anything like the desert. Ah! yes, it is very beautiful!'

" 'What did you feel there?' I asked him.

" 'Oh! that can't be described, young man! Besides, I am not always regretting my palm trees and my panther. I should have to be very melancholy for that. In the desert, you see, there is everything, and nothing.'

" 'Yes, but explain——'

" 'Well,' he said, with an impatient gesture, 'it is God without mankind.' "

THE DIARY

OF

SAMUEL

PEPYS

A CONDENSATION

*Reprinted from The Everyman's Library edition by
permission of J. M. Dent & Sons Ltd.*

HOME COURSE APPRECIATION

A SHORT MAN, MASSIVELY BEWIGGED and wearing a plum-colored velvet coat with wide skirts and lace ruffles at the throat and wrists, made his way along the London docks. Samuel Pepys (pronounced Peeps), Clerk of the Acts of the Navy, was busy in his Majesty's service.

Purveyors to the Navy knew that Mr. Pepys' sharp eyes missed nothing; since he took office they had had to abandon the lucrative business of giving the fleet short measures for full price. Samuel Pepys was the very model of a civil servant. Charles II had few officials who served him as well or as faithfully.

Pepys had an insatiable curiosity about everything. Wherever he went, whether among the beauties of the Restoration court, or down the alleys of the waterfront, or into foreign lands, he was always a keen observer. He would go from one end of town to the other to see a new plant or a strange beast. When he went to the theater, it was to watch the audience as closely as the players.

He had a way of being present at, and remembering in his diary, small as well as great events. He was on hand when Lady Castlemaine, the King's beautiful mistress, stepped into a rough crowd to comfort a hurt child. He watched scientific experiments at Gresham College (the Royal Society) and attended cockfights and bull-baitings. Every night for almost ten years he described the events of the day in his diary. He wrote only for himself, using a seventeenth century shorthand invented by Thomas Shelton. Some of the more intimate passages were written in a strange mixture of French, German, Latin, and shorthand. It was a wise precaution because, in his diary, Pepys was above all frank, and it would never have done for his wife or the servants to read some of the entries.

London was both his home and his delight. He was born there on February 23, 1633, the fifth child of John Pepys and Margaret Kite. His father was a tailor. Before her marriage, his humbly born mother had been a laundress. Because John Pepys was not a Londoner—the Pepys family were from Cambridgeshire—or a member of the all-powerful Guild of Merchant Tailors, he was forced to establish himself as one of the city's "foreign" tailors.

Samuel's great-aunt married Sir Sidney Montagu, a country squire and neighbor of the Cromwell family at Huntingdon. Her son Edward became the first Earl of Sandwich and Pepys' patron. It is this Edward who is constantly referred to in the Diary as "my Lord."

Samuel was reared in a devout but pleasant Puritan household. We sometimes make the mistake of thinking that the English Puritans disapproved of all forms of pleasure. Like the great Puritan poet, John Milton, Pepys was passionately fond of music. His father played the bass viol and taught that instrument to his son. There was nothing Pepys loved more than a concert. When, in the early years of his marriage, poverty forced him to pawn his lute, he suffered the loss acutely. Among his favorite companions in later years were the composer Matthew Lock and Henry Purcell, father of the composer of the same name.

He was sent to school at St. Paul's, not far from his father's shop. There he was given a rigorous classical education that included Latin, Greek and Hebrew. It was of value to him later when, confronted by a Dutch admiral who spoke neither French nor English, he could converse in Latin. Samuel won a scholarship in 1650 which made it possible for him to enter Trinity Hall, Cambridge, as a sizar—a student who waited on table in exchange for his tuition. The next year he transferred to Magdalene College, where he was granted a more generous scholarship.

THE MAN AND HIS TIME

Pepys reached manhood during the Commonwealth. The Civil War which set Roundhead against Royalist was over. The Stuarts were in exile and Oliver Cromwell had become Lord Protector of the realm. Pepys had relatives on both sides of the conflict, but his immediate family were staunch Roundheads and his cousin Edward Montagu was an enthusiastic follower of Cromwell. St. Paul's School was Puritan in its sympathies and when Charles I was beheaded in 1649, pious fifteen-year-old Samuel remarked to a classmate that if he were to preach a sermon on the King's execution, his text would be, "The memory of the wicked shall rot."

Pepys' father benefited from the overthrow of the monarchy. The Guild of Merchant Tailors, which completely dominated the trade and made it very difficult for non-members to practice their craft, was composed largely of Presbyterian merchants. Since the Puritans looked upon Presbyterians as little better than members of the Established Church, their status was lowered and with it their autocratic power. John Pepys was able to gain admittance to the Guild in 1653.

Oliver Cromwell died in 1658. His son Richard inherited the position of Lord Protector, and little else. His father had had the genius and energy of a great general, but even he had found it difficult to control his army officers. Under Richard they overran the country. The weak successor to sturdy Old Noll was soon the object of open contempt. "As queer as Dick's hatband" became a common expression of disgust at his attempt to hang on to the power of the Crown.

Thoughtful men began to lament the loss of the Stuart kings. In retrospect they seemed far better than they had in the turbulent 1640's, and certainly preferable to Richard Cromwell. Edward Montagu, commissioner of the Treasury and Admiralty under Cromwell, entered into secret correspondence with Charles II in exile on the Continent. Samuel Pepys, an orderly man distressed by the chaos of the government, was among those Roundheads who turned Royalist. Montagu took Pepys with him as his confidential secretary when the final arrangements were made to bring Charles II back to England.

MARRIAGE AND A CAREER

Just how Pepys earned his living when he first left the University is a matter of conjecture, but he soon made himself useful to "my Lord" and entered his employ. And he fell in love.

The young lady was Elizabeth le Marchant de St. Michel, the curly-haired daughter of an exiled French Huguenot, as penniless as he was impractical. Elizabeth, barely fifteen years old, was a petulant, headstrong, remarkably pretty girl. Though the eminently practical Mr. Pepys had few prospects, he allowed his heart to rule, and he and the young lady were married. As the reader of the *Diary* soon discovers. their married life was not one long idyll. But every quarrel was some-

Samuel Pepys as he looked when he was keeping his diary, with King Charles II at the left, the Duke of York at the right.

how reconciled and they lived out their time together very agreeably on the whole.

When they were first married the need of money was acute. Pepys performed all sorts of odd jobs for his cousin, carrying small sums of money to tradesmen, hiring coaches, and so forth. Later he graduated to more important responsibilities—the collection of rents, the management of properties and the execution of confidential errands.

It was during this period, on March 26, 1654, that Pepys had his famous operation for kidney stones. Every year he celebrated his deliverance from that affliction with a dinner party. And small wonder! In the seventeenth century, when there were neither anesthetics nor antiseptics, surgery was indeed hazardous and not too many patients survived to talk about their operations.

Pepys was working as a minor clerk in the Exchequer when Montagu asked him to accompany him on the naval expedition that resulted in the restoration of the monarchy. When they returned to England, "my Lord" obtained for him the position of Clerk of the Acts of the Navy. The Clerk of the Acts was in charge of the purchase and supply for, and the administration of, the Royal Navy. He dealt with contractors and admirals, shipbuilders and treasury officials. He was responsible for spending the equivalent of millions of dollars.

THE CIVIL SERVANT

WHEN SAMUEL PEPYS TOOK OVER his post he was under thirty; he had had no experience at sea and he was quite ill-prepared for such an important job. But he did have inexhaustible energy and little by little he made himself the master of his office. One of the first things he did was to hire a mathematics tutor to teach him the multiplication tables.

If Pepys could prevent it, his Majesty was not going to receive short weight. He rose early ("Up betimes," as he phrased it in the diary) and worked late. His letters of instructions to subordinates, which at first were vague and sketchy, grew steadily longer and more detailed as he mastered his duties. He would sit by the hour with old seamen, learning the names of ropes and sails. He made it his business to know the hardships seamen endured and took pains to remedy the more flagrant abuses.

The more he learned about the business of the King's Navy, the more clearly did Mr. Pepys perceive that his Majesty was being cheated on all sides. Up and down the vast, disorderly waterfront he hurried, investigating suppliers and raging at the graft he found. He bargained with dealers of hemp, tar and lumber. He renegotiated old contracts and found new sources of supply. He hired carpenters and fought with lords, divided prize money and assigned officers to duty.

And in carrying out his office he also improved the fortunes of Samuel Pepys. Today some of his activities might be the subject of a parliamentary inquiry, but by the standards of the seventeenth century, he was a paragon of honesty.

When the times demanded it he could rise to heroism. As the great plague of 1665 swept through London, he sent his wife and household staff to the country, while he remained at the Navy Office. "You, sir," he wrote to Sir William Coventry, "took your turn at the sword. I must not therefore grudge to take mine at the pestilence."

The fire raged every way . . . nobody endeavoring to quench it,

but to remove their goods, and leave all to the fire.

The years from 1660 to 1669, when Pepys was founding his fortune, and England, by disposing of the Dutch challenge, was laying the groundwork for her empire, are covered by the diaries. They take the diarist from his twenty-seventh to his thirty-seventh year. They take him from shabby lodgings cared for by one maid in Axe Yard to a fashionable house with several menservants and maids. They find him beginning to collect his splendid library and leave him owning a coach-and-four.

The diaries were ended when Pepys' eyesight, worn out from years of scribbling tiny shorthand pothooks by flickering candlelight, could no longer be helped by the pair of leather tubes with lenses in them that comprised his primitive spectacles. The tone of resignation to his impending blindness—which fortunately did not come about—gives the reader the feeling that Pepys was old and worn out. In fact, at thirty-six he had just reached the vigorous prime of life. And we can take pleasure in knowing that he had nearly thirty-five more years of life, during which he accomplished some of his greatest achievements.

His wife Elizabeth died shortly after the diaries were closed and he never remarried. Pepys served as Secretary of the Admiralty from 1672 to 1678, when a combination of political and business enemies charged him with disloyalty, malfeasance and complicity in the Popish plot to overthrow the government. Most of the "evidence" supporting the charges was either false or distorted, but Pepys was forced to defend himself at great expense. Ultimately he was exonerated. One of his chief accusers, a former butler, confessed on his deathbed that he had perjured himself to make a case against his one-time employer.

Pepys returned to government service and accompanied Lord Dartmouth on an inspection tour to Tangier. Pepys kept a most interesting diary during the trip. In 1684 he was again named Secretary of the Admiralty. His work to reorganize and modernize the Navy caused his biographer, the historian Arthur Bryant, to call him the "savior of the Navy." After the so-called Glorious Revolution of 1688 he was dismissed from office.

He spent the last years of his life in comfortable retirement, arranging his library, looking after his investments, and corresponding with such friends as Christopher Wren, Isaac Newton, John Evelyn and John Dryden. He was a fellow of the Royal Society and its president in 1684 and again in 1685.

When Pepys died in 1703, John Evelyn expressed his sorrow at the loss of his honored friend in a moving passage in his own diary. Pepys willed his valuable library to his nephew John Jackson, providing that he in turn would give it to Magdalene College.

SIX VOLUMES OF SHORTHAND WRITING

AMONG THE RICHLY BOUND VOLUMES in Pepys' notable collection of books were six calf-bound, untitled volumes. Their pages were covered with close, neat lines of shorthand writing. At one time it was believed that the diary was written in a secret cipher, but actually it was in a shorthand that became obsolete soon after Pepys' death.

Following the successful publication in 1818 of John Evelyn's diary, the Master of Magdalene College remembered the six shorthand volumes in the Pepys Library and called them to the attention of Lord Baybrooke. John Smith was given the task of deciphering the diaries. We are told that Smith worked from twelve to fourteen hours a day for about three years transcribing the books. In 1825 Lord Baybrooke published selections from the *Diary* as the *Memoirs of Samuel Pepys*. Between 1893–99 Henry B. Wheatley brought out a ten-volume edition of the *Diary* that is complete except for the omission of a number of "indelicate" passages.

During the busy years he was keeping a diary, Samuel Pepys set down some 1,300,000 words, or about the equivalent of seventeen average-sized novels. Only about one-quarter of the whole diary appeared in the first edition. The characters and places mentioned by Pepys have since been identified by successive editors, biographers and historians. Pepys' papers and letters supplement the original volumes and we now know more about Samuel Pepys than about almost any other Englishman, with the possible exception of James Boswell.

PEPYS AS A WRITER

It is not customary to rank Pepys very high as a writer. His style is quite unadorned, and the shorthand in which he wrote sometimes had the effect of making his prose sound quaint. He often omitted the verb from a sentence or slid from topic to topic as memory prompted him. Some of the entries are merely routine notices of business transactions. But he had a remarkable gift for sustained narrative; the *Diary* is marked by an astonishing frankness and common sense.

When he tells the story of the Great Fire of London (September 2–6, 1666), we feel that we are experiencing those tragic days. We see London ablaze from the Tower to the Temple. With the broad picture he gives us the significant, human details and touching, intimate episodes.

Pepys' finest effects often come in a way that defies art. They come from the man himself. When he visits Epsom Downs and discourses with an old shepherd, there is a gentleness to the scene which would surprise people who know of Pepys only that there are racy passages in the *Diary*.

Pepys was perhaps no better than he should be. But he was, after all, only human. He never pretended to be more than he was. The charm of the diaries lies in their utter frankness. Pepys records his faults and his virtues, so that we get an unsurpassed portrait of the whole man against the background of London life, in the exciting years of the Restoration.

[*When Samuel Pepys begins his diary, he is a minor official in the Navy Office, having been helped to the post by a distant kinsman, Edward Montagu, the Earl of Sandwich, who is called simply "My Lord" throughout the work. The year 1660 dawns amid great uncertainty. The Parliament, contemptuously called the "Rump" of the famous Long Parliament, is restless and unpredictable; the populace is uneasy. England's future is anxiously debated by generals and grandees—the Monks, Fairfaxes and Lamberts of the diary's early entries. Across the Channel, charming, ambitious Charles Stuart plots an end to the eleven-year exile during which his father has been beheaded.*]

1659–60

B LESSED BE God, at the end of the last year, I was in very good health, without any sense of my old pain, but upon taking of cold. I lived in Axe Yard, having my wife, and servant Jane, and no other in family than us three.

The condition of the State was thus: viz. the Rump, after being disturbed by my Lord Lambert, was lately returned to sit again. The officers of the Army all forced to yield. Lawson * lies still in the river,

* Admiral Sir John Lawson brought Charles back to England.

and Monk is with his army in Scotland. Only my Lord Lambert is not yet come into the Parliament, nor is it expected that he will, without being forced to it. The new Common Council of the City do speak very high; and had sent to Monk, their sword-bearer, to acquaint him with their desires for a free and full Parliament, which is at present the desires, and the hopes, and the expectations of all: twenty-two of the old secluded members having been at the House door the last week to demand entrance, but it was denied them; and it is believed that neither they nor the people will be satisfied till the House be filled. My own private condition very handsome, and esteemed rich, but indeed very poor; besides my goods of my house, and my office, which at present is somewhat certain. Mr. Downing master of my office.

JANUARY 1st. (Lord's day.) This morning, (we living lately in the garret) I rose, put on my suit with great skirts, having not lately worn any other clothes but them. Went to Mr. Gunning's chapel at Exeter House, where he made a very good sermon upon these words: "That in the fullness of time God sent his Son, made of a woman," &c.; showing, that by "made under the law" is meant the circumcision, which is solemnized this day. Dined at home in the garret, where my wife dressed the remains of a turkey, and in the doing of it she burned her hand. I stayed at home the whole afternoon, looking over my accounts; then went with my wife to my father's, and in going observed the great posts which the City workmen set up at the Conduit in Fleet Street.

2d. Walked a great while in Westminster Hall, where I heard that Lambert was coming up to London; that my Lord Fairfax was in the head of the Irish brigade, but it was not certain what he would declare for. The House was today upon finishing the act for the Council of State, which they did; and for the indemnity to the soldiers; and were to sit again thereupon in the afternoon. Great talk that many places had declared for a free Parliament; and it is believed that they will be forced to fill up the House with the old members. From the Hall I called at home, and so went to Mr. Crewe's (my wife she was to go to her father's) and Mr. Moore and I and another gentleman went out and drank a cup of ale together in the new market, and there I ate some bread and cheese for my dinner.

MARCH 6th. (Shrove Tuesday.) I called Mr. Shepley, and we both went up to my Lord's * lodgings at Mr. Crewe's, where he bids us to go home again, and get a fire against an hour after; which we did, at

* Earl of Sandwich, called so throughout

White Hall, whither he came, and after talking with him about our going to sea, he called me by myself into the garden, where he asked me how things were with me. He bid me look out now at this turn some good place, and he would use all his own, and all the interest of his friends that he had in England, to do me good; and asked me whether I could, without too much inconvenience, go to sea as his secretary, and bid me think of it. He also began to talk of things of State, and told me that he should want one in that capacity at sea, that he might trust in, and therefore he would have me to go. He told me also, that he did believe the King would come in, and did discourse with me about it, and about the affection of the people and City, at which I was full glad. Mr. Hawley brought me a seaman that had promised £10 to him if he get him a purser's place, which I think to endeavor to do. My uncle Tom inquires about the Knights of Windsor, of which he desires to be one. To see Mrs. Jem, at whose chamber door I found a couple of ladies, but she not being there, we hunted her out, and found that she and another had hid themselves behind a door. Well, they all went down into the dining-room, where it was full of tag, rag, and bobtail, dancing, singing, and drinking, of which I was ashamed, and after I had stayed a dance or two, I went away. Wrote by the post, by my Lord's command, for J. Goods to come up presently; for my Lord intends to go forth with Goods to the Swiftsure till the Nazeby be ready.

This day I hear that the Lords do intend to sit, a great store of them are now in town, and, I see, in the Hall today. Overton at Hull do stand out, but can, it is thought, do nothing; and Lawson, it is said, is gone with some ships thither, but all that is nothing. My Lord told me, that there was great endeavors to bring in the Protector again; but he told me, too, that he did believe it would not last long if he were brought in; no, nor the King neither (though he seems to think that he will come in) unless he carry himself very soberly and well. Everybody now drinks the King's health without any fear, whereas before it was very private that a man dare do it. Monk this day is feasted at Mercers' Hall, and is invited one after another to the twelve Halls in London. Many think that he is honest yet, and some or more think him to be a fool that would raise himself, but think that he will undo himself by endeavoring it.

7th. (Ash Wednesday.) Washington told me, upon my question whether he knew of any place now ready that I might have by power over friends, that this day Mr. G. Montagu was to be made Custos

Rotulorum for Westminster, and that I might get to be named by him Clerk of the Peace; but my Lord he believes Mr. Montagu had already promised it, and that it was given him only that he might gratify one person with the place I look for. Going homeward, my Lord overtook me in his coach, and called me in, and so I went with him to St. James's, and G. Montagu being gone to White Hall, we walked over the Park thither, all the way he discoursing of the times, and of the change of things since the last year, and wondering how he could bear with so great a disappointment as he did. He did give me the best advice that he could what was best for me, whether to stay or go with him, and offered all the ways that could be, how he might do me good, with the greatest liberty and love that could be.

This day, according to order, Sir Arthur appeared at the House; what was done I know not, but there was all the Rumpers almost come to the House today. My Lord did seem to wonder much why Lambert was so willing to be put into the Tower, and thinks he has some design in it; but I think that he is so poor that he cannot use his liberty for debts, if he were at liberty; and so it is as good and better for him to be there, than anywhere else. My father left my uncle with his leg very dangerous, and do believe he cannot continue long. My uncle did acquaint him, that he did intend to make me his heir, and give my brother Tom something, and to leave something to raise portions for Joh. and Pall. I pray God he may be as good as his word! This news and my Lord's great kindness makes me very cheerful within.

8th. To Westminster Hall, where there was a general damp over men's minds and faces upon some of the officers of the Army being about making a remonstrance upon Charles Stuart or any single person; but at noon it was told, that the General had put a stop to it, so all was well again. Here I met with Jasper, who was to bring me to my Lord at the lobby; whither sending a note to my Lord, he comes out to me and gives me directions to look after getting some money for him from the Admiralty, seeing that things are so unsafe, that he would not lay out a farthing for the State, till he had received some money of theirs. This afternoon, some of the officers of the Army, and some of the Parliament, had a conference at White Hall, to make all right again, but I know not what is done. At the Dog Tavern, Captain Philip Holland, with whom I advised how to make some advantage of my Lord's going to sea, told me to have five or six servants entered on board as dead men, and I to give them what wages I pleased, and so their pay to be mine; he also urged me to take the Secretary's place that my Lord did proffer me. Then in comes Mr. Wade and Mr. Sterry, secretary to the plenipotentiary in Denmark, who brought the news of the death of the King of Sweden at Gottenburg the 3d of last month, and he told me what a great change he found when he came here, the secluded members being restored.

9th. To my Lord at his lodging, and came to Westminster with him in the coach; and Mr. Dudley and he in the Painted Chamber walked a good while; and I telling him that I was willing and ready to go with him to sea, he agreed that I should, and advised me what to write to Mr. Downing about it. This day it was resolved that the writs do go out in the name of the Keepers of the Liberty, and I hear that it is resolved privately that a treaty be offered with the King; and that Monk did check his soldiers highly for what they did yesterday.

10th. To my father in his cutting * house, and told him my resolution to go to sea with my Lord, and we resolved of letting my wife be at Mr. Bowyer's.

12th. Rode to Huntsmore to Mr. Bowyer's, where I found him, and all well, and willing to have my wife come and board with them while I was at sea. Here I lay, and took a spoonful of honey and a nutmeg, scraped for my cold, by Mr. Bowyer's direction.

13th. At my Lord's lodgings, who told me that I was to be secretary, and Crewe deputy treasurer to the Fleet, at which I was troubled, but I could not help it. This day the Parliament voted all that had been done by the former Rump against the House of Lords be void, and tonight that the writs go out without any qualification. Things seem very doubtful what will be the end of all; for the Parliament seems to be strong for the King, while the soldiers do all talk against.

14th. To my Lord's, where infinity of applications to him and to me. To my great trouble, my Lord gives me all the papers that was given to him, to put in order and to give him an account of them. Here I got half a piece of a person of Mr. Wright's recommending to my Lord, to be Chaplain of the Speaker frigate. I went hence to St. James's, to speak with Mr. Clerke, Monk's secretary, about getting some soldiers removed out of Huntingdon to Oundle, which my Lord told me he did to do a courtesy to the town, that he might have the greater interest in them, in the choice of the next Parliament; not that he intends to be chosen himself, but that he might have Mr. G. Montagu and my Lord Mandeville, chose there in spite of the Bernards.

* Cutting room of his father's tailor shop

This done I saw General Monk, and methought he seemed a dull heavy man. I did promise to give my wife all that I have in the world, but my books, in case I should die at sea. After supper, I went to Westminster Hall, and the Parliament sat till ten at night, thinking and being expected to dissolve themselves today, but they did not. Great talk tonight that the discontented officers did think this night to make a stir, but prevented.

15th. Early packing up my things to be sent by cart with the rest of my Lord's. At Will's I met Tom Alcock, one that went to school with me at Huntingdon, but I had not seen him these sixteen years.

16th. To Westminster Hall, where I heard how the Parliament had this day dissolved themselves, and did pass very cheerfully through the Hall, and the Speaker without his mace. The whole Hall was joyful thereat, as well as themselves, and now they begin to talk loud of the King. Tonight I am told, that yesterday, about five o'clock in the afternoon, one came with a ladder to the Great Exchange, and wiped with a brush the inscription that was on King Charles, and that there was a great bonfire made in the Exchange, and people called out, "God bless King Charles the Second!"

17th. This day, before I went out with my wife, I did seal my will to her, whereby I did give her all that I have in the world, but my books, which I give to my brother John, excepting only French books, which my wife is to have.

20th. I took a short melancholy leave of my father and mother, without having them to drink, or say anything of business one to another. At Westminster, by reason of rain and an easterly wind, the water was so high that there was boats rowed in King Street, and all our yard was drowned, that one could not go to my house, so as no man has seen the like almost, and most houses full of water.

21st. To my Lord's, but the wind very high against us; here I did very much business, and then to my Lord Widdrington's from my Lord, with his desire that he might have the disposal of the writs of the Cinque Ports.* My Lord was very civil to me, and called for wine, and writ a long letter in answer.

22d. To Westminster, and received my warrant of Mr. Blackburne, to be Secretary to the two Generals of the Fleet. Strange how these people do now promise me anything; one a rapier, the other a vessel of wine, or a gun, and one offered me a silver hatband to do him

* Five principal military ports on the English Channel

a courtesy. I pray God to keep me from being proud, or too much lifted up hereby.

23d. Carried my Lord's will in a black box to Mr. W. Montagu, for him to keep for him. My Lord, Captain Isham, Mr. Thomas, John Crewe, W. Howe, and I to the Tower, where the barges stayed for us; my Lord and the Captain in one, and W. Howe and I, &c., in the other, to the Long Reach, where the Swiftsure lay at anchor (in our way, we saw the great breach which the late high water had made, to the loss of many £1000 to the people about Limehouse). Soon as my Lord on board, the guns went off bravely from the ships. And a little while after comes the Vice-Admiral Lawson, and seemed very respectful to my Lord, and so did the rest of the Commanders of the frigates that were thereabouts. We were late writing of orders for the getting of ships ready and also making of others to all the seaports between Hastings and Yarmouth, to stop all dangerous persons that are going or coming between Flanders and there. The cabin allotted to me was the best that any had that belonged to my Lord.

24th. At work hard all the day writing letters to the Council, &c. Mr. Creed came on board, and dined very boldly with my Lord. The boy Eliezer flung down a can of beer upon my papers, which made me give him a box of the ear, it having cost me a great deal of work.

25th. (Lord's day.) About two o'clock in the morning, letters came from London by our coxswain, so they waked me, but I bid him stay till morning, which he did, and then I rose and carried them into my Lord, who read them a-bed. Among the rest, there was the writ and mandate for him to dispose to the Cinque Ports for choice of Parliament men. There was also one for me from Mr. Blackburne, who with his own hand superscribes it to S. P., Esq., of which God knows I was not a little proud. I wrote a letter to the Clerk of Dover Castle, to come to my Lord about issuing of those writs. Mr. Ibbott prayed, and preached a good sermon. At dinner, I took place of all but the Captain. After that, sermon again, at which I slept, God forgive me!

26th. This day it is two years since it pleased God that I was cut for the stone * at Mrs. Turner's in Salisbury Court; and did resolve while I live to keep it a festival, as I did the last year at my house, and forever to have Mrs. Turner and her company with me. But now it pleased God that I am prevented to do it openly; only within my soul I can and do rejoice, and bless God, being at this time, blessed be his holy name, in as good health as ever I was in my life.

* Operated on

171

27th. This morning, the wind came about, and we fell into the Hope; and in our passing by the Vice-Admiral, he and the rest of the frigates did give us many guns, and we him, and the report of them broke all the windows in my cabin. I sat the first time with my Lord at table since my coming to sea. All the afternoon exceeding busy in writing of letters and orders. In the afternoon, Sir Harry Wright come on board us, about his business of being chosen a Parliament-man. My Lord brought him to see my cabin, where I was hard a-writing. At night supped with my Lord too, with the Captain.

APRIL 5th. We set sail at noon, and come in the evening to Lee roads and anchored.

6th. Under sail as far as the Spitts.

7th. The wind grew high, and we, being among the sands, lay at anchor; I began to be dizzy and squeamish.

8th. (Lord's day.) The lieutenant and I looked through his glass at two good merchantmen, and at the women on board them, being pretty handsome.

9th. In sight of the North and South Forelands. This afternoon I first saw France and Calais, with which I was much pleased, though it was at a distance. We came to the castles about Deal, where our fleet lay, and anchored; great was the shout of guns from the castles, and ships, and our answers.

10th. Most of the commanders in the fleet came on board, and the Vice-Admiral to us, who sat and talked, and seemed a very good-natured man. Lord Goring returned from France, and landed at Dover.

11th. A gentleman came from my Lord of Manchester to my Lord for a pass for Mr. Boyle, which was made him. All the news from London is that things go on further towards a king. That the Skinners' Company the other day, at their entertaining of General Monk, had took down the Parliament Arms in their Hall, and set up the King's. My Lord and I had a great deal of discourse about the several Captains of the Fleet and his interest among them, and had his mind clear to bring in the King. He confessed to me that he was not sure of his own Captain, to be true to him, and that he did not like Captain Stokes. Came two letters from my dear wife.

18th. Mr. Cook returned from London, bringing me this news, that the Cavaliers are something unwise to talk so high as they do. That the Lords do meet every day at my Lord of Manchester's, and resolve to sit the first day of the Parliament. That it is evident now that the

General and the Council do resolve to make way for the King's coming. And it is clear that either the Fanatics must now be undone, or the gentry and citizens throughout England, and clergy must fall, in spite of their militia and army, which is not at all possible, I think.

21st. This day dined Sir John Boys and some other gentlemen, formerly great Cavaliers, and among the rest one Mr. Norwood, for whom my Lord give a convoy to carry him to Den Briel,* but he is certainly going to the King; for my Lord commanded me that I should not enter his name in my book. My Lord do show them and that sort of people great civility. All their discourse and others are of the King's coming, and we begin to speak of it very freely; and heard how in many churches in London, and upon many signs there, and upon merchants' ships in the river, they had set up the King's arms. This night there came one with a letter from Mr. Edward Montagu to my Lord, with command to deliver it to his own hands. I do believe that he do carry some close business on for the King. This day I had a large letter from Mr. Moore, giving me an account of the present dispute at London that is like to be at the beginning of the Parliament, about the House of Lords, who do resolve to sit with the Commons, as not thinking themselves dissolved yet, which, whether it be granted or no, or whether they will sit or no, it will bring a great many inconveniences. His letter I keep, it being a very well writ one.

22d. (Easter Sunday.) Several Londoners, strangers, friends of the Captains, dined here, who, among other things, told us, how the King's Arms are every day set up in houses and churches, particularly in Allhallows' Church in Thames Street, John Simpson's church, which, being privately done, was a great eyesore to his people when they came to church and saw it. Also, they told us for certain, that the King's statue is making by the Mercers' Company, (who are bound to do it) to set up in the Exchange.

23d. I had 40s. given me by Captain Cowes of the Paradox. In the evening, for the first time, extraordinary good sport among the seamen, after my Lord had done playing at ninepins. That being done, he fell to singing a song upon the Rump, to the tune of "The Blacksmith."†

MAY 1st. It being a very pleasant day, I wished myself in Hyde Park. At supper, hearing a great noise, we all rose, and found it was to save the coxswain of the Cheriton, who, dropping overboard, was

* Dutch seaport
† Same tune as "Green Sleeves"

drowned. Today, I hear they were very merry at Deal, setting up the King's flags upon one of their Maypoles, and drinking his health upon their knees in the streets, and firing the guns, which the soldiers of the castle threatened, but dared not oppose.

2d. Mr. Dunne from London, with letters that tell us the welcome news of the Parliament's votes yesterday, which will be remembered for the happiest May Day that hath been many a year to England. The King's letter was read in the House, wherein he submits himself and all things to them, as to an Act of Oblivion to all, unless they shall please to except any, as to the confirming of the sales of the King's and Church lands, if they see good. The House, upon reading the letter, ordered £50,000 to be forthwith provided to send to His Majesty for his present supply; and a committee chosen to return an answer of thanks to His Majesty for his gracious letter; and that the letter be kept among the records of the Parliament; and in all this not so much as one no. So that Luke Robinson himself stood up, and made a recantation for what he had done, and promises to be a loyal subject to his Prince for the time to come. The City of London have put out a Declaration, wherein they do disclaim their owing any other government but that of a King, Lords, and Commons. Thanks were given by the House to Sir John Greenville, one of the bedchamber to the King, who brought the letter, and they continued bare all the time it was reading. Upon notice from the Lords to the Commons, of their desire that the Commons would join with them in their vote for King, Lords, and Commons; the Commons did concur, and voted that all books whatever that are out against the Government of Kings, Lords, and Commons, should be brought into the House and burned. Great joy all yesterday at London, and at night more bonfires than ever, and ringing of bells, and drinking of the King's health upon their knees in the streets, which methinks is a little too much. But everybody seems to be very joyful in the business, insomuch that our sea-commanders now begin to say so too, which a week ago they would not do. And our seamen, as many as had money or credit for drink, did do nothing else this evening. This day came Mr. North (Sir Dudley North's son) on board to spend a little time here, which my Lord was a little troubled at, but he seems to be a fine gentleman, and at night did play his part at music exceeding well at first sight.

3d. This morning my Lord showed me the King's declaration and his letter to the two Generals to be communicated to the fleet. The contents of the letter are his offer of grace to all that will come in within forty days, only excepting them that the Parliament shall here-after except. That the sales of lands during these troubles, and all other things, shall be left to the Parliament, by which he will stand. The letter dated at Breda, April 14, 1660, in the twelfth year of his reign. Upon the receipt of it this morning by an express, Mr. Phillips, one of the messengers of the Council from General Monk, my Lord summoned a council of war, and in the meantime did dictate to me how he would have the vote ordered which he would have pass this council. Which done, the Commanders all came on board, and the council sat in the coach (the first council of war that had been in my time), where I read the letter and declaration; and while they were discoursing upon it, I seemed to draw up a vote, which, being offered, they passed. Not one man seemed to say no to it, though I am confident many in their hearts were against it.

After this was done, I went up to the quarter-deck with my Lord and the Commanders, and there read both the papers and the vote; which done, and demanding their opinion, the seamen did all of them cry out, "God bless King Charles!" with the greatest joy imaginable. That being done, Sir R. Stayner, who had invited us yesterday, took all the Commanders and myself on board him to dinner, which not being ready, I went with Captain Hayward to the Plymouth and Essex, and did what I had to do, and returned, where very merry at dinner. After dinner, to the rest of the ships quite through the fleet, which was a very brave sight to visit all the ships, and to be received with the respect and honor that I was on board them all; and much more to see the great joy that I brought to all men; not one through the whole fleet showing the least dislike of the business.

In the evening, as I was going on board the Vice-Admiral, the General began to fire his guns, which he did all that he had in the ship, and so did all the rest of the Commanders, which was very gallant, and to hear the bullets go hissing over our heads as we were in the boat.

This done, and finished my Proclamation, I returned to the Nazeby, where my Lord was much pleased to hear how all the fleet took it in a transport of joy, showed me a private letter of the King's to him, and another from the Duke of York, in such familiar style as their common friend, with all kindness imaginable. And I found by the letters, and so my Lord told me too, that there had been many letters passed between them for a great while, and I perceive unknown to Monk. And among the rest that had carried these letters Sir John Boys is one, and Mr. Norwood, which had a ship to carry him over the other day, when my Lord would not have me put down his name in the book.

The King speaks of his being courted to come to the Hague, but do desire my Lord's advice where to come to take ship; and the Duke offers to learn the seaman's trade of him, in such familiar words as if Jack Cole and I had writ them. This was very strange to me, that my Lord should carry all things so wisely and prudently as he do, and I was over-joyful to see him in so good condition, and he did not a little please himself to tell me how he had provided for himself so great a hold on the King. After this to supper, and then to writing of letters till twelve at night, and so up again at three in the morning.

My Lord seemed to put great confidence in me, and would take my advice in many things. I perceive his being willing to do all the honor in the world to Monk, and to let him have all the honor of doing the business, though he will many times express his thoughts of him to be but a thick-skulled fool. So that I do believe there is some agreement more than ordinary between the King and my Lord to let Monk carry on the business, for it is he that can do the business, or at least that can hinder it, if he be not flattered and observed. This my Lord will hint himself sometimes. My Lord, I perceive by the King's letter, had writ to him about his father, Crewe, and the King did speak well of him; but my Lord tells me, that he is afraid that he hath too much concerned himself with the Presbyterians against the House of Lords, which will do him a great discourtesy.

4th. I wrote this morning many letters, and to all the copies of the vote of the council of war I put my name, that if it should come in print my name may be on it. I sent a copy of the vote to Doling, enclosed in this letter:

"Sir,

"He that can fancy a fleet (like ours) in her pride, with pennants loose, guns roaring, caps flying, and the loud *'Vive le Roys!'** echoed from one ship's company to another, he, and he only, can apprehend the joy this enclosed vote was received with, or the blessing he thought himself possessed of that bore it, and is

"Your humble servant."

About nine o'clock I got all my letters done, and sent them by the messenger that came yesterday. This morning came Captain Isham

* Long live the King!

on board with a gentleman going to the King, by whom very cunningly, my Lord tells me, he intends to send an account of this day's and yesterday's actions here, notwithstanding he had writ to the Parliament to have leave of them to send the King the answer of the fleet. Since my writing of the last paragraph, my Lord called me to him, to read his letter to the King, to see whether I could find any slips in it or no. And as much of the letter as I can remember is thus:

"May it please Your Most Excellent Majesty," and so begins.

That he yesterday received from General Monk his Majesty's letter and direction; and that General Monk had desired him to write to the Parliament to have leave to send the vote of the seamen before he did send it to him, which he had done by writing to both Speakers; but for his private satisfaction he had sent it thus privately (and so the copy of the proceedings yesterday was sent him) and that this came by a gentleman that came this day on board, intending to wait upon his Majesty, that he is my Lord's countryman, and one whose friends have suffered much on his Majesty's behalf. That my Lords Pembroke and Salisbury are put out of the House of Lords. That my Lord is very joyful that other countries do pay him the civility and respect due to him; and that he do much rejoice to see that the King do receive none of their assistance (or some such words) from them, he having strength enough in the love and loyalty of his own subjects to support him. That his Majesty had chosen the best place * for his embarking, and that there is nothing in the world of which he is more ambitious than to have the honor of attending his Majesty, which he hoped would be speedy. That he had commanded the vessel to attend till this gentleman returns, that so if his Majesty do not think it fit to command the fleet himself, yet that he may be there to receive his commands and bring them to his Lordship. He ends his letter, that he is confounded with the thoughts of the high expressions of love to him in the King's letter, and concludes,

"Your most loyal, dutiful, faithful, and obedient subject and servant, "E. M."

After supper at the table in the coach, my Lord talking concerning the uncertainty of the places of the Exchequer to them that had them now; he did at last think of an office which do belong to him in case the King do restore every man to his places that ever had been patent, which is to be one of the clerks of the signet, which will be a fine employment for one of his sons.

* Scheveningen, port of the Hague

In the afternoon came a minister on board, one Mr. Sharpe, who is going to the King; who tells me that Commissioners are chosen both of the Lords and Commons to go to the King; and that Dr. Clarges is going to him from the Army, and that he will be here tomorrow. My letters at night tell me that the House did deliver their letter to Sir John Greenville, in answer to the King's sending, and that they give him £500 for his pains, to buy him a jewel, and that besides the £50,000 ordered to be borrowed of the City for the present use of the King, the twelve companies of the City do give every one of them to his Majesty, as a present, £1000.

5th. All the morning very busy writing letters to London, and a packet to Mr. Downing, to acquaint him with what had been done lately in the fleet. And this I did by my Lord's command, who, I thank him, did of himself think of doing it, to do me a kindness, for he writ a letter himself to him, thanking him for his kindness to me. This evening come Dr. Clarges to Deal, going to the King; where the towns-people strewed the streets with herbs against his coming, for joy of his going. Never was there so general a content as there is now. I cannot but remember that our parson did, in his prayer tonight, pray for the long life and happiness of our King and dread Sovereign, that may last as long as the sun and moon endureth.

6th. (Lord's day.) Dr. Clarges and a dozen gentlemen to see my Lord, and after sermon dined with him: last night, my Lord told me he was a man of small *entendimiento*.† It fell very well today, a stranger preached here for Mr. Ibbot, one Mr. Stanley, who prayed for King Charles, by the Grace of God, which gave great contentment to the gentlemen that were on board here, and they said they would talk of it, when they come to Breda, as not having it done yet in London so publicly. After they were gone from on board, my Lord writ a letter to the King, and give it to me to carry privately to Sir William Compton, on board the Assistance, which I did, and after a health to his Majesty on board there, I left them under sail for Breda. I find that, all my debts paid and my preparations to sea, I have £40 clear in my purse, and so to bed.

7th. My Lord went this morning about the flag-ships in a boat, to see what alterations there must be, as to the arms and flags. He did give me orders also to write for silk flags and scarlet waistclothes. For a rich barge; for a noise of trumpets, and a set of fiddlers. Very great deal of company came today.

† Understanding

11th. This morning we began to pull down all the States' arms in the fleet, having first sent to Dover for painters and others to come to set up the King's. There dined here my Lord Crauford and my Lord Cavendish, and other Scotchmen, whom I afterwards ordered to be received on board the Plymouth, and to go along with us. After dinner, we set sail from the Downs.

14th. In the morning the Hague was clearly to be seen by us. My Lord went up in his night-gown into the cabin, to see how to dispose thereof for himself and us that belong to him, to give order for our removal today. Some nasty Dutchmen came on board to proffer their boats to carry things from us on shore, &c., to get money by us. Before noon some gentlemen came on board from the shore to kiss my Lord's hands. And by and by Mr. North and Dr. Clerke went to kiss the Queen of Bohemia's hands, from my Lord, with twelve attendants from on board to wait on them, among which I sent my boy, who, like myself, is with child to see any strange thing. After noon they came back again, after having kissed the Queen of Bohemia's hand, and were sent again by my Lord to do the same to the Prince of Orange. So I got the Captain to ask leave for me to go, which my Lord did give, and I, taking my boy and Judge Advocate with me, went in company with them.

The weather bad; we were sadly washed when we came near the shore, it being very hard to land there. The shore is like all the country between that and the Hague, all sand. The rest of the company got a coach by themselves; Mr. Creed and I went in the fore part of a coach, wherein were two very pretty ladies, very fashionable, and with black patches, who very merrily sang all the way, and that very well, and were very free to kiss two blades that were with them. The Hague is a most neat place in all respects. The houses so neat in all places and things as is possible. Here we walked up and down a great while, the town being now very full of Englishmen, for the Londoners were come on shore today. But going to see the Prince, he was gone forth with his governor, and so we walked up and down the town and court to see the place; and by the help of a stranger, an Englishman, we saw a great many places, and were made to understand many things, as the intention of Maypoles, which we saw there standing at every great man's door, of different greatness according to the quality of the person.

About ten at night the Prince comes home, and we found an easy admission. His attendance very inconsiderable as for a Prince; but

179

yet handsome, and his tutor a fine man, and himself a very pretty boy. This done, we went to a place we had taken to sup in, where a salad and two or three bones of mutton were provided for a matter of ten of us, which was very strange. The Judge and I lay in one press bed, there being two more in the same room; my boy sleeping on a bench by me.

15th. In the afternoon my Lord called me on purpose to show me his fine clothes which are now come hither, and indeed are very rich as gold and silver can make them, only his sword he and I do not like. In the afternoon my Lord and I walked together in the coach two hours, talking together upon all sorts of discourse: as religion, wherein he is, I perceive, wholly skeptical, saying, that indeed the Protestants as to the Church of Rome are wholly fanatics: he likes uniformity and form of prayer: about State-business, among other things he told me that his conversion to the King's cause (for I was saying that I wondered from what time the King could look upon him to become his friend) commenced from his being in the Sound, when he found what usage he was likely to have from a Commonwealth. My Lord, the Captain, and I, supped in my Lord's chamber, where I did perceive that he did begin to show me much more respect than ever he did yet. After supper, my Lord sent for me, intending to have me play at cards with him, but I not knowing cribbage, we fell into discourse of many things, and the ship rolled so much that I was not able to stand, and so he bid me go to bed.

22d. Up, and trimmed by a barber that has not trimmed me yet, my Spaniard being on shore. News brought that the two Dukes are coming on board, which, by and by, they did, in a Dutch boat, the Duke of York in yellow trimmings, the Duke of Gloucester in gray and red. My Lord went in a boat to meet them; the Captain, myself, and others, standing at the entering port. So soon as they were entered, we shot the guns off round the fleet. After that, they went to view the ship all over, and were most exceedingly pleased with it. They seem to be very fine gentlemen. After that done, upon the quarter-deck table, under the awning, the Duke of York and my Lord, Mr. Coventry, and I, spent an hour at allotting to every ship their service, in their return to England; which being done, they went to dinner, where the table was very full; the two Dukes at the upper end, my Lord Opdam next on one side, and my Lord on the other. Two guns given to every man while he was drinking the King's health, and so likewise to the Duke's health. I took down Monsieur d'Esquier to the great cabin below, and dined with him in state along with only one or two friends of his. All dinner, the harper belonging to Captain Sparling played to the Dukes.

After dinner, the Dukes and my Lord to sea, the Vice and Rear-Admirals and I in a boat after them. After that done, they made to the shore in the Dutch boat that brought them, and I got into the boat with them; but the shore was full of people to expect their coming. When we came near the shore, my Lord left them, and came into his own boat, and General Penn and I with him; my Lord being very well pleased with this day's work. By the time we came on board again, news is sent us that the King is on shore; so my Lord fired all his guns round twice, and all the fleet after him, which, in the end, fell into disorder, which seemed very handsome. The gun over against my cabin I fired myself to the King, which was the first time that he had been saluted by his own ships since this change; but, holding my head too much over the gun, I had almost spoiled my right eye.Nothing in the world but giving of guns almost all this day.

In the evening we began to remove to cabins; I to the carpenter's cabin, and Dr. Clerke with me, who came on board this afternoon, having been twice ducked in the sea today, and Mr. North and John Pickering the like. Many of the King's servants came on board tonight; and so many Dutch of all sorts came to see the ship till it was quite dark, that we could not pass by one another, which was a great trouble to us all. This afternoon, Mr. Downing (who was knighted yesterday by the King) was here on board, and had a ship for his passage into England with his lady and servants. By the same token, he called me to him when I was going to write the order, to tell me that I must write him Sir G. Downing. My Lord lay in the roundhouse tonight. This evening, I was late writing a French letter by my Lord's order to Mr. Krag, Danish ambassador to the Hague, which my Lord signed in bed.

23d. In the morning came infinity of people on board from the King to go along with him. My Lord, Mr. Crewe, and others, go on shore to meet the King as he comes off from shore, where Sir R. Stayner, bringing His Majesty into the boat, I hear that His Majesty did with a great deal of affection kiss my Lord upon his first meeting. The King, with the two Dukes and Queen of Bohemia, Princess Royal, and Prince of Orange, came on board, where I, in their coming in, kissed the King's, Queen's, and Princess's hands, having done the other before. Infinite shooting off of the guns, and that in a disorder on purpose, which was better than if it had been otherwise. All day, nothing but Lords and persons of honor on board, that we were exceeding full.

Dined in a great deal of state, the Royal company by themselves in the coach, which was a blessed sight to see. After dinner, the King and Duke altered the name of some of the ships, viz., the Nazeby into Charles; the Richard, James; the Speaker, Mary; the Dunbar (which was not in company with us), the Henry; Winsly, Happy Return; Wakefield, Richmond; Lambert, the Henrietta; Cheriton, the Speedwell; Bradford, the Success. That done, the Queen, Princess Royal, and Prince of Orange, took leave of the King, and the Duke of York went on board the London, and the Duke of Gloucester, the Swiftsure. Which done, we weighed anchor, and with a fresh gale and most happy weather we set sail for England.

All the afternoon the King walked here and there, up and down, (quite contrary to what I thought him to have been) very active and stirring. Upon the quarter-deck he fell into discourse of his escape from Worcester, where it made me ready to weep to hear the stories that he told of his difficulties that he had passed through, as his traveling four days and three nights on foot, every step up to his knees in dirt, with nothing but a green coat and a pair of country breeches on, and a pair of country shoes that made him so sore all over his feet, that he could scarce stir. Yet he was forced to run away from a miller and other company, that took them for rogues.

His sitting at table at one place where the master of the house that had not seen him in eight years did know him, but kept it private; when at the same table there was one, that had been of his own regiment at Worcester, could not know him, but made him drink the King's health, and said that the King was at least four fingers higher than he. At another place, he was by some servants of the house made to drink, that they might know that he was not a Roundhead, which they swore he was. In another place, at his inn, the master of the house, as the King was standing with his hands upon the back of a chair by the fireside, kneeled down and kissed his hand, privately, saying that he would not ask him who he was, but bid God bless him whither he was going. Then the difficulties in getting a boat to get into France, where he was fain to plot with the master thereof to keep his design from the foreman and a boy, (which was all the ship's company) and so get to Fécamp, in France. At Rouen he looked so poorly, that the people went into the rooms before he went away, to see whether he had not stole something or other.

In the evening, I went up to my Lord, to write letters for England, which we sent away with word of our coming by Mr. Edward

Pickering. The King supped alone in the coach; after that I got a dish, and we four supped in my cabin, as at noon. About bedtime, my Lord Bartlett (who I had offered my service to before) sent for me to get him a bed, who with much ado I did get to bed to my Lord Middlesex, in the great cabin below, but I was cruelly troubled before I could dispose of him, and quit myself of him. So to my cabin again, where the company still was, and were talking more of the King's difficulties; as how he was fain to eat a piece of bread and cheese out of a poor boy's pocket; how, at a Catholic house, he was fain to lie a good while in the house for his privacy. After that, our company broke up. We have all the Lords Commissioners on board us, and many others. Under sail all night, and most glorious weather.

24th. Up, and made myself as fine as I could, with the linen stockings on that I bought the other day at the Hague. Extraordinary press of noble company, and great mirth all the day. There dined with me in my cabin (that is, the carpenter's) Dr. Earle, and Mr. Hollis, the King's chaplains; Dr. Scarborough, Dr. Quarterman, and Dr. Clerke, physicians; Mr. Darcy and Mr. Fox, (both very fine gentlemen) the King's servants; where we had brave discourse. Walking upon the decks were persons of honor all the afternoon, among others, Thomas Killigrew, (a merry droll, but a gentleman of great esteem with the King) who told us many merry stories: one, how he wrote a letter three or four days ago to the Princess Royal, about a Queen Dowager of Judæa and Palestine, that was at the Hague *incognita,* that made love to the King, which was Mr. Cary (a courtier's) wife, that had been a nun. At supper, the three Doctors of Medicine again at my cabin; where I put Dr. Scarborough in mind of what I heard him say, that children do, in every day's experience, look several ways with both their eyes, till custom teaches them otherwise; and that we do now see but with one eye, our eyes looking in parallel lines. After this discourse, I was called to write a pass for my Lord Mandeville, to take up horses to London, which I wrote in the King's name, and carried it to him to sign, which was the first and only one that ever he signed in the ship Charles. To bed, coming in sight of land a little before night.

25th. By the morning we were come close to the land, and everybody made ready to get on shore. The King and the two Dukes did eat their breakfast before they went; and there being set some ship's diet before them, only to show them the manner of the ship's diet, they ate of nothing else but pease and pork, and boiled beef. I had

183

Mr. Darcy in my cabin; and Dr. Clerke, who ate with me, told me how the King had given £50 to Mr. Shepley for my Lord's servants, and £500 among the officers and common men of the ship. I spoke to the Duke of York about business, who called me Pepys by name, and upon my desire did promise me his future favor. Great expectation of the King's making some Knights, but there was none. About noon (though the brigantine that Beale made was there ready to carry him) yet he would go in my Lord's barge with the two Dukes. Our Captain steered, and my Lord went along bareheaded with him. I went, and Mr. Mansell, and one of the King's footmen, and a dog that the King loved, in a boat by ourselves, and so got on shore when the King did, who was received by General Monk with all imaginable love and respect at his entrance upon the land at Dover.

Infinite the crowd of people and the gallantry of the horsemen, citizens, and noblemen of all sorts. The Mayor of the town came and gave him his white staff, the badge of his place, which the King did give him again. The Mayor also presented him from the town a very rich Bible, which he took, and said it was the thing that he loved above all things in the world. A canopy was provided for him to stand under, which he did, and talked awhile with General Monk and others, and so into a stately coach there set for him, and so away through the town towards Canterbury, without making any stay at Dover. The shouting and joy expressed by all is past imagination. Seeing that my Lord did not stir out of his barge, I got into a boat, and so into his barge, and we back to the ship, seeing a man almost drowned that fell into the sea. My Lord almost transported with joy that he had done all this without any the least blur or obstruction in the world, that could give offense to any, and with the great honor he thought it would be to him. Being overtook by the brigantine, my Lord and we went out of our barge into it, and so went on board with Sir W. Batten and the Vice and Rear-Admirals. At night, I supped with the Captain, who told me what the King had given us. My Lord returned late, and at his coming did give me order to cause the mark to be gilded, and a Crown and C. R. to be made at the head of the coach table, where the King today with his own hand did mark his height, which accordingly I caused the painter to do, and is now done, as is to be seen.

26th. Mr. North, and Dr. Clerke, and all the great company being gone, I found myself very uncouth all this day for want thereof. My Lord dined with the Vice-Admiral today (who is as officious, poor man! as any spaniel can be; but I believe all to no purpose, for I believe he will not hold his place); so I dined commander at the coach table today, and all the officers of the ship with me, and Mr. White of Dover. After a game or two at ninepins, to work all the afternoon, making about twenty orders. In the evening, my Lord having been ashore, the first time that he hath been ashore since he came out of the Hope, having resolved not to go till he had brought his Majesty into England, returned on board with a great deal of pleasure. The Captain told me that my Lord had appointed me £30 out of the 1000 ducats which the King had given to the ship.

JUNE 2d. Being with my Lord in the morning about business in his cabin, I took occasion to give thanks for his love to me in the share that he had given me of his Majesty's money, and the Duke's. He told me he hoped to do me a more lasting kindness, if all things stand as they are now between him and the King; but, says he, "We must have a little patience, and we will rise together; in the meantime, I will do yet all the good jobs I can." Which was great content for me to hear from my Lord. All the morning with the Captain, computing how much the pay of the thirty ships that came with the King comes to for a month (because the King promised to give them all a month's pay), and it comes to £6538, and the Charles particularly, £777. I wish we had the money.

[*Now that the King is in his kingdom, there remain the distasteful tasks of punishing those who supported the Puritan regime of Oliver Cromwell, and the business of getting jobs for those who have shown themselves deserving. For most of these Cavaliers, the Restoration is a time of pleasure-taking. Pepys, though finding a place among them, devotes himself also to his new responsibilities.*]

AUGUST 10th. With Mr. Moore and Creed to Hyde Park by coach, and saw a fine foot-race three times round the Park, between an Irishman and Crow, that was once my Lord Claypoole's footman. (By the way, I cannot forget that my Lord Claypoole did the other day make inquiry of Mrs. Hunt concerning my house in Axe Yard, and did set her on work to get it from me for him, which methinks is a very great change.) Crow beat the other by above two miles. Unable to think of anything, because of my constant business, not having read a new book or inquiring after any news. Many people look after my house in Axe Yard, to hire it, so that I am troubled with them.

But blessed be God for my good chance of the Privy Seal, where I get every day, I believe, about £3. This place my Lord did give me by chance, neither he nor I thinking it to be of the worth that he and I find it to be.

18th. Towards Westminster by water. I landed my wife at White-friars, with £5 to buy her a petticoat, and my father persuaded her to buy a most fine cloth, of 26s. a yard, and a rich lace, that the petticoat will come to £5; but she doing it very innocently, I could not be angry. Captain Ferrers took me and Creed to the Cockpit play, the first that I have had time to see since my coming from sea, *The Loyal Subject,** where one Kinaston, a boy, acted the Duke's sister Olympia, but made the loveliest lady that ever I saw in my life. After the play done, we went to drink, and, by Captain Ferrers' means, Kinaston, and another that acted Archas the General, came and drank with us.

SEPTEMBER 16th. (Lord's day.) My Lord of Oxford, I am told, is also dead of the smallpox; in whom his family dies, after 600 years having that honor in their family and name. To the Park, where I saw how far they had proceeded in the Pall Mall, and in making a river through the Park, which I had never seen before since it was begun. Thence to White Hall Garden, where I saw the King in purple mourning for his brother. A gentleman in the Poultry had a great and dirty fall over a waterpipe that lay along the channel.

25th. I did send for a cup of tea, (a China drink) of which I never had drank before, and went away (the King and the Princess coming up the river this afternoon as we were at our pay). My Lord told me how the ship that brought the Princess and him (the Tredagh) did knock six times upon the Kentish Knock, which put them in great fear for the ship; but got off well. He told me also how the King had knighted Vice-Admiral Lawson and Sir Richard Stayner.

OCTOBER 13th. I went out to Charing Cross to see Major-General Harrison hanged, drawn, and quartered; which was done there, he looking as cheerful as any man could do in that condition. He was presently cut down, and his head and heart shown to the people, at which there was great shouts of joy. It is said, that he said that he was sure to come shortly at the right hand of Christ to judge them that now had judged him; and that his wife do expect his coming again. Thus it was my chance to see the King beheaded at White Hall, and to see the first blood shed in revenge for the King at Charing Cross.

* A tragi-comedy by Beaumont and Fletcher

Setting up shelves in my study.

15th. This morning Mr. Carew was hanged and quartered at Charing Cross, but his quarters, by a great favor, are not to be hanged up.

20th. I dined with my Lord and Lady; he was very merry, and did talk very high how he would have a French cook, and a master of his horse, and his lady and child to wear black patches; which methought was strange; but he is become a perfect courtier; and, among other things, my Lady saying that she could get a good merchant for her daughter Jem., he answered, that he would rather see her with a peddler's pack at her back, so she married a gentleman, than she should marry a citizen. This afternoon, going through London, and calling at Crowe's, the upholsterer's, in Saint Bartholomew's, I saw the limbs of some of our new traitors set upon Aldersgate, which was a sad sight to see; and a bloody week this and the last have been, there being ten hanged, drawn, and quartered.

NOVEMBER 1st. This morning, Sir W. Penn and I were mounted early, and had very merry discourse all the way, he being very good company. We came to Sir W. Batten's, where he lives like a prince, and we were made very welcome. Among other things, he showed me my Lady's closet, wherein was great store of rarities; as also a chair, which he calls King Harry's chair, where he that sits down is caught with two irons, that come round about him, which makes good sport. Here dined with us two or three more country gentlemen; among the rest, Mr. Christmas, my old school-fellow, with whom I had much talk. He did remember that I was a great Roundhead when I was a boy, and I was much afraid that he would have remembered the words that I said the day the King was beheaded (that, were I to preach upon him, my text should be—"The memory of the wicked shall rot"); but I found afterwards that he did go away from school before that time. He did make us good sport in imitating Mr. Case, Ash, and Nye, the ministers; but a deadly drinker he is, and grown very fat.

22d. This morning came the carpenters to make me a door at the other side of my house, going into the entry. My wife and I walked to the Old Exchange, and there she bought her a white scarf, and put it on, and I a pair of gloves. To Mr. Fox's, where we found Mrs. Fox within, and an alderman of London paying £1000 or £1400 in gold upon the table for the King. Mr. Fox came in presently, and did receive us with a great deal of respect; and then did take my wife and I to the Queen's presence-chamber, where he got my wife placed behind the Queen's chair, and the two Princesses came to dinner. The

Queen, a very little, plain old woman, and nothing more in her presence in any respect nor garb than any ordinary woman. The Princess of Orange I had often seen before. The Princess Henrietta is very pretty, but much below my expectation; and her dressing of herself with her hair frizzed short up to her ears did make her seem so much the less to me. But my wife standing near her with two or three black patches on, and well dressed, did seem to me much handsomer than she. Dinner being done, we went to Mr. Fox's again, where many gentlemen dined with us, and most princely dinner—all provided for me and my friends, but I bringing none but myself and wife, he did call the company to help to eat up so much good victuals. At the end of the dinner my Lord Sandwich's health was drunk in the gilt tankard that I did give to Mrs. Fox the other day. To White Hall at about nine at night, and there, with Laud, the page that went with me, we could not get out of Henry the Eighth's gallery into the farther part of the boarded gallery, where my Lord was walking with my Lord Ormond; and we had a key of Sir S. Morland's, but all would not do; till at last, by knocking, Mr. Harrison, the door-keeper, did open the door, and, after some talk with my Lord about getting a boat to carry my Lord St. Albans's goods to France, I parted and went home on foot.

DECEMBER 1st. This morning, observing some things to be laid up not as they should be by my girl, I took a broom and basted her till she cried extremely, which made me vexed; but, before I went out, I left her appeased. Went to my Lord St. Albans's lodgings, and found him in bed, talking to a priest (he looked like one) that leaned along over the side of the bed; and there I desired to know his mind about making the ship stay longer, which I got ready for him the other day. He seems to be a fine, civil gentleman. There fell into our company old Mr. Flower and another gentleman, who did tell us how a Scotch knight was killed basely the other day at the Fleece Tavern in Covent Garden, where there had been a great many formerly killed.

4th. To the Duke of York, and he took us into his closet, and we did open to him our project of stopping the growing charge of the fleet, by paying them in hand one half, and the other four months hence. This he do like. This day the Parliament voted that the bodies of Oliver, Ireton, Bradshaw, and Thomas Pride, should be taken up out of their graves in the Abbey, and drawn to the gallows, and there hanged and buried under it: which (methinks) do trouble me that a man of so great courage as Cromwell have that dishonor, though otherwise he might deserve it enough.

31st. In Paul's Churchyard I bought the play of *Henry the Fourth,** and so went to the new theater and saw it acted; but my expectation being too great, it did not please me, as otherwise I believe it would; and my having a book, I believe did spoil it a little. That being done, I went to my Lord's, where I found him private at cards with my Lord Lauderdale, and some persons of honor, my boy taking a cat home with him from my Lord's, which Sarah had given him for my wife, we being much troubled with mice. At White Hall inquiring for a coach, there was a Frenchman with one eye that was going my way, so he and I hired the coach between us, and he set me down in Fenchurch Street. Strange, how the fellow, without asking, did tell me all what he was, and how he had run away from his father, and come into England to serve the King, and now going back again.

1661

At the end of the last and the beginning of this year, I do live in one of the houses belonging to the Navy Office, as one of the principal officers, and have done now about half a year; my family being myself, my wife, Jane, Will Hewer, and Wayneman, my girl's brother. Myself in constant good health, and in a most handsome and thriving condition. Blessed be Almighty God for it! As to things of State—the King settled, and loved of all. The Duke of York matched to my Lord Chancellor's daughter, which do not please many. The Queen upon her return to France with the Princess Henrietta. The Princess of Orange lately dead, and we into new mourning for her. We have been lately frighted with a great plot, and many taken up on it, and the fright not quite over. The Parliament, which had done all this great good to the King, beginning to grow factious, the King did dissolve it December 29th last, and another likely to be chosen speedily. I take myself now to be worth £300 clear in money, and all my goods, and all manner of debts paid, which are none at all.

January 7th. This morning, news was brought to me to my bedside, that there had been a great stir in the City this night by the Fanatics, who had been up and killed six or seven men, but all are fled. My Lord Mayor and the whole City had been in arms, above

* By Shakespeare

40,000. Tom and I and my wife to the theater, and there saw *The Silent Woman.** Among other things here, Kinaston, the boy, had the good turn to appear in three shapes: first, as a poor woman in ordinary clothes, to please Morose; then in fine clothes, as a gallant; and in them was clearly the prettiest woman in the whole house; and lastly, as a man; and then likewise did appear the handsomest man in the house.

FEBRUARY 10th. (Lord's day.) Took a physic all day, and, God forgive me, did spend it in reading of some little French romances. At night my wife and I did please ourselves talking of our going into France, which I hope to effect this summer.

12th. By water to Salisbury Court Playhouse, where not liking to sit, we went out again, and by coach to the Killigrew theater, and there saw *The Scornful Lady,* now done by a woman, which makes the play much better than ever it did to me.

13th. To Sir W. Batten's, whither I sent for my wife, and we chose Valentines for tomorrow. My wife chose me, which did much please me; my Lady Batten, Sir W. Penn, &c.

14th. (Valentine's day.) Up early, and to Sir W. Batten's, but could not go in till I asked whether they that opened the door was a man or a woman, and Mingo, who was there, answered a woman, which, with his tone, made me laugh: so up I went, and took Mrs. Martha for my Valentine, (which I do only for complacency) and Sir W. Batten he go in the same manner to my wife, and so we were very merry. About ten o'clock, we with a great deal of company went down by our barge to Deptford, and there only went to see how forward Mr. Pett's yacht is; and so all into the barge again, and so to Woolwich, on board the Rosebush, Captain Brown's ship, that is brother-in-law to Sir W. Batten, where we had a very fine dinner, dressed on shore, and great mirth, and all things successful: the first time I ever carried my wife shipboard, as also my boy Wayneman, who hath all this day been called young Pepys, as Sir W. Penn's boy young Penn. The talk of the town now is, who the King is like to have for his Queen: and whether Lent shall be kept with the strictness of the King's proclamation; which is thought cannot be, because of the poor, who cannot buy fish. And also the great preparation for the King's crowning is now much thought upon and talked of.

15th. Making up my accounts for my Lord tomorrow; and that being done, I found myself to be clear (as I think) £350 in the

* By Ben Jonson

world, besides my goods in my house, and all things paid for.

16th. To my Lord in the morning, who looked over my accounts, and agreed to them. I do also get him to sign a bill (which do make my heart merry) for £60 to me, in consideration of my work extraordinary at sea this last voyage, which I hope to get paid. To the theater, where I saw the *Virgin Martyr,* a good, but too sober a play for the company.

17th. (Lord's day.) A most tedious, unreasonable, and impertinent sermon, by an Irish doctor. His text was, "Scatter them, O Lord, that delight in war." Sir W. Batten and I very much angry with the parson.

APRIL 2d. To St. James's Park, where I saw the Duke of York playing at Pellmell, the first time that ever I saw the sport. Then to my Lord's, where I dined with my Lady, and after we had dined, in comes my Lord and Ned Pickering hungry, and there was not a bit of meat left in the house, the servants having eat up all, at which my Lord was very angry, and at last got something dressed. So to Whitefriars, and saw *The Little Thief,** which is a very merry and pretty play, and the little boy do very well. Then to the Dolphin to Sir W. Batten, and Penn, and other company; among others Mr. Delabar; where strange how these men, who at other times are all wise men, do now, in their drink, twit and reproach one another with their former conditions, and their actions as in public concerns, till I was ashamed to see it.

3d. Up among my workmen, my head aching all day from last night's debauch. At noon dined with Sir W. Batten and Penn, who would have me drink two good draughts of sack today, to cure me of my last night's disease, which I thought strange, but I think find it true.

22d. The King's going from the Tower to White Hall. Up early, and made myself as fine as I could, and put on my velvet coat, the first day that I put it on, though made half a year ago. And being ready, Sir W. Batten, my Lady, and his two daughters, and his son and wife, and Sir W. Penn and his son and I, went to Mr. Young's, the flagmaker, in Cornhill; and there we had a good room to ourselves, with wine and good cake, and saw the show very well. In which it is impossible to relate the glory of this day, expressed in the clothes of them that rode, and their horses and horse-clothes. Among others, my Lord Sandwich's embroidery and diamonds were not ordinary among them. The Knights of the Bath was a brave sight of itself; and their Esquires, among which Mr. Armiger was an Esquire to one of

* A comedy by John Fletcher

the Knights. Remarkable were the two men that represent the two Dukes of Normandy and Aquitaine. The Bishops came next after Barons, which is the higher place; which makes me think that the next Parliament will be called to the House of Lords. My Lord Monk rode bareheaded after the King, and led in his hand a spare horse, being Master of the Horse. The King, in a most rich embroidered suit and cloak, looked most noble. Wadlow, the vintner, at the Devil, in Fleet Street, did lead a fine company of soldiers, all young, comely men, in white doublets. There followed the Vice-Chamberlain, Sir G. Carteret, a company of men all like Turks; but I know not yet what they are for. The streets all graveled and the houses hung with carpets before them made brave show, and the ladies out of the windows. So glorious was the show with gold and silver, that we were not able to look at it, our eyes at last being so much overcome. Both the King and the Duke of York took notice of us, as they saw us at the window. In the evening, by water to White Hall to my Lord's, and there I spoke with my Lord. He talked with me about his suit, which was made in France, and cost him £200, and very rich it is with embroidery.

The show being ended, Mr. Young did give us a dinner, at which we very merry, and pleased above imagination at what we had seen. Sir W. Batten going home, he and I called, and drunk some wine, and laid our wager about my Lady Faulconbridge's name, which he says not to be Mary, and so I won above 20*s*. So home, where Will and the boy stayed, and saw the show upon Tower Hill, and Jane at T. Pepys's and my wife at Charles Glasscock's in Fleet Street.

Coronation Day

23d. About four I rose and got to the Abbey, where I followed Sir J. Denham, the surveyor, with some company he was leading in. And with much ado, by the favor of Mr. Cooper, his man, did get up into a great scaffold across the north end of the Abbey, where with a great deal of patience I sat from past four till eleven before the King came in. And a great pleasure it was to see the Abbey raised in the middle, all covered with red, and a throne (that is, a chair) and footstool on the top of it; and all the officers of all kinds, so much as the very fiddlers, in red vests. At last came in the Dean and Prebendaries of Westminster, with the Bishops, (many of them in cloth of gold copes) and after them the Nobility, all in their Parliament robes, which was a most magnificent sight. Then the Duke, and the King with a scepter (carried by my Lord Sandwich) and sword and wand before him, and the crown too. The King in his robes, bareheaded, which was very fine.

And after all had placed themselves, there was a sermon and the service; and then in the choir at the high altar, the King passed through all the ceremonies of the Coronation, which to my great grief I and most in the Abbey could not see. The crown being put upon his head, a great shout began, and he came forth to the throne, and passed through more ceremonies: as taking the oath, and having things read to him by the Bishop; and his lords (who put on their caps as soon as the King put on his crown) and Bishops came, and kneeled before him. And three times the King at Arms went to the three open places on the scaffold, and proclaimed that if anyone could show any reason why Charles Stuart should not be King of England, that now he should come and speak. And a General Pardon also was read by the Lord Chancellor, and medals flung up and down by my Lord Cornwallis, of silver, but I could not come by any. But so great a noise that I could make but little of the music; and indeed, it was lost to everybody. I went out a little while before the King had done all his ceremonies, and went round the Abbey to Westminster Hall, all the way within rails, and 10,000 people with the ground covered with blue cloth; and scaffolds all the way.

Into the Hall I got, where it was very fine with hangings and scaffolds one upon another full of brave ladies; and my wife in one little one, on the right hand. Here I stayed walking up and down, and at last upon one of the side stalls I stood and saw the King come in with all the persons (but the soldiers) that were yesterday in the cavalcade; and a most pleasant sight it was to see them in their several robes. And the King came in with his crown on, and his scepter in his hand, under a canopy borne up by six silver staves, carried by Barons of the Cinque Ports, and little bells at every end. And after a long time, he got up to the farther end, and all set themselves down at their several tables; and that was also a brave sight: and the King's first course carried up by the Knights of the Bath.

And many fine ceremonies there was of the Heralds leading up people before him, and bowing; and my Lord of Albemarle's going to the kitchen and eating a bit of the first dish that was to go to the King's table. But, above all, was these three Lords, Northumberland, and Suffolk, and the Duke of Ormond, coming before the courses on horseback, and staying so all dinner time, and at last bringing up Dymock, the King's Champion, all in armor on horseback, with his spear and target carried before him. And a Herald proclaims "That if any dare deny Charles Stuart to be lawful King of England, here was a Champion that would fight with him"; and with these words, the Champion flings down his gauntlet, and all this he do three times in his going up towards the King's table. To which, when he is come, the King drinks to him, and then sends him the cup which is of gold, and he drinks it off, and then rides back again with the cup in his hand.

I went from table to table to see the Bishops and all others at their dinner, and was infinitely pleased with it. And at the Lords' table, I met with William Howe, and he spoke to my Lord for me, and he did give him four rabbits and a pullet, and so Mr. Creed and I got Mr. Minshell to give us some bread, and so we at a stall ate it, as everybody else did what they could get. I took a great deal of pleasure to go up and down, and look upon the ladies, and to hear the music of all sorts, but above all, the 24 violins. About six at night they had dined, and I went up to my wife. And strange it is to think, that these two days have held up fair till now that all is done, and the King gone out of the Hall; and then it fell a-raining and thundering and lightning as I have not seen it do for some years: which people did take great notice of; God's blessing of the work of these two days, which is a foolery to take too much notice of such things. I observed little disorder in all this, only the King's footmen had got hold of the canopy, and would keep it from the Barons of the Cinque Ports, which they endeavored to force from them again, but could not do it till my Lord Duke of Albemarle caused it to be put into Sir R. Pye's hand till tomorrow to be decided.

At Mr. Bowyer's; a great deal of company, some I knew, others I did not. Here we stayed upon the leads and below till it was late, expecting to see the fireworks, but they were not performed tonight: only the City had a light like a glory round about it, with bonfires. At last, I went to King Street, and there sent Crockford to my father's and my house, to tell them I could not come home tonight, because of the dirt, and a coach could not be had. And so I took my wife and Mrs. Frankleyn (who I proffered the civility of lying with my wife at Mrs. Hunt's tonight) to Axe Yard, in which, at the further end, there were three great bonfires, and a great many gallants, men and women; and they laid hold of us, and would have us drink the King's health upon our knees, kneeling upon a fagot, which we all did, they drinking to us one after another, which we thought a strange frolic; but these gallants continued there a great while, and I wondered to see how the ladies did tipple.

At last, I sent my wife and her bedfellow to bed, and Mr. Hunt and I went in with Mr. Thornbury (who did give the company all their wine, he being yeoman of the wine-cellar to the King); and there, with his wife and two of his sisters, and some gallant sparks that were there, we drank the King's health, and nothing else, till one of the gentlemen fell down stark drunk, and there lay; and I went to my Lord's pretty well. But no sooner a-bed with Mr. Shepley but my head began to turn, and I to vomit, and if ever I was foxed, it was now, which I cannot say yet, because I fell asleep, and slept till morning. Thus did the day end with joy everywhere; and blessed be God, I have not heard of any mischance to anybody through it all, but only to Sergeant Glynne, whose horse fell upon him yesterday, and is like to kill him, which people do please themselves to see how just God is to punish the rogue at such a time as this; he being now one of the King's Sergeants, and rode in the cavalcade with Maynard, to whom people wish the same fortune. There was also this night, in King Street, a woman had her eye put out by a boy's flinging a firebrand into the coach. Now, after all this, I can say, that, besides the pleasure of the sight of these glorious things, I may now shut my eyes against any other objects, nor for the future trouble myself to see things of state and show, as being sure never to see the like again in this world.

24th. Waked in the morning, with my head in a sad taking through the last night's drink, which I am very sorry for: so rose, and went out with Mr. Creed to drink our morning draught, which he did give me in chocolate to settle my stomach. At night, set myself to write down these three days' diary, and, while I am about it, I hear the noise of the chambers, and other things of the fireworks, which are now playing upon the Thames before the King; and I wish myself with them, being sorry not to see them.

MAY 23d. To the Rhenish wine-house, and there Mr. Jonas Moore, the mathematician, to us, and there he did by discourse make us fully believe that England and France were once the same continent, by very good arguments, and spoke very many things not so much to prove the Scripture false, as that the time therein is not well computed nor understood. In my black silk suit (the first day I have put it on this year) to my Lord Mayor's by coach, with a great deal of honorable company, and great entertainment. At table I had very good discourse with Mr. Ashmole, wherein he did assure me that frogs and many insects do often fall from the sky, ready formed. Dr. Bates's singularity in not rising up nor drinking the King's nor other healths at the table was very much observed. From thence we all took coach, and to our office, and there sat till it was late; and so I home and to bed by daylight. This day was kept a holiday through the town; and it pleased me to see the little boys walk up and down in procession with their broom-staffs in their hands, as I had myself long ago done.

JULY 24th. This morning my wife in bed tells me of our being robbed of our silver tankard, which vexed me all day for the negligence of my people to leave the door open. To the Wardrobe, but came too late, and dined with the servants. And then to my Lady, who do show my wife and me the greatest favor in the world, in which I take great content. To the office all the afternoon, which is a great pleasure to me again, to talk with persons of quality, and to be in command, and I give it out among them that the estate left me is £200 a year in land, besides moneys, because I would put an esteem upon myself. I hear that my man Will lost his clock with my tankard, at which I am very glad.

AUGUST 24th. Called to Sir W. Batten's, to see the strange creature that Captain Holmes brought with him from Guinea; it is a great baboon, but so much like a man in most things, that, though they say there is a species of them, yet I cannot believe but that it is a monster got of a man and she-baboon. I do believe that it already understands much English, and I am of the mind that it might be taught to speak or make signs. To the Opera, and there saw *Hamlet, Prince of Denmark*.

DECEMBER 31st. My wife and I this morning to the painter's and there she sat the last time, and I stood by, and did tell him some little things to do, that now her picture I think will please me very well; and after her, her little black dog sat in her lap, and was drawn, which made us very merry: so home to dinner. To the office; and there late finishing our estimate of the debts of the Navy to this day; and it came to near £374,000. So home, and after supper and my barber had trimmed me, I sat down to end my journal for this year, and my condition at this time, by God's blessing, is that my health is very good, and so my wife's, in all respects: my servants, W. Hewer, Sarah, Nell, and Wayneman: my house at the Navy Office. I suppose myself to be worth about £500 clear in the world, and my goods of my house my own, and what is coming to me from Brampton, when my father dies, which God defer. But, by my uncle's death, the whole care and trouble, and settling of all, lies upon me, which is very great, because of lawsuits, especially that with T. Trice, about the interest of £200, which will, I hope, be ended soon. My chiefest thought is now to get a good wife for Tom, there being one offered by the Joyces, a cousin of theirs, worth £200 in ready money. I am upon writing a little treatise to present to the Duke, about our privilege in the seas, as to other nations striking their flags to us.

But my greatest trouble is, that I have for this last half year been a very great spendthrift in all manner of respects, that I am afraid to cast up my accounts, though I hope I am worth what I say above. But I will cast them up very shortly. I have newly taken a solemn oath about abstaining from plays and wine, which I am resolved to keep, according to the letter of the oath which I keep by me. The fleet hath been ready to sail for Portsmouth, but hath lacked wind this fortnight, and by that means my Lord is forced to keep at sea all this winter, till he brings home the Queen, which is the expectation of all now, and the greatest matter of public talk.

1 6 6 2

FEBRUARY 3d. After music practice, I dined with Sir W. Batten with many friends more, it being his wedding day, and among other frolic, it being their third year, they had three pies, whereof the middlemost was made of an oval form in an oval hole within the other two, which made much mirth, and was called the middle piece; and above all the rest, we had great striving to steal a spoonful out of it; and I remember Mrs. Mills, the minister's wife, did steal one for me, and did give it to me; and to end all, Mrs. Shippman did fill the pie full of white wine, it holding at least a pint and a half, and did drink it off for a health to Sir William and my Lady—it being the greatest draught that ever I did see a woman drink in my life. I went along with my Lady and the rest of the gentlewomen to Major Holmes's, and there we had a fine supper—among others, excellent lobsters, which I never ate at this time of the year before. The Major hath good lodgings at the Trinity House. At last home, and, being in my chamber, we hear great noise of mirth at Sir William Batten's, tearing the ribbands from my Lady and him.

4th. To Westminster Hall, where it was full term. Here all the morning, and at noon to my Lord Crewe's, where one Mr. Templer, an ingenious man and a person of honor he seems to be, dined; and, discoursing of the nature of serpents, he told us some in the waste places of Lancashire grow to a great bigness, and feed upon larks, which they take thus: they observe, when the lark is soared to the highest, and crawl till they come to be just underneath them; and there they place themselves with their mouths uppermost, and there, as is conceived, they eject poison upon the bird; for the bird suddenly comes down again in its course of a circle, and falls directly into the mouth of the serpent; which is very strange. He is a great traveler; and, speaking of the tarantula, he says that all the harvest long, about which times they are most busy, there are fiddlers who go up and down the fields everywhere, in expectation of being hired by those that are stung.

28th. The boy failing to call us up as I commanded, I was angry, and resolved to whip him for that and many other faults today. Early with Sir W. Penn by coach to White Hall, to the Duke of York's chamber, and there I presented him from my Lord a fine map of Tangier, done by one Captain Beckman, a Swede, that is with my Lord. We stayed looking it over a great while with the Duke after he was ready. I bade Will get me a rod, and he and I called the boy up to one of the upper rooms of the Comptroller's house towards the garden, and there I reckoned all his faults, and whipped him soundly, but the rods were so small that I fear they did not much hurt to him, but only to my arm, which I am already, within a quarter of an hour, not able to stir almost.

March 5th. To the pewterer's to buy a poor-box, to put my forfeits in, upon breach of my late vows.* To my office, and there sat looking over my papers of my voyage, when we fetched over the King, and tore so many of these that were worth nothing, as filled my closet as high as my knees.

26th. Up early. This being, by God's great blessing, the fourth solemn day of my cutting for the stone this day four years ago and I am, by God's mercy, in very good health, and like to do well; the Lord's name be praised for it! At noon came my good guest, Madam Turner and cousin Norton, and a gentleman, one Mr. Lewin, of the

* See entry of December 31, 1661

King's Life Guard; by the same token he told us of one of his fellows killed this morning in a duel. I had a pretty dinner for them: a brace of stewed carps, six roasted chickens, and a jowl of salmon, hot, for the first course; a tansy † and two ox tongues and cheese, the second. Merry all the afternoon, talking, and singing, and piping on the flute. We had a man-cook to dress dinner today, and sent for Jane to help us.

MAY 21st. My wife and I to my Lord's lodging; where she and I went walking in White Hall Garden. And in the Privy-garden saw the finest smocks and linen petticoats of my Lady Castlemaine's, laced with rich lace at the bottom, that ever I saw; and did me good to look at them. Sarah told me how the King dined at my Lady Castlemaine's, and supped, every day and night the last week; and that the night that the bonfires were made for joy of the Queen's arrival, the King was there; but there was no fire at her door, though at all the rest of the doors almost in the street; which was much observed: and that the King and she did send for a pair of scales and weighed one another; and she, being with child, was said to be the heaviest. But she is now a most disconsolate creature, and comes not out of doors, since the King's going. But we went to Killigrew's Theater, to see *The French Dancing Master,* and there with much pleasure we saw and gazed upon Lady Castlemaine; but it troubles us to see her look dejectedly, and slighted by people already. The play pleased us very well; but Lacy's part, the Dancing Master, pleased us the best in the world.

29th. At home all the morning. At noon to the Wardrobe, and dined with my Lady, and, after dinner, stayed long talking with her; then homeward, and, in Lombard Street, was called out of a window by Alderman Backwell, where I went, and saluted his lady, a very pretty woman. Here was Mr. Creed, and it seems they have been under some disorder in fear of a fire next door, and had been removing their goods, but the fear was over before I came. Thence home, and with my wife and the two maids and the boy took boat and to Foxhall, where I had not been a great while. To the old Spring Garden, and there walked long, and the wenches gathered pink flowers. Here we stayed, and seeing that we could not have anything to eat but what was very dear, and with long stay, we went forth again without any notice taken of us, and so we might have done if we had had anything. Thence to the New Spring Garden, where I never was before, which much exceeds the other; and here we also walked, and

† A pudding made with tansy herbs

the boy crept through the hedge, and gathered abundance of roses, and after a long walk, passed out of doors as we did in the other place, and so to another house that was an ordinary house, and here we had cakes and powdered beef and ale, and so home again by water, with much pleasure. This day, being the King's birthday, was very solemnly observed; and the more, for that the Queen this day comes to Hampton Court. In the evening, bonfires were made, but nothing to the great number that was heretofore at the burning of the Rump.

JUNE 14th. Up by four o'clock in the morning, and upon business at my office. Then we sat down to business, and about 11 o'clock, having a room got ready for us, we all went out to the Tower-hill; and there, over against the scaffold, made on purpose this day, saw Sir Henry Vane brought. A very great press of people. He made a long speech, many times interrupted by the Sheriff and others there; and they would have taken his paper out of his hand, but he would not let it go. But they caused all the books of those who wrote after him * to be given to the Sheriff; and the trumpets were brought under the scaffold that he might not be heard. Then he prayed, and so fitted himself, and received the blow; but the scaffold was so crowded that we could not see it done. But Boreman, who had been upon the scaffold, told us that first he began to speak of the irregular proceeding against him; that he was against Magna Charta, denied to have his exceptions against the indictment allowed; and that there he was stopped by the Sheriff.

Then he drew out his paper of notes, and began to tell them first his life; that he was born a gentleman; he had been, till he was seventeen years old, a good fellow, but then it pleased God to lay a foundation of grace in his heart, by which he was persuaded, against his worldly interest, to leave all preferment and go abroad, where he might serve God with more freedom. Then he was called home, and made a member of the Long Parliament; where he never did, to this day, anything against his conscience, but all for the glory of God. Here he would have given them an account of the proceedings of the Long Parliament, but they so often interrupted him that at last he was forced to give over: and so fell into prayer for England in general, then for the churches in England, and then for the City of London: and so fitted himself for the block, and received the blow.

He had a blister, or issue, upon his neck, which he desired them not to hurt: he changed not his color or speech to the last, but died

* Shorthand copiers of his speech

justifying himself and the cause he had stood for; and spoke very confidently of his being presently at the right hand of Christ; and in all things appeared the most resolved man that ever died in that manner, and showed more of heat than cowardice, but yet with all humility and gravity. One asked him why he did not pray for the King. He answered, "You shall see I can pray for the King: I pray God bless him!" The King had given his body to his friends; and, therefore, he told them that he hoped they would be civil to his body when dead; and desired they would let him die like a gentleman and a Christian, and not crowded and pressed as he was.

So to the office a little, and to the Trinity House, and there all of us to dinner; and to the office again all the afternoon till night.

JULY 21st. Up early. I did take boat and down to Greenwich, to Captain Cocke's, who hath a most pleasant seat, and neat. Here I drank wine, and ate some fruit off the trees; and he showed a great rarity, which was two or three of a great number of silver dishes and plates, which he bought from an ambassador that did lack money, in the edges and basins of which was placed silver and gold medals, very ancient. To Woolwich to the Rope Yard; and there looked over several sorts of hemp, and did fall upon my great survey of seeing the working and experiments of the strength and the charge in the dressing of every sort; and I do think have brought it to so great a certainty, as I have done the King some service in it: and do propose to get it ready for the Duke's coming to town to present to him. I see it is impossible for the King to have things done as cheap as other men.

AUGUST 23d. Mr. Coventry and I did walk together a great while in the garden, where he did tell me his mind about Sir G. Carteret's having so much the command of the money, which must be removed; and indeed it is the bane of all our business. He observed to me also how Sir W. Batten begins to struggle and to look after his business. I also put him upon getting an order from the Duke for our inquiries into the Chest, which he will see done. Mr. Creed and I walked down to the Steelyard,* and so all along Thames Street, but could not get a boat: I offered eight shillings for a boat to attend me this afternoon, and they would not, it being the day of the Queen's coming to town from Hampton Court.

So we fairly walked it to White Hall, and through my Lord's lodgings we got into White Hall Garden, and so to the Bowling Green, and up to the top of the new Banqueting House there, over the

* Home of the Hanseatic merchants

Thames, which was a most pleasant place as any I could have got; and all the show consisted chiefly in the number of boats and barges; and two pageants, one of a King, and another of a Queen, with her Maids of Honor sitting at her feet very prettily; and they tell me the Queen is Sir Richard Ford's daughter. Anon came the King and Queen in a barge under a canopy, with one thousand barges and boats I know, for we could see no water for them, nor discern the King nor Queen. And so they landed at White Hall Bridge, and the great guns on the other side went off. But that which pleased me best was that my Lady Castlemaine stood over against us upon a piece of White Hall. I thought it was strange to see her Lord and her upon the same place walking up and down without taking notice of one another, only at first entry he put off his hat, and she made him a very civil salute, but afterwards took no notice of one another; but both of them now and then would take their child, which the nurse held in her arms, and dandle it.

One thing more: there happened a scaffold below to fall, and we feared some hurt, but there was none, but she of all the great ladies only ran down among the common rabble to see what hurt was done, and did take care of a child that received some little hurt, which I thought was so noble. Anon there came one there booted and spurred that she talked long with; and by and by, she being in her hair, she put on his hat, which was but an ordinary one, to keep the wind off; but it became her mightily, as everything else does. I went away, not weary with looking at her.

Observations

This I take to be as bad a juncture as ever I observed: the King and his new Queen minding their pleasures at Hampton Court. All people discontented; some that the King do not gratify them enough; and the others, Fanatics of all sorts, that the King do take away their liberty of conscience; and the height of the Bishops, who I fear will ruin all again. They do much cry up the manner of Sir H. Vane's death, and he deserves it. Much clamor against the chimney-money; and the people say, they will not pay it without force. And in the meantime, likely to have war abroad; and Portugal to assist, when we have not money to pay for any ordinary layings-out at home. All in dirt about building of my house, and Sir W. Batten's, a story higher. Into a good way, fallen on minding my business and saving money, which God increase; and I do take great delight in it, and see the benefit of it. In a longing mind of going to see Brampton, but cannot get three days time, do what I can. In very good health, my wife and myself.

OCTOBER 2d. At night, hearing that there was a play at the Cockpit, and my Lord Sandwich, who came to town last night to it, I do go thither, and by very great fortune did follow four or five gentlemen who were carried to a little private door in a wall, and so crept through a narrow place, and came into one of the boxes next the King's, so I could not see the King or Queen, but many of the fine ladies, who are not really so handsome generally as I used to take them to be, but are finely dressed. Then we saw *The Cardinal,* a tragedy I had never seen before, nor is there any great matter in it. The company that came with me into the box were all Frenchmen who could speak no English; but Lord! what sport they made to ask a pretty lady that they got among them, that understood both French and English, to make her tell them what the actors said.

DECEMBER 31st. William Bowyer tells me how the difference comes between his fair cousin Butler and Colonel Dillon, upon his opening letters of her brother's from Ireland, complaining of his knavery, and forging others to the contrary; and so they are long ago quite broke off. Mr. Povy and I went to White Hall; he taking me to carry me into the ball this night before the King. He brought me first to the Duke's chamber, where I saw him and the Duchess at supper; and then into the room where the ball was to be, crammed with fine ladies, the greatest of the Court. By and by comes the King and Queen, the Duke and Duchess, and all the great ones; and after seating themselves, the King takes out the Duchess of York; and the Duke, the Duchess of Buckingham; the Duke of Monmouth, my Lady Castlemaine; and so other lords other ladies; and they dance. After that, the King led a lady in a single coranto; * and then the rest of the lords, one after another, other ladies: very noble it was, and great pleasure to see. Then to country dances; the King leading the first, which he called for; which was, says he, "Cuckolds all awry," the old dance of England. Of the ladies that danced, the Duke of Monmouth's mistress, and my Lady Castlemaine, and a daughter of Sir Harry de Vicke's, were the best. The manner was, when the King dances, all the ladies in the room, and the Queen herself, stand up; and indeed he dances rarely, and much better than the Duke of York. Having

* Swift, lively dance

stayed here as long as I thought fit, to my infinite content, it being the greatest pleasure I could wish now to see at Court, I went home, leaving them dancing.

Thus ends this year, with great mirth to me and my wife. Our condition being thus: we are at present spending a night or two at my Lord's lodgings at White Hall. Our home at the Navy Office, which is and hath a pretty while been in good condition, finished and made very convenient. By my last year's diligence in my office, blessed be God! I am come to a good degree of knowledge therein; and am acknowledged so by all the world, even the Duke himself, to whom I have a good access: and by that, and by my being Commissioner for Tangier, he takes much notice of me; and I doubt not but, by the continuance of the same endeavors, I shall in a little time come to be a man much taken notice of in the world, especially being come to so great an esteem with Mr. Coventry.

Public matters stand thus: the King is bringing, it is said, his family, and Navy, and all his other charges, to a less expense. In the meantime, himself following his pleasures more than with good advice he should do; at least, seen to all the world to do so. His dalliance with my Lady Castlemaine being public, every day, to his great reproach; and his favoring of none at Court so much as those that are the confidants of his pleasure, as Sir H. Bennet and Sir Charles Barkeley; which, good God, put it into his heart to mend, before he makes himself too much condemned by his people for it! The Duke of Monmouth is in so great splendor at Court, and so dandled by the King, that some doubt, if the King should have no child by the Queen (which there is yet no appearance of), whether he would not be acknowledged for a lawful son; and that there will be a difference follow between the Duke of York and him; which God prevent!

My Lord Chancellor is threatened by people to be questioned, the next sitting of the Parliament, by some spirits that do not love to see him so great: but certainly he is a good servant to the King. The Queen Mother is said to keep too great a Court now; and her being married to my Lord St. Albans is commonly talked of; and that they had a daughter between them in France; how true, God knows. The Bishops are high, and go on without any diffidence in pressing uniformity; and the Presbyters seem silent in it, and either conform or lay down, though without doubt they expect a turn, and would be glad if these endeavors of the other Fanatics would take effect; there having been a plot lately found, for which four have been publicly tried at the Old Bailey and hanged.

My Lord Sandwich is still in good esteem, and now keeping his Christmas in the country; and I in good esteem, I think, as any man can be with him. Mr. Moore is very sickly, and I doubt will hardly get over his late fit of sickness that still hangs on him. In fine, for the good condition of myself, wife, family, and estate, in the great degree that it is, and for the public state of the nation, so quiet as it is, the Lord God be praised!

1663

JANUARY 9th. My wife began to speak again of the necessity of our keeping somebody to bear her company; for her familiarity with the other servants spoils them all, and other company she hath none, which is too true. Comes Major Tolhurst, one of my old acquaintance in Cromwell's time, and sometimes of our club, to see me, and I could do no less than carry him to the Miter, Tolhurst telling me the manner of their collieries in the North.

13th. My poor wife rose by five o'clock in the morning, before day, and went to market and bought fowls and many other things for dinner, with which I was highly pleased, and the cut of beef was down also before six o'clock, and my own spit roasts it very well, things being put in order, and the cook come. By and by comes Dr. Clerke and his lady, his sister, and a she-cousin, and Mr. Pierce and his wife, which was all my guests. I had for them, after oysters, at first course, a hash of rabbits and lamb, and a rare cut of beef. Next, a great dish of roasted fowl, that cost me about 30s., and a tart, and then fruit and cheese. My dinner was noble, and enough. I had my house mighty clean and neat; my room below with a good fire in it; my dining room above, and my chamber being made a withdrawing chamber; and my wife's a good fire, also. I find my new table very proper, and will hold nine or ten people well, but eight with great room. At supper, had a good sack posset * and cold meat, and sent my guests away about ten o'clock at night, both them and myself

* Hot spiced drink

highly pleased with our management of this day; and indeed their company was very fine, and Mrs. Clerke a very witty, fine lady, though a little conceited and proud. I believe this day's feast will cost me near £5.

FEBRUARY 8th. (Lord's day.) Up, and it being a very great frost, I walked to White Hall to chapel, where there preached little Dr. Duport of Cambridge upon Joshua's words: "But I and my house, we will serve the Lord." Then with Mr. Creed to the King's Head Tavern. After dinner, Sir Thomas Willis and another stranger and Creed and I fell talking; they of the errors and corruption of the Navy, and great expense thereof, not knowing who I was, which at last I did undertake to confute and disabuse them: and they took it very well, and I hope it was to good purpose, they being Parliament men. Creed and I and Captain Ferrers withdrew to the Park, and there walked finely, seeing people slide, we talking all the while; and Captain Ferrers telling me, among other Court passages, how, about a month ago at a ball at Court, a child was dropped by one of the ladies in dancing, but nobody knew who, it being taken up by somebody in their handkerchief. The next morning all the Ladies of Honor appeared early at Court for their vindication, so that nobody could tell whose this mischance should be. But it seems Mrs. Wells fell sick that afternoon, and hath disappeared ever since, so that it is concluded it was her. Another story was how Lady Castlemaine, a few days since, had Mrs. Stuart to an entertainment, and at night began a frolic that they two must be married—and married they were, with ring and all other ceremonies of church service, and ribbands and a sack posset in bed, and flinging the stocking; but, in the close, it is said that my Lady Castlemaine, who was the bridegroom, rose, and the King came and took her place. This is said to be very true. Another story was how Captain Ferrers and W. Howe both have often, through my Lady Castlemaine's window, seen her go to bed, and Sir Charles Barkeley in the chamber. The little Duke of Monmouth, it seems, is ordered to take place of all Dukes, and so follows Prince Rupert now, before the Duke of Buckingham or any else.

APRIL 25th. In the evening, merrily practicing the dance which my wife hath begun to learn this day from Mr. Pembleton, but I fear will hardly do any great good at it, because she is conceited that she do well already, though I think no such thing.

MAY 4th. The dancing master came, while I stood by, seeing him instructing my wife; when he had done with her, he would needs have me try the steps of a coranto; and what with his desire and my wife's importunity, I did begin, and then was obliged to give him entry money 10*s.*, and am become his scholar. The truth is, I think it is a thing very useful for any gentleman.

8th. By water to the Strand, and there viewed the Queen Mother's works at Somerset House, and then to the new playhouse, but could not get in to see it: so to visit my Lady Jemimah, who is grown much since I saw her; but lacks mightily to be brought into the fashion of the Court to set her off. Took my wife and Ashwell to the Theater Royal, being the second day of its being opened. The house is made with extraordinary good convenience, and yet hath some faults, as the narrowness of the passages in and out of the pit, and the distance from the stage to the boxes, which I am confident cannot hear; but for all other things, is well; only, above all, the music being below, and most of it sounding under the very stage, there is no hearing of the basses at all, nor very well of the trebles, which sure must be mended.

The play was *The Humorous Lieutenant,* a play that hath little good in it, nor much in the very part which, by the King's command, Lacy now acts, instead of Clun. In the dance, the tall devil's actions were very pretty. The play being done, we home by water, having been a little shamed that my wife and woman were in such a pickle, all the ladies being finer and better dressed in the pit than they used, I think, to be. To my office, to set down this day's passage, and though my oath against going to plays does not oblige me against this house, because it was not then in being, yet, believing that at the time my meaning was against all public houses, I am resolved to deny myself the liberty of two plays at Court, which are in arrears to me for the months of March and April. At supper comes Pembleton, and afterwards we all up to dancing till late. They say that I am like to make a dancer.

12th. A little angry with my wife for minding nothing now but the dancing master, having him come twice a day, which is folly.

16th. After dinner comes Pembleton again, and I did go up to them to practice, and did make an end of La Duchesse, which I think I should, with a little pains, do very well.

JUNE 1st. The Duke having been a-hunting today, and so lately come home and gone to bed, we could not see him, and we walked away. And I with Sir J. Minnes to the Strand Maypole; and there alighted from his coach, and walked to the New Theater, which, since the King's players are gone to the Royal one, is this day begun to be employed by the fencers to play at prizes. And here I came and saw the first prize I ever saw in my life: and it was between one Mathews, who did beat at all weapons, and one Westwick, who was soundly cut several times both in the head and legs, that he was all over blood: and other deadly blows they did give and take in very good earnest, till Westwick was in a sad pickle. They fought at eight weapons, three bouts at each weapon. This being upon a private quarrel, they did it in good earnest; and I felt one of their swords, and found it to be very little, if at all, blunter on the edge than the common swords are. Strange to see what a deal of money is flung to them both upon the stage between every bout. So, well pleased for once with this sight, I walked home.

JULY 13th. I walked to the Temple; and there, from my cousin Roger, hear that the Judges have this day brought in their answer to the Lords: that the articles against my Lord Chancellor are not treason; and tomorrow they are to bring in their arguments to the House for the same. This day also the King did send by my Lord Chamberlain to the Lords to tell them from him that most of the articles against my Lord Chancellor he himself knows to be false. I met the Queen Mother walking in the Pall Mall, led by my Lord St. Albans. And finding many coaches at the Gate, I found upon inquiry that the Duchess is brought to bed of a boy; and hearing that the King and Queen rode abroad with the Ladies of Honor to the Park; and seeing a great crowd of gallants staying here to see their return, I also stayed walking up and down.

By and by the King and Queen, who looked in this dress, a white-laced waistcoat and a crimson short petticoat, and her hair dressed mighty pretty: and the King rode hand in hand with her. Here was also my Lady Castlemaine, who rode among the rest of the ladies; but the King took, methought, no notice of her; nor when she alighted did anybody press (as she seemed to expect and stayed for it) to take her down, but was taken down by her own gentleman. She looked mighty out of humor, and had a yellow plume in her hat, which all took notice of, and yet is very handsome, but very melancholy; nor did anybody speak to her, or she so much as smile or speak to anybody.

I followed them up into White Hall and into the Queen's presence, where all the ladies walked, talking and fiddling with their hats and feathers, and changing and trying one another's by one another's heads, and laughing. But it was the finest sight to me, considering their great beauties and dress, that ever I did see in all my life. But, above all, Mrs. Stuart in this dress, with her hat cocked and a red plume, with her sweet eye, little Roman nose, and excellent figure, is now the greatest beauty I ever saw, I think, in my life; and, if ever woman can, exceeds my Lady Castlemaine, at least in this dress: nor do I wonder if the King changes, which I verily believe is the reason for his coldness to my Lady Castlemaine.

31st. Mr. Grant showed me letters of Sir William Petty's, wherein he says that his vessel which he hath built upon two keels, a model whereof built for the King he showed me, hath this month won a wager of £50, in sailing between Dublin and Holyhead with the packet-boat, the best ship or vessel the King hath there; and he offers to lay with any vessel in the world. It is about thirty ton in burden, and carries thirty men, with good accommodation, as much more as any ship of her burden, and so any vessel of this figure shall carry more men, with better accommodation by half, than any other ship. This carries also ten guns of about five tons weight. In their coming back from Holyhead, they started together, and this vessel came to Dublin by five at night, and the packet-boat not before eight the next morning; and when they came, they did believe that this vessel had been drowned, or at least left behind, not thinking she could have lived in that sea. Strange things are told of this vessel and he concludes his letter with this position: "I only affirm that the perfection of sailing lies in my principle; find it out who can."

DECEMBER 21st. To my Lord Sandwich's, and there I had a pretty kind salute from my Lord. To Shoe Lane, to see cock-fighting at a new pit there, a spot I was never at in my life: but Lord! to see the strange variety of people, from a Parliament man, by name Wildes, that was Deputy Governor of the Tower when Robinson was Lord Mayor, to the poorest 'prentices, bakers, brewers, butchers, draymen, and what not; and all these fellows one with another cursing and betting. I soon had enough of it. It is strange to see how people of this poor rank, that look as if they had not bread to put in their mouths, shall bet three or four pounds at a time, and lose it and yet bet as much the next battle; so that one of them will lose 10 or £20 at a meeting.

Thence to my Lord Sandwich's, where I find him within with Captain Cooke and his boys, Dr. Childe, Mr. Madge, and Mallard, playing and singing over my Lord's anthem, which he hath made to sing in the King's Chapel: my Lord saluted me kindly, and took me into the withdrawing room to hear it: and indeed it sounds very pretty, and is a good thing, I believe, to be made by him, and they all commend it. My Lord going to White Hall, I went along with him, and made a desire to have his coach go along with my cousin Edward Pepys's hearse through the city on Wednesday next, which he granted me presently, though he cannot yet come to speak to me in the familiar style that he used to do, nor can I expect it.

31st. To dinner, my wife and I, a fine turkey and a minced pie, and dined in state, poor wretch, she and I, and have thus kept our Christmas together all alone almost, having not once been out. At the Coffee House, hearing some simple discourse about Quakers being charmed by a string about their wrists. I bless God I do, after a large expense, even this month, find that I am worth, in money, besides all my household stuff or anything of Brampton, above £800, whereof in my Lord Sandwich's hand £700, and the rest in my hand. I do live at my lodgings in the Navy Office, my family being, besides my wife and I, Jane Gentleman, Besse, our excellent, good-natured cook-maid, and Susan, a little girl; having neither man nor boy, nor like to have again a good while, living now in most perfect content and quiet, and very frugally also; my health pretty good.

At the office I am well, though envied to the devil by Sir William Batten, who hates me to death, but cannot hurt me. The rest either love me, or at least do not show otherwise, though I know Sir William Penn to be a false knave touching me, though he seems fair. My father and mother well in the country; and at this time the young ladies of Hinchingbroke with them—their house having the smallpox in it. The Queen, after a long and sore sickness, is become well again; and the King minds his mistress a little too much, if it pleased God! but I hope all things will go well, and in the Navy particularly, wherein I shall do my duty, whatever comes of it. The great talk is the design of the King of France, whether against the Pope or King of Spain nobody knows; but a great and most promising Prince he is, and all the Princes of Europe have their eye upon him.

My wife's brother came to great unhappiness by the ill disposition, my wife says, of his wife, and her poverty which she now professes, after all her husband's pretense of a great portion. At present, I am concerned for my cousin Angier of Cambridge, lately broke in his trade, and this day am sending his son John, a very rogue, to sea. My brother Tom I know not what to think of; for I cannot hear whether he minds his business or not; and my brother John at Cambridge, with as little hopes of doing good there; for when he was here, he did give me great cause of dissatisfaction with his manner of life. Pall with my father; and God knows what she does there, or what will become of her; for I have not anything yet to spare her, and she grows now old, and must be disposed of one way or other.

The Duchess of York is growing well again. The Turk very far entered into Germany, and all that part of the world at a loss what to expect from his proceeding. Myself, blessed be God! in a good way, and design and resolution of sticking to my business to get a little money, doing the best service I can to the King also—which God continue! So ends the old year.

1664

FEBRUARY 1st. I hear how two men last night, jostling for the wall about the new Exchange, did kill one another, each thrusting the other through; one of them of the King's Chapel, one Cave, and the other a retainer of my Lord General Middleton's. I to White Hall; where, in the Duke's chamber, the King came and stayed an hour or two laughing at Sir W. Petty, who was there, about his boat; and at Gresham College in general: at which poor Petty was, I perceive, at some loss; but did argue discreetly, and bear the unreasonable follies of the King's objections and other bystanders with great discretion; and offered to take odds against the King's best boats: but the King would not lay, but cried him down with words only. Gresham College he mightily laughed at, for spending time only in weighing of air, and doing nothing else since they sat. Mr. Pierce tells me how the King, coming the other day to his theater to see *The Indian Queen,* which he commends for a very fine thing, my Lady Castlemaine was in the next box before he came; and, leaning over other ladies awhile to whisper with the King, she rose out of the box, and went into the King's, and set herself on the King's right hand, between the King and the Duke of York; which, he swears, put the King himself, as well as everybody else, out of countenance; and believes that she did it only to show the world that she is not out of favor yet, as was believed.

To the King's Theater, and there saw *The Indian Queen* acted; which indeed is a most pleasant show, and beyond my expectation;

the play good, but spoiled with the rhyme, which breaks the sense. But above my expectation most, the eldest Marshal did her part most excellently well as I ever heard a woman in my life; but her voice is not so sweet as Ianthe's: however, we came home mightily contented.

3d. To the Miter Tavern, and there met with W. Howe, who had come to buy wine for my Lord for his going down to Hinchingbroke, and I was private with him a great while discoursing of my Lord's strangeness to me; but he answers that I have no reason to think any such thing, but that my Lord is only in general a more reserved man than he was before. My wife is full of sad stories of her good-natured father, and roguish brother, who is going for Holland to be a soldier. In Covent Garden tonight, going to fetch home my wife, I stopped at the great Coffee House there, where I never was before: where Dryden, the poet, I knew at Cambridge, and all the wits of the town, and Harris the player, and Mr. Hoole of our College. And, had I had time then, or could at other times, it will be good coming thither, for there, I perceive, is very witty and pleasant discourse. But I could not tarry, and, as it was late, they were all ready to go away.

JUNE 14th. By coach to Kensington. In the way overtaking Mr. Laxton, the apothecary, with his wife and daughters—very fine young lasses—in a coach; and so both of us to my Lady Sandwich, who hath lain this fortnight here, at Dean Hodges's. Much company come hither today—my Lady Carteret, Sir William Wheeler and his lady, and, above all, Mr. Beck of Chelsea, and wife and daughter, my Lord's mistress, and one that hath not one good feature in her face, and yet is a fine lady, very well carriaged and mighty discreet. I took all the occasion I could to discourse with the young ladies in her company to give occasion to her to talk, which now and then she did, and that mighty finely, and is, I perceive, a woman of such an air, as I wonder the less at my Lord's favor to her, and I dare warrant him she hath brains enough to entangle him. Two or three hours we were in her company, going into Sir H. Finch's garden, and seeing the fountain, and singing there with the ladies, and a mighty fine cool place it is, with a great laver of water in the middle, and the bravest place for music I ever heard. After much mirth, discoursing to the ladies in defense of the city against the country or court, and giving them occasion to invite themselves tomorrow to dinner to my venison pasty, I got their mother's leave, and so good night, very well pleased with my day's work, and, above all, that I have seen my Lord's mistress.

15th. At home, to look after things for dinner. And anon at noon comes Mr. Creed by chance, and by and by the three young ladies: and very merry we were with our pasty, very well baked; and a good dish of roasted chickens; pease, lobsters, strawberries. And after dinner to cards: and about five o'clock, by water down to Greenwich; and up to the top of the hill, and there played upon the ground at cards. And so to the Cherry Garden, and then by water singing finely to the Bridge, and there landed; and so took boat again, and to Somerset House. And by this time, the tide being against us, it was past ten of the clock; and such a troublesome passage, in regard to my Lady Paulina's fearfulness, that in all my life I never did see any poor wretch in that condition.

Being come hither, there waited for them their coach; but, it being so late, I doubted what to do how to get them home. After half an hour's stay in the street, I sent my wife home by coach with Mr. Creed's boy: and myself and Creed in the coach home with them. But Lord! the fear that my Lady Paulina was in every step of the way: and indeed, at this time of the night, it was no safe thing to go that road; so that I was even afraid myself, though I appeared otherwise. We came safe, however, to their house; where we knocked them up, my Lady and all the family being in bed. So put them into doors; and, leaving them with the maids, bade them good night. Then into the town—Creed and I, it being about twelve o'clock and past; and to several inns, but could get no lodging, all being in bed. At last, we found some people drinking and roaring; and, after drinking, got an ill bed.

16th. I lay in my drawers and stockings and waistcoat till five of the clock, and so up; and, being well pleased with our frolic, walked to Knightsbridge, and there ate a mess of cream, and so to St. James's, and I to White Hall, and took coach, and found my wife got home well last night, and now in bed.

JULY 14th. I rose a little after four o'clock, and went abroad. Walked to my Lord's, and nobody up, but the porter rose out of bed to me: so back again to Fleet Street, and there bought a little book of law; and thence hearing a psalm sung I went into St. Dunstan's, and there heard prayers read, which, it seems, is done there every morning at six o'clock—a thing I never did at a chapel, but the College chapel, in all my life. Thence to my Lord's again, and my Lord being up, was sent for, and he and I were alone. He did begin with a most solemn profession of the same confidence in and love for me that he ever had, and then told me what a misfortune was fallen upon me and him: on me, by a displeasure which my Lord Chancellor did show to him last night against me, in the highest and most passionate manner that ever any man did speak, even to the not hearing of anything to be said to him; but he told me that he did say all that could be said for a man as to my faithfulness and duty to his Lordship, and did me the greatest right imaginable.

And what should the business be, but that I should be forward to have the trees in Clarendon Park marked and cut down, which he, it seems, hath bought from my Lord Albemarle; when, God knows! I am the most innocent man in the world in it, and did nothing of myself, nor knew of his concernment therein, but barely obeyed my Lord Treasurer's warrant for the doing thereof. And said that I did most ungentlemanly-like with him, and had justified the rogues in cutting down a tree of his; and that I had sent the veriest Fanatic that is in England to mark them, on purpose to nose him. All which, I did assure my Lord, was most properly false, and nothing like it true; and told my Lord the whole passage. My Lord do seem most nearly affected with him; partly, I believe, for me, and partly for himself. So he advised me to wait presently upon my Lord, and clear myself in the most perfect manner I could, with all submission and assurance that I am his creature both in this and all other things; and that I do own that all I have is derived through my Lord Sandwich from his Lordship.

So, full of horror, I went, and found him busy in trials of law in his great room; and, it being sitting day, I dared not stay, but went to my Lord and told him so: whereupon he directed me to take him after dinner; and so away I went home, leaving my Lord mightily concerned for me. So I to my Lord Chancellor's; and there, coming out after dinner, I accosted him, telling him that I was the unhappy Pepys that had fallen into his high displeasure, and came to desire him to give me leave to make myself better understood to his Lordship, assuring him of my duty and service. He answered me very pleasingly, that he was confident upon the score of my Lord Sandwich's character of me, but that he had reason to think what he did, and desired me to call upon him some evening. I named tonight, and he accepted it.

To my Lord Chancellor's, and there heard several trials, wherein I perceive my Lord is a most able and ready man. After all done, he himself called, "Come, Mr. Pepys, you and I will take a turn in the garden." So he was led downstairs, having the gout, and there walked with me, I think, above an hour, talking most friendly, yet cunningly. I told him clearly how things were; how ignorant I was of his Lordship's concernment in it; how I did not do nor say one word singly, but what was done was the act of the whole Board. He told me by name that he was more angry with Sir G. Carteret than with me, and also with the whole body of the Board. But, thinking who it was of the Board that did know him least, he did place his fear upon me; but he finds that he is indebted to none of his friends there. I think I did thoroughly appease him, till he thanked me for my desire and pains to satisfy him; and, upon my desiring to be directed who I should of his servants advise with about this business, he told me nobody, but would be glad to hear from me himself. He told me he would not direct me in anything, that it might not be said that the Lord Chancellor did labor to abuse the King; or, as I offered, direct the suspending the Report of the Purveyors: but I see what he means, and will make it my work to do him service in it. But Lord! to see how he is incensed against poor Dean, as a fanatic rogue, and I know not what: and what he did was done in spite to his Lordship among all his friends and tenants. He did plainly say that he would not direct me in anything, for he would not put himself into the power of any man to say that he did so and so; but plainly told me, as if he would be glad I did something.

Lord! to see how we poor wretches dare not do the King good service for fear of the greatness of these men. He named Sir G. Carteret and Sir J. Minnes and the rest; and that he was as angry with them all as with me. But it was pleasant to think that, while he was talking to me, into the garden comes Sir G. Carteret; and my Lord avoided speaking with him, and made him and many others stay expecting him, while I walked up and down above an hour, I think; and he would have me walk with my hat on. And yet, after all, there has been so little ground for his jealousy of me that I am sometimes afraid that he does this only in policy to bring me to his side by scaring me; or else, which is worse, to try how faithful I would be to the King: but I rather think the former of the two. I parted with great assurance how I acknowledged all I had to come from his Lordship; which he did not seem to refuse, but, with great kindness and respect, parted.

AUGUST 13th. Comes Mr. Reeve, with a microscope and scotoscope. For the first I did give him £5 10s., a great price, but a most curious bauble it is, and, he says, the best he knows in England. The other he gives me and is of value; and a curious curiosity it is to discover objects in a dark room with. Mr. Creed dining with me, I got him to give my wife and me a play this afternoon, lending him money to do it, which is a fallacy that I have found now once, to avoid my vow with, but never to be more practiced, I swear. To the new play, at the Duke's house, of *Henry the Fifth,* a most noble play writ by my Lord Orrery; wherein Betterton, Harris, and Ianthe's parts are most incomparably wrote and done, and the whole play the most full of height and raptures of wit and sense that ever I heard; having but one incongruity, that King Harry promises to plead for Tudor to their mistress, Princess Katherine of France, more than, when it comes to it, he seems to do; and Tudor refused by her with some kind of indignity, not with a difficulty and honor that it ought to have been done in to him.

SEPTEMBER 16th. Mr. Gauden coming to me, I had a good opportunity to speak to him about his present, which hitherto hath been a burden to me, because I was doubtful that he meant it as a temptation to me, to stand by him in the business of Tangier victualling; but he clears me it was not, and that what he did was for my old kindnesses to him, and dispatching of his business. Met Sir W. Warren, and afterwards to the Sun Tavern, where he brought to me, being all alone, £100 in a bag, which I offered him to give him my receipt for, but he told me no, it was my own, which he had a little while since promised me; and so most kindly he did give it to me, and I as joyfully, even out of myself, carried it home in a coach—he himself expressly taking care that nobody might see this business done, though I was willing enough to have carried a servant with me to have received it, but he advised me to do it myself.

DECEMBER 31st. To my accounts of the whole year till past twelve at night, it being bitter cold, but yet I was well satisfied with my work; and above all, to find myself, by the great blessing of God, worth £1349, by which, as I have spent very largely, so I have laid up above £500 this year above what I was worth this day twelvemonth. The Lord make me forever thankful to his holy name for it! Soon as ever the clock struck one, I kissed my wife in the kitchen by the fireside, wishing her a merry new year.

So ends the old year, I bless God, with great joy to me, not only from my having made so good a year of profit, as having spent £420 and laid up £540 and upwards; but I bless God I never have been in so good plight as to my health in so very cold weather as this is, nor indeed in any hot weather, these ten years, as I am at this day, and have been these four or five months. But I am at a great loss to know whether it be my hare's foot, or taking every morning of a pill of turpentine, or my having left off the wearing of a gown. My family is my wife, in good health, and happy with her; her woman Mercer, a pretty, modest, quiet maid; her chambermaid Besse, her cook-maid Jane, the little girl Susan, and my boy, which I have had about half a year, Tom Edwards, which I took from the King's Chapel; and as pretty and loving, quiet a family I have as any man in England.

My credit in the world and my office grows daily, and I am in good esteem with everybody, I think.

1665

JUNE 7th. This morning my wife and mother rose about two o'clock; and with Mercer, Mary, the boy, and W. Hewer, as they had designed, took boat, and down to refresh themselves on the water to Gravesend. To the Dolphin Tavern, where Sir J. Minnes, Lord Brouncker, Sir Thomas Harvy, and myself dined, upon Sir G. Carteret's charge, and very merry we were, Sir Thomas Harvy being very droll. To the New Exchange, and there drank whey, with much entreaty getting it for our money, and they would not be entreated to let us have one glass more. So took water to Foxhall, to the Spring Garden, and there walked an hour or two with great pleasure, saving our minds ill at ease concerning the fleet and my Lord Sandwich: but we have no news of them, and ill reports run up and down of his being killed, but without ground. Here stayed, pleasantly walking, and spending but 6d. till nine at night. The hottest day that ever I felt in my life. This day, much against my will, I did in Drury Lane see two or three houses marked with a red cross upon the doors, and "Lord have mercy upon us!" writ there; which was a sad sight to me, being the first of the kind that, to my remembrance, I ever saw. It put me into an ill conception of myself and my smell, so that I was forced to buy some roll-tobacco to smell and chew, which took away the apprehension.

10th. In the evening home to supper; and there, to my great trouble, hear that the plague is come into the City, though it hath, these three or four weeks since its beginning, been wholly out of the City; but where should it begin but in my good friend and neighbor's, Dr. Burnett, in Fenchurch Street: which, in both points, troubles me mightily.

15th. Up, and put on my new stuff suit with close knees, which becomes me most nobly, as my wife says. The town grows very sickly, and people to be afraid of it: there dying this last week of the plague 112, from 43 the week before; whereof but one in Fenchurch Street, and one in Broad Street, by the Treasurer's office.

17th. At the office find Sir W. Penn come home, who looks very well; and I am gladder to see him than otherwise I should be because of my hearing so well of him for his serviceableness at this time. It struck me very deep this afternoon going with a hackney coach from Lord Treasurer's down Holborn, the coachman I found to drive easily and easily, at last stood still, and came down hardly able to stand, and told me that he was suddenly struck very sick, and almost blind— he could not see; so I alighted, and went into another coach, with a sad heart for the poor man and for myself also, lest he should have been struck with the plague. Sir John Lawson, I hear, is worse than yesterday; the King went to see him today most kindly. It seems his wound is not very bad; but he hath a fever, a thrush, and a hiccup, all three together, which are, it seems, very bad symptoms.

JULY 13th. By water, at night late, to Sir G. Carteret's, but, there being no oars to carry me, I was fain to call a sculler that had a gentleman already in it, and he proved a man of love to music, and he and I sang together the way down with great pleasure. Above 700 died of the plague this week.

20th. To Deptford, and after dinner saw my Lady Sandwich and Mr. Carteret and his two sisters over the water, going to Dagenhams, and my Lady Carteret toward Cranburne. Walked to Redriffe, where I hear the sickness is, and indeed is scattered almost everywhere, there dying 1089 of the plague this week. My Lady Carteret did this day give me a bottle of plague-water home with me. I received yesterday a letter from my Lord Sandwich, giving me thanks for my care about their marriage business, and desiring it to be dispatched, that no disappointment may happen therein. Lord! to see how the plague spreads! it being now all over King's Street, at the Axe, and next door to it, and in other places.

AUGUST 3d. Up, and betimes to Deptford to Sir G. Carteret's, where, not knowing the horse which had been hired by Mr. Unthwayt for me, I did desire Sir G. Carteret to let me ride his new £40 horse;

and so to the ferry, where I was forced to stay a great while before I could get my horse brought over, and then mounted, and rode very finely to Dagenhams; all the way, people, citizens, walking to and fro, inquire how the plague is in the City this week by the Bill; which, by chance, at Greenwich, I had heard was 2020 of the plague, and 3000 and odd, of all diseases; but methought it was a sad question to be so often asked me.

Coming to Dagenhams, I there met our company coming out of the house, having stayed as long as they could for me; so I let them go a little way before, and went and took leave of my Lady Sandwich, good woman, who seems very sensible of my service, in this late business, and having her directions in some things—among others, to get Sir G. Carteret and my Lord to settle the portion, and what Sir G. Carteret is to settle, into land, soon as may be, she not liking it should lie long undone, for fear of death on either side. So took leave of her, and down to the buttery, and ate a piece of cold venison pie, and drank, and took some bread and cheese in my hand; and so mounted after them, Mr. Marr very kindly staying to lead me the way.

By and by met Lord Crewe returning; Mr. Marr telling me, by the way, how a maid servant of Mr. John Wright's, who lives thereabouts, falling sick of the plague, she was removed to an outhouse, and a nurse appointed to look to her; who, being once absent, the maid got out of the house at the window, and ran away. The nurse coming and knocking, and, having no answer, believed she was dead, and went and told Mr. Wright so; who and his lady were in great turmoil what to do to get her buried. At last, resolved to go to Burntwood, hard by, being in the parish, and there get people to do it. But they would not: so he went home full of trouble, and on the way met the wench walking over the Common, which frightened him worse than before; and was forced to send people to take her, which he did; and they got one of the pest-coaches, and put her into it, to carry her to a pest-house. And, passing in a narrow lane, Sir Anthony Browne, with his brother and some friends in the coach, met this coach with the curtains drawn close. The brother, being a young man, and believing there might be some lady in it that would not be seen, and the way being narrow, he thrust his head out of his own into her coach, and to look, and there saw somebody looking very ill, and in a silk dress, and stunk mightily; which the coachman also cried out upon. And presently they came up to some people that stood looking after it, and told our gallants that it was a maid of Mr. Wright's carried away sick of the plague; which put the young gentleman into a fright had almost cost him his life, but is now well again.

10th. My she-cousin Porter, the turner's wife, to tell me that her husband was carried to the Tower, for buying some of the King's powder, and would have my help, but I could give her none, not daring to appear in the business. By and by to the office, where we sat all the morning; in great trouble to see the Bill this week rise so high, to above 4000 in all, and of them above 3000 of the plague. Home, to draw over anew my will, which I had bound myself by oath to dispatch by tomorrow night; the town growing so unhealthy that a man cannot depend upon living two days.

12th. The people die so, that now it seems they are fain to carry the dead to be buried by daylight, the nights not sufficing to do it in. And my Lord Mayor commands people to be within at nine at night, as they say, so that the sick may have liberty to go abroad for air. There is one also dead out of one of our ships at Deptford, which troubles us mightily—the Providence, fire-ship, which was just fitted to go to sea; but they tell me, today, no more sick on board. And this day W. Bodham tells me that one is dead at Woolwich, not far from the Rope Yard. I am told, too, that a wife of one of the grooms at Court is dead at Salisbury; so that the King and Queen are speedily to be all gone to Wilton. So God preserve us!

30th. Abroad, and met with Hadley, our clerk, who, upon my asking how the plague goes, told me it increases much, and much in our parish; for, says he, there died nine this week, though I have returned but six: which is a very ill practice, and makes me think it is so in other places; and therefore the plague much greater than people take it to be. I went forth, and walked towards Moorefields to see, God forgive my presumption! whether I could see any dead corpse going to the grave; but, as God would have it, did not. But Lord! how everybody's looks and discourse in the street is of death and nothing else; and few people going up and down, so that the town is like a place distressed and forsaken.

31st. Up, and after putting several things in order to my removal, to Woolwich; the plague having a great increase this week, beyond all expectation, of almost 2000, making the general Bill 7000, odd 100; and the plague above 6000. Thus this month ends with great sadness upon the public, through the greatness of the plague everywhere through the kingdom almost. Every day sadder and sadder news of its increase. In the City died this week 7496, and of them

220

6102 of the plague. But it is feared that the true number of the dead this week is near 10,000; partly from the poor that cannot be taken notice of, through the greatness of the number, and partly from the Quakers and others that will not have any bell ring for them.

SEPTEMBER 4th. Walked home, my Lord Brouncker giving me a very neat cane to walk with; but it troubled me to pass by Coome farm, where about twenty-one people have died of the plague.

5th. After dinner comes Colonel Blunt in his new chariot made with springs; as that was of wicker, wherein a while since we rode at his house. And he hath rode, he says, now his journey, many miles in it with one horse, and out-drives any coach, and out-goes any horse, and so easy, he says. So, for curiosity, I went into it to try it, and up the hill to the heath, and over the cart-ruts, and found it pretty well, but not so easy as he pretends.

6th. To London, to pack up more things; and there I saw fires burning in the street, as it is through the whole City, by the Lord Mayor's order. Thence by water to the Duke of Albemarle's: all the way fires on each side of the Thames, and strange to see in broad daylight two or three burials upon the bankside, one at the very heels of another: doubtless, all of the plague; and yet at least forty or fifty people going along with every one of them. The Duke mighty pleasant with me; telling me that he is certainly informed that the Dutch did not come home upon the first instant, and so he hopes our fleet may meet with them.

7th. To the Tower, and there sent for the weekly Bill, and find 8252 dead in all, and of them 6978 of the plague; which is a most dreadful number, and shows reason to fear that the plague hath got that hold that it will yet continue among us.

20th. Up, and after being trimmed, the first time I have been touched by a barber these twelve months, I think, and more, by and by Sir J. Minnes and Sir W. Batten met, to go into my Lord Brouncker's coach, and so we four to Lambeth, and thence to the Duke of Albemarle, to inform him what we have done as to the fleet, which is very little, and to receive his direction. But Lord! what a sad time it is to see no boats upon the river; and grass grows all up and down White Hall Court, and nobody but poor wretches in the streets! And, which is worst of all, the Duke showed us the number of the plague this week, brought in the last night from the Lord Mayor; that it is increased about 600 more than the last, which is quite contrary to our hopes and expectations, from the coldness of the late season.

221

For the whole general number is 8297, and of them the plague 7165; which is more in the whole, by above 50, than the biggest Bill yet: which is very grievous to us all.

NOVEMBER 30th. At noon comes Sir Thomas Allen, and I made him dine with me, and very friendly he is, and a good man, I think, but one that professes he loves to get and to save. Great joy we have this week in the weekly Bill, it being come to 544 in all, and but 333 of the plague; so that we are encouraged to get to London soon as we can. And my father writes as great news of joy to them, that he saw York's wagon go again this week to London, and full of passengers; and tells me that my aunt Bell hath been dead of the plague these seven weeks.

DECEMBER 6th. Up betimes, it being fast-day; and by water to the Duke of Albemarle, who came to town from Oxford last night. He is mighty brisk, and very kind to me, and asks my advice principally in every thing. He surprises me with the news that my Lord Sandwich goes Ambassador to Spain speedily; though I know not whence this arises, yet I am heartily glad of it. I spent the afternoon upon a song of Solomon's words to Roxalana that I have set, and so with my wife walked and Mercer to Mrs. Pierce's, where Captain Rolt and Mrs. Knipp, Mr. Coleman and his wife, and Laneare, Mrs. Worshipp and her singing daughter, met; and by and by, unexpectedly comes Mr. Pierce from Oxford. Here the best company for music I ever was in in my life and wish I could live and die in it, both for music and the face of Mrs. Pierce, and my wife, and Knipp, who is pretty enough; but the most excellent, mad-humored thing, and sings the noblest that ever I heard in my life, and Rolt, with her, some things together, most excellently. I spent the night in an ecstasy almost; and, having invited them to my house a day or two hence, we broke up.

30th. All the afternoon to my accounts; and there find myself, to my great joy, a great deal worth, above £4000, for which the Lord be praised! and is principally occasioned by my getting £500 from Cocke, for my profit in his bargains of prize goods, and from Mr. Gauden's making me a present of £500 more, when I paid him £800 for Tangier.

31st. (Lord's day.) Thus ends this year, to my great joy, in this manner. I have raised my estate from £1300 in this year to £4400. I have got myself greater interest, I think, by my diligence, and my employments increased by that of Treasurer for Tangier and Surveyor of the Victuals.

It is true we have gone through great melancholy because of the great plague, and I was put to great charges by it, by keeping my family long at Woolwich; and myself and another part of my family, my clerks at my charge at Greenwich, and a maid at London; but I hope the King will give us some satisfaction for that. But now the plague is abated almost to nothing, and I intending to get to London as fast as I can. The Dutch war goes on very ill, by reason of lack of money; having none to hope for, all being put into disorder by a new act that is made as an experiment to bring credit to the Exchequer, for goods and money to be advanced upon the credit of that act.

The great evil of this year, and the only one indeed, is the fall of my Lord Sandwich, whose mistake about the prizes hath undone him, I believe, as to interest at Court; though sent, for a little palliating it, Ambassador into Spain, which he is now fitting himself for. But the Duke of Albemarle goes with the Prince to sea this next year, and my Lord is very meanly spoken of; and, indeed, his miscarriage about the prize-goods is not to be excused, to suffer a company of rogues to go away with ten times as much as himself, and the blame of all to be deservedly laid upon him.

My whole family hath been well all this while, and all my friends I know of, saving my aunt Bell, who is dead, and some children of my cousin Sarah's, of the plague. But many of such as I know very well, dead; yet, to our great joy, the town fills apace, and shops begin to be open again. Pray God continue the plague's decrease! for that keeps the Court away from the place of business, and so all goes to rack as to public matters, they at this distance not thinking of it.

1666

JANUARY 28th. (Lord's day.) Took coach, and to Hampton Court, where we find the King and Duke and Lords, all in council; so we walked up and down: there being none of the ladies come, and so much the more business I hope will be done. The Council being up, out comes the King, and I kissed his hand, and he grasped me very kindly by the hand. The Duke also, I kissed his, and he mighty kind, and Sir W. Coventry. I found my Lord Sandwich there, poor man! I see with a melancholy face, and suffers his beard to grow on his upper lip more than usual. I took him a little aside, to know when I should wait on him, and where: he told me, that it would be best to meet at his lodgings, without being seen to walk together, which I liked very well; and Lord! to see in what difficulty I stand, that I dare not walk with Sir W. Coventry, for fear my Lord or Sir G. Carteret should see me; nor with either of them, for fear Sir W. Coventry should.

I went down into one of the Courts, and there met the King and Duke; and the Duke called me to him. And the King came to me by himself, and told me, "Mr. Pepys," says he, "I do give you thanks for your good service all this year, and I assure you I am very sensible of it." And the Duke of York did tell me with pleasure that he had read over my discourse about pursers, and would have it ordered in my way, and so fell from one discourse to another. I walked with them quite out of the Court into the fields, and then back, and to my Lord Sandwich's chamber, where I find him very melancholy, and not well satisfied, I perceive, with my carriage to Sir G. Carteret, but I did satisfy him that I have a very hard game to play; and he told me that he was sorry to see it, and the inconveniences which likely may fall upon me with him; but, for all that, I am not much afraid, if I can but keep out of harm's way. He hath got over the business of the prizes, so far as to have a privy seal passed for all that was in his distribution to the officers, which I am heartily glad of; and, for the rest, he must be answerable for what he is proved to have. But for his pardon for anything else, he thinks it not seasonable to ask it, and not useful to him; because that will not stop a Parliament's mouth, and for the King, he is not sure of him. Took boat, and by water to Kingston, and so to our lodgings.

APRIL 17th. To the office, but Lord! what a conflict I had with myself, my heart tempting me a thousand times to go abroad about some pleasure or other, notwithstanding the foul weather. However, I did not budge; and, to my great content, did a great deal of business.

MAY 9th. To White Hall, and heard the Duke commend Dean's ship, the Rupert, before the Defiance, built by Castle, in hearing of Sir W. Batten, which pleased me mightily. To Pierce's, where I find Knipp. Thence with them to Cornhill, to call and choose a chimney-piece for Pierce's closet. My wife mightily vexed at my being abroad with these women; and, when they were gone, called them I know not what, which vexed me, having been so innocent with them.

JULY 10th. To the office; the yard being very full of women, I believe above three hundred, coming to get money for their husbands and friends that are prisoners in Holland; and they lay clamoring, and swearing, and cursing us, that my wife and I were afraid to send a venison-pasty that we have for supper tonight to the cook's to be baked, for fear of their offering violence to it: but it went, and no hurt done. To the Tower, to speak with Sir John Robinson about the bad condition of the pressed men for want of clothes. Home, and there find my wife and the two Mrs. Bateliers walking in the garden; and then they and we and Mrs. Mercer, the mother, and her daughter Anne, and our Mercer, to supper to a good venison pasty and other good things, and had a good supper, and very merry—Mistresses Bateliers being both very good-humored. We sang and talked, and then led them home, and there they made us drink; and, among other things, did show us, in cages, some birds brought from Bordeaux, that are all fat, and, examining one of them, they are so, almost all fat. Their name is Ortolans, which are brought over to the King for him to eat, and indeed are excellent things.

AUGUST 19th. (Lord's day.) Comes by agreement Mr. Reeves, bringing me a lantern, with pictures in glass, to make strange things appear on a wall, very pretty. We did also at night see Jupiter and his girdle and satellites, very fine, with my twelve-foot glass, but not Saturn, he being very dark. Spong and I had also several fine discourses upon the globes this afternoon, particularly why the fixed stars do not rise and set at the same hour all the year long, which he could not demonstrate, nor I neither.

21st. Mr. Batelier told me how, being with some others at Bordeaux, making a bargain with another man at a tavern for some clarets, they did hire a fellow to thunder, which he had the art of doing, upon a deal board, and to rain and hail, that is, make the noise of, so as did give them a pretense of undervaluing their merchants' wines, by saying this thunder would spoil and turn them, which was so reasonable to the merchant, that he did abate two pistols per ton for the wine, in belief of that.

22d. I to St. James's, and there with the Duke of York. I had opportunity of much talk with Sir W. Penn today, he being newly come from the fleet; and he do much undervalue the honor that is given to the conduct of Holmes in burning the ships and town, saying it was a great thing indeed, and of great profit to us in being of great loss to the enemy, but that it was wholly a business of chance. Mrs. Knipp tells me my song of "Beauty, Retire" is mightily cried up, which I am not a little proud of; and do think I have done "It is Decreed" better,

225

but I have not finished it. My closet is being done by an upholsterer, which I am pleased with, but fear my purple will be too sad for that melancholy room. My wife, Knipp, and Mercer, by coach to Moorfields, and there saw *Polichinello,** which pleases me mightily.

31st. Much pleased today with thoughts of gilding the backs of all my books alike, in all my new presses.

SEPTEMBER 1st. My wife and I to *Polichinello,* but were there horribly frighted to see Young Killigrew come in, with a great many more young sparks: but we hid ourselves, so as we think they did not see us.

2d. (Lord's day.) Some of our maids sitting up late last night to get things ready for our feast today, Jane called us up about three in the morning, to tell us of a great fire they saw in the City. So I rose, and slipped on my night-gown, and went to her window; and thought it to be on the back side of Mark Lane at the farthest; but, being unused to such fires as followed, I thought it far enough off; and so went to bed again, and to sleep. About seven rose again to dress myself, and there looked out of the window, and saw the fire not so much as it was, and farther off. So to my closet to set things to rights, after yesterday's cleaning. By and by Jane comes and tells me that she hears that above 300 houses have been burned down tonight by the fire we saw, and that it is now burning down all Fish Street, by London Bridge.

So I made myself ready presently, and walked to the Tower; and there got up upon one of the high places, Sir J. Robinson's little son going up with me; and there I did see the houses at that end of the bridge all on fire, and an infinite great fire on this and the other side of the end of the bridge; which, among other people, did trouble me for poor little Michell and our Sarah on the bridge. So down, with my heart full of trouble, to the Lieutenant of the Tower, who tells me that it began this morning in the King's baker's house in Pudding Lane, and that it hath burned down St. Magnus's Church and most part of Fish Street already. So I down to the waterside, and there got a boat, and through the bridge, and there saw a lamentable fire. Poor Michell's house, as far as the Old Swan, already burned that way, and the fire running farther, that, in a very little time, it got as far as the Steel Yard, while I was there. Everybody endeavoring to remove their goods, and flinging them into the river, or bringing them into lighters that lay off; poor people staying in their houses as long as till the very fire touched them, and then running into boats, or clambering from

* Punch and Judy show

one pair of stairs, by the waterside, to another. And, among other things, the poor pigeons, I perceive, were loath to leave their houses, but hovered about the windows and balconies, till they burned their wings and fell down.

Having stayed, and in an hour's time seen the fire rage every way; and nobody, to my sight, endeavoring to quench it, but to remove their goods, and leave all to the fire; and, having seen it get as far as the Steel Yard, and the wind mighty high, and driving it into the City; and everything, after so long a drought, proving combustible, even the very stones of churches; and, among other things, the poor steeple whereof my old schoolfellow Elborough is parson, taken fire in the very top, and there burned till it fell down; I to White Hall, with a gentleman with me, who desired to go off from the Tower, to see the fire, in my boat; and there up to the King's closet in the Chapel, where people come about me, and I did give them an account, dismayed them all, and word was carried in to the King.

So I was called for, and did tell the King and Duke of York what I saw; and that, unless his Majesty did command houses to be pulled down, nothing could stop the fire. They seemed much troubled, and the King commanded me to go to my Lord Mayor from him, and command him to spare no houses, but to pull down before the fire every way. The Duke of York bid me tell him, that if he would have any more soldiers, he shall; and so did my Lord Arlington afterwards, as a great secret. Here meeting with Captain Cocke, I in his coach, which he lent me, and Creed with me to Paul's; and there walked along Watling Street, as well as I could, every creature coming away laden with goods to save, and, here and there, sick people carried away in beds. Extraordinary good goods carried in carts and on backs. At last met my Lord Mayor in Canning Street, like a man spent, with a handkerchief about his neck. To the King's message, he cried, like a fainting woman, "Lord! what can I do? I am spent: people will not obey me. I have been pulling down houses; but the fire overtakes us faster than we can do it." That he needed no more soldiers; and that, for himself, he must go and refresh himself, having been up all night.

So he left me, and I him, and walked home; seeing people all almost distracted, and no manner of means used to quench the fire. The houses, too, so very thick thereabouts, and full of matter for burning, as pitch and tar, in Thames Street; and warehouses of oil, and wines, and brandy, and other things. Here I saw Mr. Isaac Houblon, the handsome man, prettily dressed and dirty at his door at Dowgate, receiving some of his brother's things, whose houses were on fire; and, as he says, have been removed twice already; and he doubts, as it soon proved, that they must be, in a little time, removed from his house also, which was a sad consideration. And to see the churches all filling with goods by people who themselves should have been quietly there at this time.

By this time, it was about twelve o'clock; and so home, and there find my guests, who were Mr. Wood and his wife Barbary Shelden, and also Mr. Moone: she mighty fine, and her husband, for aught I see, a likable man. But Mr. Moone's design and mine, which was to look over my closet, and please him with the sight thereof, which he hath long desired, was wholly disappointed; for we were in great trouble and disturbance at this fire, not knowing what to think of it. However, we had an extraordinary good dinner, and as merry as at this time we could be. While at dinner, Mrs. Batelier come to inquire after Mr. Woolfe and Stanes, who, it seems, are related to them, whose houses in Fish Street are all burned, and they in a sad condition. She would not stay in the fright.

Soon as we dined, I and Moone away, and walked through the City, the streets full of nothing but people; and horses and carts laden with goods, ready to run over one another, and removing goods from one burned house to another. They now removing out of Canning Street, which received goods in the morning, into Lombard Street, and farther: and, among others, I now saw my little goldsmith Stokes, receiving some friend's goods, whose house itself was burned the day after. We parted at Paul's; he home, and I to Paul's Wharf, where I had appointed a boat to attend me, and took in Mr. Carcasse and his brother, whom I met in the street, and carried them below and above bridge too. And again to see the fire, which was now got farther, both below and above, and no likelihood of stopping it.

Met with the King and Duke of York in their barge, and with them to Queenhithe, and there called Sir Richard Browne to them. Their order was only to pull down houses apace, and so below bridge at the waterside; but this little was or could be done, the fire coming upon them so fast. Good hopes there was of stopping it at the Three Cranes above, and at Buttulph's Wharf below bridge, if care be used; but the wind carries it into the City, so as we know not, by the waterside, what it does there. River full of lighters and boats taking in goods, and good goods swimming in the water; and only I observed that hardly one lighter or boat in three that had the goods of a house in, but there was a pair of virginals * in it. Having seen as much as I could now, I away to White Hall by appointment, and there walked to St. James's Park; and there met my wife, and Creed, and Wood and his wife, and walked to my boat; and there upon the water again, and to the fire up and down, it still increasing, and the wind great. So near the fire as we could for smoke; and all over the Thames, with one's face in the wind, you were almost burned with a shower of fire-drops. This is very true: so as houses were burned by these drops and flakes of fire, three or four, nay, five or six houses, one from another. When we could endure no more upon the water, we went to a little alehouse on the Bankside, over against the Three Cranes, and there stayed till it was dark almost, and saw the fire grow; and, as it grew darker, appeared more and more; and in corners and upon steeples, and between churches and houses, as far as we could see up the hill of the City, in a most horrid, malicious, bloody flame, not like the fine flame of an ordinary fire. Barbary and her husband away before us.

We stayed till, it being darkish, we saw the fire as only one entire arch of fire from this to the other side of the bridge, and in a bow up the hill for an arch of above a mile long: it made me weep to see it. The churches, houses, and all on fire, and flaming at once; and a horrid noise the flames made, and the cracking of houses at their ruin. So home with a sad heart, and there find everybody discoursing and lamenting the fire; and poor Tom Hater came with some few of his goods saved out of his house, which was burned upon Fish Street Hill. I invited him to lie at my house, and did receive his goods; but was deceived in his lying there, the news coming every moment of the growth of the fire; so as we were forced to begin to pack up our own goods, and prepare for their removal; and did by moonshine (it being brave, dry, and moonshine and warm weather) carry much of my goods into the garden; and Mr. Hater and I did remove my money and iron chests into my cellar, as thinking that the safest place. And got my bags of gold into my office, ready to carry away, and my chief papers of accounts also there, and my tallies into a box by themselves. So great was our fear, as Sir W. Batten hath carts come out of the country to fetch away his goods this night. We did put Mr. Hater, poor man! to bed a little; but he got but very little rest, so much noise being in my house, taking down of goods.

3d. About four o'clock in the morning, my Lady Batten sent me a cart to carry away all my money and plate and best things to Sir W.

* An early spinet

Rider's at Bednall Green, which I did, riding myself in my night-gown, in the cart; and Lord! to see how the streets and the highways are crowded with people running and riding, and getting of carts at any rate to fetch away things. I find Sir W. Rider tired with being called up all night, and receiving things from several friends. His house full of goods, and much of Sir W. Batten's and Sir W. Penn's. I am eased at my heart to have my treasure so well secured. Then home, and with much ado to find a way, nor any sleep all this night to me nor my poor wife. But then all this day she and I and all my people laboring to get away the rest of our things, and did get Mr. Tooker to get me a lighter to take them in, and we did carry them, myself some, over Tower Hill, which was by this time full of people's goods, bringing their goods thither; and down to the lighter, which lay at the next quay, above the Tower Dock. And here was my neighbor's wife with her pretty child, and some few of her things, which I did willingly give way to be saved with mine; but there was no passing with anything through the postern, the crowd was so great.

The Duke of York came this day by the office, and spoke to us, and did ride with his guard up and down the City to keep all quiet, he being now General, and having the care of all. This day, Mercer being not at home, but against her mistress's order gone to her mother's, and my wife going thither to speak with W. Hewer, beat her there, and was angry; and her mother saying that she was not a 'prentice girl, to ask leave every time she goes abroad, my wife with good reason was angry; and, when she came home, did bid her be gone again. And so she went away, which troubled me, but yet less than it would, because of the condition we are in, in fear of coming in a little time to being less able to keep one in her quality. At night, lay down a little upon a quilt of W. Hewer's in the office, all my own things being packed up or gone; and, after me, my poor wife did the like, we having fed upon the remains of yesterday's dinner, having no fire nor dishes, nor any opportunity of dressing anything.

4th. Up by break of day, to get away the remainder of my things; which I did by a lighter at the Iron Gate: and my hands so full, that it was afternoon before we could get them all away. Sir W. Penn and I to the Tower Street, and there met the fire burning, three or four doors beyond Mr. Howell's, whose goods, poor man, his trays, and dishes, shovels, &c., were flung all along Tower Street in the kennels, and people working therewith from one end to the other; the fire coming on in that narrow street, on both sides, with infinite fury.

Sir W. Batten not knowing how to remove his wine, did dig a pit in the garden, and laid it in there; and I took the opportunity of laying all the papers of my office that I could not otherwise dispose of. And in the evening Sir W. Penn and I did dig another, and put our wine into it; and I my Parmesan cheese, as well as my wine and some other things.

The Duke of York was at the office this day, at Sir W. Penn's; but I happened not to be within. This afternoon, sitting melancholy with Sir W. Penn in our garden, and thinking of the certain burning of this office, without extraordinary means, I did propose for the sending up of all our workmen from the Woolwich and Deptford yards, none whereof yet appeared, and to write to Sir W. Coventry to have the Duke of York's permission to pull down houses, rather than lose this office, which would much hinder the King's business. So Sir W. Penn went down this night, in order to send them up tomorrow morning; and I wrote to Sir W. Coventry about the business, but received no answer.

This night, Mrs. Turner, who, poor woman, was removing her goods all this day (good goods, into the garden, and knows not how to dispose of them) and her husband supped with my wife and me at night in the office upon a shoulder of mutton from the cook's without any napkin or anything, in a sad manner, but they were merry. Only now and then, walking into the garden, saw how horribly the sky looks, all on fire in the night; was enough to put us out of our wits; and, indeed, it was extremely dreadful, for it looks just as if it was at us, and the whole heaven on fire. I after supper walked in the dark down to Tower Street, and there saw it all on fire, at the Trinity House on that side, and the Dolphin Tavern on this side, which was very near us; and the fire with extraordinary vehemence. Now begins the practice of blowing up of houses in Tower Street, those next the Tower, which at first did frighten people more than anything; but it stopped the fire where it was done, it bringing down the houses to the ground in the same places they stood, and then it was easy to quench what little fire was in it, though it kindled nothing almost.

W. Hewer this day went to see how his mother did, and comes late home, telling us how he hath been forced to remove her to Islington, her house in Pye Corner being burned; so that the fire is got so far that way, and to the Old Bailey, and was running down to Fleet Street; and Paul's is burned, and all Cheapside. I wrote to my father this night, but the posthouse being burned, the letter could not go.

231

5th. I lay down in the office again upon W. Hewer's quilt, being mighty weary, and sore in my feet with going till I was hardly able to stand. About two in the morning my wife calls me up, and tells me of new cries of fire, it being come to Barking Church, which is at the bottom of our lane. I up; and finding it so, resolved presently to take her away, and did, and took my gold, which was about £2350, W. Hewer and Jane down by Proundy's boat to Woolwich; but Lord! what a sad sight it was by moonlight to see the whole city almost on fire, that you might see it as plain at Woolwich, as if you were by it. There, when I came, I find the gates shut, but no guard kept at all; which troubled me, because of discourses now begun, that there is a plot in it, and that the French had done it. I got the gates open, and to Mr. Shelden's, where I locked up my gold, and charged my wife and W. Hewer never to leave the room without one of them in it, night or day.

So back again, by the way seeing my goods well in the lighters at Deptford, and watched well by people. Home, and whereas I expected to have seen our house on fire, it being now about seven o'clock, it was not. But to the fire, and there find greater hopes than I expected; for my confidence of finding our office on fire was such, that I dared not ask anybody how it was with us, till I came and saw it was not burned. But, going to the fire, I find, by the blowing up of houses, and the great help given by the workmen out of the King's yards, sent up by Sir W. Penn, there is a good stop given to it, as well at Mark Lane End as ours; it having only burned the dial of Barking Church, and part of the porch, and was there quenched. I up to the top of Barking steeple, and there saw the saddest sight of desolation that I ever saw; everywhere great fires, oil-cellars, and brimstone, and other things burning. I became afraid to stay there long, and therefore down again as fast as I could, the fire being spread as far as I could see it; and to Sir W. Penn's, and there ate a piece of cold meat, having eaten nothing since Sunday but the remains of Sunday's dinner.

Here I met with Mr. Young and Whistler; and, having removed all my things, and received good hopes that the fire at our end is stopped, they and I walked into the town, and find Fenchurch Street, Gracious Street, and Lombard Street all in dust. The Exchange a sad sight, nothing standing there of all the statues or pillars but Sir Thomas Gresham's picture in the corner. Into Moorfields, our feet ready to burn, walking through the town among the hot coals, and find that full of people, and poor wretches carrying their goods there, and everybody keeping his goods together by themselves; and a great blessing it is to them that it is fair weather for them to keep abroad night and day; drank there, and paid twopence for a plain penny loaf. Thence homeward, having passed through Cheapside, and Newgate market, all burned; and seen Anthony Joyce's house in fire; and took up, which I keep by me, a piece of glass of the Mercers' chapel in the street, where much more was, so melted and buckled with the heat of the fire like parchment. I also did see a poor cat taken out of a hole in a chimney, joining to the wall of the Exchange, with the hair all burnt off the body, and yet alive. So home at night, and find there good hopes of saving our office; but great endeavors of watching all night, and having men ready; and so we lodged them in the office, and had drink and bread and cheese for them. And I lay down and slept a good night about midnight: though, when I rose, I heard that there had been a great alarm of French and Dutch being risen, which proved nothing. But it is a strange thing to see how long this time did look since Sunday, having been always full of variety of actions, and little sleep, that it looked like a week or more, and I had forgot almost the day of the week.

6th. Up about five o'clock, and met Mr. Gauden at the gate of the office, I intending to go out, as I used, every now and then, today, to see how the fire is, to call our men to Bishop's Gate, where no fire had yet been near, and there is now one broke out: which did give great grounds to people, and to me too, to think that there is some kind of plot in this, on which many by this time have been taken, and it hath been dangerous for any stranger to walk in the streets, but I went with the men, and we did put it out in a little time; so that that was well again. It was pretty to see how hard the women did work in the canals, sweeping water; but then they would scold for drink, and be as drunk as devils. I saw good butts of sugar broke open in the street, and people give and take handfuls out, and put into beer, and drink it. And now all being pretty well, I took boat, and over to Southwark, and took boat on the other side the bridge, and so to Westminster, thinking to shift myself, being all in dirt from top to bottom; but could not there find any place to buy a shirt or a pair of gloves, Westminster Hall being full of people's goods, those in Westminster having removed all their goods, and the Exchequer money put into vessels to carry to Nonsuch; but to the Swan, and there was trimmed: and then to White Hall, but saw nobody; and so home.

A sad sight to see how the river looks: no houses nor church near it to the Temple, where it stopped. At home, did go with Sir W. Batten, and our neighbor, Knightly, who, with one more, was the only man of any fashion left in all the neighborhood thereabouts, they all removing their goods, and leaving their houses to the mercy of the fire; to Sir R. Ford's, and there dined in an earthen platter—a fried breast of mutton; a great many of us, but very merry, and indeed as good a meal, though as ugly a one as ever I had in my life.

Thence down to Deptford, and there with great satisfaction landed all my goods at Sir G. Carteret's safe, and nothing missed I could see or hear. This being done to my great content, I home, and to Sir W. Batten's, and there, with Sir R. Ford, Mr. Knightly, and one Withers, a professed lying rogue, supped well, and mighty merry, and our fears over. From them to the office, and there slept with the office full of laborers, who talked, and slept, and walked all night long there. But strange it is to see Clothworkers' Hall on fire these three days and nights in one body of flame, it being the cellar full of oil.

7th. Up by five o'clock; and, blessed be God! find all well; and by water to Pane's Wharf. Walked thence, and saw all the town burned, and a miserable sight of Paul's church, with all the roofs fallen, and the body of the choir fallen into St. Faith's; Paul's school also, Ludgate, and Fleet Street. My father's house, and the church, and a good part of the Temple the like. So to Creed's lodging, near the New Exchange, and there find him laid down upon a bed; the house all unfurnished, there being fears of the fire's coming to them. There borrowed a shirt from him, and washed.

To Sir W. Coventry at St. James's, who lay without curtains, having removed all his goods; as the King at White Hall, and everybody had done, and was doing. He hopes we shall have no public distractions upon this fire, which is what everybody fears, because of the talk of the French having a hand in it. And it is a proper time for discontents; all men's minds are full of care to protect themselves and save their goods: the militia is in arms everywhere. Our fleets, he tells me, have been in sight of one another, and most unhappily by foul weather were parted, to our great loss, as in reason they do conclude; the Dutch being come out only to make a show, and please their people; but in very bad condition as to stores, victuals, and men. They are at Boulogne, and our fleet come to St. Ellen's. We have got nothing, but have lost one ship, but he knows not what. Thence to the Swan, and there drank; and so home, and find all well. My Lord Brouncker, at Sir W. Batten's, tells us the General is sent for, to come to advise with the King about business at this juncture, and to keep all quiet; which is great honor to him, but I am sure is but a piece of dissimulation.

So home, and did give orders for my house to be made clean; and then down to Woolwich, and there find all well. Dined, and Mrs. Markham came to see my wife. This day our Merchants first met at Gresham College, which, by proclamation, is to be their Exchange. Strange to hear what is bid for houses all up and down here; a friend of Sir W. Rider's having £150 for what he used to let for £40 per annum. Much dispute where the Custom House shall be; thereby the growth of the City again to be foreseen. My Lord Treasurer, they say, and others, would have it at the other end of the town. I home late to Sir W. Penn's, who did give me a bed, but without curtains or hangings, all being down. So here I went the first time into a naked bed, only my drawers on; and did sleep pretty well: but still both sleeping and waking had a fear of fire in my heart, that I took little rest. People do all the world over cry out of the simplicity of my Lord Mayor in general; and more particularly in this business of the fire, laying it all upon him. A proclamation is come out for markets to be kept at Leadenhall and Mile End Green, and several other places about the town; and Tower Hill, and all churches to be set open to receive poor people.

8th. I stopped with Sir G. Carteret to desire him to go with us, and to enquire after money. But the first he cannot do, and the other as little, or says, "When can we get any?" or "What shall we do for it?" He, it seems, is employed in the correspondence between the City and the King every day, in settling of things. I find him full of trouble to think how things will go. I left him, and to St. James's, where we met first at Sir W. Coventry's chamber, and there did what business we could, without any books. Our discourse, as everything else, was confused. The fleet is at Portsmouth, there staying a wind to carry them to the Downs, or towards Boulogne, where they say the Dutch fleet is gone, and stays. We concluded upon private meetings for a while, not having any money to satisfy any people that may come to us. I bought two eels upon the Thames, cost me six shillings.

Thence with Sir W. Batten to the Cock-pit, whither the Duke of Albemarle is come. It seems the King holds him so necessary at this time, that he hath sent for him, and will keep him here. Indeed, his interest in the City, being acquainted, and his care in keeping things quiet, is reckoned that, wherein he will be very serviceable. We to him: he is courted in appearance by everybody. He is very kind to us; and I

235

perceive he lays by all business of the fleet at present, and minds the City, and is now hastening to Gresham College, to discourse with the aldermen. Sir W. Batten and I home, where met my brother John, come to town to see how things are done with us, and then presently he with me to Gresham College; where infinity of people, partly through novelty to see the new place, and partly to find out and hear what is become one man of another. I met with many people undone, and more that have extraordinary great losses. People speaking their thoughts variously about the beginning of the fire, and the rebuilding of the City.

Then to Sir W. Batten's, and took my brother with me, and there dined with a great company of neighbors, and much good discourse; among others, of the low spirits of some rich men in the City, in sparing any encouragement to the poor people that wrought for the saving their houses. Among others, Alderman Starling, a very rich man, without children, the fire next door to him in our lane, after our men had saved his house, did give 2*s*. 6*d*. among thirty of them, and did quarrel with some that would remove the rubbish out of the way of the fire, saying that they came to steal. Sir W. Coventry told me of another this morning in Holborn, which he showed the King: that when it was offered to stop the fire near his house for such a reward that came but to 2*s*. 6*d*. a man, among the neighbors, he would give but 18*d*. Thence to Bednall Green by coach, my brother with me, and saw all well there, and fetched away my journal book, to enter for five days past. I was much frighted and kept awake in my bed, by some noise I heard a great while below stairs; and the boys not coming up to me when I knocked. It was by their discovery of some people stealing some neighbors' wine that lay in vessels in the streets. So to sleep; and all well all night.

9th. (Sunday.) Up; and was trimmed, and sent my brother to Woolwich to my wife, to dine with her. I to church, where our parson made a melancholy but good sermon; and many and most in the church cried, specially the women. The church mighty full; but few of fashion, and most strangers. I walked to Bednall Green, and there dined well, but a bad venison pasty, at Sir W. Rider's. Good people they are, and good discourse, and his daughter Middleton a fine woman, discreet. Thence home, and to church again, and there preached Dean Harding; but, methinks, a bad, poor sermon, though proper for the time; nor eloquent, in saying at this time that the City is reduced from a large folio to a decimo-tertio. So to my office, there to write down my journal, and take leave of my brother, whom I send back this afternoon, though raining, which it hath not done a good while before. But I had no room or convenience for him here till my house was fitted; but I was very kind to him, and do take very well of him his journey. I did give him 40s. for his pocket, and so, he being gone, and it presently raining, I was troubled for him, though it is good for the fire. Anon to Sir W. Penn's to bed, and made my boy Tom read me asleep.

10th. All the morning clearing our cellars, and breaking in pieces all my old lumber to make room and to prevent fire. And then to Sir W. Batten's and dined; and there hear that Sir W. Rider says that the town is full of the report of the wealth that is in his house, and he would be glad that his friends would provide for the safety of their goods there. This made me get a cart; and thither, and there brought my money all away. Took a hackney-coach myself, the hackney-coaches now standing at Allgate. Much wealth indeed there is at his house. Blessed be God! I got all mine well thence, and lodged it in my office; but vexed to have all the world see it, and with Sir W. Batten, who would have taken away my hands before they were stowed. But by and by comes brother Balty from sea, which I was glad of; and so got him and Mr. Tooker, and the boy, to watch with them all in the office all night, while I went down to my wife to Woolwich.

22d. My house is so clean as I never saw it, or any other house, in my life, and everything in as good condition as ever before the fire; but with about £20 cost, one way or other, besides about £20 charge, in removing my goods, and do not find that I have lost anything but two little pictures of ships and sea, and a little gold frame for one of my sea-cards. My glazier, indeed, is so full of work that I cannot get him to come to perfect my house. In the afternoon I paid for the two lighters that carried my goods to Deptford, and they cost me £8.

NOVEMBER 1st. Up, and was presented by Burton, one of our smiths' wives, with a very noble cake, which I presently resolved to have my wife go with today, and some wine, and house-warm Betty Michell, which she readily resolved to do. From dinner, my wife and my brother, and W. Hewer and Barker, away to Betty Michell's to Shadwell.

2d. On board the Ruby, French prize, the only ship of war we have taken from any of our enemies this year. It seems a very good ship, but with galleries quite round the stern, to walk in as a balcony, which will be taken down. She had also about forty good brass guns, but will make little amends to our loss in the Prince. I also did buy some apples and pork, by the same token the butcher commended it as the best in England for cloth and color. And for his beef, says he, "look how fat it is; the lean appears only here and there a speck, like beauty-spots."

14th. Dr. Croone told me that at the meeting at Gresham College* tonight which, it seems, they now have every Wednesday again, there was a pretty experiment of the blood of one dog let out, till he died, into the body of another on one side, while all his own ran out on the other side. The first died upon the place, and the other very well, and likely to do well. This did give occasion to many pretty wishes, as of the blood of a Quaker to be let into an Archbishop, and such like; but as Dr. Croone says, it may, if it takes, be of mighty use to man's health, for the mending of bad blood by borrowing from a better body.

16th. This noon I met with Mr. Hooke, and he tells me the dog which was filled with another dog's blood at the College the other day is very well and like to be so as ever, and doubts not its being found of great use to men; and so does Dr. Whistler, who dined with us at the tavern.

December 31st. To my accounts, wherein, at last, I find them clear and right; but, to my great discontent, do find that my gettings this year have been £573 less than my last: it being this year in all but £2986; whereas the last, I got £3560. And then again my spendings this year have exceeded my spendings the last by £644: my whole spendings last year being but £509; whereas this year, it appears I have spent £1154, which is a sum not fit to be said that ever I should spend in one year before I am master of a better estate than I am. Yet, blessed be God! and I pray God make me thankful for it, I do find myself worth in money, all good, above £6200; which is above £1800 more than I was the last year.

Thus ends this year of public wonder and mischief to this nation, and therefore generally wished by all people to have an end. Myself and family well, having four maids and one clerk, Tom, in my house, and my brother, now with me, to spend time in order to his preferment. Our health all well, public matters in a most sad condition; seamen discouraged for want of pay, and are not to be governed: nor, as matters are now, can any fleet go out next year. Our enemies, French and Dutch, great, and grow more by our poverty. The Parliament

* The Royal Society

backward in raising, because jealous of the spending of the money; the City less and less likely to be built again, everybody settling elsewhere, and nobody encouraged to trade. A sad, vicious, negligent Court, and all sober men there fearful of the ruin of the whole kingdom this next year; from which good God deliver us! One thing I reckon remarkable in my own condition is that I am come to abound in good plate, so as at all entertainments to be served wholly with silver plates, having two dozen and a half.

1667

J ANUARY 23d. Took up my wife and Mercer to Temple Bar to the Ordinary, and had a dish of meat for them, they having not dined, and thence to the King's house, and there saw *The Humorous Lieutenant:* a silly play, I think; only the Spirit in it that grows very tall and then sinks again to nothing, having two heads breeding upon one, and then Knipp's singing did please us. Here, in a box above, we spied Mrs. Pierce; and, going out, they called us, and so we stayed for them; and Knipp took us all in, and brought to us Nelly,* a most pretty woman, who acted the great part of Cœlia today very fine, and did it pretty well: I kissed her and so did my wife; and a mighty pretty soul she is. We also saw Mrs. Hall, which is my little Roman-nose black girl, who is mighty pretty: she is usually called Betty. Knipp made us stay in a box and see the dancing preparatory to tomorrow for *The Goblins,* a play of Suckling's, not acted these twenty-five years; which was pretty; and so away thence, pleased with this sight also, and specially kissing of Nell.

In our way home, we find the Guards of horse in the street, and hear the occasion to be news that the seamen are in a mutiny; which put me into a great fright; and, when I come home, I hear of no disturbance there of the seamen, but that one of them, being arrested today, others do go and rescue him.

24th. At the office, we were frighted with news of fire at Sir W. Batten's by a chimney taking fire, and it put me into much fear and trouble, but with a great many hands and pains it was soon stopped. I home, where most of my company come of this end of the town—

* Nell Gwynn, favored by King Charles II

Mercer and her sister, Mr. Batelier and Pembleton, my Lady Penn, and Peg, and Mr. Lowther, but did not stay long and I believe it was by Sir W. Penn's order; for they had a great mind to have stayed, and also Captain Rolt. And anon, at about seven or eight o'clock, comes Mr. Harris, of the Duke's playhouse, and brings Mrs. Pierce with him, and also one dressed like a country maid with a straw hat on; and, at first, I could not tell who it was, though I expected Knipp: but it was she coming off the stage just as she acted this day in *The Goblins;* a merry jade. Now my house is full, and four fiddlers that play well. Harris I first took to my closet; and I find him a very curious and understanding person in all pictures and other things, and a man of fine conversation; and so is Rolt.

So away with all my company down to the Office, and there fell to dancing, and continued at it an hour or two, there coming Mrs. Anne Jones, a merchant's daughter hard by, who dances well, and all in mighty good humor, and danced with great pleasure; and then sang and then danced, and then sang many things of three voices—both Harris and Rolt singing their parts excellently. Among other things, Harris sang his Irish song—the strangest in itself, and the prettiest sung by him, that ever I heard.

Then to supper in the Office, a cold, good supper, and wondrous merry. Here was Mrs. Turner, also, and Mrs. Markham: after supper to dancing again and singing, and so continued till almost three in the morning, and then, with extraordinary pleasure, broke up—only towards morning, Knipp fell a little ill, and so my wife home with her to put her to bed, and we continued dancing and singing; and among other things, our Mercer unexpectedly did happen to sing an Italian song I know not, of which they two sung the other two parts—two that did almost ravish me and made me in love with her more than ever with her singing. As late as it was, yet Rolt and Harris would go home tonight, and walked it, though I had a bed for them; and it proved dark, and a misty night, and very windy.

The company being all gone to their homes, I up with Mrs. Pierce to Knipp, who was in bed; and we waked her, and sang a song, and then left my wife to see Mrs. Pierce in bed to her in our best chamber, and so to bed myself, my mind mightily satisfied: only the music did not please me, they not being contented with less than 30s.

FEBRUARY 12th. With my Lord Brouncker by coach to his house, there to hear some Italian music: and here we met Tom Killigrew, Sir Robert Murray, and the Italian Signor Baptista, who hath proposed a play in Italian for the Opera, which T. Killigrew do intend to have up; and here he did sing one of the acts. He himself is the poet as well as the musician; which is very much, and did sing the whole from the words without any music, and played all along upon a harpsichord most admirably, and the composition most excellent. The words I did not understand, and so know not how they are fitted, but believe very well, and all in the recitative very fine. But I perceive there is a proper accent in every country's discourse, and that do reach in their setting of notes to words, which, therefore, cannot be natural to anybody else but them; so that I am not so much smitten with it as, it may be, I should be if I were acquainted with their accent. But the whole composition is certainly most excellent; and the poetry, T. Killigrew and Sir R. Murray, who understood the words, did say most excellent. I confess I was mightily pleased with the music. He pretends not to voice, though it be good, but not excellent.

This done, T. Killigrew and I to talk: and he tells me how the audience at his house is not above half so much as it used to be before the late fire. That Knipp is like to make the best actor that ever came upon the stage, she understanding so well: that they are going to give her £30 a year more. That the stage is now by his pains a thousand times better and more glorious than ever heretofore. Now, wax candles, and many of them; then, not above 3lbs. of tallow: now, all things civil, no rudeness anywhere; then, as in a bear-garden: then, two or three fiddlers; now, nine or ten of the best: then, nothing but rushes upon the ground, and everything else mean; now, all otherwise: then, the Queen seldom and the King never would come; now, not the King only for state, but all civil people do think they may come as well as any.

He tells me that he hath gone several times, eight or ten times, he tells me, hence to Rome, to hear good music; so much he loves it, though he never did sing or play a note. That he hath ever endeavored in the late King's time, and in this, to introduce good music, but he never could do it, there never having been any music here better than ballads. And says, "Hermit poor" and "Chevy Cheese" was all the music we had; and yet no ordinary fiddlers get so much money as ours do here, which speaks our rudeness still. That he hath gathered our Italians from several courts in Christendom, to come to make a concert for the King, which he do give £200 a year apiece to: but badly paid, and do keep four ridiculous gundilows,* he having got the King

* Gondolas

to put them away, and lay out money this way; and indeed I do commend him for it, for I think it is a very noble undertaking.

He do intend to have sometimes these operas performed at the two present theaters, since he is defeated in what he intended in Moorfields on purpose for it; and he tells me plainly that the City audience was as good as the Court, but now they are most gone. Baptista tells me that Giacomo Carissimi is still alive at Rome, who was master to Vinnecotio, who is one of the Italians that the King hath here, and the chief composer of them. My great wonder is, how this man do keep in memory so perfectly the music of the whole act, both for the voice and the instrument too. I confess I do admire it: but in recitative the sense much helps him, for there is but one proper way of discoursing and giving the accents. Having done our discourse, we all took coaches, my Lord's and T. Killigrew's, and to Mrs. Knipp's chamber, where this Italian is to teach her to sing her part. And so we all thither, and there she did sing an Italian song or two very fine, while he played the bass upon a harpsichord there; and exceedingly taken I am with her singing, and believe that she will do miracles at that and acting. Her little girl is mighty pretty and witty.

18th. To the King's house, to *The Maid's Tragedy;* but vexed all the while with two talking ladies and Sir Charles Sedley; yet pleased to hear their discourse, he being a stranger. And one of the ladies would and did sit with her mask on all the play, and being exceeding witty as ever I heard a woman, did talk most pleasantly with him; but was, I believe, a virtuous woman and of quality. He would fain know who she was, but she would not tell; yet did give him many pleasant hints of her knowledge of him, by that means setting his brains at work to find out who she was, and did give him leave to use all means to find out who she was, but pulling off her mask. He was mighty witty, and she also making sport with him very inoffensively, that a more pleasant exchange I never heard. But by that means lost the pleasure of the play wholly, to which now and then Sir Charles Sedley's exceptions against both words and pronouncing were very pretty.

25th. Lay long in bed, talking with pleasure with my poor wife, how she used to make coal fires, and wash my foul clothes with her own hand for me, poor wretch! in our little room at my Lord Sandwich's; for which I ought forever to love and admire her, and do; and persuade myself she would do the same thing again, if God should reduce us to it. At my goldsmith's did observe the King's new medal, where, in little, there is Mrs. Stuart's face as well-done as ever I saw anything in my whole life, I think: and a pretty thing it is that he should choose her face to represent Britannia by.

MARCH 2d. After dinner with my wife to the King's house to see *The Maiden Queen,* a new play of Dryden's, mightily commended for the regularity of it, and the strain and wit; and, the truth is, there is a comical part done by Nell, which is Florimell, that I never can hope ever to see the like done again by man or woman. The King and Duke of York were at the play. But so great performance of a comical part was never, I believe, in the world before as Nell do this, both as a mad girl, then most and best of all when she comes in like a young gallant; and hath the motions and carriage of a spark the most that ever I saw any man have. It makes me, I confess, admire her.

MAY 1st. To Westminster; in the way meeting many milkmaids with their garlands upon their pails, dancing with a fiddler before them; and saw pretty Nelly standing at her lodgings' door in Drury Lane in her smock sleeves and bodice, looking upon one: she seemed a mighty pretty creature.

JULY 14th. (Lord's day.) Up with my wife a little before four to make us ready; and by and by Mrs. Turner came to us, by agreement, and she and I stayed talking below, while my wife dressed herself, which vexed me that she was so long about it, keeping us till past five o'clock before she was ready. She ready; and taking some bottles of wine and beer and some cold fowl with us, we took coach and four horses which I had provided last night, and so away. A very fine day and so towards Epsom, talking all the way pleasantly, and particularly of the pride and ignorance of Mrs. Lowther, in having her train carried up. The country very fine, only the way very dusty.

To Epsom, by eight o'clock, to the well; where much company, and I drank the water: they did not, but I did drink four pints. And to the town, to the King's Head; and hear that my Lord Buckhurst and Nelly are lodged at the next house, and Sir Charles Sedley with them: and keep a merry house. Poor girl! I pity her; but more the loss of her at the King's house. W. Hewer rode with us, and I left him and the women, and by myself walked to church, where few people to what I expected, and none I knew, but all the Houblons, brothers, and them after sermon I did salute, and walk with towards my inn. James did tell me that I was the only happy man of the Navy, of whom, he says, during all this freedom the people have taken to speaking treason, he hath not heard one bad word of me, which is a great joy to me; for I hear the same of others, but know that I have deserved as well as most.

We parted to meet anon, and I to my women into a better room, which the people of the house borrowed for us, and there to a good dinner, and were merry, and Pembleton came to us, who happened to be in the house, and there talked and was merry. After dinner, he gone, we all lay down, the day being wonderful hot, to sleep, and each of us took a good nap, and then rose; and here Tom Wilson came to see me, and sat and talked an hour; and I perceive he hath been much acquainted with Dr. Fuller and Dr. Pierson and several of the great cavalier parsons during the late troubles; and I was glad to hear him talk of them, which he did very ingenuously, and very much of Dr. Fuller's art of memory, which he did tell me several instances of. By and by he parted, and we took coach to take the air, there being a fine breeze abroad; and I carried them to the well, and there filled some bottles of water to carry home with me; and there I talked with the two women that farm the well, at £12 per annum, of the lord of the manor. Mr. Evelyn with his lady, and also my Lord George Barkeley's lady, and their fine daughter, that the King of France liked so well, and did dance so rich in jewels before the King at the ball I was at, at our Court, last winter, and also their son, a Knight of the Bath, were at church this morning. Here W. Hewer's horse broke loose, and we had the sport to see him taken again.

Then I carried them to see my cousin Pepys's house, and walked round about it, and they liked it, as indeed it deserves, very well, and is a pretty place; and then I walked them to the wood hard by, and there got them in the thickets till they had lost themselves, and I could not find the way into any of the walks in the wood, which indeed are very pleasant, if I could have found them. At last got out of the wood again; and I, by leaping down the little bank, coming out of the wood, did sprain my right foot, which brought me great pain, but presently, with walking, it went away for the present, and so the women and W. Hewer and I walked upon the downs, where a flock of sheep was; and the most pleasant and innocent sight that ever I saw in my life.

We found a shepherd and his little boy reading, far from any houses or sight of people, the Bible to him; so I made the boy read to me, which he did, with the forced tone that children do usually read, that

244

was mighty pretty, and then I did give him something, and went to the father, and talked with him; and I find he had been a servant in my cousin Pepys's house, and told me what was become of their old servants. He did content himself mightily in my liking his boy's reading, and did bless God for him, the most like one of the old patriarchs that ever I saw in my life, and it brought those thoughts of the old age of the world in my mind for two or three days after.

We took notice of his woolen knit stockings of two colors mixed, and of his shoes shod with iron, both at the toe and heels, and with great nails in the soles of his feet, which was mighty pretty: and, taking notice of them, "Why," says the poor man, "the downs, you see, are full of stones, and we are fain to shoe ourselves thus; and these," says he, "will make the stones fly till they ring before me." I did give the poor man something, for which he was mighty thankful. He values his dog mightily, that would turn a sheep any way which he would have him, when he goes to fold them: told me there was about eighteen score sheep in his flock, and that he hath four shillings a week the year round for keeping them: and Mrs. Turner, in the common fields here, did gather one of the prettiest nosegays that ever I saw in my life.

So to our coach, and through Mr. Minnes's wood, and looked upon Mr. Evelyn's house; and so over the common, and through Epsom to our inn, on the way stopping a poor woman with her milk-pail, and in one of my gilt tumblers, did drink our bellyfuls of milk, better than any cream; and so to our inn, and there had a dish of cream, but it was sour, and so had no pleasure in it; and so paid our reckoning and took coach, it being about seven at night, and passed and saw the people walking with their wives and children to take the air, and we set out for home, the sun by and by going down, and we in the cool of the evening all the way with much pleasure home, talking and pleasing ourselves with the pleasures of this day's work. Mrs. Turner mightily pleased with my resolution, which, I tell her, is never to keep a country-house, but to keep a coach, and with my wife on Saturday to go sometimes for a day to this place, and then to another place; and there is more variety and as little charge, and no trouble, as there is in a country-house. Anon it grew dark, and we had the pleasure to see several glowworms, which were mighty pretty, but my foot begins more and more to pain me, which Mrs. Turner, by keeping her warm hand upon it, did much ease; but when we came home, which was just at eleven at night, I was not able to walk from the lane's end to my house without being helped. So to bed, and there had a cerecloth laid to my foot, but in great pain all night long.

21st. (Lord's day.) I and my wife and Mercer up by water to Barn Elms, where we walked by moonshine, and called at Lambeth, and drank and had cold meat in the boat, and did eat and sang, and down home, by almost twelve at night, very fine and pleasant, only could not sing ordinary songs with the freedom that otherwise I would. Here Mercer tells me that the pretty maid of the Ship Tavern is married there, which I am glad of. So having spent this night, with much serious pleasure to consider that I am in condition to fling away an angel * in such a refreshment to myself and family, we home and to bed, leaving Mercer by the way at her own door.

AUGUST 18th. To Cree Church, to see it how it is: but I find no alteration there, as they say there was, for my Lord Mayor and aldermen to come to sermon, as they do every Sunday, as they did formerly to Paul's. There dined with me Mr. Turner and his daughter Betty. Betty is grown a fine young lady as to carriage and discourse. We had a good haunch of venison, powdered and boiled, and a good dinner. I walked towards White Hall, but, being wearied, turned into St. Dunstan's Church, where I heard an able sermon of the minister of the place; and stood by a pretty, modest maid, whom I did labor to take by the hand; but she would not, but got farther and farther from me; and, at last, I could perceive her to take pins out of her pocket to prick me if I should touch her again—which seeing, I did forbear, and was glad I did spy her design. And then I fell to gaze upon another pretty maid in a pew close to me and she on me; and I did go about to take her by the hand, which she suffered a little, and then withdrew. So the sermon ended, and the church broke up, and my amours ended also. Took coach home and there took up my wife to Islington.

NOVEMBER 29th. Waked about seven o'clock this morning with a noise I supposed I heard near our chamber of knocking, which by and by increased: and I, more awake, could distinguish it better. I then waked my wife and both of us wondered at it, and lay so great a while, while that increased, and at last heard it plainer, knocking, as if it were breaking down a window for people to get out; and then removing stools and chairs; and plainly, by and by, going up and down our stairs. We lay, both of us, afraid; yet I would have rose, but my

* Old coin, valued at ten shillings

wife would not let me. Besides, I could not do it without making noise; and we did both conclude that thieves were in the house, but wondered what our people did, whom we thought either killed, or afraid, as we were. Thus we lay till the clock struck eight, and high day. At last I removed my gown and slippers safely to the other side of the bed over my wife; and there safely rose, and put on my gown and breeches, and then, with a firebrand in my hand, safely opened the door, and neither saw nor heard anything. Then with fear, I confess, I went to the maid's chamber door, and found all quiet and safe. Called Jane up and went down safely, and opened my chamber door, where all well. Then more freely about, and to the kitchen, where the cook-maid up, and all safe. So up again, and when Jane came, and we demanded whether she heard no noise, she said, "Yes, but was afraid," but rose with the other maid, and found nothing; but heard a noise in the great stack of chimneys that goes from Sir J. Minnes through our house; and so we sent, and their chimneys have been swept this morning, and the noise was that, and nothing else. It is one of the most extraordinary accidents in my life, and gives ground to think of Don Quixote's adventures how people may be surprised, and the more from an accident last night, that our young tomcat did leap down our stairs from top to bottom, at two leaps and frighted us, that we could not tell well whether it was the cat or a spirit, and do sometimes think this morning that the house might be haunted.

James Otis

ARGUES AGAINST

THE WRITS OF

ASSISTANCE

February 24, 1761

HOME COURSE APPRECIATION

JAMES OTIS (1725–1783) WAS ONE OF THOSE MEN who thrive on contention and who are at their best in troubled times. In this respect, fortune smiled on him, for he came of age at a time when the American colonists were beginning to protest against the oppressive colonial policies of Britain.

Otis graduated from Harvard in 1743 and then read law in the office of Jeremiah Gridley. Shortly after being admitted to the bar, he was one of the most successful lawyers in the colonies. His mind was quick and supple, his flow of words brilliant. He was interested in the theory and history of the law and was a keen student of the classics. He was particularly famous and successful because he did not base his cases on legal technicalities, but tried to understand the basic intention of the law. In token of his unusual learning, Governor Pownall appointed him King's advocate-general of the vice-admiralty court in Boston.

In 1760, the British government ordered its agents in the colonies to collect the taxes on sugar authorized by the Sugar Act of 1733. Colonial merchants had ignored the act and the authorities had not troubled to enforce it. The royal customs officers promptly applied to the court for writs of assistance to entitle them to search Boston houses for sugar on which import duties had not been paid. As the King's advocate-general, it was Otis' task to argue for the writs. Instead, he resigned his well-paid position and with Oxenbridge Thatcher undertook the case of the Boston merchants who contended that the writs were illegal.

The case was tried in February, 1761, in Boston's Old State House. Otis' good friend and former law teacher, Jeremiah Gridley argued the case for the Crown. While much of the text of Otis' long speech has been lost, there is no doubt that he created a sensation. "Otis was a flame of fire!" wrote John Adams. "He hurried away everything before him. American independence was then and there born; the seeds of patriots and heroes were then and there sown." Tradition assigns to James Otis and to this occasion the watchwords of the American Revolution, "Taxation without representation is tyranny."

Otis lost his case. But his arguments against the writs of assistance gave the colonies a legal basis for their quarrel with the arbitrary power of the mother country. For what Otis did was to rise above mere quibbles about some section of the law. He appealed, as throughout history men have so often appealed, to a higher law, a law beyond mere acts of parliament, to the natural law which no man-made statute can violate with impunity.

After his famous speech, Otis continued to wield great influence in the cause of American independence. He took part in the activities of the "Sons of Liberty"; he spoke boldly and wrote effectively for the cause of the colonies. In 1769 he was severely wounded during a fight in the British Coffee House when a British officer struck him on the head with a dagger. The quarrel arose because Otis had publicly branded a number of British officials as liars. The blow affected Otis' reason and although he had lucid intervals he became quite insane. In 1775, when the bullets were flying on Bunker Hill, Otis was found in the thick of them, firing a borrowed musket and forwarding the cause of liberty with sword and shot, as he had done previously with pen and tongue. He died as dramatically as he had lived, struck down by a bolt of lightning on May 23, 1783.

May it please your Honors,

I WAS DESIRED by one of the Court to look into the books, and consider the question now before them concerning Writs of Assistance. I have accordingly considered it, and now appear not only in obedience to your order, but likewise in behalf of the inhabitants of this town, who have presented another petition, and out of regard to the liberties of the subject. And I take this opportunity to declare, that whether under a fee or not, (for in such a cause as this I despise a fee,) I will to my dying day oppose with all the powers and faculties God has given me, all such instruments of slavery on the one hand, and villainy on the other, as this writ of assistance is.

It appears to me the worst instrument of arbitrary power, the most destructive of English liberty and the fundamental principles of law, that ever was found in an English law book. I must therefore beg your Honors' patience and attention to the whole range of an argument that may perhaps appear uncommon in many things, as well as to points of learning that are more remote and unusual: that the whole tendency of my design may the more easily be perceived, the conclusions better descend, and the force of them be better felt. I shall not think much of my pains in this cause, as I engaged in it from principle. I was solicited to argue this cause as Advocate General; and because I would not, I have been charged with desertion from my office. To this charge I can give a very sufficient answer. I renounced that office, and I argue this cause from the same principle; and I argue it with the greater pleasure, as it is in favor of British liberty, at a time when we hear the greatest monarch upon earth declaring from his throne, that he glories in the name of Briton, and that the privileges of his people are dearer to him than the most valuable prerogatives of his crown; and it is in opposition to a kind of power, the exercise of which in former periods of English history, cost one king of England his head, and another his throne. I have taken more pains in this cause, than I ever will take again, although my engaging in this and another popular cause has raised much resentment. But I think I can sincerely declare, that I cheerfully submit myself to every odious name for conscience' sake: and from my soul I despise all those whose guilt, malice, or folly has made them my foes. Let the consequences be what they will, I am determined to proceed. The only principles of public conduct that are worthy of a gentleman or a man, are to sacrifice estate, ease, health, and applause, and even life, to the sacred calls of his country.

These manly sentiments, in private life, make the good citizen; in public life, the patriot and the hero. I do not say, that when brought to the test, I shall be invincible. I pray God I may never be brought to the melancholy trial, but if ever I should, it will be then known how far I can reduce to practice, principles which I know to be founded in truth. In the meantime I will proceed to the subject of this writ.

Your Honors will find in the old books concerning the office of a Justice of the Peace, precedents of general warrants to search suspected houses. But in more modern books, you will find only special warrants to search such and such houses, specially named, in which the complainant has before sworn that he suspects his goods are concealed; and will find it adjudged, that special warrants only are legal. In the same manner I rely on it, that the writ prayed for in this petition, being general, is illegal. It is a power that places the liberty of every man in the hands of every petty officer. I say I admit that special writs of assistance, to search special places, may be granted to certain persons on oath; but I deny that the writ now prayed for can be granted, for I beg leave to make some observations on the writ itself, before I proceed to other acts of Parliament.

In the first place, the writ is universal, being directed "to all and singular Justices, Sheriffs, Constables, and all other officers and subjects"; so that, in short, it is directed to every subject in the King's dominions. Every one with this writ may be a tyrant in a legal manner, also may control, imprison, or murder any one within the realm. In the next place, it is perpetual, there is no return. A man is accountable to no person for his doings. Every man may reign secure in his petty tyranny, and spread terror and desolation around him, until the trump of the archangel shall excite different emotions in his soul. In the third place, a person with this writ, in the daytime, may enter all houses, shops, etc., at will, and command all to assist him. Fourthly, by this writ, not only deputies, but even their menial servants, are allowed to lord it over us. What is this but to have the curse of Canaan with a witness on us; to be the servant of servants, the most despicable of God's creation?

Now one of the most essential branches of English liberty is the freedom of one's house. A man's house is his castle; and while he is quiet, he is as well guarded as a prince in his castle. This writ, if it should be declared legal, would totally annihilate this privilege. Customhouse officers may enter our houses when they please; we are commanded to permit their entry. Their menial servants may enter, may break locks, bars, and everything in their way: and whether they break through malice or revenge, no man, no court, can inquire. Bare suspicion without oath is sufficient. This wanton exercise of this power is not a chimerical suggestion of a heated brain. I will mention some facts.

Mr. Pew had one of these writs, and when Mr. Ware succeeded him, he endorsed this writ over to Mr. Ware: so that, these writs are negotiable from one officer to another; and so your Honors have no opportunity of judging the persons to whom this vast power is delegated. Another instance is this: Mr. Justice Walley had called this same Mr. Ware before him, by a constable, to answer for a breach of the Sabbath Day acts, or that of profane swearing. As soon as he had finished, Mr. Ware asked him if he had done. He replied: "Yes." "Well then," said Mr. Ware, "I will show you a little of my power. I command you to permit me to search your house for uncustomed goods"; and went on to search the house from the garret to the cellar; and then served the constable in the same manner! But to show another absurdity in this writ, if it should be established, I insist upon it every person by the 14th Charles II, has this power as well as the customhouse officers. The words are: "It shall be lawful for any person or persons authorized, etc." What a scene does this open! Every man prompted by revenge, ill humor, or wantonness to inspect the inside of his neighbor's house, may get a writ of assistance. Others will ask it from self-defense; one arbitrary exertion will provoke another, until society be involved in tumult and in blood.

253

THE

CONFESSIONS

OF

SAINT

AUGUSTINE

TRANSLATED BY

E. B. Pusey

A CONDENSATION

HOME COURSE APPRECIATION

ANYONE WHO SETS OUT TO EXPLAIN OR PRAISE Saint Augustine must surely feel some misgivings. For the work of Saint Augustine is one of those peaks in the history of thought which are so permanently established that they scarcely need definition or allow commendation. We can hardly talk about Augustine without using ideas which he helped to form; we can hardly judge him without using values which he did much to create. He was a philosopher, an orator, and a mighty figure not only of the Catholic Church but of Western civilization in general.

THE BACKGROUND OF AUGUSTINE'S LIFE

Saint Augustine was a man of remarkable achievements. But we cannot fully appreciate the enthusiasm and devotion which he aroused, until we see something of the background against which the great drama of his life was enacted. The world into which Augustine was born strikes us as one of the most confused ever. On one hand, a great empire was nearing its end, and the terrific weight of the past hung heavy on men's spirits; the physical world seemed worn beyond repair. On the other hand, a great new religion was taking shape, inspiring new hopes for a better world of the spirit. Working against both these forces was a great barbaric wave descending from the northern forests and the eastern plains, urged forward by even more primitive hordes from Asia. It was a time of growing darkness, of lawlessness and disorder. Ignorance was widespread and cruelty had become almost too common to be protested. Yet Christianity was strengthening the fragments of the civilized world. And at this time of decay and growth, of worldly pessimism and spiritual optimism,

Saint Augustine found the chaos a perpetual challenge to the resources of the soul and a great chance to establish a peace with God.

Aurelius Augustinus, son of Patricius and Monica, was born in the year 354 A.D. in the little town of Thagaste in Northern Africa. His family was probably pure Roman, though it is possible that there was some native blood in them. His father was a respectable landowner, hasty and irascible of temper, rough in manner, and little interested in any form of religion. His mother was a pious woman—meek, forgiving and, one guesses, just a shade too saintly for her rough-and-ready husband. From the first, Augustine's strongest attachment was for his mother; he had few good words to say for his father.

THAGASTE AND CARTHAGE

IN AUGUSTINE'S LIFETIME Thagaste lay in the Roman province of Numidia. The town is known today as Souk Ahras, and lies in Algeria. It is close to the edge of the Sahara desert on the south and to the shore of the Mediterranean Sea on the north. North Africa was not quite the stony, semi-arid land that it is today, nor was the climate quite so merciless. The native population consisted of tribesmen, dark-eyed and olive-complexioned, by no means uncivilized, but impetuous, violent and quick of temper.

The yoke of Roman rule and taxation had lain heavy on Numidia for a long time, but very little Roman culture had filtered down to Thagaste to console its disgruntled taxpayers. The town had a wretched little theater, a small bath, a dusty forum; it was a slow-paced, dull, rough-mannered town even for provincial Numidia. In good seasons the land, which was cultivated by slaves, yielded plentiful crops of oil and fruits. After harvest, the family of a wealthy landowner like Patricius might look forward to visiting the great city of Carthage, a hundred miles to the northwest, where it might enjoy the diversions of city life.

Carthage had long before been utterly destroyed by Rome in the Punic Wars of 241–146 B.C.; but she had been rebuilt over the centuries and now provided a metropolis thronging with dancing girls, pirates, priests of obscure cults and merchant princes whose only god was their belly. It was a splendid, barbaric city which Augustine visited as a child, and to which he came, in 371 A.D., as a student.

CARTHAGE AND ROME

Carthage was rich and magnificent, but Rome, although it was now corrupt and decadent, was still the spiritual center of the known world, still the symbol of empire and authority. Saint Augustine did not see Rome until he was thirty years old and he has not left us any distinct description of it. Apparently he did not feel very comfortable in the big city, because he never stayed long. He spoke Latin with a provincial, African accent, and seems to have been awed by the courtly ways of Roman society.

The Roman Empire had already passed into the hands of Christian emperors. In 323 Constantine had been drawn to the cross by the motto he had seen in the sky, *In hoc signo vinces* ("In this sign thou shalt conquer.") But the Empire, pressed from the North by Goths, Visigoths, Huns, Vandals and Teutons, was no longer in a position to conquer anyone. Valentinian and Theodosius did their best to stave off the inevitable; but in 410 the Visigoths, under Alaric, sacked the capital and slaughtered its helpless inhabitants.

From a practical point of view, the fall of Rome cannot have meant a great deal to the provincial towns strung out around the rim of the Mediterranean. The tribute they had been paying to Rome for hundreds of years, they would have to pay elsewhere. The seat of government had been for some time in Milan or Ravenna, or wherever the Emperor of the moment chose to hold his court. The Roman Forum, like the Roman Senate, was a mere figurehead; and the Roman Church, though famous and pre-eminent, was not yet recognized throughout Christendom as the Mother Church. Thus the importance of Rome was largely symbolic. But the loss of Rome to Alaric and its looting by his barbarian hordes struck a terrible blow at the conscience of the civilized world. Voices rose on every side, declaring that the city had been safe under pagan emperors; only when the leaders turned to Christianity did the barbarians succeed in defeating them. It was against those who drew this conclusion from the misfortunes of the age that Saint Augustine composed his great work of exhortation, argument, and invective, *The City of God*.

THE TEMPERING OF CHRISTIANITY

BY THE TIME OF AUGUSTINE, the age of imperial persecution had long since passed. The last pagan Emperor, Julian, died just nine years after Augustine's birth. If Christianity was not everywhere the official state religion, it was in some form or other the favored religion. After the bitter early days, when the poverty of the Church and the perils of persecution kept the number of believers small though fervent, Christianity fell upon evil days of heresy and opportunism. Men professed Christianity for their own earthly advantage; and, perhaps more dangerous, they began to offer different interpretations of major points of doctrine. The great conflict between Athanasius, representing the Western church, and Arius, representing the Eastern, had been ended, not decided, by the council of Nicaea in 325. Now lesser heresies were being spawned everywhere by ignorant or misguided men, with Manichaeans, Donatists and Pelagians springing up on every hand to menace the unity of the faith.

To describe the many heresies against which Augustine waged relentless warfare would be confusing. For purposes of his story, the two most important heresies are Manichaeism, to which he himself was addicted from his twentieth to his thirtieth year; and Donatism, against which he spent the last years of his life in bitter struggle. Manichaeism incorporated Christian belief with a great deal of pagan matter. Its founder was a Persian artist named Mani, who lived some time during the third century A.D. According to Mani, the universe consisted of two kingdoms, one of light and good under the leadership of God, one of dark and evil under the rule of Satan. These two kingdoms once had a war, in the course of which the particles of good got mixed with the particles of evil. It was the purpose of human life to separate them again, with the help of the Sun (which also stands for Primal Man) and the Moon (Primal Woman). In this strange hodgepodge were mingled beliefs from Abraham, Zoroaster, Buddha, Christ and Saint Paul. Because it was so rich in images and vague in its total outline, Manichaeism appealed tremendously to the young Augustine's rhetorical mind, his dramatic instincts, and his deep sense of pervasive sin. Augustine refuted this heresy by proclaiming that every work of God is good and that the freedom of creatures is the sole source of moral evil.

The Donatist heresy, although typically African, was not in the least congenial to Augustine. The monk Donatus carried religious strictness to an extreme by asserting that the character of the priest determined the efficacy of the sacrament which he administered. It is hard for us to see why anyone should want to believe a doctrine that made salvation so precarious and that regarded every parish difference in terms of salvation and damnation for all the members. In crushing the heresy, Augustine held the basic belief that the Church can tolerate sinners within the fold in the hope of converting them without suffering any loss of holiness.

The story of Augustine's early life is told in the *Confessions* with an abundance of detail and a wealth of psychological insight. But the Saint Augustine who captured the imagination of the Christian world was not the awkward, earnest young professor of rhetoric of the *Confessions*. It was Saint Augustine, the Bishop of Hippo, the great teacher and defender of the faith who won the reverence of later ages. We may well approach the *Confessions* themselves at the point where they leave off, through the personality that they show Augustine becoming.

Hippo, or Hippo Regius, now the town of Bône in French Algeria, was a seaport town in Numidia. Augustine went there in 390 A.D., just three years after his conversion, on an errand of Christian mercy. The bishop of the town, a Greek named Valerius, was old and tired, and, because of his language, not an effective preacher to a congregation which spoke largely Latin and Punic. When the people heard Augustine had come, they carried him by force to the cathedral, where they insisted that he be made a presbyter at once. It was the beginning of a relationship between the unruly townspeople and their patient leader that lasted for forty rich and eventful years. The citizens of Hippo were proud of Bishop Augustine and yet they delighted in putting his many virtues to the test; they loved to show that anybody less than Augustine would be unable to manage them. They loved and bothered and revered and tormented him.

THE SHEPHERD OF A TRYING FLOCK

THE GREAT BISHOP was busy among the citizens of Hippo even while he was sending letters to every corner of the Christian world, solving problems, teaching and composing those enormous treatises which often seem like a life's work in themselves. He preached volubly, dramatically at least five times a week and sometimes twice a day, to an audience which expected him to answer all its problems immediately. He conferred with disputants; he taught the elements of the Christian religion to new converts; and while a lesser man might have been exhausted by these endless labors, Saint Augustine drew sustenance from them.

No experience was alien to him. In all his writings he showed a gift for the homely image, the ready anecdote, the pointed detail, which he drew from the daily business of the diocese. In the middle of a textbook of *Christian Instruction,* for example, while ridiculing certain superstitions, he reports that some people had the habit "of striking a harmless child a box on the ear if he runs between two people walking together. But," he continues with grim satisfaction, "it is only fitting that the dogs avenge the children. For when they strike a dog that has run between them, the dog sometimes sends his smiter away from a ridiculous practice to a real physician."

Over and over again, one finds in Saint Augustine this vivid detail. In the middle of the heaviest treatises, he tells his reader little tales of curious lore: of a two-headed monster just born in the East, of a new comet and its effect on earthly life, of a snake which still wriggled after being cut in two (if it had a soul, which half would the soul be in?), of a notable demon which appeared before a pagan philosopher. He used the things of daily life to build the great intellectual edifice by which he explained both this world and the next.

THE GREAT CATHEDRAL OF AUGUSTINE'S THOUGHT

He created his structure in the shadow of doom, for even as he wrote his last works, the Goths and Vandals had overwhelmed Rome and were invading Africa. The last days of Augustine were spent under siege in the city of Hippo, which he steadfastly refused to leave, and where he died on August 28, 430 A.D., in his seventy-sixth year. In those last years, the whole civilized world must have seemed a spectacle of barbarian triumph. Yet with all these excuses for despair, with every reason to doubt that his works would survive, the great Bishop of Hippo continued to work at the massive structure of his religious thought.

Saint Augustine was a philosopher of profound insight and vast scope, whose equal would not be found again in the Church till the days of Saint Thomas Aquinas, nearly 800 years later. His thinking was influenced chiefly by Plato and the Platonists, to whom he always acknowledged his indebtedness; but it was also bold and original. Augustine's deep and pervasive sense of human sin did much to strengthen the Christian belief in predestination. His way of reading the Scriptures allegorically was ingeniously elaborated by medieval scholars. And his profound meditations on time and on the nature of evil have exercised the minds of philosophers, both Catholic and non-Catholic, ever since. The philosopher-mystic was a student of his own heart, and of the hearts of all men. His gifts of psychological insight found their highest expression in the *Confessions.*

SAINT AUGUSTINE'S REASONS FOR WRITING THE "CONFESSIONS"

THE "CONFESSIONS" OF SAINT AUGUSTINE were written between the years 397 and 400 A.D.—that is, about ten years after the religious conversion which is their central episode. Their purpose is to edify, not to scandalize, as we sometimes think confessions must. Augustine undertook to tell only as much of his life as would cast a light upon his moral development. To understand this is to comprehend the many exaggerated remarks about the sinfulness of the bishop's youth. It is true that he describes himself as having been terribly wicked, and then, to prove his point, mentions the famous affair of the stolen pears. We tend to think that any young fellow is unnaturally good whose conscience accuses him of nothing worse than a raided pear-orchard. But Augustine is not interested in scandalous sins or impressive quantities of sin. What he does is simply to analyze the moral quality of that one theft down to its essential meanness and cowardice: the young thieves didn't eat the fruit, they threw it away; none of them would have dared to commit the theft alone. But that we would be quite wrong in concluding that Augustine could have told us nothing more about the desires of the flesh, his prayer stands to prove: "Lord, give me chastity . . . but not yet!"

One of the supreme achievements of the *Confessions* is their insight into the complexity of the soul. One of the most famous passages is the description of Alypius' unwilling visit to the gladiatorial games. We see the gentle young convert dragged by his noisy friends to the arena, and we shrink with him from the bloody display. Then his character changes before our eyes. "He beheld, shouted, kindled, and carried thence with him the madness which should goad him to return not only with them who first drew him thither, but also before them, yea and to draw in others."

The passages of self-analysis that led to Augustine's conversion are also artfully constructed:

> The very toys of toys and vanities of vanities, my ancient mistresses, still held me; they plucked my fleshly garment, and whispered softly, "Dost thou cast us off? and from that moment shall we no more be with thee forever?". . . muttering as it were behind my back, and privily plucking me, as I was departing, but to look back at them. Yet they did retard me, so that I hesitated to burst and shake myself free from them, and to spring over whither I was called; a violent habit saying to me, "Thinkest thou, thou canst live without them?"

Skillfully the passage builds from gentle allurements toward a note of violence. The man who wrote in this way of his lusts was no simple ascetic, unacquainted with the passions of the world or immune to them. As Saint Augustine tells us over and over again, the desire to love and be loved was powerful within him and subdued only after bitter struggle. This struggle is recorded in the *Confessions* with a wonderful truthfulness and subtlety. One need only call to mind that scene in the garden near Milan, where he heard a child singing "Take up and read, take up and read," and turning to a volume of Saint Paul's *Epistles,* he read, and was immediately filled with the light of certainty. Or, perhaps, one thinks of the supreme passage in the *Confessions,* describing a mystical vision that occurred during a conversation with his mother, at Ostia.

We read the *Confessions,* then, for the record which they contain of a great and powerful mind undergoing religious conversion. The anguish and ecstasy of being terribly lost and then wonderfully found have never been recorded as dramatically. We read the *Confessions* also because they are the work of a master psychologist, who turned the white light of moral inquiry into the darkest caverns of his own heart and found there much that can help us illuminate our own lives. Finally, we read Saint Augustine because he gives us the record of an age much like our own, when men were confused and discouraged, when things at times looked hopeless, but when an honest heart, a clear mind, and a devoted faith could bring peace.

BOOK I

Confessions of the greatness and unsearchableness of God, of God's mercies in infancy and boyhood, and human willfulness; of his own sins of idleness, abuse of his studies, and of God's gifts up to his fifteenth year.

Great art Thou, O Lord, and greatly to be praised; great is Thy power, and Thy wisdom infinite. And Thee would man praise; man, but a particle of Thy creation; man that bears about him his mortality, the witness of his sin, the witness that *Thou resistest the proud:* yet would man praise Thee; he, but a particle of Thy creation. Thou awakest us to delight in Thy praise; for Thou madest us for Thyself, and our heart is restless, until it repose in Thee. Grant me, Lord, to know and understand which is first, to call on Thee or to praise Thee? and, again, to know Thee or to call on Thee? For who can call on Thee, not knowing Thee? For he that knoweth Thee not, may call on Thee as other than Thou art. Or, is it rather, that we call on Thee that we may know Thee? But *how shall they call on Him in whom they have not believed? or how shall they believe without a preacher?* And *they that seek the Lord shall praise Him.* For *they that seek shall find Him,* and they that find shall praise Him. I will seek Thee, Lord, by calling on Thee; and will call on Thee, believing in Thee; for to us hast Thou been preached. My faith, Lord, shall call on Thee, which Thou hast given me, wherewith Thou hast inspired me, through the Incarnation of Thy Son, through the ministry of the Preacher.*

* Saint Ambrose, by whom Saint Augustine was baptized.

257

And how shall I call upon my God, my God and Lord, since, when I call for Him, I shall be calling Him to myself? and what room is there within me, whither my God can come into me? Whither can God come into me, God who made heaven and earth? Is there, indeed, O Lord my God, aught in me that can contain Thee? Do then heaven and earth, which Thou hast made, and wherein Thou hast made me, contain Thee? or, because nothing which exists could exist without Thee, doth therefore whatever exists contain Thee? Since, then, I too exist, why do I seek that Thou shouldest enter into me, who were not, wert Thou not in me? Why? Because I am not gone down in hell, and yet Thou art there also. For *if I go down into hell, Thou art there.* I could not be then, O my God, could not be at all, wert Thou not in me; or, rather, unless I were in Thee, *of whom are all things, by whom are all things, in whom are all things?* Even so, Lord, even so. Whither do I call Thee, since I am in Thee? or whence canst Thou enter into me? For whither can I go beyond heaven and earth, that thence my God should come into me, who hath said, *I fill the heaven and the earth?* . . .

Narrow is the mansion of my soul; enlarge Thou it, that Thou mayest enter in. It is ruinous; repair Thou it. It has that within which must offend Thine eyes; I confess and know it. But who shall cleanse it? or to whom should I cry, save Thee? *Lord, cleanse me from my secret faults, and spare Thy servant from the power of the enemy. I believe, and therefore do I speak.* Lord, Thou knowest. *Have I not confessed against myself my transgressions unto Thee, and Thou, my God, hast forgiven the iniquity of my heart? I contend not in judgment with Thee,* who art the truth; I fear to deceive myself; *lest mine iniquity lie unto itself.* Therefore I contend not in judgment with Thee; *for if Thou, Lord, shouldest mark iniquities, O Lord, who shall abide it?*

Yet suffer me to speak unto Thy mercy, me, *dust and ashes.* Yet suffer me to speak, since I speak to Thy mercy, and not to scornful man. Thou too, perhaps, despisest me, yet wilt Thou *return and have compassion* upon me. For what would I say, O Lord my God, but that I know not whence I came into this dying life (shall I call it?) or living death. Then immediately did the comforts of Thy compassion take me up, as I heard (for I remember it not) from the parents of my flesh, out of whose substance Thou didst sometime fashion me. Thus there received me the comforts of woman's milk. For neither my mother nor my nurses stored their own breasts for me; but Thou didst bestow the food of my infancy through them, according to Thine ordinance, whereby Thou distributest Thy riches through the hidden springs of all things. Thou also gavest me to desire no more than Thou gavest; and to my nurses willingly to give me what Thou gavest them. For they, with a heaven-taught affection, willingly gave me, what they abounded with from Thee. For this my good from them, was good for them. Nor, indeed, from them was it, but through them; for from Thee, O God, are all good things, and *from my God is all my health*. This I since learned, Thou, through these Thy gifts, within me and without, proclaiming Thyself unto me. For then I knew but to suck; to repose in what pleased, and cry at what offended my flesh; nothing more.

Afterwards I began to smile; first in sleep, then waking: for so it was told me of myself, and I believed it; for we see the like in other infants, though of myself I remember it not. Thus, little by little, I became conscious where I was; and to have a wish to express my wishes to those who could content them, and I could not; for the wishes were within me, and they without; nor could they by any sense of theirs enter within my spirit. So I flung about at random limbs and voice, making the few signs I could, and such as I could, like, though in truth very little like, what I wished. And when I was not presently obeyed (my wishes being hurtful or unintelligible) then I was indignant with my elders for not submitting to me, with those owing me no service, for not serving me; and avenged myself on them by tears. Such have I learned infants to be from observing them; and, that I was myself such, they, all unconscious, have shown me better than my nurses who knew it. . . .

Hear, O God. Alas, for man's sin! So saith man, and Thou pitiest him; for Thou madest him, but sin in him Thou madest not. Who remindeth me of the sins of my infancy? *for in Thy sight none is pure from sin, not even the infant whose life is but a day upon the earth.* Who remindeth me? Doth not each little infant, in whom I see what of myself I remember not? What then was my sin? Was it that I hung upon the breast and cried? For should I now so do for food suitable to my age, justly should I be laughed at and reproved. What I then did was worthy reproof; but since I could not understand reproof, custom and reason forbade me to be reproved. For those habits, when grown, we root out and cast away. Now no man, though he prunes, wittingly casts away what is good. Or was it then good, even for a while, to cry for what, if given, would hurt? bitterly to resent, that

259

persons free, and its own elders, yea, the very authors of its birth, served it not? that many besides, wiser than it, obeyed not the nod of its good pleasure? to do its best to strike and hurt, because commands were not obeyed, which had been obeyed to its hurt? The weakness then of infant limbs, not its will, is its innocence. Myself have seen and known even a baby envious; it could not speak, yet it turned pale and looked bitterly on its foster brother. Who knows not this? Mothers and nurses tell you, that they allay these things by I know not what remedies. Is that too innocence, when the fountain of milk is flowing in rich abundance, not to endure one to share it, though in extremest need, and whose very life as yet depends thereon? We bear gently with all this, not as being no or slight evils, but because they will disappear as years increase; for, though tolerated now, the very same tempers are utterly intolerable when found in riper years.

Thou, then, O Lord my God, who gavest life to this my infancy, furnishing thus with senses (as we see) the frame Thou gavest, compacting its limbs, ornamenting its proportions and, for its general good and safety, implanting in it all vital functions, Thou commandest me to praise Thee in these things, *to confess unto Thee, and sing unto Thy name, Thou most Highest.* For Thou art God, Almighty and Good, even hadst Thou done nought but only this, which none could do but Thou: whose Unity is the mold of all things; who out of Thy own fairness makest all things fair; and orderest all things by Thy law. This age then, Lord, whereof I have no remembrance, which I take on others' word, and guess from other infants that I have passed, true though the guess be, I am yet loath to count in this life of mine which I live in this world. For no less than that which I spent in my mother's womb, is it hid from me in the shadows of forgetfulness. But if *I was shapen in iniquity, and in sin did my mother conceive me,* where, I beseech Thee, O my God, where, Lord, or when was I Thy servant guiltless? But, lo! that period I pass by; and what have I now to do with that, of which I can recall no vestige?

Passing hence from infancy, I came to boyhood, or rather it came to me, displacing infancy. Nor did that depart (for whither went it?) and yet it was no more. For I was no longer a speechless infant, but a speaking boy. This I remember; and have since observed how I learned to speak. It was not that my elders taught me words (as, soon after, other learning) in any set method; but I, longing by cries and broken accents and various motions of my limbs to express my thoughts, that so I might have my will, and yet unable to express all I willed, or to whom I willed, did myself, by the understanding which Thou, my God, gavest me, practice the sounds in my memory. When they named anything, and as they spoke turned toward it, I saw and remembered that they called what they would point out, by the name they uttered. And that they meant this thing and no other, was plain from the motions of their body, the natural language, as it were, of all nations, expressed by the countenance, glances of the eye, gestures of the limbs, and tones of the voice, indicating the affections of the mind, as it pursues, possesses, rejects, or shuns. And thus by constantly hearing words, as they occurred in various sentences, I collected gradually for what they stood; and having broken in my mouth to these signs, I thereby gave utterance to my will. Thus I exchanged with those about me these current signs of our wills, and so launched deeper into the stormy intercourse of human life, yet depending on parental authority and the beck of elders.

O God my God, what miseries and mockeries did I now experience, when obedience to my teachers was proposed to me, as proper in a boy, in order that in this world I might prosper, and excel in tongue science, which should serve to the "praise of men," and to deceitful riches. Next I was put to school to get learning, in which I, poor wretch, knew not what use there was; and yet, if idle in learning, I was beaten. For this was judged right by our forefathers; and many, passing the same course before us, framed for us weary paths, through which we were fain to pass; multiplying toil and grief upon the sons of Adam. But, Lord, we found that men called upon Thee, and we learned from them to think of Thee, according to our powers, as of some great One, who, though hidden from our senses, couldst hear and help us. For so I began, as a boy, to pray to Thee, my aid and refuge; and broke the fetters of my tongue to call on Thee, praying Thee, though small, yet with no small earnestness, that I might not be beaten at school. And when Thou heardest me not (*not thereby giving me over to folly*), my elders, yea, my very parents, who yet wished me no ill, mocked my stripes, my then great and grievous ill.

Is there, Lord, any of soul so great, and cleaving to Thee with so intense affection (for a sort of stupidity will in a way do it); but is there anyone who, from cleaving devoutly to Thee, is endued with so great a spirit, that he can think as lightly of the racks and hooks and other torments (against which, throughout all lands, men call on Thee with extreme dread), mocking at those by whom they are feared most bitterly, as our parents mocked the torments which we suffered in boyhood from our masters? For we feared not our torments less; nor prayed we less to Thee to escape them. And yet we sinned, in writing or reading or studying less than was exacted of us. For we wanted not, O Lord, memory or capacity, whereof Thy will gave enough for our age; but our sole delight was play; and for this we were punished by those who yet themselves were doing the like. But elder folks' idleness is called "business"; that of boys, being really the same, is punished by those elders; and none commiserates either boys or men. For will any of sound discretion approve of my being beaten as a boy, because, by playing at ball, I made less progress in studies which I was to learn, only that, as a man, I might play more unbeseemingly? And what else did he, who beat me? who, if worsted in some trifling discussion with his fellow tutor, was more embittered and jealous than I, when beaten at ball by a playfellow? . . .

In boyhood itself, however (so much less dreaded for me than youth), I loved not study, and hated to be forced to it. Yet I was forced; and this was well done toward me, but I did not well; for, unless forced, I had not learned. But no one doth well against his will, even though what he doth, be well. Yet neither did they well who forced me, but what was well came to me from Thee, my God. For they were regardless how I should employ what they forced me to learn, except to satiate the insatiate desires of a wealthy beggary and a shameful glory. But Thou, *by whom the very hairs of our head are numbered,* didst use for my good the error of all who urged me to learn; and my own, who would not learn, Thou didst use for my punishment—a fit penalty for one, so small a boy and so great a sinner. So by those who did not well, Thou didst well for me; and by my own sin Thou didst justly punish me. For Thou hast commanded, and so it is, that every inordinate affection should be its own punishment.

But why did I so much hate the Greek, which I studied as a boy? I do not yet fully know. For the Latin I loved; not what my first masters, but what the so-called grammarians taught me. For those first lessons, reading, writing, and arithmetic, I thought as great a burden and penalty as any Greek. And yet whence was this too, but from the sin and vanity of this life, because *I was flesh, and a breath that passeth away and cometh not again?* For those first lessons were better certainly, because more certain; by them I obtained, and still retain, the power of reading what I find written, and myself writing what I will; whereas in the others, I was forced to learn the wanderings of one Aeneas, forgetful of my own, and to weep for dead Dido, because she killed herself for love; the while, with dry eyes, I endured my miserable self dying among these things, far from Thee, O my God my life.

For what more miserable than a miserable being who commiserates not himself; weeping the death of Dido for love to Aeneas, but weeping not his own death for want of love to Thee, O God. Thou light of my heart, Thou bread of my inmost soul, Thou Power who givest vigor to my mind, who quickenest my thoughts, I loved Thee not. I committed fornication against Thee, and all around me thus fornicating there echoed "Well done! well done!" *for the friendship of this world is fornication against Thee;* and "Well done! well done!" echoes on till one is ashamed not to be thus a man. And all this I wept not, I who wept for Dido slain, and "seeking by the sword a stroke and wound extreme," myself seeking the while a worse extreme, the extremest and lowest of Thy creatures, having forsaken Thee, earth passing into the earth. And if forbidden to read all this, I was grieved that I might not read what grieved me. Madness like this is thought a higher and a richer learning, than that by which I learned to read and write. . . .

Bear with me, my God, while I say somewhat of my wit, Thy gift, and on what dotages I wasted it. For a task was set me, troublesome enough to my soul, upon terms of praise or shame, and fear of stripes, to speak the words of Juno, as she raged and mourned that she could not

This Trojan prince from Latium turn.

Which words I had heard that Juno never uttered; but we were forced to go astray in the footsteps of these poetic fictions, and to say in prose much what he expressed in verse. And his speaking was most applauded, in whom the passions of rage and grief were most preeminent, and clothed in the most fitting language, maintaining the dignity of the character. What is it to me, O my true life, my God, that my declamation was applauded above so many of my own age and class? Is not all this smoke and wind? And was there nothing else whereon to exercise my wit and tongue? Thy praises, Lord, Thy praises might have stayed the yet tender shoot of my heart by the prop of Thy Scriptures; so had it not trailed away amid these empty trifles, a defiled prey for the fowls of the air. For in more ways than one do men sacrifice to the rebellious angels.

But what marvel that I was thus carried away to vanities, and went

263

out from Thy presence, O my God, when men were set before me as models, who, if in relating some action of theirs, in itself not ill, they committed some barbarism or solecism, being censured, were abashed; but when in rich and adorned and well-ordered discourse they related their own disordered life, being bepraised, they gloried? These things Thou seest, Lord, and holdest Thy peace; *long-suffering, and plenteous in mercy and truth*. Wilt Thou hold Thy peace forever? And even now Thou drawest out of this horrible gulf the soul that seeketh Thee, that thirsteth for Thy pleasures, *whose heart saith unto Thee, I have sought Thy face; Thy face, Lord, will I seek*. For *darkened* affections is removal from Thee. For it is not by our feet, or change of place, that men leave Thee, or return unto Thee. Or did that Thy younger son look out for horses or chariots, or ships, fly with visible wings, or journey by the motion of his limbs, that he might in a far country waste in riotous living all Thou gavest at his departure? A loving Father, when Thou gavest, and more loving unto him, when he returned empty. So then in lustful, that is, in darkened affections, is the true distance from Thy face.

Behold, O Lord God, yea, behold patiently as Thou art wont, how carefully the sons of men observe the covenanted rules of letters and syllables received from those who spoke before them, neglecting the eternal covenant of everlasting salvation received from Thee. Insomuch, that a teacher or learner of the hereditary laws of pronunciation will more offend men, by speaking without the aspirate, of a *"uman* being," in despite of the laws of grammar, than if he, a "human being," hate a "human being" in despite of Thine. As if any enemy could be more hurtful than the hatred with which he is incensed against him; or could wound more deeply him whom he persecutes, than he wounds his own soul by his enmity. Assuredly no science of letters can be so innate as the record of conscience, "that he is doing to another what from another he would be loath to suffer." How deep are Thy ways, O God, Thou only great, *that sittest* silent *on high* and by an unwearied law dispensing penal blindness to lawless desires. In quest of the fame of eloquence, a man standing before a human judge, surrounded by a human throng, declaiming against his enemy with fiercest hatred, will take heed most watchfully, lest, by an error of the tongue, he murder the word "human being"; but takes no heed, lest, through the fury of his spirit, he murder the real human being.

This was the world at whose gate unhappy I lay in my boyhood;

this the stage, where I had feared more to commit a barbarism, than having committed one, to envy those who had not. These things I speak and confess to Thee, my God; for which I had praise from them, whom I then thought it all virtue to please. For I saw not the abyss of vileness, wherein *I was cast away from Thine eyes*. Before them what more foul than I was already, displeasing even such as myself? with innumerable lies deceiving my tutor, my masters, my parents, from love of play, eagerness to see vain shows, and restlessness to imitate them! Thefts also I committed, from my parents' cellar and table, enslaved by greediness, or that I might have to give to boys, who sold me their play, which all the while they liked no less than I. In this play, too, I often sought unfair conquests, conquered myself meanwhile by vain desire of pre-eminence. And what could I so ill endure, or when I detected it, upbraided I so fiercely, as that I was doing to others? and for which if detected, I was upbraided, I chose rather to quarrel, than to yield. And is this the innocence of boyhood? Not so, Lord, not so; I cry Thy mercy, O my God. For these very sins, as riper years succeed, these very sins are transferred from tutors and masters, from nuts and balls and sparrows, to magistrates and kings, to gold and manors and slaves, just as severer punishments displace the cane. It was the low stature then of childhood, which Thou our King didst commend as an emblem of lowliness, when Thou saidst, *Of such is the kingdom of heaven*.

Yet, Lord, to Thee, the Creator and Governor of the universe, most excellent and most good, thanks were due to Thee our God, even hadst Thou destined for me boyhood only. For even then I was, I lived, and felt; and had an implanted providence over my own well-being—a trace of that mysterious Unity, whence I was derived. I guarded by the inward sense the entireness of my senses, and in these minute pursuits, and in my thoughts on things minute, I learned to delight in truth. I hated to be deceived, had a vigorous memory, was gifted with speech, was soothed by friendship, avoided pain, baseness, ignorance. In so small a creature, what was not wonderful, not admirable? But all are gifts of my God; it was not I, who gave them me; and good these are, and these together are myself. Good, then, is He that made me, and He is my good; and before Him will I exult for every good which of a boy I had. For it was my sin, that not in Him, but in His creatures—myself and others—I sought for pleasures, sublimities, truths, and so fell headlong into sorrows, confusions, errors. Thanks be to Thee, my joy and my glory and my confidence, my God, thanks be to Thee for Thy gifts; but do Thou preserve them to me. For so wilt Thou preserve me, and those things shall be enlarged and perfected, which Thou hast given me, and I myself shall be with Thee, since even to be Thou hast given me.

BOOK II

Object of these Confessions. Further ills of idleness developed in his sixteenth year. Evils of ill society, which betrayed him into theft.

I WILL NOW call to mind my past foulness, and the carnal corruptions of my soul: not because I love them, but that I may love Thee, O my God. For love of Thy love I do it; reviewing my most wicked ways in the very bitterness of my remembrance, that Thou mayest grow sweet unto me (Thou sweetness never failing, Thou blissful and assured sweetness) and gathering me again out of that my dissipation, wherein I was torn piecemeal, while turned from Thee, the One Good, I lost myself among a multiplicity of things. For I even burned in my youth heretofore, to be satiated in things below; and I dared to grow wild again, with these various and shadowy loves: *my beauty consumed away,* and I stank in Thine eyes; pleasing myself, and desirous to please in the eyes of men.

And what was it that I delighted in, but to love, and be beloved? but I kept not the measure of love, or mind to mind, friendship's bright boundary; but out of the muddy concupiscence of the flesh, and the bubblings of youth, mists fumed up which beclouded and overcast my heart, that I could not discern the clear brightness of love, from the fog of lustfulness. Both did confusedly boil in me, and hurried my unstayed youth over the precipice of unholy desires, and sunk me in a gulf of flagitiousness. Thy wrath had gathered over me, and I knew it not. I was grown deaf by the clanking of the chain of my mortality, the punishment of the pride of my soul, and I strayed further from Thee, and Thou lettest me alone, and I was tossed about, and wasted, and dissipated, and I boiled over in my fornications, and Thou heldest Thy peace, O Thou my tardy joy! Thou then heldest Thy peace, and I wandered further and further from Thee, into more and more fruitless seed-plots of sorrows, with a proud dejectedness, and a restless weariness. . . .

For that year were my studies intermitted: while after my return from Madaura (a neighbor city, whither I had journeyed to learn grammar and rhetoric), the expenses for a further journey to Carthage were being provided for me; and that, rather by the resolution than the means of my father, who was but a poor freeman of Thagaste. . . . Who did not extol my father, that beyond the ability of his means, he would furnish his son with all necessaries for a far journey for his studies' sake? For many far abler citizens did no such thing for their children. But yet this same father had no concern, how I grew towards Thee, or how chaste I was; so that I were but copious in speech, however barren I were to Thy culture, O God, who art the only true and good Lord of Thy field, my heart.

But while in that my sixteenth year I lived with my parents, leaving all school for a while (a season of idleness being interposed through the narrowness of my parents' fortunes), the briers of unclean desires grew rank over my head, and there was no hand to root them out. When that my father saw me at the baths, now growing toward manhood, and endued with a restless youthfulness, he, as already hence anticipating his descendants, gladly told it to my mother; rejoicing in that tumult of the senses wherein the world forgetteth Thee its Creator, and becometh enamored of Thy creature, instead of Thyself, through the fumes of that invisible wine of its self-will, turning aside and bowing down to the very basest things. But in my mother's breast Thou hadst already begun Thy temple, and the foundation of Thy holy habitation, whereas my father was as yet but a catechumen, and that but recently. She then was startled with a holy fear and trembling; and though I was not as yet baptized, feared for me those crooked ways, in which they walk, who *turn their back to Thee, and not their face.*

Woe is me! and dare I say that Thou heldest Thy peace, O my God, while I wandered further from Thee? Didst Thou then indeed hold Thy peace to me? And whose but Thine were these words which by my mother, Thy faithful one, Thou sangest in my ears? Nothing whereof sunk into my heart, so as to do it. For she wished, and I remember in private with great anxiety warned me, "not to commit fornication; but especially never to defile another's wife." These seemed to me womanish advices, which I should blush to obey. But they were Thine, and I knew it not: and I thought Thou wert silent, and that it was she who spoke; by whom Thou wert not silent unto me; and in her wast despised by me, her son, *the son of Thy hand-*

267

maid, Thy servant. But I knew it not; and ran headlong with such blindness, that among my equals I was ashamed of a less shamelessness, when I heard them boast of their flagitiousness, yea, and the more boasting, the more they were degraded: and I took pleasure, not only in the pleasure of the deed, but in the praise. What is worthy of dispraise but Vice? But I made myself worse than I was, that I might not be dispraised; and when in anything I had not sinned as the abandoned ones, I would say that I had done what I had not done, that I might not seem contemptible in proportion as I was innocent; or of less account, the more chaste.

Behold with what companions I walked the streets of Babylon, and wallowed in the mire thereof, as if in a bed of spices, and precious ointments. And that I might cleave the faster to its very center, the invisible enemy trod me down, and seduced me, for that I was easy to be seduced. Neither did the mother of my flesh (who had now *fled out of the center of Babylon,* yet went more slowly in the skirts thereof) as she advised me to chastity, so heed what she had heard of me from her husband, as to restrain within the bounds of conjugal affection (if it could not be pared away to the quick), what she felt to be pestilent at present, and for the future dangerous. She heeded not this, for she feared, lest a wife should prove a clog and hindrance to my hopes. Not those hopes of the world to come, which my mother reposed in Thee; but the hope of learning, which both my parents were too desirous I should attain; my father, because he had next to no thought of Thee, and of me but vain conceits; my mother, because she accounted that those usual courses of learning would not only be no hindrance, but even some furtherance toward attaining Thee. For this I conjecture, recalling, as well as I may, the disposition of my parents. The reins, meantime, were slackened to me, beyond all temper of due severity, to spend my time in sport, yea, even unto dissoluteness in whatsoever I affected. And in all was a mist, intercepting from me, O my God, the brightness of Thy truth; and *mine iniquity burst out as from very fatness.*

Theft is punished by Thy law, O Lord, and the law written in the hearts of men, which iniquity itself effaces not. For what thief will abide a thief? not even a rich thief, one stealing through want. Yet I lusted to thieve, and did it, compelled by no hunger, nor poverty, but through a cloyedness of welldoing, and a pamperedness of iniquity. For I stole that, of which I had enough, and much better. Nor cared I to enjoy what I stole, but joyed in the theft and sin itself. A pear tree there was near our vineyard, laden with fruit, tempting neither for color nor taste. To shake and rob this, some lewd young fellows of us went, late one night (having according to our pestilent custom prolonged our sports in the streets till then), and took huge loads, not for our eating, but to fling to the very hogs, having only tasted them. And this, but to do what we liked only because it was misliked. Behold my heart, O God, behold my heart, which Thou hadst pity upon in the bottom of the bottomless pit. Now, behold let my heart tell Thee, what it sought there, that I should be gratuitously evil, having no temptation to ill, but the ill itself. It was foul, and I loved it. I loved to perish, I loved mine own fault, not that for which I was faulty, but my fault itself. Foul soul, falling from Thy firmament to utter destruction; not seeking aught through the shame, but the shame itself!

For there is an attractiveness in beautiful bodies, in gold and silver, and all things; and in bodily touch, sympathy hath much influence, and each other sense hath his proper object answerably tempered. Worldly honor hath also its grace, and the power of overcoming, and of mastery; whence springs also the thirst of revenge. But yet, to obtain all these, we may not depart from Thee, O Lord, nor decline from Thy law. The life also which here we live hath its own enchantment, through a certain proportion of its own, and a correspondence with all things beautiful here below. Human friendship also is endeared with a sweet tie, by reason of the unity formed of many souls. Upon occasion of all these, and the like, is sin committed, while through an immoderate inclination toward these goods of the lowest order, the better and higher are forsaken—Thou, our Lord God, Thy truth, and Thy law. For these lower things have their delights, but not like my God, who made all things: for *in Him doth the righteous delight, and He is the joy of the upright in heart.* . . .

What then did wretched I so love in thee, thou theft of mine, thou deed of darkness, in that sixteenth year of my age? Lovely thou wert not, because thou wert theft. But art thou anything, that thus I speak to thee? Fair were the pears we stole, because they were Thy creation, Thou fairest of all, Creator of all, Thou good God; God, the sovereign good and my true good. Fair were those pears, but not them did my wretched soul desire; for I had store of better, and those I gathered, only that I might steal. For, when gathered, I flung them away, my only feast therein being my own sin, which I was pleased to enjoy. For if aught of those pears came within my mouth, what sweetened it was the sin. And now, O Lord my God, I inquire what in that theft delighted me; and behold it hath no loveliness; I mean not such loveliness as in justice and wisdom; nor such as is in the mind and memory, and senses, and animal life of man; nor yet as the stars are glorious and beautiful in their orbs; or the earth, or sea, full of embryo life, replacing by its birth that which decayeth; nay, nor even that false and shadowy beauty, which belongeth to deceiving vices. . . .

What fruit had I then (wretched man!) *in those things, of the remembrance whereof I am now ashamed?* Especially, in that theft which I loved for the theft's sake; and it too was nothing, and therefore the more miserable I, who loved it. Yet alone I had not done it: such was I then, I remember, alone I had never done it. I loved then in it also the company of the accomplices, with whom I did it. I did not then love nothing else but the theft, yea rather I did love nothing else; for that circumstance of the company was also nothing. What is, in truth? who can teach me, save He that enlighteneth my heart, and discovereth its dark corners? What is it which hath come into my mind to inquire, and discuss, and consider? For had I then loved the pears I stole, and wished to enjoy them, I might have done it alone, had the bare commission of the theft sufficed to attain my pleasure; nor needed I have inflamed the itching of my desires, by the excitement of accomplices. But since my pleasure was not in those pears, it was in the offense itself, which the company of fellow sinners occasioned.

What then was this feeling? For of a truth it was too foul: and woe was me, who had it. But yet what was it? *Who can understand his errors?* It was the sport, which, as it were, tickled our hearts, that we beguiled, those who little thought what we were doing, and much misliked it. Why then was my delight of such sort, that I did it not alone? Because none doth ordinarily laugh alone? ordinarily no one; yet laughter sometimes masters men alone and singly when no one whatever is with them, if any thing very ludicrous presents itself to their senses or mind. Yet I had not done this alone; alone I had never never done it. Behold my God, before Thee, the vivid remembrance of my soul; alone, I had never committed that theft, wherein what I stole pleased me not, but that I stole; nor had it alone liked me to do it, nor had I done it. O friendship too unfriendly! thou incomprehensible inveigler of the soul, thou greediness to do mischief out of mirth and wantonness; thou thirst of others' loss, without lust of my own gain or revenge: but when it is said, "Let's go, let's do it," we are ashamed not to be shameless.

270

Who can disentangle that twisted and intricate knottiness? Foul is it: I hate to think on it, to look on it. But Thee I long for, O Righteousness and Innocence, beautiful and comely to all pure eyes, and of a satisfaction unsating. With Thee is rest entire, and life imperturbable. Whoso enters into Thee, *enters into the joy of his Lord:* and shall not fear, and shall do excellently in the All Excellent. I sank away from Thee, and I wandered, O my God, too much astray from Thee my stay, in these days of my youth, and I became to myself a barren land.

BOOK III

His residence at Carthage from his seventeenth to his nineteenth year. Source of his disorders. Love of shows. Advance in studies and love of wisdom. Distaste for Scripture. Led astray to the Manichaeans. Refutation of some of their tenets. Grief of his mother Monica at his heresy, and prayers for his conversion. Her vision from God, and answer through a Bishop.

To CARTHAGE I came, where there sang all around me in my ears a caldron of unholy loves. I loved not yet, yet I loved to love, and out of a deep-seated want, I hated myself for wanting not. I sought what I might love, in love with loving, and safety I hated, and a way without snares. For within me was a famine of that inward food, Thyself, my God; yet, through that famine I was not hungered; but was without all longing for incorruptible sustenance, not because filled therewith, but the more empty, the more I loathed it. For this cause my soul was sickly and full of sores, it miserably cast itself forth, desiring to be scraped by the touch of objects of sense. Yet if these had not a soul, they would not be objects of love. To love then, and to be beloved, was sweet to me; but more, when I obtained to enjoy the person I loved. I defiled, therefore, the spring of friendship with the filth of concupiscence, and I beclouded its brightness with the hell of lustfulness; and thus foul and unseemly, I would fain, through exceeding vanity, be fine and courtly. I fell headlong then into the love, wherein I longed to be ensnared. My God, my Mercy, with how much gall didst thou out of thy great goodness besprinkle for me that sweetness? For I was both beloved, and secretly arrived at the bond of

271

enjoying; and was with joy fettered with sorrow-bringing bonds, that I might be scourged with the iron-burning rods of jealousy, and suspicions, and fears, and angers, and quarrels.

Stage-plays also carried me away, full of images of my miseries, and of fuel to my fire. Why is it, that man desires to be made sad, beholding doleful and tragical things, which yet himself would by no means suffer? yet he desires as a spectator to feel sorrow at them, and this very sorrow is his pleasure. What is this but a miserable madness? for a man is the more affected with these actions, the less free he is from such affections. Howsoever, when he suffers in his own person, it uses to be styled misery: when he compassionates others, then it is mercy. But what sort of compassion is this for feigned and scenical passions? for the auditor is not called on to relieve, but only to grieve: and he applauds the actor of these fictions the more, the more he grieves. And if the calamities of those persons (whether of old times, or mere fiction) be so acted, that the spectator is not moved to tears, he goes away disgusted and criticizing; but if he be moved to passion, he stays intent, and weeps for joy. . . .

And Thy faithful mercy hovered over me afar. Upon how grievous iniquities consumed I myself, pursuing a sacrilegious curiosity, that having forsaken Thee, it might bring me to the treacherous abyss, and the beguiling service of devils, to whom I sacrificed my evil actions, and in all these things thou didst scourge me! I dared even, while Thy solemnities were celebrated within the walls of Thy Church, to desire, and to compass a business, deserving death for its fruits, for which Thou scourgedst me with grievous punishments, though nothing to my fault, O Thou my exceeding mercy, my God, my refuge from those terrible destroyers, among whom I wandered with a stiff neck, withdrawing further from Thee, loving mine own ways, and not Thine; loving a vagrant liberty. . . .

Among such as these, in that unsettled age of mine, learned I books of eloquence, wherein I desired to be eminent, out of a damnable and vainglorious end, a joy in human vanity. In the ordinary course of study, I fell upon a certain book of Cicero, whose speech almost all admire, not so his heart. This book of his contains an exhortation to philosophy, and is called *Hortensius*. But this book altered my affections, and turned my prayers to Thyself, O Lord; and made me have other purposes and desires. Every vain hope at once became worthless to me; and I longed with an incredibly burning desire for an immortality of wisdom, and began now to arise, that I might return to Thee. For not to sharpen my tongue (which thing I seemed to be purchasing with my mother's allowances, in that my nineteenth year, my father being dead two years before), not to sharpen my tongue did I employ that book; nor did it infuse into me its style, but its matter.

How did I burn then, my God, how did I burn to remount from earthly things to Thee, nor knew I what Thou wouldest do with me? For with Thee is wisdom. But the love of wisdom is in Greek called "philosophy," with which that book inflamed me. Some there be that seduce through philosophy, under a great, and smooth, and honorable name coloring and disguising their own errors: and almost all who in that and former ages were such, are in that book censured and set forth: there also is made plain that wholesome advice of Thy Spirit, by Thy good and devout servant; *Beware lest any man spoil you through philosophy and vain deceit, after the tradition of men, after the rudiments of the world, and not after Christ. For in Him dwelleth all the fullness of the Godhead bodily.* And since at that time (Thou, O light of my heart, knowest) Apostolic Scripture was not known to me, I was delighted with that exhortation, so far only, that I was thereby strongly roused, and kindled, and inflamed to love, and seek, and obtain, and hold, and embrace not this or that sect, but wisdom itself whatever it were; and this alone checked me thus enkindled, that the name of Christ was not in it. For this name, according to Thy mercy, O Lord, this name of my Saviour Thy Son, had my tender heart, even with my mother's milk, devoutly drunk in, and deeply treasured; and whatsoever was without that name, though never so learned, polished, or true, took not entire hold of me.

I resolved then to bend my mind to the holy Scriptures, that I might see what they were. But behold, I see a thing not understood by the proud, nor laid open to children, lowly in access, in its recesses lofty, and veiled with mysteries; and I was not such as could enter into it, or stoop my neck to follow its steps. For not as I now speak, did I feel when I turned to those Scriptures; but they seemed to me unworthy to be compared to the stateliness of Tully: for my swelling pride shrunk from their lowliness, nor could my sharp wit pierce the interior thereof. Yet were they such as would grow up in a little one. But I disdained to be a little one; and, swollen with pride, took myself to be a great one.

Translated by E. B. Pusey

Therefore I fell among men * proudly doting, exceeding carnal and prating, in whose mouths were the snares of the Devil, lined with the mixture of the syllables of Thy name, and of our Lord Jesus Christ, and of the Holy Ghost, the Paraclete, our Comforter. These names departed not out of their mouth, but so far forth, as the sound only and the noise of the tongue, for the heart was void of truth. Yet they cried out "Truth, Truth," and spoke much thereof to me, yet *it was not in them:* but they spoke falsehood, not of Thee only, who truly art Truth, but even of those elements of this world, Thy creatures. And I indeed ought to have passed by even philosophers who spoke truth concerning them, for love of Thee, my Father, supremely good, Beauty of all things beautiful. O Truth, Truth, how inwardly did even then the marrow of my soul pant after Thee, when they often and diversely, and in many and huge books, echoed of Thee to me, though it was but an echo? And these were the dishes wherein to me, hungering after Thee, they, instead of Thee, served up the Sun and Moon, beautiful works of Thine, but yet Thy works, not Thyself, no nor Thy first works. For Thy spiritual works are before these corporeal works, celestial though they be, and shining. But I hungered and thirsted not even after those first works of Thine, but after Thee Thyself, the Truth, *in whom is no variableness, neither shadow of turning:* yet they still set before me in those dishes, glittering fantasies. . . .

These things I being ignorant of, scoffed at those Thy holy servants and prophets. And what gained I by scoffing at them, but to be scoffed at by Thee, being insensibly and step by step drawn on to those follies, as to believe that a fig tree wept when it was plucked, and the tree, its mother, shed milky tears? Which fig notwithstanding (plucked by some other's, not his own, guilt) had some (Manichaean) saint eaten, and mingled with his bowels, he should breathe out of it angels, yea, there shall burst forth particles of divinity, at every moan or groan in his prayer, which particles of the most high and true God had remained bound in that fig, unless they had been set at liberty by the teeth or belly of some "Elect" saint! . . .

And Thou *sentest Thine hand from above,* and drewest my soul out of that profound darkness, my mother, Thy faithful one, weeping to Thee for me, more than mothers weep the bodily deaths of their children. For she, by that faith and spirit which she had from Thee, discerned the death wherein I lay, and Thou heardest her, O Lord; Thou heardest her, and despisedst not her tears, when streaming

* The Manichaeans

274

down, they watered the ground * under her eyes in every place where she prayed; yea Thou heardest her. For whence was that dream whereby Thou comfortedst her; so that she allowed me to live with her, and to eat at the same table in the house, which she had begun to shrink from, abhorring and detesting the blasphemies of my error? For she saw herself standing on a certain wooden rule, and a shining youth coming towards her, cheerful and smiling upon her, herself grieving, and overwhelmed with grief. But he having (in order to instruct, as is their wont, not to be instructed) inquired of her the causes of her grief and daily tears, and she answering that she was bewailing my perdition, he bade her rest contented, and told her to look and observe, "That where she was, there was I also." And when she looked, she saw me standing by her in the same rule. Whence was this, but that Thine ears were toward her heart? O Thou Good omnipotent, who so carest for every one of us, as if Thou caredst for him only; and so for all, as if they were but one!

Whence was this also, that when she had told me this vision, and I would fain bend it to mean, "That she rather should not despair of being one day what I was"; she presently, without any hesitation, replies "No; for it was not told me that, 'where he, there thou also'; but 'where thou, there he also.'" I confess to Thee, O Lord, that to the best of my remembrance (and I have oft spoken of this), that Thy answer, through my waking mother—that she was not perplexed by the plausibility of my false interpretation, and so quickly saw what was to be seen, and which I certainly had not perceived, before she spoke—even then moved me more than the dream itself, by which a joy to the holy woman, to be fulfilled so long after, was, for the consolation of her present anguish, so long before foresignified. For almost nine years passed, in which I wallowed in the mire of that deep pit, and the darkness of falsehood, often assaying to rise, but dashed down the more grievously. All which time that chaste, godly, and sober widow, such as Thou lovest, now more cheered with hope, yet no whit relaxing in her weeping and mourning, ceased not at all hours of her devotions to bewail my case unto Thee. And her *prayers entered into Thy presence;* and yet Thou sufferest me to be yet involved and reinvolved in that darkness.

Thou gavest her meantime another answer, which I call to mind; for much I pass by, hastening to those things which more press me

* Saint Augustine is alluding to the devout manner of the ancients who used to lie flat on their faces in prayer.

to confess unto Thee, and much I do not remember. Thou gavest her then another answer, by a Priest of Thine, a certain Bishop brought up in Thy Church, and well studied in Thy books. Whom when this woman had entreated to vouchsafe to converse with me, refute my errors, unteach me ill things, and teach me good things (for this he was wont to do, when he found persons fitted to receive it), he refused, wisely, as I afterward perceived. For he answered, that I was yet unteachable, being puffed up with the novelty of that heresy, and had already perplexed divers unskillful persons with captious questions, as she had told him. "But let him alone a while," saith he, "only pray God for him, he will of himself by reading find what that error is, and how great its impiety." At the same time he told her, how himself, when a little one, had by his seduced mother been consigned over to the Manichees, and had not only read, but frequently copied out almost all their books, and had (without any argument or proof from anyone) seen how much that sect was to be avoided; and had avoided it. Which when he had said, and she would not be satisfied, but urged him more, with entreaties and many tears, that he would see me, and discourse with me; he, a little displeased at her importunity, saith, "Go thy ways, and God bless thee, for it is not possible that the son of these tears should perish." Which answer she took (as she often mentioned in her conversations with me) as if it had sounded from heaven.

BOOK IV

Saint Augustine's life from nineteen to twenty-eight; himself a Manichaean, and seducing others to the same heresy; partial obedience amidst vanity and sin, consulting astrologers, only partially shaken herein; loss of an early friend, who is converted by being baptized when in a swoon; reflections on grief, on real and unreal friendship, and love of fame; writes on "the fair and fit," yet cannot rightly, though God had given him great talents, since he entertained wrong notions of God; and so even his knowledge he applied ill.

FOR THIS SPACE of nine years then (from my nineteenth year, to my eight-and-twentieth) we lived seduced and seducing, deceived and deceiving, in divers lusts; openly, by sciences which they call liberal; secretly, with a false-named religion; here proud, there superstitious, everywhere vain! Here, hunting after the emptiness of popular praise, down even to theatrical applauses, and poetic prizes, and strifes for grassy garlands, and the follies of shows, and the intemperance of desires. There, desiring to be cleansed from these defilements, by carrying food to those who were called "elect" and "holy," out of which, in the workhouse of their stomachs, they should forge for us Angels and Gods, by whom we might be cleansed. These things did I follow, and practice with my friends, deceived by me, and with me. Let the arrogant mock me, and such as have not been, to their soul's health, stricken and cast down by Thee, O my God; but I would still confess to Thee mine own shame in Thy praise. . . .

In those years I taught rhetoric, and, overcome by cupidity, made sale of a loquacity to overcome by. Yet I preferred (Lord, Thou knowest) honest scholars (as they are accounted), and these I, without artifice, taught artifices, not to be practiced against the life of the guiltless, though sometimes for the life of the guilty. And Thou, O God, from afar perceivedst me stumbling in that slippery course, and amid much smoke sending out some sparks of faithfulness, which I showed in that my guidance of *such as loved vanity,* and *sought after leasing,* myself their companion. In those years I had one—not in that which is called lawful marriage, but whom I had found out in a wayward passion, void of understanding; yet but one, remaining faithful even to her; in whom I in my own case experienced, what difference there is betwixt the self-restraint of the marriage covenant, for the sake of issue, and the bargain of a lustful love, where children are born against their parents' will, although, once born, they constrain love.

I remember also, that when I had settled to enter the lists for a theatrical prize, some wizard asked me what I would give him to win: but I, detesting and abhorring such foul mysteries, answered, "Though the garland were of imperishable gold, I would not suffer a fly to be killed to gain me it." For he was to kill some living creatures in his sacrifices, and by those honors to invite the devils to favor me. But this ill also I rejected, not out of a pure love for Thee, O God of my heart; for I knew not how to love Thee, who knew not how to conceive aught beyond a material brightness. And doth not a soul, sighing after such fictions, commit fornication against Thee, trust in things unreal, and *feed the wind?* Still I would not forsooth have sacrifices offered to devils for me, to whom I was sacrificing myself by that superstition. For, what else is it *to feed the wind,* but to feed them, that is, by going astray to become their pleasure and derision?

277

Translated by E. B. Pusey

Those impostors then, whom they style Mathematicians, I consulted without scruple; because they seemed to use no sacrifice, nor to pray to any spirit for their divinations: which art, however, Christian and true piety consistently rejects and condemns. For, *it is a good thing to confess unto Thee,* and to say, *Have mercy upon me, heal my soul, for I have sinned against Thee;* and not to abuse Thy mercy for a license to sin, but to remember the Lord's words, *Behold, thou art made whole, sin no more, lest a worse thing come unto thee.* All which wholesome advice they labor to destroy, saying, "The cause of thy sin is inevitably determined in heaven"; and "This did Venus, or Saturn, or Mars": that man, forsooth, flesh and blood, and proud corruption, might be blameless; while the Creator and Ordainer of heaven and the stars is to bear the blame. And who is He but our God? the very sweetness and wellspring of righteousness, who *renderest to every man according to his works:* and *a broken and contrite heart wilt Thou not despise.*

There was in those days a wise man, very skillful in physic, and renowned therein, who had with his own proconsular hand put the Agonistic garland upon my distempered head, but not as a physician: for this disease Thou only curest, *who resistest the proud, and givest grace to the humble.* But didst Thou fail me even by that old man, or forbear to heal my soul? For having become more acquainted with him, and hanging assiduously and fixedly on his speech (for though in simple terms, it was vivid, lively, and earnest), when he had gathered by my discourse, that I was given to the books of nativity-casters, he kindly and fatherly advised me to cast them away, and not fruitlessly bestow a care and diligence, necessary for useful things, upon these vanities; saying, that he had in his earliest years studied that art, so as to make it the profession whereby he should live, and that, understanding Hippocrates, he could soon have understood such a study as this; and yet he had given it over, and taken to physic, for no other reason, but that he found it utterly false; and he, a grave man would not get his living by deluding people. "But thou," saith he, "hast rhetoric to maintain thyself by, so that thou followest this of free choice, not of necessity: the more then oughtest thou to give me credit herein, who labored to acquire it so perfectly, as to get my living by it alone." Of whom when I had demanded, how then could many true things be foretold by it, he answered me (as he could), "that the force of chance, diffused throughout the whole order of things, brought this about. For if when a man by haphazard opens the pages of some poet, who sang and thought of something wholly different, a verse oftentimes fell out, wondrously agreeable to the present business: it were not to be wondered at, if out of the soul of man, unconscious what takes place in it, by some higher instinct an answer should be given, by hap, not by art, corresponding to the business and actions of the demander."

And thus much, either from or through him, Thou conveyedst to me, and tracedst in my memory, what I might hereafter examine for myself. But at that time neither he, nor my dearest Nebridius, a youth singularly good and of a holy fear, who derided the whole body of divination, could persuade me to cast it aside, the authority of the authors swaying me yet more, and as yet I had found no certain proof (such as I sought) whereby it might without all doubt appear, that what had been truly foretold by those consulted was the result of haphazard, not of the art of the stargazers.

In those years when I first began to teach rhetoric in my native town, I had made one my friend, but too dear to me, from a community of pursuits, of mine own age, and, as myself, in the first opening flower of youth. He had grown up of a child with me, and we had been both schoolfellows, and playfellows. But he was not yet my friend as afterward, nor even then, as true friendship is; for true it cannot be, unless in such as Thou cementest together, cleaving unto Thee, by that *love which is shed abroad in our hearts by the Holy Ghost, which is given unto us.* Yet was it but too sweet, ripened by the warmth of kindred studies: for, from the true faith (which he as a youth had not soundly and thoroughly imbibed), I had warped him also to those superstitious and pernicious fables, for which my mother bewailed me. With me he now erred in mind, nor could my soul be without him. But behold Thou wert close on the steps of Thy fugitives, at once *God of vengeance,* and Fountain of mercies, turning us to Thyself by wonderful means; Thou tookest that man out of this life, when he had scarce filled up one whole year of my friendship, sweet to me above all sweetness of that my life.

Who can recount all Thy praises, which he hath felt in his one self? What didst Thou then, my God, and how unsearchable is the *abyss of Thy judgments?* For long, sore sick of a fever, he lay senseless in a deathsweat; and his recovery being despaired of, he was baptized, unknowing; myself meanwhile little regarding, and presuming that his soul would retain rather what it had received of me, not what was wrought on his unconscious body. But it proved far otherwise: for

279

he was refreshed, and restored. Forthwith, as soon as I could speak
with him (and I could, so soon as he was able, for I never left him,
and we hung but too much upon each other), I essayed to jest with
him, as though he would jest with me at that baptism which he had
received, when utterly absent in mind and feeling, but had now understood that he had received. But he so shrunk from me, as from an
enemy; and with a wonderful and sudden freedom bade me, as I
would continue his friend, forbear such language to him. I, all astonished and amazed, suppressed all my emotions till he should grow
well, and his health were strong enough for me to deal with him, as I
would. But he was taken away from my frenzy, that with Thee he
might be preserved for my comfort; a few days after, in my absence,
he was attacked again by the fever, and so departed.

At this grief my heart was utterly darkened; and whatever I beheld
was death. My native country was a torment to me, and my father's
house a strange unhappiness; and whatever I had shared with him,
wanting him, became a distracting torture. Mine eyes sought him
everywhere, but he was not granted them; and I hated all places, for
that they had not him; nor could they now tell me, "he is coming," as
when he was alive and absent. I became a great riddle to myself, and
I asked my soul, *why she was so sad, and why she disquieted me
sorely:* but she knew not what to answer me. And if I said, *Trust in
God,* she very rightly obeyed me not; because that most dear friend,
whom she had lost, was, being man, both truer and better, than that
phantasm she was bid to trust in. Only tears were sweet to me, for
they succeeded my friend, in the dearest of my affections. . . .

Wretched I was; and wretched is every soul bound by the friendship of perishable things; he is torn asunder when he loses them, and
then he feels the wretchedness, which he had, ere yet he lost them.
So was it then with me; I wept most bitterly, and found my repose in
bitterness. Thus was I wretched, and that wretched life I held dearer
than my friend. For though I would willingly have changed it, yet was
I more unwilling to part with it, than with him; yea, I know not
whether I would have parted with it even for him, as is related (if not
feigned) of Pylades and Orestes, that they would gladly have died
for each other or together, not to live together being to them worse
than death. But in me there had arisen some unexplained feeling, too
contrary to this, for at once I loathed exceedingly to live, and feared
to die. I suppose, the more I loved him, the more did I hate, and
fear (as a most cruel enemy) death, which had bereaved me of him:

280

and I imagined it would speedily make an end of all men, since it had power over him. Thus was it with me, I remember. . . .

O madness, which knowest not how to love men, like men! O foolish man that I then was, enduring impatiently the lot of man! I fretted then, sighed, wept, was distracted; had neither rest nor counsel. For I bore about a shattered and bleeding soul, impatient of being borne by me, yet where to repose it, I found not. Not in calm groves, not in games and music, nor in fragrant spots, nor in curious banquetings, nor in the pleasures of the bed and the couch; nor, finally, in books of poesy, found it repose. All things looked ghastly, yea, the very light; whatsoever was not what he was, was revolting and hateful, except groaning and tears. For in those alone found I a little refreshment. But when my soul was withdrawn from them, a huge load of misery weighed me down. . . . For whither should my heart flee from my heart? Whither should I flee from myself? Whither not follow myself? And yet I fled out of my country; for so should mine eyes less look for him, where they were not wont to see him. And thus from Thagaste, I came to Carthage.

Times lose no time; nor do they roll idly by; through our senses they work strange operations on the mind. Behold, they went and came day by day; and by coming and going, introduced into my mind other imaginations, and other remembrances; and little by little patched me up again with my old kind of delights, unto which that my sorrow gave way. And yet there succeeded, not indeed other griefs, yet the causes of other griefs. For whence had that former grief so easily reached my very inmost soul, but that I had poured out my soul upon the dust, in loving one that must die, as if he would never die? For what restored and refreshed me chiefly, was the solaces of other friends, with whom I did love, what instead of Thee I loved: and this was a great fable, and protracted lie, by whose adulterous stimulus, our soul, which lay itching in our ears, was being defiled. But that fable would not die to me, so oft as any of my friends died. There were other things which in them did more take my mind; to talk and jest together, to do kind offices by turns; to read together honeyed books; to play the fool or to be earnest together; to dissent at times without discontent, as a man might with his own self; and even with the seldomness of these dissentings, to season our more frequent consentings; sometimes to teach, and sometimes learn; long for the absent with impatience; and welcome the coming with joy. These and the like expressions, proceeding out of the hearts of those that loved

281

and were loved again, by the countenance, the tongue, the eyes, and a thousand pleasing gestures, were so much fuel to melt our souls together, and out of many make but one. . . .

I loved these lower beauties, and I was sinking to the very depths, and to my friends I said, "Do we love anything but the beautiful? What then is the beautiful? and what is beauty? What is it that attracts and wins us to the things we love? for unless there were in them a grace and beauty, they could by no means draw us unto them." And I marked and perceived that in bodies themselves, there was a beauty, from their forming a sort of whole, and again, another from apt and mutual correspondence, as of a part of the body with its whole, or a shoe with a foot, and the like. And this consideration sprang up in my mind, out of my inmost heart, and I wrote "On the Fair and Fit," I think, two or three books. Thou knowest, O Lord, for it is gone from me; for I have them not, but they are strayed from me, I know not how. . . .

I was then some six- or seven-and-twenty years old when I wrote those volumes; revolving within me corporeal fictions, buzzing in the ears of my heart, which I turned, O sweet truth, to thy inward melody, meditating on the "fair and fit," and longing to stand and hearken to Thee, and *to rejoice greatly at the Bridegroom's voice,* but could not; for by the voices of mine own errors, I was hurried abroad, and through the weight of my own pride, I was sinking into the lowest pit. For Thou didst not *make me to hear joy and gladness,* nor did *the bones exult which were not yet humbled.* . . .

And what did it profit me, that all the books I could procure of the so-called liberal arts, I, the vile slave of vile affections, read by myself, and understood? And I delighted in them, but knew not whence came all, that therein was true or certain. For I had my back to the light, and my face to the things enlightened; whence my face, with which I discerned the things enlightened, itself was not enlightened. Whatever was written, either on rhetoric, or logic, geometry, music, and arithmetic, by myself without much difficulty or any instructor, I understood. Thou knowest, O Lord my God; because both quickness of understanding, and acuteness in discerning, is Thy gift: yet did I not thence sacrifice to Thee. So then it served not to my use, but rather to my perdition, since I went about to get so good a *portion of my substance* into my own keeping; and I *kept not my strength for Thee,* but wandered from Thee *into a far country, to spend it upon harlotries.* For what profited me good abilities, not employed to good uses? For I felt not that those arts were attained with great difficulty, even by the studious and talented, until I attempted to explain them to such; when he most excelled in them, who followed me not altogether slowly.

But what did this further me, imagining that Thou, O Lord God, the Truth, wert a vast and bright body, and I a fragment of that body? Perverseness too great! But such was I. Nor do I blush, O my God, to *confess to Thee Thy mercies toward me,* and to call upon Thee, who blushed not then to profess to men my blasphemies, and to bark against Thee. What profited me then my nimble wit in those sciences and all those most knotty volumes, unraveled by me, without aid from human instruction; seeing I erred so foully, and with such sacrilegious shamefulness, in the doctrine of piety? Or what hindrance was a far slower wit to Thy little ones, since they departed not far from Thee, that in the nest of Thy Church they might securely be fledged, and nourish the wings of charity, by the food of a sound faith. O Lord our God, *under the shadow of Thy wings let us hope;* protect us, and carry us. Thou wilt carry us both when little, and *even to hoar hairs wilt Thou carry us;* for our firmness, when it is Thou, then is it firmness; but when our own, it is infirmity. Our good ever lives with Thee; from which when we turn away, we are turned aside. Let us now, O Lord, return, that we may not be overturned, because with Thee our good lives without any decay, which good art Thou; nor need we fear, lest there be no place whither to return, because we fell from it: for through our absence, our mansion fell not—Thy eternity.

BOOK V

Saint Augustine's twenty-ninth year. Faustus, a snare of Satan to many, made an instrument of deliverance to Saint Augustine, by showing the ignorance of the Manichees on those things, wherein they professed to have divine knowledge. Augustine gives up all thought of going further among the Manichees: is guided to Rome and Milan, where he hears Saint Ambrose, leaves the Manichees, and becomes again a catechumen in the Catholic Church.

I WOULD LAY open before my God that nine-and-twentieth year of mine age. There had then come to Carthage, a certain Bishop of the Manichees, Faustus by name, a great snare of the Devil, and many were entangled by him through that lure of his smooth language: which though I did commend, yet could I separate from the truth of the things which I was earnest to learn: nor did I so much regard the service of oratory, as the science which this Faustus, so praised among them, set before me to feed upon. Fame had before bespoken him most knowing in all valuable learning, and exquisitely skilled in the liberal sciences. And since I had read and well remembered much of the philosophers, I compared some things of theirs with those long fables of the Manichees, and found the former the more probable; even although they *could only prevail so far as to make judgment of this lower world, the Lord of it they could by no means find out. For Thou art great, O Lord, and hast respect unto the humble, but the proud Thou beholdest afar off.* Nor dost thou *draw near;* but to *the contrite in heart,* nor art found by the proud, no, not though by curious skill they could number the stars and the sand, and measure the starry heavens, and track the courses of the planets. . . .

And for almost all those nine years, wherein with unsettled mind I had been their disciple, I had longed but too intensely for the coming of this Faustus. For the rest of the sect, whom by chance I had lighted upon, when unable to solve my objections about these things, still held out to me the coming of this Faustus, by conference with whom, these and greater difficulties, if I had them, were to be most readily and abundantly cleared. When then he came, I found him a man of pleasing discourse, and who could speak fluently and in better terms, yet still but the selfsame things which they were wont to say. But what availed the utmost neatness of the cupbearer to my thirst for a more precious draught? Mine ears were already cloyed with the like, nor did they seem to me therefore better, because better said; nor therefore true, because eloquent; nor the soul therefore wise, because the face was comely, and the language graceful. But they who held him out to me, were no good judges of things; and therefore to them he appeared understanding and wise, because in words pleasing. I felt however that another sort of people were suspicious even of truth, and refused to assent to it, if delivered in a smooth and copious discourse. But Thou, O my God, hadst already taught me by wonderful and secret ways, and therefore I believe that Thou taughtest me, because it is truth, nor is there besides Thee any teacher of truth, where or whencesoever it may shine upon us. Of Thyself therefore had I now learned, that neither ought anything to seem to be spoken truly, because eloquently; nor therefore falsely, because the utterance of

284

the lips is inharmonious; nor, again, therefore true, because rudely delivered; nor therefore false, because the language is rich; but that wisdom and folly, are as wholesome and unwholesome food; and adorned or unadorned phrases, as courtly or country vessels; either kind of meats may be served up in either kind of dishes.

That greediness then, wherewith I had of so long time expected that man, was delighted verily with his action and feeling when disputing, and his choice and readiness of words to clothe his ideas. I was then delighted, and, with many others and more than they, did I praise and extol him. It troubled me, however, that in the assembly of his auditors, I was not allowed to put in, and communicate those questions that troubled me, in familiar converse with him. Which when I might, and with my friends began to engage his ears at such times as it was not unbecoming for him to discuss with me, and had brought forward such things as moved me; I found him first utterly ignorant of liberal sciences, save grammar, and that but in an ordinary way. But because he had read some of Tully's Orations, a very few books of Seneca, some things of the poets, and such few volumes of his own sect, as were written in Latin and neatly, and was daily practiced in speaking, he acquired a certain eloquence, which proved the more pleasing and seductive, because under the guidance of a good wit, and with a kind of natural gracefulness. . . .

For after it was clear, that he was ignorant of those arts in which I thought he excelled, I began to despair of his opening and solving the difficulties which perplexed me (of which indeed however ignorant, he might have held the truths of piety, had he not been a Manichee). For their books are fraught with prolix fables, of the heaven, and stars, sun, and moon, and I now no longer thought him able satisfactorily to decide what I much desired, whether, on comparison of these things with the calculations I had elsewhere read, the account given in the books of Manichaeus were preferable, or at least as good. Which when I proposed to be considered and discussed, he, so far modestly, shrunk from the burden. For he knew that he knew not these things, and was not ashamed to confess it. For he was not one of those talking persons, many of whom I had endured, who undertook to teach me these things, and said nothing. But this man had a heart, though not right toward Thee, yet neither altogether treacherous to himself. For he was not altogether ignorant of his own ignorance, nor would he rashly be entangled in a dispute, whence he could neither retreat, nor extricate himself fairly. Even for this I liked

285

him the better. For fairer is the modesty of a candid mind, than the knowledge of those things which I desired; and such I found him, in all the more difficult and subtle questions.

My zeal for the writings of Manichaeus being thus blunted, and despairing yet more of their other teachers, seeing that in divers things which perplexed me, he, so renowned among them, had so turned out; I began to engage with him in the study of that literature, on which he also was much set (and which as rhetoric-reader I was at that time teaching young students at Carthage), and to read with him, either what himself desired to hear, or such as I judged fit for his genius. But all my efforts whereby I had purposed to advance in that sect, upon knowledge of that man, came utterly to an end; not that I detached myself from them altogether, but as one finding nothing better, I had settled to be content meanwhile with what I had in whatever way fallen upon, unless by chance something more eligible should dawn upon me. Thus that Faustus, to so many a snare of death, had now, neither willing nor witting it, begun to loosen that wherein I was taken. . . .

Thou didst deal with me, that I should be persuaded to go to Rome, and to teach there rather, what I was teaching at Carthage. And how I was persuaded to this, I will not neglect to confess to Thee: because herein also the deepest recesses of Thy wisdom, and Thy most present mercy to us, must be considered and confessed. I did not wish therefore to go to Rome, because higher gains and higher dignities were warranted me by my friends who persuaded me to this (though even these things had at that time an influence over my mind), but my chief and almost only reason was, that I heard that young men studied there more peacefully, and were kept quiet under a restraint of more regular discipline; so that they did not, at their pleasures, petulantly rush into the school of one, whose pupils they were not, nor were even admitted without his permission. Whereas at Carthage, there reigns among the scholars a most disgraceful and unruly license. They burst in audaciously, and with gestures almost frantic, disturb all order which any one hath established for the good of his scholars. Divers outrages they commit, with a wonderful stolidity, punishable by law, did not custom uphold them; that custom evincing them to be the more miserable, in that they now do as lawful, what by Thy eternal law shall never be lawful; and they think they do it unpunished, whereas they are punished with the very blindness whereby they do it, and suffer incomparably worse than what they do. The manners then which, when a student, I would not make my own, I was fain, as a teacher, to endure in others: and so I was well pleased to go where, all that knew it, assured me that the like was not done. But Thou, *my refuge and my portion in the land of the living,* that I might change my earthly dwelling for the salvation of my soul, at Carthage didst goad me, that I might thereby be torn from it; and at Rome didst proffer me allurements, whereby I might be drawn thither, by men in love with a dying life, the one doing frantic, the other promising vain things; and, to correct my steps, didst secretly use their and my own perverseness. For both they who disturbed my quiet, were blinded with a disgraceful frenzy, and they who invited me elsewhere, savored of earth. And I, who here detested real misery, was there seeking unreal happiness.

But why I went hence, and went thither, Thou knewest, O God, yet showedst it neither to me, nor to my mother, who grievously bewailed my journey, and followed me as far as the sea. But I deceived her, holding me by force, that either she might keep me back, or go with me, and I feigned that I had a friend whom I could not leave, till he had a fair wind to sail. And I lied to my mother, and such a mother, and escaped: for this also hast Thou mercifully forgiven me, preserving me, thus full of execrable defilements, from the waters of the sea, for the water of Thy Grace; whereby when I was cleansed, the streams of my mother's eyes should be dried, with which for me she daily watered the ground under her face. And yet refusing to return without me, I scarcely persuaded her to stay that night in a place hard by our ship, where was an Oratory * in memory of the blessed Cyprian. That night I privily departed, but she was not behind in weeping and prayer. And what, O Lord, was she with so many tears asking of Thee, but that Thou wouldest not suffer me to sail? But Thou, in the depth of Thy counsels and hearing the main point of her desire, regardest not what she then asked, that Thou mightest make me what she ever asked. The wind blew and swelled our sails, and withdrew the shore from our sight; and she on the morrow was there, frantic with sorrow, and with complaints and groans filled Thine ears, who didst then disregard them; whilst through my desires, Thou wert hurrying me to end all desire, and the earthly part of her affection to me was chastened by the allotted scourge of sorrows. For she loved my being with her, as mothers do, but much more than many; and she knew not how great joy Thou wert about to work for her out of my absence. She knew not; therefore did she weep and wail, and by this

* In Augustine's time a church built over the grave of a martyr

agony there appeared in her the inheritance of Eve, with sorrow seeking, what in sorrow she had brought forth. And yet, after accusing my treachery and hardheartedness, she betook herself again to intercede to Thee for me, went to her wonted place, and I to Rome. . . .

But now despairing to make proficiency in that false doctrine, even those things (with which if I should find no better, I had resolved to rest contented) I now held more laxly and carelessly. For there half arose a thought in me, that those philosophers, whom they call Academics, were wiser than the rest, for that they held, men ought to doubt everything, and laid down that no truth can be comprehended by man: for so, not then understanding even their meaning, I also was clearly convinced that they thought, as they are commonly reported. Yet did I freely and openly discourage that host of mine from that overconfidence which I perceived him to have in those fables, which the books of Manichaeus are full of. Yet I lived in more familiar friendship with them, than with others who were not of this heresy. Nor did I maintain it with my ancient eagerness; still my intimacy with that sect (Rome secretly harboring many of them) made me slower to seek any other way: especially since I despaired of finding the truth, from which they had turned me aside. . . .

Furthermore, what the Manichees had criticized in Thy Scriptures, I thought could not be defended; yet at times verily I had a wish to confer upon these several points with someone very well skilled in those books, and to make trial what he thought thereon: for the words of one Helpidius, as he spoke and disputed face to face against the said Manichees, had begun to stir me even at Carthage: in that he had produced things out of the Scriptures, not easily withstood, the Manichees' answer whereto seemed to me weak. And this answer they liked not to give publicly, but only to us in private. It was, that the Scriptures of the New Testament had been corrupted by I know not whom, who wished to engraft the law of the Jews upon the Christian faith: yet themselves produced not any uncorrupted copies. But I, conceiving of things corporeal only, was mainly held down, vehemently oppressed and in a manner suffocated by those "masses"; panting under which after the breath of Thy truth, I could not breathe it pure and untainted.

I began then diligently to practice that for which I came to Rome, to teach rhetoric; and first, to gather some to my house, to whom, and through whom, I had begun to be known; when lo, I found other offenses committed in Rome, to which I was not exposed in Africa. . . .

288

When therefore they of Milan had sent to Rome to the prefect of the city, to furnish them with a rhetoric reader for their city, and send him at the public expense, I made application . . . that Symmachus, then prefect of the city, would try me by setting me some subject, and so send me. To Milan I came, to Ambrose the Bishop, known to the whole world as among the best of men, Thy devout servant. His eloquent discourse did then plentifully dispense unto Thy people the flour of Thy wheat, the gladness of Thy oil, and the sober inebriation of Thy wine. To him was I unknowing led by Thee, that by him I might knowingly be led to Thee. That man of God received me as a father, and showed me an Episcopal kindness on my coming. Thenceforth I began to love him, at first indeed not as a teacher of the truth (which I utterly despaired of in Thy Church), but as a person kind toward myself. And I listened diligently to him preaching to the people, not with that intent I ought, but, as it were, trying his eloquence, whether it answered the fame thereof, or flowed fuller or lower than was reported; and I hung on his words attentively; but of the matter I was as a careless and scornful looker-on; and I was delighted with the sweetness of his discourse, more recondite, yet in manner, less winning and harmonious, than that of Faustus. Of the matter, however, there was no comparison; for the one was wandering amid Manichaean delusions, the other teaching salvation most soundly. But *salvation is far from sinners,* such as I then stood before him; and yet was I drawing nearer by little and little, and unconsciously.

For though I took no pains to learn what he spoke, but only to hear how he spoke (for that empty care alone was left me, despairing of a way, open for man, to Thee); yet together with the words which I would choose, came also into my mind the things which I would refuse; for I could not separate them. And while I opened my heart to admit "how eloquently he spoke," there also entered "how truly he spoke"; but this by degrees. For first, these things also had now begun to appear to me capable of defense; and the Catholic faith, for which I had thought nothing could be said against the Manichees' objections, I now thought might be maintained without shamelessness; especially after I had heard one or two places of the Old Testament resolved, and ofttimes *"in a figure,"* which when I understood literally, I was slain spiritually. Very many places then of those books having been explained, I now blamed my despair, in believing, that no answer could be given to such as hated and scoffed at the Law and the Prophets. Yet did I not therefore then see, that the Catholic way was to be held, because it also could find learned maintainers, who could at large and with some show of reason answer objections; nor that what I held was therefore to be condemned, because both sides could be maintained. For the Catholic cause seemed to me in such sort not vanquished, as still not as yet to be victorious.

Hereupon I earnestly bent my mind, to see if in any way I could by any certain proof convict the Manichees of falsehood. Could I once have conceived a spiritual substance, all their strongholds had been beaten down, and cast utterly out of my mind; but I could not. Notwithstanding, concerning the frame of this world, and the whole of nature, which the senses of the flesh can reach to, as I more and more considered and compared things, I judged the tenets of most of the philosophers to have been much more probable. So then after the manner of the Academics (as they are supposed) doubting of everything, and wavering between all, I settled so far, that the Manichees were to be abandoned; judging that, even while doubting, I might not continue in that sect, to which I already preferred some of the philosophers; to which philosophers notwithstanding, for that they were without the saving Name of Christ, I utterly refused to commit the cure of my sick soul. I determined therefore so long to be a catechumen in the Catholic Church, to which I had been commended by my parents, till something certain should dawn upon me, whither I might steer my course.

BOOK VI

Arrival of Monica at Milan; her obedience to Saint Ambrose, and his value for her; Saint Ambrose's habits; Augustine's gradual abandonment of error; finds that he has blamed the Catholic Church wrongly; desire of absolute certainty, but struck with the contrary analogy of God's natural Providence; how shaken in his worldly pursuits; God's guidance of his friend Alypius; Augustine debates with himself and his friends about their mode of life; his inveterate sins, and dread of judgment.

MY MOTHER HAD now come to me, resolute through piety, following me over sea and land, in all perils confiding in Thee. For in perils of the sea, she comforted the very mariners (by whom passengers unacquainted with the deep, use rather to be comforted when troubled), assuring them of a safe arrival, because Thou hadst by a vision assured her thereof. She found me in grievous peril, through despair of ever finding truth. But when I had discovered to her, that I was now no longer a Manichee, though not yet a Catholic Christian, she was not overjoyed, as at something unexpected; although she was now assured concerning that part of my misery, for which she bewailed me as one dead, though to be reawakened by Thee, carrying me forth upon the *bier* of her thoughts, that Thou mightest say to the *son of the widow, Young man, I say unto Thee, Arise; and he should revive, and begin to speak, and thou shouldest deliver him to his mother.* Her heart then was shaken with no tumultuous exultation, when she heard that what she daily with tears desired of Thee, was already in so great part realized; in that, though I had not yet attained the truth, I was rescued from falsehood. But, as being assured, that Thou, who hadst promised the whole, wouldest one day give the rest, most calmly, and with a heart full of confidence, she replied to me, "She believed in Christ, that before she departed this life, she should see me a Catholic believer." Thus much to me. But to Thee, Fountain of mercies, poured she forth more copious prayers and tears, that Thou wouldest hasten Thy help, and enlighten my darkness; and she hastened the more eagerly to the Church, and hung upon the lips of Ambrose, praying for *the fountain of that water,* which springeth up unto life everlasting.* But that man she loved *as an angel of God,* because she knew that by him I had been brought for the present to that doubtful state of faith I now was in, through which she anticipated most confidently, that I should pass from sickness unto health, after the access, as it were, of a sharper fit, which physicians call "the crisis.". . .

Nor did I yet groan in my prayers, that Thou wouldest help me; but my spirit was wholly intent on learning, and restless to dispute. And Ambrose himself, as the world counts happy, I esteemed a happy man, whom personages so great held in such honor; only his celibacy seemed to me a painful course. But what hope he bore within him, what struggles he had against the temptations which beset his very excellencies, or what comfort in adversities, and what sweet joys Thy Bread had for the hidden mouth of his spirit, when chewing the cud thereof, I neither could conjecture, nor had experienced. Nor did he know the tides of my feelings, or the abyss of my danger. For I could not ask of him, what I would as I would, being shut out both from his

* Baptism

ear and speech by multitudes of busy people, whose weaknesses he served. With whom when he was not taken up (which was but a little time), he was either refreshing his body with the sustenance absolutely necessary, or his mind with reading. But when he was reading, his eye glided over the pages, and his heart searched out the sense, but his voice and tongue were at rest. Ofttimes when we had come (for no man was forbidden to enter, nor was it his wont that any who came should be announced to him), we saw him thus reading to himself, and never otherwise; and having long sat silent (for who durst intrude on one so intent?) we were fain to depart, conjecturing, that in the small interval, which he obtained, free from the din of others' business, for the recruiting of his mind, he was loath to be taken off. Perchance he dreaded lest if the author he read should deliver any thing obscurely, some attentive or perplexed hearer should desire him to expound it, or to discuss some of the harder questions; so that his time being thus spent, he could not turn over so many volumes as he desired; although the preserving of his voice (which a very little speaking would weaken) might be the truer reason for his reading to himself. But with what intent soever he did it, certainly in such a man it was good. . . .

Then Thou, O Lord, little by little with most tender and most merciful hand, touching and composing my heart, didst persuade me . . . that not they who believed Thy Books (which Thou hast established in so great authority among almost all nations), but they who believed them not, were to be blamed; and that they were not to be heard, who should say to me, "How knowest thou those Scriptures to have been imparted unto mankind by the Spirit of the one true and most true God?" For this very thing was of all most to be believed, since no contentiousness of blasphemous questionings, of all that multitude which I had read in the self-contradicting philosophers, could wring this belief from me, "That Thou art" whatsoever Thou wert (what I knew not), and "That the government of human things belongs to Thee."

This I believed, sometimes more strongly, more weakly otherwhile; yet I ever believed both that Thou wert, and hadst a care of us; though I was ignorant, both what was to be thought of Thy substance, and what way led or led back to Thee. Since then we were too weak by abstract reasonings to find out truth: and for this very cause needed the authority of Holy Writ; I had now begun to believe, that Thou wouldest never have given such excellency of authority to that Writ in all lands, hadst Thou not willed thereby to be believed in, thereby sought. For now what things, sounding strangely in the Scripture, were wont to offend me, having heard divers of them expounded satisfactorily, I referred to the depth of the mysteries, and its authority appeared to me the more venerable, and more worthy of religious credence, in that, while it lay open to all to read, it reserved the majesty of its mysteries within its profounder meaning, stooping to all in the great plainness of its words and lowliness of its style, yet calling forth the intensest application of such as are not light of heart; that so it might receive all in its open bosom, and through narrow passages waft over toward Thee some few, yet many more than if it stood not aloft on such a height of authority, nor drew multitudes within its bosom by its holy lowliness. These things I thought on, and Thou wert with me; I sighed, and Thou heardest me; I wavered, and Thou didst guide me; I wandered through the broad way of the world, and Thou didst not forsake me.

I panted after honors, gains, marriage; and Thou deridedst me. In these desires I underwent most bitter crosses, Thou being the more gracious, the less Thou sufferedst aught to grow sweet to me, which was not Thou. Behold my heart, O Lord, who wouldest I should remember all this, and confess to Thee. Let my soul cleave unto Thee, now that Thou hast freed it from that fast-holding birdlime of death. How wretched was it! and Thou didst irritate the feeling of its wound, that forsaking all else, it might be converted unto Thee, who art above all, and without whom all things would be nothing; be converted, and be healed. How miserable was I then, and how didst Thou deal with me, to make me feel my misery on that day, when I was preparing to recite a panegyric of the Emperor, wherein I was to utter many a lie, and lying, was to be applauded by those who knew I lied, and my heart was panting with these anxieties, and boiling with the feverishness of consuming thoughts. For, passing through one of the streets of Milan, I observed a poor beggar, then, I suppose, with a full belly, joking and joyous: and I sighed, and spoke to the friends around me, of the many sorrows of our frenzies; for that by all such efforts of ours, as those wherein I then toiled, dragging along, under the goading of desire, the burden of my own wretchedness, and, by dragging, augmenting it, we yet looked to arrive only at that very joyousness, whither that beggarman had arrived before us, who should never perchance attain it. For what he had obtained by means of a few begged pence, the same was I plotting for by many a toilsome turning

293

and winding; the joy of a temporary felicity. For he verily had not the true joy; but yet I with those my ambitious designs was seeking one much less true. And certainly he was joyous, I anxious; he void of care, I full of fears. But should any ask me, had I rather be merry or fearful? I would answer, merry. Again, if he asked had I rather be such as he was, or what I then was? I should choose to be myself, though worn with cares and fears; but out of wrong judgment; for, was it the truth? For I ought not to prefer myself to him, because more learned than he, seeing I had no joy therein, but sought to please men by it; and that not to instruct, but simply to please. Wherefore also Thou didst break my bones with the staff of thy correction.

Away with those then from my soul, who say to her, "It makes a difference, whence a man's joy is. That beggarman joyed in drunkenness; Thou desiredst to joy in glory." What glory, Lord? That which is not in Thee. For even as his was no true joy, so was that no true glory: and it overthrew my soul more. He that very night should digest his drunkenness; but I had slept and risen again with mine, and was to sleep again, and again to rise with it, how many days, Thou, God, knowest. But "it doth make a difference whence a man's joy is." I know it, and the joy of a faithful hope lieth incomparably beyond such vanity. Yea, and so was he then beyond me: for he verily was the happier; not only for that he was thoroughly drenched in mirth, I disembowelled with cares: but he, by fair wishes, had gotten wine; I, by lying was seeking for empty, swelling praise. Much to this purpose said I then to my friends: and I often marked in them how it fared with me; and I found it went ill with me, and grieved, and doubled that very ill; and if any prosperity smiled on me, I was loath to catch at it, for almost before I could grasp it, it flew away.

These things we, who were living as friends together, bemoaned together, but chiefly and most familiarly did I speak thereof with Alypius and Nebridius, of whom Alypius was born in the same town with me, of persons of chief rank there, but younger than I. For he had studied under me, both when I first lectured in our town, and afterwards at Carthage, and he loved me much, because I seemed to him kind, and learned; and I him, for his great towardliness to virtue, which was eminent enough in one of no greater years. Yet the whirlpool of Carthaginian habits (amongst whom those idle spectacles are hotly followed) had drawn him into the madness of the Circus. . . .

He, not forsaking that secular course which his parents had

charmed him to pursue, had gone before me to Rome, to study law, and there he was carried away incredibly with an incredible eagerness after the shows of gladiators. For being utterly averse to and detesting such spectacles, he was one day by chance met by divers of his acquaintance and fellow students coming from dinner, and they with a familiar violence haled him, vehemently refusing and resisting, into the Amphitheater, during these cruel and deadly shows, he thus protesting, "Though you hale my body to that place, and there set me, can you force me also to turn my mind or my eyes to those shows? I shall then be absent while present, and so shall overcome both you and them." They hearing this, led him on nevertheless, desirous perchance to try that very thing, whether he could do as he said. When they were come thither, and had taken their places as they could, the whole place kindled with that savage pastime. But he, closing the passages of his eyes, forbade his mind to range abroad after such evils; and would he had stopped his ears also! For in the fight, when one fell, a mighty cry of the whole people striking him strongly, overcome by curiosity, and as if prepared to despise and be superior to it whatsoever it were, even when seen, he opened his eyes, and was stricken with a deeper wound in his soul, than the other, whom he desired to behold, was in his body; and he fell more miserably than he, upon whose fall that mighty noise was raised, which entered through his ears, and unlocked his eyes, to make way for the striking and beating down of a soul, bold rather than resolute, and the weaker, in that it had presumed on itself, which ought to have relied on Thee. For so soon as he saw that blood, he therewith drunk down savageness; nor turned away, but fixed his eye, drinking in frenzy, unawares, and was delighted with that guilty fight, and intoxicated with the bloody pastime. Nor was he now the man he came, but one of the throng he came unto, yea, a true associate of theirs that brought him thither. Why say more? He beheld, shouted, kindled, carried thence with him the madness which should goad him to return not only with them who first drew him thither, but also before them, yea and to draw in others. Yet thence didst Thou with a most strong and most merciful hand pluck him, and taughtest him to have confidence not in himself, but in Thee. But this was after. . . .

Him then I had found at Rome, and he cleaved to me by a most strong tie, and went with me to Milan, both that he might not leave me, and might practice something of the law he had studied, more to please his parents, than himself. There he had thrice sat as Assessor with an uncorruptness, much wondered at by others, he wondering at others rather, who could prefer gold to honesty. . . .

Nebridius also, who having left his native country near Carthage, yea and Carthage itself, where he had much lived, leaving his excellent family estate and house, and a mother behind, who was not to follow him, had come to Milan, for no other reason, but that with me he might live in a most ardent search after truth and wisdom. Like me he sighed, like me he wavered, an ardent searcher after true life, and a most acute examiner of the most difficult of questions. Thus were there the mouths of three indigent persons, sighing out their wants one to another, and *waiting upon Thee that Thou mightest give them their meat in due season.* And in all the bitterness, which by Thy mercy followed our worldly affairs, as we looked towards the end, why we should suffer all this, darkness met us; and we turned away groaning, and saying, *How long shall these things be?* This too we often said; and so saying forsook them not, for as yet there dawned nothing certain, which, these forsaken, we might embrace.

And I, viewing and reviewing things, most wondered at the length of time from that my nineteenth year, wherein I had begun to kindle with the desire of wisdom, settling when I had found her, to abandon all the empty hopes and lying frenzies of vain desires. And lo, I was now in my thirtieth year, sticking in the same mire, greedy of enjoying things present, which passed away and wasted my soul; while I said to myself, "Tomorrow I shall find it; it will appear manifestly, and I shall grasp it; lo, Faustus the Manichee will come, and clear every thing! O you great men, ye Academicians, it is true then, that no certainty can be attained for the ordering of life! Nay, let us search the more diligently, and despair not. Lo, things in the ecclesiastical books are not absurd to us now, which sometimes seemed absurd, and may be otherwise taken, and in a good sense. I will take my stand, where, as a child, my parents placed me, until the clear truth be found out. But where shall it be sought or when? Ambrose has no leisure; we have no leisure to read; where shall we find even the books? Whence, or when procure them? from whom borrow them? Let set times be appointed, and certain hours be ordered for the health of our soul. Great hope has dawned; the Catholic Faith teaches not what we thought, and vainly accused it of; her instructed members hold it profane, to believe God to be bounded by the figure of a human body: and do we doubt to 'knock,' that the rest 'may be opened'? The forenoons our scholars take up; what do we during the rest? Why not this? But when then pay we court to our great friends, whose favor we need? When compose what we may sell to scholars? When refresh ourselves, unbending our minds from this intenseness of care?". . .

Alypius indeed kept me from marrying; alleging, that so could we by no means with undistracted leisure live together in the love of wisdom, as we had long desired. For himself was even then most pure in this point, so that it was wonderful; and that the more, since in the outset of his youth he had entered into that course, but had not stuck fast therein; rather had he felt remorse and revolting at it, living thenceforth until now most continently. But I opposed him with the examples of those, who as married men had cherished wisdom, and served God acceptably, and retained their friends, and loved them faithfully. Of whose greatness of spirit I was far short; and bound with the disease of the flesh, and its deadly sweetness, drew along my chain, dreading to be loosed, and as if my wound had been fretted, put back his good persuasions, as it were the hand of one that would unchain me. Moreover, by me did the serpent speak unto Alypius himself, by my tongue weaving and laying in his path pleasurable snares, wherein his virtuous and free feet might be entangled.

For when he wondered that I, whom he esteemed not slightly, should stick so fast in the birdlime of that pleasure, as to protest (so oft as we discussed it) that I could never lead a single life; and urged in my defense when I saw him wonder, that there was great difference between his momentary and scarce-remembered knowledge of that life, which so he might easily despise, and my continued acquaintance whereto if but the honorable name of marriage were added, he ought not to wonder why I could not contemn that course; he began also to desire to be married; not as overcome with desire of such pleasure, but out of curiosity. For he would fain know, he said, what that should be, without which my life, to him so pleasing, would to me seem not life but a punishment. For his mind, free from that chain, was amazed at my thralldom; and through that amazement was going on to a desire of trying it, thence to the trial itself, and thence perhaps to sink into that bondage whereat he wondered, seeing he was willing to *make a covenant with death; and, he that loves danger, shall fall into it*. For whatever honor there be in the office of well-ordering a married life, and a family, moved us but slightly. But me for the most part the habit of satisfying an insatiable appetite tormented, while it held me captive; him, an admiring wonder was leading captive. So were we, until

297

Thou, O Most High, not forsaking our dust, commiserating us miserable, didst come to our help, by wondrous and secret ways.

Continual effort was made to have me married. I wooed, I was promised, chiefly through my mother's pains, that so once married, the health-giving baptism might cleanse me, toward which she rejoiced that I was being daily fitted, and observed that her prayers, and Thy promises, were being fulfilled in my faith. At which time verily, both at my request and her own longing, with strong cries of heart she daily begged of Thee, that Thou wouldest by a vision discover unto her something concerning my future marriage; Thou never wouldest. She saw indeed certain vain and fantastic things, such as the energy of the human spirit, busied thereon, brought together; and these she told me of, not with that confidence she was wont, when Thou showed her anything, but slighting them. For she could, she said, through a certain feeling, which in words she could not express, discern betwixt Thy revelations, and the dreams of her own soul. Yet the matter was pressed on, and a maiden asked in marriage, two years under the fit age; and, as pleasing, was waited for. . . .

Meanwhile my sins were being multiplied, and my concubine being torn from my side as a hindrance to my marriage, my heart which cleaved unto her was torn and wounded and bleeding. And she returned to Africa, vowing unto Thee never to know any other man, leaving with me my son by her. But unhappy I, who could not imitate a very woman, impatient of delay, inasmuch as not till after two years was I to obtain her I sought, not being so much a lover of marriage, as a slave to lust, procured another, though no wife, that so by the servitude of an enduring custom, the disease of my soul might be kept up and carried on in its vigor or even augmented, into the dominion of marriage. Nor was that my wound cured, which had been made by the cutting away of the former, but after inflammation and most acute pain, it mortified, and my pains became less acute, but more desperate.

BOOK VII

Augustine's thirty-first year; gradually extricated from his errors, but still with material conceptions of God; much aided by an argument of Nebridius; sees that the cause of sin lies in free will, rejects the Manichaean heresy, but cannot altogether embrace the doctrine of the Church; recovered from the belief in Astrology, but miserably perplexed about the origin of evil; is led to find in the Platonists the seeds of the doctrine of the Divinity of the WORD, but not of His humiliation; hence he obtains clearer notions of God's majesty, but, not knowing Christ to be the Mediator, remains estranged from Him; all his doubts removed by the study of Holy Scripture, especially Saint Paul.

DECEASED WAS NOW my evil and abominable youth, and I was passing into early manhood; the more defiled by vain things as I grew in years, who could not imagine any substance, but such as is wont to be seen with these eyes. I thought not of Thee, O God, under the figure of a human body; since I began to hear aught of wisdom, I always avoided this; and rejoiced to have found the same in the faith of our spiritual mother, Thy Catholic Church. But what else to conceive Thee I knew not. And I, a man, and such a man, sought to conceive of Thee the sovereign, only, true God; and I did in my inmost soul believe that Thou wert incorruptible, and uninjurable, and unchangeable; because though not knowing whence or how, yet I saw plainly and was sure, that that which may be corrupted, must be inferior to that which cannot; what could not be injured I preferred unhesitatingly to what could receive injury; the unchangeable to things subject to change. My heart passionately cried out against all my phantoms, and with this one blow I sought to beat away from the eye of my mind all that unclean troop, which buzzed around it. And lo, being scarce put off, in the twinkling of an eye they gathered again thick about me, flew against my face, and beclouded it; so that though not under the form of the human body, yet was I constrained to conceive of Thee (that incorruptible, uninjurable, and unchangeable, which I preferred before the corruptible, and injurable, and changeable) as being in space, whether infused into the world, or diffused infinitely without it. Because whatsoever I conceived, deprived of this space, seemed to me nothing, yea altogether nothing, not even a void, as if a body were taken out of its place, and the place should remain empty of any body at all, of earth and water, air and heaven, yet would it remain a void place, as it were a spacious nothing. . . .

Although I held and was firmly persuaded, that Thou our Lord the true God, who madest not only our souls, but our bodies, and not only our souls and bodies, but all beings, and all things, wert undefilable and unalterable, and in no degree mutable; yet understood I not, clearly and without difficulty, the cause of evil. And yet whatever it

299

were, I perceived it was in such wise to be sought out, as should not constrain me to believe the immutable God to be mutable, lest I should become that evil I was seeking out. I sought it out then, thus far free from anxiety, certain of the untruth of what these held, from whom I shrunk with my whole heart: for I saw, that through inquiring the origin of evil, they were filled with evil, in that they preferred to think that Thy substance did suffer ill than their own did commit it.

And I strained to perceive what I now heard, that free will was the cause of our doing ill, and Thy just judgment, of our suffering ill. But I was not able clearly to discern it. So then endeavoring to draw my soul's vision out of that deep pit, I was again plunged therein, and endeavoring often, I was plunged back as often. But this raised me a little into Thy light, that I knew as well that I had a will, as that I lived: when then I did will or not will anything, I was most sure, that no other than myself did will and not will: and I all but saw that there was the cause of my sin. But what I did against my will, I saw that I suffered rather than did, and I judged not to be my fault, but my punishment; whereby however, holding thee to be just, I speedily confessed myself to be not unjustly punished. But again I said, Who made me? Did not my God, who is not only good, but goodness itself? Whence then came I to will evil and not will good, so that I am thus justly punished? who set this in me, and ingrafted into me this plant of bitterness, seeing I was wholly formed by my most sweet God? If the devil were the author, whence is that same devil? And if he also by his own perverse will, of a good angel became a devil, whence, again, came in him that evil will, whereby he became a devil, seeing the whole nature of angels was made by that most good Creator? By these thoughts I was again sunk down and choked; yet not brought down to that hell of error (where no man confesseth unto Thee), to think rather that Thou dost suffer ill, than that man doth it. . . .

By this time also had I rejected the lying divinations and impious dotages of the astrologers. Let Thine own mercies, out of my very inmost soul, confess unto Thee for this also, O my God. For Thou, Thou altogether (for who else calls us back from the death of all errors, save the Life which cannot die, and the Wisdom which needing no light enlightens the minds that need it, whereby the universe is directed, down to the whirling leaves of trees?), Thou madest provision for my obstinacy wherewith I struggled against Vindicianus, an acute old man, and Nebridius, a young man of admirable talents. Vindicianus vehemently affirmed, and Nebridius often (though with some doubtfulness) said, "That there was no such art whereby to foresee things to come, but that men's conjectures were a sort of lottery, and that out of many things, which they said should come to pass, some actually did, unawares to them who spoke it, who stumbled upon it, through their oft speaking." Thou providedst then a friend for me, no negligent consulter of the astrologers; nor yet well skilled in those arts, but, as I said, a curious consulter with them, and yet knowing something, which he said he had heard of his father, which how far it went to overthrow the estimation of that art, he knew not. This man, Firminus by name, having had a liberal education, and well taught in Rhetoric, consulted me, as one very dear to him, what, according to his so-called constellations, I thought on certain affairs of his, wherein his worldly hopes had risen. And I, who had herein now begun to incline towards Nebridius' opinion, did not altogether refuse to conjecture, and tell him what came into my unresolved mind; but added, that I was now almost persuaded, that these were but empty and ridiculous follies. Thereupon he told me, that his father had been very curious in such books, and had a friend as earnest in them as himself, who with joint study and conference fanned the flame of their affections to these toys, so that they would observe the moments, whereat the very dumb animals, which bred about their houses, gave birth, and then observed the relative position of the heavens, thereby to make fresh experiments in this so-called art. Firminus said that he had heard of his father, that about the time his mother was to give birth to him, a womanservant of his father's friend was also with child, which could not escape her master, who took care with most exact diligence to know the births of his very puppies. And so it was, that the one for his wife, and the other for his servant, with the most careful observation, reckoned days, hours, nay, the lesser divisions of the hours. Both women were delivered at the same instant; so that both were constrained to allow the same constellations, even to the minutest points, the one for his son, the other for his newborn slave. For so soon as the women began to be in labor, they each gave notice to the other what was fallen out in their houses, and had messengers ready to send to one another, as soon as they had notice of the actual birth, of which they had easily provided, each in his own province, to give instant intelligence. Thus then the messengers of the respective parties met, he averred, at such an equal distance from either house, that neither of them could make out any difference in the position of the stars, or any other minutest points; and yet Firminus, born in a high estate in his parents' house, ran his course through the gilded paths of life, was increased in riches, raised to honors; whereas that slave continued to serve his master, without any relaxation of his yoke, as Firminus, who knew him, told me.

Upon hearing and believing these things, told by one of such credibility, all my resistance gave way; and first I endeavored to reclaim Firminus himself from that curiosity, by telling him, that upon inspecting his constellations, I ought, if I were to predict truly, to have seen in them, parents eminent among their neighbors, a noble family in its own city, high birth, good education, liberal learning. But if that servant had consulted me upon the same constellations, since they were his also, I ought again (to tell him too truly) to see in them a lineage the most abject, a slavish condition, and every thing else, utterly at variance with the former. Whence then if I spoke the truth, I should, from the same constellations, speak diversely, or if I spoke the same, speak falsely: thence it followed most certainly, that whatever, upon consideration of the constellations, was spoken truly, was spoken not out of art, but chance; and whatever spoken falsely, was not out of ignorance in the art, but the failure of the chance. . . .

Now then, O my Helper, hadst Thou loosed me from those fetters: and I sought "whence is evil," and found no way. But Thou sufferedst me not by any fluctuations of thought to be carried away from the Faith whereby I believed Thee both to be, and Thy substance to be unchangeable, and that Thou hast a care of, and wouldest judge men, and that in Christ, Thy Son, our Lord, and the Holy Scriptures, which the authority of Thy Catholic Church pressed upon me, Thou hadst set the way of man's salvation, to that life which is to be after this death. These things being safe and immovably settled in my mind, I sought anxiously "whence was evil?" What were the pangs of my teeming heart, what groans, O my God! yet even there were Thine ears open, and I knew it not: and when in silence I vehemently sought, those silent contritions of my soul were strong cries unto Thy mercy. . . . And this was the true temperament, and middle region of my safety, to remain in Thy Image, and by serving Thee, rule the body. But when I rose proudly against Thee, and *ran against the Lord with my neck, with the thick bosses of my buckler,* even these inferior things were set above me, and pressed me down, and nowhere was there respite or space of breathing. They met my sight on all sides by heaps and troops, and in thought the images thereof presented themselves unsought, as I would return to Thee, as if they would say unto me,

302

"Whither goest thou, unworthy and defiled?" And these things had grown out of my wound; for Thou "humbledst the proud like one that is wounded," and through my own swelling was I separated from Thee; yea, my pride-swollen face closed up mine eyes.

But Thou, Lord, *abidest forever,* yet not forever art Thou angry with us; because Thou pitiest our dust and ashes, and it was pleasing in Thy sight to reform my deformities; and by inward goads didst Thou rouse me, that I should be ill at ease, until Thou wert manifested to my inward sight. Thus, by the secret hand of Thy medicining, was my swelling abated, and the troubled and bedimmed eyesight of my mind, by the smarting anointings of healthful sorrows, was from day to day healed. . . .

And being thence admonished to return to myself, I entered even into my inward self, Thou being my Guide: and able I was, for Thou wert become my Helper. And I entered and beheld with the eye of my soul (such as it was), above the same eye of my soul, above my mind, the Light Unchangeable. Not this ordinary light, which all flesh may look upon, nor as it were a greater of the same kind, as though the brightness of this should be manifold brighter, and with its greatness take up all space. Not such was this light, but other, yea, far other from all these. Nor was it above my soul, as oil is above water, nor yet as heaven above earth: but above to my soul, because It made me; and I below It, because I was made by It. He that knows the Truth, knows what that Light is; and he that knows It, knows eternity. Love knoweth it. O Truth Who art Eternity! and Love Who art Truth! and Eternity Who art Love! Thou art my God, to Thee do I sigh night and day. Thee when I first knew, Thou liftedst me up, that I might see there was what I might see, and that I was not yet such as to see. And Thou didst beat back the weakness of my sight, streaming forth Thy beams of light upon me most strongly, and I trembled with love and awe: and I perceived myself to be far off from Thee, in the region of unlikeness, as if I heard this Thy voice from on high: "I am the food of grown men; grow, and thou shalt feed upon Me; nor shalt thou convert Me, like the food of thy flesh, into thee, but thou shalt be converted into Me." And I learned, that *Thou for iniquity chastenest man, and Thou madest my soul to consume away like a spider.* And I said, "Is Truth therefore nothing because it is not diffused through space finite or infinite?" And Thou criedst to me from afar: "Yea verily, *I AM that I AM.*" And I heard, as the heart heareth, nor had I room to doubt, and I should sooner doubt that I live, than that Truth is not,

303

which is clearly seen being understood by those things which are made.

And I beheld the other things below Thee, and I perceived, that they neither altogether are, nor altogether are not, for they are, since they are from Thee, but are not, because they are not, what Thou art. For that truly is, which remains unchangeably. *It is good then for me to hold fast unto God; for if I remain not in Him, I cannot in myself; but He remaining in himself, reneweth all things. And Thou art the Lord* my God, since Thou *standest not in need of my goodness.* . . .

And I wondered that I now loved Thee, and no phantasm for Thee. And yet did I not press on to enjoy my God; but was borne up to Thee by Thy beauty, and soon borne down from Thee by mine own weight, sinking with sorrow into these inferior things. This weight was carnal custom. Yet dwelt there with me a remembrance of Thee; nor did I any way doubt, that there was One to Whom I might cleave, but that I was not yet such as to cleave to Thee: for that *the body which is corrupted, presseth down the soul, and the earthly tabernacle weigheth down the mind that museth upon many things.* And most certain I was, *that Thy invisible works from the creation of the world are clearly seen, being understood by the things that are made, even Thy eternal power and Godhead.* For examining, whence it was that I admired the beauty of bodies celestial or terrestrial; and what aided me in judging soundly on things mutable, and pronouncing, "This ought to be thus, this not"; examining, I say, whence it was that I so judged, seeing I did so judge, I had found the unchangeable and true Eternity of Truth, above my changeable mind. And thus by degrees, I passed from bodies to the soul, which through the bodily senses perceives; and thence to its inward faculty, to which the bodily senses represent things external, whitherto reaches the faculties of beasts; and thence again to the reasoning faculty, to which what is received from the senses of the body, is referred to be judged. Which finding itself also to be in me a thing variable, raised itself up to its own understanding, and drew away my thoughts from the power of habit, withdrawing itself from those troops of contradictory phantasms; that so it might find what that light was, whereby it was bedewed, when, without all doubting it cried out, "That the unchangeable was to be preferred to the changeable"; whence also it knew That Unchangeable, which, unless it had in some way known, it had had no sure ground to prefer it to the changeable. And thus with that flash of one trembling glance it arrived at THAT WHICH Is. And then I saw Thy *invisible things understood by the things which are made.* But I could not fix my gaze thereon; and my infirmity being struck back, I was thrown again on my wonted habits, carrying along with me only a loving memory thereof, and a longing for what I had, as it were, perceived the odor of, but was not yet able to feed on.

Then I sought a way of obtaining strength, sufficient to enjoy Thee; and found it not, until I embraced *that Mediator betwixt God and men, the Man Christ Jesus, who is over all, God blessed for evermore,* calling unto me, and saying, *I am the way, the truth, and the life,* and mingling that food which I was unable to receive, with our flesh. . . .

Most eagerly then did I seize that venerable writing of Thy Spirit; and chiefly the Apostle Paul. Whereupon those difficulties vanished away, wherein he once seemed to me to contradict himself, and the text of his discourse not to agree with the testimonies of the Law and the Prophets. And the face of that pure word appeared to me one and the same; and I learned to *rejoice with trembling.* So I began; and whatsoever truth I had read in those other books, I found here amid the praise of Thy Grace; that whoso sees, may not *so glory as if he had not received,* not only what he sees, but also that he sees (*for what hath he, which he hath not received?*) and that he may be not only admonished to behold Thee, *Who art* ever *the same,* but also healed, to hold Thee; and that *he who cannot see afar off,* may yet walk on the way, whereby he may arrive, and behold, and hold Thee. . . . These things did wonderfully sink into my bowels, when I read that *least of Thy Apostles,* and had meditated upon Thy works, and trembled exceedingly.

BOOK VIII

Augustine's thirty-second year. He consults Simplicianus, from him hears the history of the conversion of Victorinus, and longs to devote himself entirely to God, but is mastered by his old habits; is still further roused by the history of Saint Antony, and the conversion of two courtiers; during a severe struggle, hears a voice from heaven, opens Scripture, and is converted, with his friend Alypius. His mother's vision fulfilled.

O MY GOD, of Thy eternal life I was now certain, though I saw it in a figure and as *through a glass.* Yet I had ceased to doubt that there was an incorruptible substance, whence was all other substance; nor did I now desire to be more certain of Thee, but more steadfast in Thee. But for my temporal life, all was wavering, and *my heart had to be purged from the old leaven. The Way,* the Saviour Himself, well pleased me, but as yet I shrunk from going through its straitness. And Thou didst put into my mind, and it seemed good in my eyes, to go to Simplicianus, who seemed to me a good servant of Thine; and Thy grace shone in him. I had heard also, that from his very youth he had lived most devoted unto Thee. Now he was grown into years; and by reason of so great age spent in such zealous following of Thy ways, he seemed to me likely to have learned much experience; and so he had. Out of which store, I wished that he would tell me (setting before him my anxieties) which were the fittest way for one in my case to walk in Thy paths.

For, I saw the church full; and one went this way, and another that way. But I was displeased, that I led a secular life; yea now that my desires no longer inflamed me, as of old, with hopes of honor and profit, a very grievous burden it was to undergo so heavy a bondage. For, in comparison of Thy sweetness, *and the beauty of Thy house which I loved,* those things delighted me no longer. But still I was enthralled with the love of woman; nor did the Apostle forbid me to marry, although he advised me to something better, chiefly wishing *that all men were as himself was.* But I being weak, chose the more indulgent place; and because of this alone, was tossed up and down in all beside, faint and wasted with withering cares, because in other matters, I was constrained against my will to conform myself to a married life, to which I was given up and enthralled. . . .

To Simplicianus then I went, the father of Ambrose (a Bishop now) in receiving Thy grace, and whom Ambrose truly loved as a father. To him I related the mazes of my wanderings. But when I mentioned that I had read certain books of the Platonists, which Victorinus, sometime Rhetoric Professor of Rome (who had died a Christian, as I had heard), had translated into Latin, he testified his joy that I had not fallen upon the writings of other philosophers, full of *fallacies and deceits, after the rudiments of this world,* whereas the Platonists many ways led to the belief in God, and His Word. Then to exhort me to the humility of Christ, *hidden from the wise, and revealed to little ones,* he spoke of Victorinus himself whom while at Rome he had most intimately known: and of him he related what I will not conceal. For it contains great *praise of Thy grace,* to be confessed unto Thee, how that aged man, most learned and skilled in the liberal sciences, and who had read, and weighed so many works of the philosophers; the instructor of so many noble Senators, who also, as a monument of his excellent discharge of his office, had (which men of this world esteem a high honor) both deserved and obtained a statue in the Roman Forum; he, to that age a worshipper of idols, and a partaker of the sacrilegious rites, to which almost all the nobility of Rome were given up, and had inspired the people with the love of

> Anubis, barking Deity, and all
> The monster Gods of every kind, who fought
> 'Gainst Neptune, Venus and Minerva: *

whom Rome once conquered, now adored, all which the aged Victorinus had with thundering eloquence so many years defended; he now blushed not to be the child of Thy Christ, and the newborn babe of Thy fountain; submitting his neck to the yoke of humility, and subduing his forehead to the reproach of the Cross.

O Lord, Lord, *Which hast bowed the heavens and come down, touched the mountains and they did smoke,* by what means didst Thou convey Thyself into that breast? He used to read (as Simplicianus said) the holy Scripture, most studiously sought and searched into all the Christian writings, and said to Simplicianus (not openly, but privately and as a friend), "Understand that I am already a Christian." Whereto he answered, "I will not believe it, nor will I rank you among Christians, unless I see you in the Church of Christ." The other, in banter, replied, "Do walls then make Christians?" And this he often said, that he was already a Christian; and Simplicianus as often made the same answer, and the conceit of the "walls" was by the other as often renewed. For he feared to offend his friends, proud demon-worshippers, from the height of whose Babylonian dignity, as from *cedars of Lebanon,* which *the Lord* had not yet *broken down,* he supposed the weight of enmity would fall upon him. But after that by reading and earnest thought he had gathered firmness, and feared to be *denied by Christ before the holy angels, should he now be afraid to confess him before men,* and appeared to himself guilty of a heavy offense, in being ashamed of the Sacraments of the humility of Thy Word, and not being ashamed of the sacrilegious rites of those proud demons, whose pride he had imitated and their rites adopted, he became bold-faced against vanity, and shamefaced toward the truth, and suddenly and unexpectedly said to Simplicianus (as himself told me), "Go we to the Church; I wish to be made a Christian." But he, not

* Vergil, *The Aeneid,* Book VIII

containing himself for joy, went with him. And having been admitted to the first Sacrament and become a catechumen, not long after he further gave in his name, that he might be regenerated by baptism, Rome wondering, the Church rejoicing. The proud *saw, and were wroth; they gnashed with their teeth, and melted away.* But the *Lord God was the hope of* Thy servant, and *he regarded not vanities and lying* madness.

To conclude, when the hour had come for making profession of his faith (which at Rome they, who are about to approach to Thy grace, deliver, from an elevated place, in the sight of all the faithful, in a set form of words committed to memory), the presbyters, he said, offered Victorinus (as was done to such, as seemed likely through bashfulness to be alarmed) to make his profession more privately. But he chose rather to profess his salvation in the presence of the holy multitude. "For it was not salvation that he taught in rhetoric, and yet that he had publicly professed. How much less then ought he, when pronouncing Thy word, to dread Thy meek flock, who, when delivering his own words, had not feared a mad multitude!" When he went up to make his profession, all, as they knew him, whispered his name one to another with the voice of congratulation. And who there knew him not? and there ran a low murmur through all the mouths of the rejoicing multitude, Victorinus! Victorinus! Sudden was the burst of rapture, that they saw him; suddenly were they hushed that they might hear him. He pronounced the true faith with an excellent boldness, and all wished to draw him into their very heart: yea by their love and joy they drew him thither; such were the hands wherewith they drew him.

Good God! what takes place in man, that he should more rejoice at the salvation of a soul despaired of, and freed from greater peril, than if there had always been hope of him, or the danger had been less? For so Thou also, merciful Father, *dost more rejoice over one penitent, than over ninety-nine just persons, that need no repentance.* And with much joyfulness do we hear, so often as we hear with what joy *the sheep which had strayed, is brought back upon the shepherd's shoulder,* and *the groat is restored to Thy treasury, the neighbors rejoicing with the woman who found it;* and the joy of the solemn service of Thy house forceth to tears, when in Thy house it is read of Thy *younger son, that he was dead, and lived again; had been lost, and is found.* For Thou *rejoicest* in us, and in Thy holy angels, holy through holy charity. For Thou art ever the same; for all things which abide not the same nor for ever, Thou for ever knowest in the same way.

What then takes place in the soul, when it is more delighted at finding or recovering the things it loves, than if it had ever had them? yea, and other things witness hereunto; and all things are full of witnesses, crying out, "so is it." The conquering commander triumpheth; yet had he not conquered, unless he had fought; and the more peril there was in the battle, so much the more joy is there in the triumph. The storm tosses the sailors, threatens shipwreck; all wax pale at approaching death; sky and sea are calmed, and they are exceeding joyed, as having been exceeding afraid. A friend is sick, and his pulse threatens danger; all who long for his recovery, are sick in mind with him. He is restored, though as yet he walks not with his former strength; yet there is such joy, as was not, when before he walked sound and strong. Yea, the very pleasures of human life men acquire by difficulties, not those only which fall upon us unlooked for, and against our wills, but even by self-chosen, and pleasure-seeking trouble. Eating and drinking have no pleasure, unless there precede the pinching of hunger and thirst. Men, given to drink, eat certain salt meats, to procure a troublesome heat, which the drink allaying, causes pleasure. It is also ordered, that the affianced bride should not at once be given, lest as a husband he should hold cheap whom, as betrothed, he sighed not after.

This law holds in foul and accursed joy; this in permitted and lawful joy; this in the very purest perfection of friendship; this, in him *who was dead, and lived again; had been lost, and was found*. Everywhere the greater joy is ushered in by the greater pain. What means this, O Lord my God, whereas Thou art everlastingly joy to Thyself, and some things around Thee evermore rejoice in Thee? What means this, that this portion of things thus ebbs and flows alternately displeased and reconciled? Is this their allotted measure? Is this all Thou hast assigned to them, whereas from the highest heavens to the lowest earth, from the beginning of the world to the end of ages, from the angel to the worm, from the first motion to the last. Thou settest each in its place, and realizest each in their season, every thing good after its kind? Woe is me! how high art Thou in the highest, and how deep in the deepest! and Thou never departest, and we scarcely return to Thee.

Up, Lord, and do; stir us up, and recall us; kindle and draw us; inflame, grow sweet unto us; let us now love, *let us run*. Do not many, out of a deeper hell of blindness than Victorinus, return to Thee, approach, and are enlightened, receiving that *Light,* which *they who receive, receive power from Thee to become Thy sons?* But if they be less known to the nations, even they that know them, rejoice less for them. For when many rejoice together, each also has more exuberant joy; for that they are kindled and inflamed one by the other. Again, because those known to many, influence the more toward salvation, and lead the way with many to follow. And therefore do they also who preceded them, much rejoice in them, because they rejoice not in them alone. For far be it, that in Thy tabernacle the persons of the rich should be accepted before the poor, or the noble before the ignoble; seeing rather *Thou hast chosen the weak things of the world, to confound the strong; and the base things of this world, and the things despised hast Thou chosen, and those things which are not, that Thou mightest bring to nought things that are.* . . .

But when that man of Thine, Simplicianus, related to me this of Victorinus, I was on fire to imitate him; for for this very end had he related it. But when he had subjoined also, how in the days of the Emperor Julian, a law was made, whereby Christians were forbidden to teach the liberal sciences or oratory; and how he, obeying this law, chose rather to give over the wordy school, than Thy *Word,* by which Thou *makest eloquent the tongues of the dumb;* he seemed to me not more resolute than blessed, in having thus found opportunity to wait on Thee only. Which thing I was sighing for, bound as I was, not with another's irons, but by my own iron will. My will the enemy held, and thence had made a chain for me, and bound me. For of a froward will, was a lust made; and a lust served, became custom; and custom not resisted, became necessity. By which links, as it were, joined together (whence I called it a chain) a hard bondage held me enthralled. But that new will which had begun to be in me, freely to serve Thee, and to wish to enjoy Thee, O God, the only assured pleasantness, was not yet able to overcome my former willfulness, strengthened by age. Thus did my two wills, one new, and the other old, one carnal, the other spiritual, struggle within me; and by their discord, undid my soul.

Thus I understood, by my own experience, what I had read, how *the flesh lusteth against the spirit and the spirit against the flesh.* Myself verily either way; yet more myself, in that which I approved in myself, than in that which in myself I disapproved. For in this last, it was now for the more part not myself, because in much I rather endured against my will, than acted willingly. And yet it was through me, that custom had obtained this power of warring against me, because I had come willingly, whither I willed not. . . .

And how Thou didst deliver me out of the bonds of desire, wherewith I was bound most straitly to carnal concupiscence, and out of the drudgery of worldly things, I will now declare, and confess unto Thy name, *O Lord, my helper and my redeemer*. Amid increasing anxiety, I was doing my wonted business, and daily sighing unto Thee. I attended Thy Church, whenever free from the business under the burden of which I groaned. Alypius was with me, now after the third sitting released from his law business, and awaiting to whom to sell his counsel, as I sold the skill of speaking, if indeed teaching can impart it. Nebridius had now, in consideration of our friendship, consented to teach under Verecundus, a citizen and a grammarian of Milan, and a very intimate friend of us all; who urgently desired, and by the right of friendship challenged from our company, such faithful aid as he greatly needed. Nebridius then was not drawn to this by any desire of advantage (for he might have made much more of his learning had he so willed), but as a most kind and gentle friend, he would not be wanting to a good office, and slight our request. But he acted herein very discreetly, shunning to become known to personages great according to this world, avoiding the distraction of mind thence ensuing, and desiring to have it free and at leisure, as many hours as might be, to seek, or read, or hear something concerning wisdom.

Upon a day then, Nebridius being absent (I recollect not why) lo, there came to see me and Alypius, one Pontitianus, our countryman so far as being an African, in high office in the Emperor's court. What he would with us, I know not, but we sat down to converse, and it happened that upon a table for some game, before us, he observed a book, took, opened it, and contrary to his expectation, found it the Apostle Paul; for he had thought it some of those books, which I was wearing myself in teaching. Whereat smiling, and looking at me, he expressed his joy and wonder, that he had on a sudden found this book, and this only before my eyes. For he was a Christian, and baptized, and often bowed himself before Thee our God in the Church, in frequent and continued prayers. When then I had told him, that I bestowed very great pains upon those Scriptures, a conversation arose (suggested by his account) on Antony the Egyptian Monk: whose name was in high reputation among Thy servants, though to that hour unknown to us. Which when he discovered, he dwelt the more upon

311

that subject, informing and wondering at our ignorance of one so eminent. But we stood amazed, hearing Thy wonderful works most fully attested, in times so recent, and almost in our own, wrought in the true Faith and Catholic Church. We all wondered; we, that they were so great, and he, that they had not reached us.

Thence his discourse turned to the flocks in the monasteries, and their holy ways, a sweet-smelling savor unto Thee, and the fruitful deserts of the wilderness, whereof we knew nothing. And there was a monastery at Milan, full of good brethren, without the city walls, under the fostering care of Ambrose, and we knew it not. . . .

But Thou, O Lord, while Pontitianus was speaking, didst turn me round toward myself, taking me from behind my back, where I had placed me, unwilling to observe myself; and setting me before my face, that I might see how foul I was, how crooked and defiled, bespotted and ulcerous. And I beheld and stood aghast; and whither to flee from myself I found not. And if I sought to turn mine eye from off myself, he went on with his relation, and Thou again didst set me over against myself, and thrustedst me before my eyes, that *I might find out mine iniquity, and hate it.* I had known it, but made as though I saw it not, winked at it, and forgot it.

But now, the more ardently I loved those, whose healthful affections I heard of, that they had resigned themselves wholly to Thee to be cured, the more did I abhor myself, when compared with them. For many of my years (some twelve) had now run out with me since my nineteenth, when, upon the reading of Cicero's *Hortensius,* I was stirred to an earnest love of wisdom; and still I was deferring to reject mere earthly felicity, and give myself to search out that, whereof not the finding only, but the very search, was to be preferred to the treasures and kingdoms of the world, though already found, and to the pleasures of the body, though spread around me at my will. But I wretched, most wretched, in the very commencement of my early youth, had begged chastity of Thee, and said, "Give me chastity and continency, only not yet." For I feared lest Thou shouldest hear me soon, and soon cure me of the disease of concupiscence, which I wished to have satisfied, rather than extinguished. And I had wandered through crooked ways in a sacrilegious superstition, not indeed assured thereof, but as preferring it to the others which I did not seek religiously, but opposed maliciously. . . .

Then in this great contention of my inward dwelling, which I had strongly raised against my soul, in *the chamber* of my heart, troubled in mind and countenance, I turned upon Alypius. "What ails us?" I exclaim: "what is it? what heardest thou? The unlearned start up and *take heaven by force,* and we with our learning, and without heart, lo, where we wallow in flesh and blood! Are we ashamed to follow, because others are gone before, and not ashamed not even to follow?" Some such words I uttered, and my fever of mind tore me away from him, while he, gazing on me in astonishment, kept silence. For it was not my wonted tone; and my forehead, cheeks, eyes, color, tone of voice, spoke my mind more than the words I uttered. A little garden there was to our lodging, which we had the use of, as of the whole house; for the master of the house, our host, was not living there. Thither had the tumult of my breast hurried me, where no man might hinder the hot contention wherein I had engaged with myself, until it should end as Thou knewest, I knew not. Only I was healthfully distracted and dying, to live; knowing what evil thing I was, and not knowing what good thing I was shortly to become. I retired then into the garden, and Alypius, on my steps. For his presence did not lessen my privacy; or how could he forsake me so disturbed? We sat down as far removed as might be from the house. I was troubled in spirit, most vehemently indignant that I entered not into Thy will and covenant, O my God, which *all my bones cried out* unto me to enter, and praised it to the skies. And therein we enter not by ships, or chariots, or feet, or move not so far as I had come from the house to that place where we were sitting. For, not to go only, but to go in thither was nothing else but to will to go, but to will resolutely and thoroughly; not to turn and toss, this way and that, a maimed and half-divided will, struggling, with one part sinking as another rose.

Lastly, in the very fever of my irresoluteness, I made with my body many such motions as men sometimes would, but cannot, if either they have not the limbs, or these be bound with bands, weakened with infirmity, or any other way hindered. Thus, if I tore my hair, beat my forehead, if locking my fingers I clasped my knee; I willed, I did it. But I might have willed, and not done it, if the power of motion in my limbs had not obeyed. So many things then I did, when "to will" was not in itself "to be able"; and I did not what both I longed incomparably more to do, and which soon after, when I should will, I should be able to do; because soon after, when I should will, I should will thoroughly. For in these things the ability was one with the will, and to will was to do; and yet was it not done: and more easily did my body obey the weakest willing of my soul, in moving its limbs at its nod, than the soul obeyed itself to accomplish in the will alone this its momentous will. . . .

Thus soul-sick was I, and tormented, accusing myself much more severely than my wont, rolling and turning me in my chain, till that were wholly broken, whereby I now was but just, but still was, held. And Thou, O Lord, pressedst upon me in my inward parts by a severe mercy, redoubling the lashes of fear and shame, lest I should again give way, and not bursting that same slight remaining tie, it should recover strength, and bind me the faster. For I said within myself, "Be it done now, be it done now." And as I spoke, I all but enacted it. I all but did it, and did it not: yet sunk not back to my former state, but kept my stand hard by, and took breath. And I essayed again, and wanted somewhat less of it, and somewhat less, and all but touched and laid hold of it; and yet came not at it, nor touched, nor laid hold of it: hesitating to die to death and to live to life: and the worse whereto I was inured, prevailed more with me than the better, whereto I was unused: and the very moment wherein I was to become other than I was, the nearer it approached me, the greater horror did it strike into me; yet did it not strike me back, nor turned me away, but held me in suspense.

The very toys of toys, and vanities of vanities, my ancient mistresses, still held me; they plucked my fleshly garment, and whispered softly, "Dost thou cast us off? and from that moment shall we no more be with thee for ever? and from that moment shall not this or that be lawful for thee for ever?" And what was it which they suggested in that I said, "this or that," what did they suggest, O my God? Let Thy mercy turn it away from the soul of Thy servant. What defilements did they suggest! what shame! And now I much less than half heard them, and not openly showing themselves and contradicting me, but muttering as it were behind my back, and privily plucking me, as I was departing, but to look back on them. Yet they did retard me, so that I hesitated to burst and shake myself free from them, and to spring over whither I was called; a violent habit saying to me, "Thinkest thou, thou canst live without them?"

But now it spoke very faintly. For on that side whither I had set my face, and whither I trembled to go, there appeared unto me the chaste dignity of Continency, serene, yet not relaxedly gay, honestly alluring me to come, and doubt not; and stretching forth to receive and embrace me, her holy hands full of multitudes of good examples.

314

There were so many young men and maidens here, a multitude of youth and every age, grave widows and aged virgins; and Continency herself in all, not barren, but a *fruitful mother of children* of joys, by Thee her Husband, O Lord. And she smiled on me with a persuasive mockery, as would she say, "Canst not thou what these youths, what these maidens can? or can they either in themselves, and not rather in the Lord their God? The Lord their God gave me unto them. Why standest thou in thyself, and so standest not? Cast thyself upon Him, fear not He will not withdraw Himself that thou shouldest fall; cast thyself fearlessly upon Him, He will receive, and will heal thee." And I blushed exceedingly, for that I yet heard the muttering of those toys, and hung in suspense. And she again seemed to say, "Stop thine ears against *those* thy unclean *members on the earth,* that they may be *mortified. They tell thee of delights, but not as doth the law of the Lord thy God."* This controversy in my heart was self against self only. But Alypius sitting close by my side, in silence waited the issue of my unwonted emotion.

But when a deep consideration had from the secret bottom of my soul drawn together and heaped up all my misery in the sight of my heart, there arose a mighty storm, bringing a mighty shower of tears. Which that I might pour forth wholly in its natural expressions, I rose from Alypius: solitude was suggested to me as fitter for the business of weeping; so I retired so far that even his presence could not be a burden to me. Thus was it then with me, and he perceived something of it; for something I suppose I had spoken, wherein the tones of my voice appeared choked with weeping, and so had risen up. He then remained where we were sitting, most extremely astonished. I cast myself down I know not how, under a certain fig tree, giving full vent to my tears; and the floods of mine eyes gushed out, an *acceptable sacrifice to Thee.* And, not indeed in these words, yet to this purpose, spoke I much unto Thee: *And Thou, O Lord, how long? how long, Lord, wilt Thou be angry, forever? Remember not our former iniquities,* for I felt that I was held by them. I sent up these sorrowful words: How long? how long, "tomorrow, and tomorrow?" Why not now? why not is there this hour an end to my uncleanness?

So was I speaking, and weeping in the most bitter contrition of my heart, when, lo! I heard from a neighboring house a voice, as of a boy or girl, I know not, chanting, and oft repeating, "Take up and read; Take up and read." Instantly, my countenance altered, I began

315

to think most intently, whether children were wont in any kind of play to sing such words: nor could I remember ever to have heard the like. So checking the torrent of my tears, I arose; interpreting it to be no other than a command from God, to open the book, and read the first chapter I should find. For I had heard of Antony, that coming in during the reading of the Gospel, he received the admonition, as if what was being read, was spoken to him; *Go, sell all that thou hast, and give to the poor, and thou shalt have treasure in heaven, and come and follow me.* And by such oracle he was forthwith converted unto Thee. Eagerly then I returned to the place where Alypius was sitting; for there had I laid the volume of the Apostle, when I arose thence. I seized, opened, and in silence read that section, on which my eyes first fell: *Not in rioting and drunkenness, not in chambering and wantonness, not in strife and envying: but put ye on the Lord Jesus Christ, and make not provision for the flesh,* in concupiscence. No further would I read; nor needed I: for instantly at the end of this sentence, by a light as it were of serenity infused into my heart, all the darkness of doubt vanished away.

Then putting my finger between, or some other mark, I shut the volume, and with a calmed countenance made it known to Alypius. And what was wrought in him, which I knew not, he thus showed me. He asked to see what I had read: I showed him; and he looked even further than I had read, and I knew not what followed. This followed, *him that is weak in the faith, receive;* which he applied to himself, and disclosed to me. And by this admonition was he strengthened; and by a good resolution and purpose, and most corresponding to his character, wherein he did always very far differ from me, for the better, without any turbulent delay he joined me. Thence we go into my mother; we tell her; she rejoiceth: we relate in order how it took place; she leaps for joy, and triumpheth, and blesseth Thee, *Who art able to do above that which we ask or think;* for she perceived that Thou hadst given her more for me, than she was wont to beg by her pitiful and most sorrowful groanings. For Thou convertedst me unto Thyself, so that I sought neither wife, nor any hope of this world, standing in that rule of faith, where Thou hadst showed me unto her in a vision, so many years before. And Thou didst *convert her mourning into joy,* much more plentiful than she had desired, and in a much more precious and purer way than she previously required, by having grandchildren of my body.

316

Augustine determines to devote his Life to God, and to abandon his profession of Rhetoric; retires to the country to prepare himself to receive the grace of baptism, and is baptized with Alypius, and his son Adeodatus. At Ostia, on his way to Africa, his mother Monica dies, in her fifty-sixth year, the thirty-third of Augustine. Her life and character.

Now was my soul free from the biting cares of canvassing and getting, and weltering in filth, and scratching off the itch of lust. And my infant tongue spoke freely to Thee, my brightness, and my riches, and my health, the Lord my God.

And I resolved in Thy sight, not tumultuously to tear, but gently to withdraw, the service of my tongue from the marts of lip-labor: that the young, neither students in Thy law, nor in Thy peace, but in lying drivel and law-skirmishes, should no longer buy at my mouth arms for their madness. And very seasonably, it now wanted but very few days unto the Vacation of the Vintage, and I resolved to endure them, then in a regular way to take my leave, and having been purchased by Thee, no more to return for sale. Our purpose then was known to Thee; but to men, other than our own friends, was it not known. For we had agreed among ourselves not to let it out abroad to any because . . . it seemed like ostentation not to wait for the vacation now so near, but to quit beforehand a public profession, which was before the eyes of all; so that all looking on this act of mine, and observing how near was the time of vintage which I wished to anticipate, would talk much of me, as if I had desired to appear some great one. And what end had it served me, that people should repute and dispute upon my purpose, and that *our good should be evil spoken of?*

Moreover, it had at first troubled me, that in this very summer my lungs began to give way, amid too great literary labor, and I began to breathe deeply with difficulty, and by the pain in my chest to show that my lungs were injured, and to refuse any full or lengthened speaking. This had troubled me, for it almost constrained me of necessity to lay down that burden of teaching, or, if I could be cured and recover, at least to intermit it. But when the full wish for leisure, that I might *see how that Thou art the Lord,* arose, and was fixed, in

317

me; my God, Thou knowest, I began even to rejoice that I had this secondary, and that no feigned, excuse, which might something moderate the offense taken by those, who for their sons' sake, wished me never to have the freedom of Thy sons. Full then of such joy, I endured till that interval of time were run; it may have been some twenty days, yet they were endured manfully; endured, for the covetousness which aforetime bore a part of this heavy business, had left me, and I remained alone, and had been overwhelmed, had not patience taken its place. Perchance, some of Thy servants, my brethren, may say, that I sinned in this, that with a heart fully set on Thy service, I suffered myself to sit even one hour in the chair of lies. Nor would I be contentious. But hast not Thou, O most merciful Lord, pardoned and remitted this sin also, with my other most horrible and deadly sins, in the holy water? . . .

Now was the day come, wherein I was indeed to be freed of my Rhetoric Professorship, whereof in thought I was already freed. And it was done. Thou didst rescue my tongue, whence Thou hadst before rescued my heart. And I blessed Thee, rejoicing; retiring with all mine to the villa. What I there did in writing, which was now enlisted in Thy service, though still, in this breathing-time as it were, panting from the school of pride, my books may witness, as well what I debated with others, as what with myself alone, before Thee: what with Nebridius, who was absent, my Epistles bear witness. And when shall I have time to rehearse all Thy great benefits toward us at that time, especially when hasting on to yet greater mercies? For my remembrance recalls me, and pleasant is it to me, O Lord, to confess to Thee, by what inward goads Thou tamedst me; and how Thou hast evened me, *lowering the mountains and hills of my high imaginations, straightening my crookedness, and smoothing my rough ways;* and how Thou also subduedst the brother of my heart, Alypius, unto the Name of Thy Only Begotten, our Lord and Saviour Jesus Christ, which he would not at first vouchsafe to have inserted in our writings. For rather would he have them savor of the lofty *cedars* of the Schools, which *the Lord* hath now *broken down,* than of the wholesome herbs of the Church, the antidote against serpents.

Oh in what accents spoke I unto Thee, my God, when I read the Psalms of David, those faithful songs, and sounds of devotion, which allow of no swelling spirit, as yet a catechumen, and a novice in Thy real love, resting in that villa, with Alypius, a catechumen, my mother cleaving to us, in female garb with masculine faith, with the tranquillity of age, motherly love, Christian piety. Oh, what accents did I utter unto Thee in those Psalms, and how was I by them kindled toward Thee, and on fire to rehearse them, if possible, through the whole world, against the pride of mankind. . . .

When shall I recall all which passed in those holy days? Yet neither have I forgotten, nor will I pass over the severity of Thy scourge, and the wonderful swiftness of Thy mercy. Thou didst then torment me with pain in my teeth; which when it had come to such height, that I could not speak, it came into my heart to desire all my friends present to pray for me to Thee, the God of all manner of health. And this I wrote on wax, and gave it them to read. Presently so soon as with humble devotion we had bowed our knees, that pain went away. But what pain? or how went it away? I was affrighted, O my Lord, my God; for from infancy I had never experienced the like. And the power of Thy Nod was deeply conveyed to me, and rejoicing in faith, I praised Thy Name. And that faith suffered me not to be at ease about my past sins, which were not yet forgiven me by Thy baptism.

The vintage-vacation ended, I gave notice to the Milanese to provide their scholars with another master to sell words to them; for that I had both made choice to serve Thee, and through my difficulty of breathing and pain in my chest, was not equal to the Professorship. And by letters I signified to Thy Prelate, the holy man Ambrose, my former errors and present desires, begging his advice what of Thy Scriptures I had best read, to become readier and fitter for receiving so great grace. He recommended Isaiah the Prophet: I believe, because he above the rest is a more clear foreshower of the Gospel and of the calling of the Gentiles. But I, not understanding the first lesson in him, and imagining the whole to be like it, laid it by, to be resumed when better practiced in our Lord's own words.

Thence, when the time was come, wherein I was to give in my name, we left the country and returned to Milan. It pleased Alypius also to be with me born again in Thee, being already clothed with the humility befitting Thy sacraments; and a most valiant tamer of the body, so as, with unwonted venture, to wear the frozen ground of Italy with his bare feet. We joined with us the boy Adeodatus, born after the flesh, of my sin. Excellently hadst Thou made him. He was not quite fifteen, and in wit surpassed many grave and learned men. I confess unto Thee Thy gifts, O Lord my God, Creator of all, and abundantly able to reform our deformities: for I had no part in that boy, but the sin. For that we brought him up in Thy discipline, it was

319

Thou, none else, had inspired us with it. I confess unto Thee Thy gifts. There is a book of ours entitled *The Master;* it is a dialogue between him and me. Thou knowest, that all there ascribed to the person conversing with me, were his ideas, in his sixteenth year. Much besides, and yet more admirable, I found in him. That talent struck awe into me. And who but Thou could be the workmaster of such wonders? Soon didst Thou take his life from the earth: and I now remember him without anxiety, fearing nothing for his childhood or youth, or his whole self. Him we joined with us, our contemporary in grace, to be brought up in Thy discipline; and we were baptized, and anxiety for our past life vanished from us. Nor was I sated in those days with the wondrous sweetness of considering the depth of Thy counsels concerning the salvation of mankind. How did I weep, in Thy Hymns and Canticles, touched to the quick by the voices of Thy sweet-attuned Church! The voices flowed into mine ears, and the Truth distilled into my heart, whence the affections of my devotion overflowed, and tears ran down, and happy was I therein. . . .

Thou *that makest men to dwell of one mind in one house,* didst join with us Euodius also, a young man in our own city. Who being an officer of Court, was before us converted to Thee and baptized: and quitting his secular warfare, girded himself to Thine. We were together, about to dwell together in our devout purpose. We sought where he might serve Thee most usefully, and were together returning to Africa: whitherward being as far as Ostia, my mother departed this life. Much I omit, as hastening much. Receive my confessions and thanksgivings, O my God, for innumerable things whereof I am silent. But I will not omit whatsoever my soul would bring forth concerning that Thy handmaid, who brought me forth, both in the flesh, that I might be born to this temporal light, and in heart, that I might be born to Light eternal. Not her gifts, but Thine in her, would I speak of; for neither did she make nor educate herself. Thou createdst her; nor did her father and mother know what a one should come from them. And the scepter of Thy Christ, the discipline of Thine only Son, in a Christian house, a good member of Thy Church, educated her in Thy fear. Yet for her good discipline, was she wont to commend not so much her mother's diligence, as that of a certain decrepit maidservant, who had carried her father when a child, as little ones used to be carried at the backs of elder girls. For which reason, and for her great age, and excellent conversation, was she, in

320

that Christian family, well respected by its heads. Whence also the charge of her master's daughters was entrusted to her, to which she gave diligent heed, restraining them earnestly, when necessary, with a holy severity, and teaching them with a grave discretion. For, except at those hours, wherein they were most temperately fed at their parents' table, she would not suffer them, though parched with thirst, to drink even water; preventing an evil custom, and adding this wholesome advice; "Ye drink water now, because you have not wine in your power; but when you come to be married, and be made mistresses of cellars and cupboards, you will scorn water, but the custom of drinking will abide." By this method of instruction, and the authority she had, she restrained the greediness of childhood, and molded their very thirst to such an excellent moderation, that what they should not, that they would not. . . .

Brought up thus modestly and soberly, and made subject rather by Thee to her parents, than by her parents to Thee, so soon as she was of marriageable age, being bestowed upon a husband, she served him as her lord; and did her diligence to win him unto Thee, preaching Thee unto him by her conversation; by which Thou ornamentedst her, making her reverently amiable, and admirable unto her husband. And she so endured the wronging of her bed, as never to have any quarrel with her husband thereon. For she looked for Thy mercy upon him, that believing in Thee, he might be made chaste. But besides this, he was fervid, as in his affections, so in anger: but she had learned, not to resist an angry husband, not in deed only, but not even in word. Only when he was smoothed and tranquil, and in a temper to receive it, she would give an account of her actions, if haply he had overhastily taken offense. In a word, while many matrons, who had milder husbands, yet bore even in their faces marks of shame, would in familiar talk blame their husbands' lives, she would blame their tongues, giving them, as in jest, earnest advice; "That from the time they heard the marriage writings read to them, they should account them as indentures, whereby they were made servants; and so, remembering their condition, ought not to set themselves up against their lords." And when they, knowing what a choleric husband she endured, marveled, that it had never been heard, nor by any token perceived, that Patricius had beaten his wife, or that there had been any domestic difference between them, even for one day, and confidentially asking the reason, she taught them her practice above mentioned. Those wives who observed it found the good, and returned thanks; those who observed it not, found no relief, and suffered.

Her mother-in-law also, at first by whisperings of evil servants incensed against her, she so overcame by observance and persevering endurance and meekness, that she of her own accord discovered to her son the meddling tongues, whereby the domestic peace betwixt her and her daughter-in-law had been disturbed, asking him to correct them. Then, when in compliance with his mother, and for the well-ordering of the family, and the harmony of its members, he had with stripes corrected those discovered, at her will who had discovered them, she promised the like reward to any who, to please her, should speak ill of her daughter-in-law to her: and, none now venturing, they lived together with a remarkable sweetness of mutual kindness.

This great gift also Thou bestowedst, O my God, my mercy, upon that good handmaid of Thine, in whose womb Thou createdst me, that between any disagreeing and discordant parties where she was able, she showed herself such a peacemaker, that hearing on both sides most bitter things, such as swelling and undigested choler uses to break out into, when the crudities of enmities are breathed out in sour discourses to a present friend against an absent enemy, she never would disclose aught of the one unto the other, but what might tend to their reconcilement. . . .

Finally, her own husband, towards the very end of his earthly life, did she gain unto Thee; nor had she to complain of that in him as a believer, which before he was a believer she had borne from him. She was also the servant of thy servants; whosoever of them knew her, did in her much praise and honor and love Thee; for that through the witness of the fruits of a holy conversation they perceived Thy presence in her heart. For she had been *the wife of one man,* had *requited her parents, had governed her house* piously, *was well reported of for good works, had brought up children,* so often *travailing in birth of them,* as she saw them swerving from Thee. Lastly, of all of us Thy servants, O Lord (whom on occasion of Thy own gift Thou sufferest to speak), us, who before her sleeping in Thee lived united together, having received the grace of Thy baptism, did she so take care of, as though she had been mother of us all; so served us, as though she had been child to us all.

The day now approaching whereon she was to depart this life, (which day Thou well knewest, we knew not) it came to pass, Thyself, as I believe, by Thy secret ways so ordering it, that she and I stood alone, leaning in a certain window, which looked into the garden of the house where we now lay, at Ostia; where removed from the din of men, we were recruiting from the fatigues of a long journey, for the voyage. We were discoursing then together, alone, very sweetly; and *forgetting those things which are behind, and reaching forth unto those things which are before,* we were inquiring between ourselves in the presence of the Truth, which Thou art, of what sort the eternal life of the saints was to be, *which eye hath not seen, nor ear heard, nor hath it entered into the heart of man.* But yet we gasped with the mouth of our heart, after those heavenly streams of Thy fountain, *the fountain of life,* which is *with Thee;* that being bedewed thence according to our capacity, we might in some sort meditate upon so high a mystery.

And when our discourse was brought to that point, that the very highest delight of the earthly senses, in the very purest material light, was, in respect of the sweetness of that life, not only not worthy of comparison, but not even of mention; we raising up ourselves with a more glowing affection towards the "Selfsame," did by degrees pass through all things bodily, even the very heaven, whence sun and moon, and stars shine upon the earth; yea, we were soaring higher yet, by inward musing, and discourse, and admiring of Thy works; and we came to our own minds, and went beyond them, that we might arrive at that region of never-failing plenty, where *Thou feedest Israel* for ever with the food of truth, and where life is the *Wisdom by whom all* these *things are made,* and what have been, and what shall be, and she is not made, but is, as she hath been, and so shall she be ever; yea rather, to "have been," and "hereafter to be," are not in her, but only "to be," seeing she is eternal. For to "have been," and to "be hereafter," are not eternal. And while we were discoursing and panting after her, we slightly touched on her with the whole effort of our heart; and we sighed, and there we leave bound *the first fruits of the Spirit;* and returned to vocal expressions of our mouth, where the word spoken has beginning and end. And what is like unto Thy Word, our Lord, who *endureth in Himself* without becoming old, and *maketh all things new?*

We were saying then: If to any the tumult of the flesh were hushed, hushed the images of earth, and waters, and air, hushed also the poles of heaven, yea the very soul be hushed to herself, and by not thinking on self surmount self, hushed all dreams and imaginary revelations, every tongue and every sign, and whatsoever exists only in transition, since if any could hear, all these say, *We made ourselves, but He made us that abideth for ever*—If then having uttered this, they too should be hushed, having roused only our ears to Him who made them, and He alone speak, not by them, but by Himself, that we may hear His Word, not through any tongue of flesh, nor Angel's voice, nor sound of thunder, nor in the dark riddle of a similitude, but might hear Whom in these things we love, might hear His Very Self without these (as we two now strained ourselves, and in swift thought touched on that Eternal Wisdom, which abideth over all) could this be continued on, and other visions of kind far unlike be withdrawn, and this one ravish, and absorb, and wrap up its beholder amid these inward joys, so that life might be forever like that one moment of understanding which now we sighed after; were not this, *Enter into thy Master's joy*? And when shall that be? When *we shall all rise again,* though we *shall not all be changed.*

Such things was I speaking, and even if not in this very manner, and these same words, yet, Lord, Thou knowest, that in that day when we were speaking of these things, and this world with all its delights became, as we spoke, contemptible to us, my mother said, "Son, for mine own part I have no further delight in anything in this life. What I do here any longer, and to what end I am here, I know not, now that my hopes in this world are accomplished. One thing there was, for which I desired to linger for a while in this life, that I might see thee a Catholic Christian before I died. My God hath done this for me more abundantly, than I should now see thee withal, despising earthly happiness, become His servant: what do I here?"

What answer I made her unto these things, I remember not. For scarce five days after, or not much more, she fell sick of a fever; and in that sickness one day she fell into a swoon, and was for a while withdrawn from these visible things. We hastened round her; but she was soon brought back to her senses; and looking on me and my brother standing by her, said to us inquiringly, "Where was I?" And then looking fixedly on us, with grief amazed, "Here," saith she, "shall you bury your mother." I held my peace and refrained weeping; but my brother spoke something, wishing for her, as the happier lot, that she might die, not in a strange place, but in her own land. Whereat, she with anxious look, checking him with her eyes, for that he still *savored such things,* and then looking upon me; "Behold," saith she, "what he saith": and soon after to us both, "Lay," she saith, "this body anywhere; let not the care for that any way disquiet you: this only I request, that you would remember me at the Lord's altar, wherever you be." And having delivered this sentiment in what words she could, she held her peace, being exercised by her growing sickness. . . . On the ninth day then of her sickness, and the fifty-sixth year of her age, and the three and thirtieth of mine, was that religious and holy soul freed from the body.

I closed her eyes; and there flowed withal a mighty sorrow into my heart, which was overflowing into tears; mine eyes at the same time, by the violent command of my mind, drank up their fountain wholly dry; and woe was me in such a strife! But when she breathed her last, the boy Adeodatus burst out into a loud lament; then, checked by us all, held his peace. In like manner also a childish feeling in me, which was, through my heart's youthful voice, finding its vent in weeping, was checked and silenced. For we thought it not fitting to solemnize that funeral with tearful lament, and groanings: for thereby do they for the most part express grief for the departed, as though unhappy, or altogether dead; whereas she was neither unhappy in her death, nor altogether dead. Of this, we were assured on good grounds, the testimony of her good conversation and her *faith unfeigned*.

What then was it which did grievously pain me within, but a fresh wound wrought through the sudden wrench of that most sweet and dear custom of living together? I joyed indeed in her testimony, when, in that her last sickness, mingling her endearments with my acts of duty, she called me "dutiful," and mentioned, with great affection of love, that she never had heard any harsh or reproachful sound uttered by my mouth against her. But yet, O my God, Who madest us, what comparison is there between that honor that I paid to her, and her slavery for me? Being then forsaken of so great comfort in her, my soul was wounded, and that life rent asunder as it were, which, of hers and mine together, had been made but one.

The boy then being stilled from weeping, Euodius took up the Psalter, and began to sing, our whole house answering him, the Psalm, *I will sing of mercy and judgment to Thee, O Lord*. But hearing what we were doing, many brethren and religious women came together; and whilst they (whose office it was) made ready for the burial, as the manner is, I (in a part of the house, where I might properly), together with those who thought not fit to leave me, discoursed upon something fitting the time; and by this balm of truth, assuaged that torment, known to Thee, they unknowing and listening intently, and con-

325

ceiving me to be without all sense of sorrow. But in Thy ears, where none of them heard, I blamed the weakness of my feelings, and refrained my flood of grief, which gave way a little unto me; but again came, as with a tide, yet not so as to burst out into tears, nor to a change of countenance; still I knew what I was keeping down in my heart. And being very much displeased, that these human things had such power over me, which in the due order and appointment of our natural condition, must needs come to pass, with a new grief I grieved for my grief, and was thus worn by a double sorrow. . . .

And then by little and little I recovered my former thoughts of Thy handmaid, her holy conversation toward Thee, her holy tenderness and observance towards us, whereof I was suddenly deprived: and I was minded to weep in Thy sight, for her and for myself, in her behalf and in my own. And I gave way to the tears which I before restrained, to overflow as much as they desired; reposing my heart upon them; and it found rest in them, for it was in Thy ears, not in those of man, who would have scornfully interpreted my weeping. And now, Lord, in writing I confess it unto Thee. Read it, who will, and interpret it, how he will: and if he finds sin therein, that I wept for my mother for a small portion of an hour (the mother who for the time was dead to mine eyes, who had for many years wept for me, that I might live in Thine eyes), let him not deride me; but rather, if he be one of large charity, let him weep himself for my sins unto Thee, the Father of all the brethren of Thy Christ. . . .

May she rest then in peace with the husband, before and after whom she had never any; whom she obeyed, *with patience bringing forth fruit* unto Thee, that she might win him also unto Thee. And inspire, O Lord my God, inspire Thy servants my brethren, Thy sons my masters, whom with voice, and heart, and pen I serve, that so many as shall read these *Confessions,* may at Thy Altar remember Monica Thy handmaid, with Patricius, her sometimes husband, by whose bodies Thou broughtest me into this life, how, I know not. May they with devout affection remember my parents in this transitory light, my brethren under Thee our Father in our Catholic Mother, and my fellow citizens in that eternal Jerusalem, which Thy pilgrim people sigheth after from their Exodus, even unto their return thither. That so, my mother's last request of me, may through my confessions, more than through my prayers, be, through the prayers of many, more abundantly fulfilled to her.

BOOK X

Having in the former books spoken of himself before his receiving the grace of baptism, in this Augustine confesses what he then was. But first, he inquires by what faculty we can know God at all, whence he enlarges on the mysterious character of the memory, wherein God, being made known, dwells, but which could not discover Him. Then he examines his own trials under the triple division of temptation, "lust of the flesh, lust of the eyes, and pride"; what Christian continency prescribes as to each. On Christ the Only Mediator, who heals and will heal all infirmities.

LET ME KNOW Thee, O Lord, who knowest me: *let me know Thee, as I am known.* Power of my soul, enter into it, and fit it for Thee, that Thou mayest have and hold it *without spot or wrinkle.* This is my hope, *therefore do I speak;* and in this hope do I rejoice, when I rejoice healthfully. Other things of this life are the less to be sorrowed for, the more they are sorrowed for; and the more to be sorrowed for, the less men sorrow for them. For behold, Thou *lovest the truth,* and *he that doth it, cometh to the light.* This would I do in my heart before Thee in confession: and in my writing, before many witnesses. . . .

This is the fruit of my confessions of what I am, not of what I have been, to confess this, not before Thee only, in a secret *exultation with trembling,* and a secret sorrow with hope; but in the ears also of the believing sons of men, sharers of my joy, and partners in my mortality, my fellow citizens, and fellow pilgrims, who are gone before, or are to follow on, companions of my way. These are Thy servants, my brethren, whom Thou willest to be Thy sons; my masters whom Thou commandest me to serve, if I would live with Thee, of Thee. But this Thy Word were little did it only command by speaking, and not go before in performing. This then I do in deed and word, this I do *under Thy wings;* in over great peril, were not my soul subdued unto Thee under Thy wings, and my infirmity known unto Thee. I am a little one, but my Father ever liveth, and my Guardian is *sufficient for me.* For He is the same who begat me, and defends me: and Thou Thyself art all my good; Thou, Almighty, Who art with me, yea, before I am with Thee. To such then whom Thou commandest me to serve will I discover, not what I have been, but what I now am, and

327

what I yet am. *But neither do I judge myself.* Thus therefore I would be heard. . . .

Not with doubting, but with assured consciousness, do I love Thee, Lord. Thou hast stricken my heart with Thy word, and I loved Thee. Yea also *heaven, and earth, and all that therein is,* behold, on every side they bid me love Thee; nor cease to say so unto all, *that they may be without excuse.* But more deeply *wilt Thou have mercy on whom Thou wilt have mercy, and wilt have compassion on whom Thou hast had compassion:* else in deaf ears do the heaven and the earth speak Thy praises. But what do I love, when I love Thee? not beauty of bodies, nor the fair harmony of time, nor the brightness of the light, so gladsome to our eyes, nor sweet melodies of varied songs, nor the fragrant smell of flowers, and ointments, and spices, not manna and honey, not limbs acceptable to embracements of flesh. None of these I love, when I love my God; and yet I love a kind of light, and melody, and fragrance, and meat, and embracement, when I love my God, the light, melody, fragrance, meat, embracement of my inner man: where there shineth unto my soul, what space cannot contain, and there soundeth, what time beareth not away and there smelleth, what breathing disperseth not, and there tasteth, what eating diminisheth not, and there clingeth, what satiety divorceth not. This is it which I love, when I love my God.

"And what is this?" I asked the earth, and it answered me, "I am not He"; and whatsoever are in it, confessed the same. I asked the sea and the deeps, and the living creeping things, and they answered, "We are not thy God, seek above us." I asked the moving air; and the whole air with his inhabitants answered, "Anaximenes was deceived, I am not God." I asked the heavens, sun, moon, stars, "Nor (say they) are we the God whom thou seekest." And I replied unto all the things which encompass the door of my flesh, "Ye have told me of my God, that ye are not He; tell me something of Him." And they cried out with a loud voice, "He made us." My questioning them was my thoughts on them: and their form of beauty gave the answer. And I turned myself unto myself, and said to myself, "Who art thou?" And I answered, "A man." And behold, in me there present themselves to me soul and body, one without, the other within. By which of these ought I to seek my God? I had sought Him in the body from earth to heaven, so far as I could send messengers, the beams of mine eyes. But the better is the inner, for to it as presiding and judging, all the bodily messengers reported the answers of heaven and earth, and

all things therein, who said, "We are not God, but He made us."
These things did my inner man know by the ministry of the outer: I
the inner, knew them; I, the mind, through the senses of my body. I
asked the whole frame of the world about my God; and it answered
me, "I am not He, but He made me.". . .

What then do I love, when I love my God? who is He above the
head of my soul? By my very soul will I ascend to Him. I will pass
beyond that power whereby I am united to my body, and fill its whole
frame with life. Nor can I by that power find my God; for so *horse
and mule that have no understanding,* might find Him; seeing it is the
same power, whereby even their bodies live. But another power there
is, not that only whereby I animate, but that too whereby I imbue
with sense my flesh, which the Lord hath framed for me: commanding the eye not to hear, and the ear not to see; but the eye, that
through it I should see, and the ear, that through it I should hear; and
to the other senses severally, what is to each their own peculiar seats
and offices; which, being divers, I the one mind, do through them
enact. I will pass beyond this power of mine also; for this also have
the horse and mule, for they also perceive through the body.

I will pass then beyond this power of my nature also, rising by degrees unto Him, who made me. And I come to the fields and spacious
palaces of my memory, where are the treasures of innumerable
images, brought into it from things of all sorts perceived by the
senses. There is stored up, whatsoever besides we think, either by en-
larging or diminishing, or any other way varying those things which
the sense hath come to; and whatever else hath been committed and
laid up, which forgetfulness hath not yet swallowed up and buried.
When I enter there, I require what I will, to be brought forth, and
something instantly comes; others must be longer sought after, which
are fetched, as it were, out of some inner receptacle; others rush out
in troops, and while one thing is desired and required, they start forth,
as who should say, "Is it perchance I?" These I drive away with the
hand of my heart, from the face of my remembrance; until what I
wished for be unveiled, and appear in sight, out of its secret place.
Other things come up readily, in unbroken order, as they are called
for; those in front making way for the following; and as they make
way, they are hidden from sight, ready to come when I will. All which
takes place, when I repeat a thing by heart.

There are all things preserved distinctly and under general heads,
each having entered by its own avenue: as light, and all colors and

forms of bodies, by the eyes; by the ears all sorts of sounds; all smells by the avenue of the nostrils; all tastes by the mouth; and by the sensation of the whole body, what is hard or soft; hot or cold; smooth or rugged; heavy or light; either outwardly or inwardly to the body. All these doth that great harbor of the memory receive in her numberless secret and inexpressible windings, to be forthcoming, and brought out at need; each entering in by his own gate, and there laid up. Nor yet do the things themselves enter in; only the images of the things perceived, are there in readiness, for thought to recall. Which images, how they are formed, who can tell, though it doth plainly appear by which sense each hath been brought in and stored up? For even while I dwell in darkness and silence, in my memory I can produce colors, if I will, and discern betwixt black and white, and what others I will: nor yet do sounds break in, and disturb the image drawn in by my eyes, which I am reviewing, though they also are there, lying dormant, and laid up, as it were, apart. For these too I call for, and forthwith they appear. And though my tongue be still, and my throat mute, so can I sing as much as I will; nor do those images of colors, which notwithstanding be there, intrude themselves and interrupt, when another store is called for, which flowed in by the ears. So the other things, piled in and up by the other senses, I recall at my pleasure. Yea, I discern the breath of lilies from violets, though smelling nothing; and I prefer honey to sweet wine, smooth before rugged, at the time neither tasting, nor handling, but remembering only.

These things do I within, in that vast court of my memory. For there are present with me, heaven, earth, sea, and whatever I could think on therein, besides what I have forgotten. There also meet I with myself, and recall myself, and when, where, and what I have done, and under what feelings. There be all which I remember, either on my own experience, or others' credit. Out of the same store do I myself with the past continually combine fresh and fresh likenesses of things, which I have experienced, or, from what I have experienced, I have believed: and thence again infer future actions, events and hopes, and all these again I reflect on, as present. "I will do this or that," say I to myself, in that great receptacle of my mind, stored with the images of things so many and so great, "and this or that will follow." "O that this or that might be!" "God avert this or that!" So speak I to myself: and when I speak, the images of all I speak of are present, out of the same treasury of memory; nor would I speak of any thereof were the images wanting.

Great is this force of memory, excessive great, O my God; a large and boundless chamber! whoever sounded the bottom thereof? yet is this a power of mine, and belongs unto my nature; nor do I myself comprehend all that I am. Therefore is the mind too strait to contain itself. And where should that be which it containeth not of itself? Is it without it, and not within? how then doth it not comprehend itself? A wonderful admiration surprises me, amazement seizes me upon this. And men go abroad to admire the heights of mountains, the mighty billows of the sea, the broad tides of rivers, the compass of the ocean, and the circuits of the stars, and pass themselves by; nor wonder, that when I spoke of all these things, I did not see them with mine eyes, yet could not have spoken of them, unless I then actually saw the mountains, billows, rivers, stars, which I had seen, and that ocean which I believe to be, inwardly in my memory, and that, with the same vast spaces between, as if I saw them abroad. Yet did not I by seeing draw them into myself, when with mine eyes I beheld them; nor are they themselves with me, but their images only. And I know by what sense of the body, each was impressed upon me.

Yet not these alone does the unmeasurable capacity of my memory retain. Here also is all, learned of the liberal sciences and as yet unforgotten; removed as it were to some inner place, which is yet no place: nor are they the images thereof, but the things themselves. For, what is literature, what the art of disputing, how many kinds of questions there be, whatsoever of these I know, in such manner exists in my memory, as that I have not taken in the image, and left out the thing, or that it should have sounded and passed away like a voice fixed on the ear by that impress, whereby it might be recalled, as if it sounded, when it no longer sounded; or as a smell while it passes, and evaporates into air affects the sense of smell, whence it conveys into the memory an image of itself, which remembering, we renew, or as meat, which verily in the belly hath now no taste, and yet in the memory still in a manner tasteth; or as any thing which the body by touch perceiveth, and which when removed from us, the memory still conceives. For those things are not transmitted into the memory, but their images only are with an admirable swiftness caught up, and stored as it were in wondrous cabinets, and thence wonderfully by the act of remembering, brought forth. . . .

Great is the power of memory, a fearful thing, O my God, a deep and boundless manifoldness; and this thing is the mind, and this am I myself. What am I then, O my God? What nature am I? A life various and manifold, and exceeding immense. Behold in the plains, and caves, and caverns of my memory, innumerable and innumerably full of innumerable kinds of things, either through images, as all bodies; or by actual presence, as the arts; or by certain notions or impressions, as the affections of the mind, which, even when the mind doth not feel, the memory retaineth, while yet whatsoever is in the memory, is also in the mind—over all these do I run, I fly; I dive on this side and on that, as far as I can, and there is no end. So great is the force of memory, so great the force of life, even in the mortal life of man. What shall I do then, O Thou my true life, my God? I will pass even beyond this power of mine which is called memory: yea, I will pass beyond it, that I may approach unto Thee, O sweet Light. What sayest Thou to me? See, I am mounting up through my mind towards Thee who abidest above me. Yea I now will pass beyond this power of mine which is called memory, desirous to arrive at Thee, whence Thou mayest be arrived at; and to cleave unto Thee, whence one may cleave unto Thee. For even beasts and birds have memory; else could they not return to their dens and nests, nor many other things they are used unto: nor indeed could they be used to any thing, but by memory. I will pass then beyond memory also, that I may arrive at Him who hath separated me from the four-footed beasts and made me wiser than the fowls of the air, I will pass beyond memory also, and where shall I find Thee, Thou truly good and certain sweetness? And where shall I find Thee? If I find Thee without my memory, then do I not retain Thee in my memory. And how shall I find Thee, if I remember Thee not? . . .

See what a space I have gone over in my memory seeking Thee, O Lord; and I have not found Thee, without it. Nor have I found any thing concerning Thee, but what I have kept in memory, ever since I learned Thee. For since I learned Thee, I have not forgotten Thee. For where I found Truth, there found I my God, the Truth Itself, which since I learned, I have not forgotten. Since then I learned Thee, Thou residest in my memory; and there do I find Thee, when I call Thee to remembrance, and delight in Thee. These be my holy delights, which Thou hast given me in Thy mercy, having regard to my poverty.

Where then did I find Thee, that I might learn Thee? For in my memory Thou wert not, before I learned Thee. Where then did I find Thee, that I might learn Thee, but in Thee above me? Place there is none; *we go backward and forward,* and there is no place. Everywhere, O Truth, dost Thou give audience to all who ask counsel of

Thee, and at once answerest all, though on manifold matters they ask Thy counsel. Clearly dost Thou answer, though all do not clearly hear. All consult Thee on what they will, though they hear not always what they will. He is thy best servant, who looks not so much to hear that from Thee, which himself willeth; as rather to will that, which from Thee he heareth.

Too late loved I Thee, O Thou Beauty of ancient days, yet ever new! too late I loved Thee! And behold, Thou wert within, and I abroad, and there I searched for Thee; deformed I, plunging amid those fair forms, which Thou hadst made. Thou wert with me, but I was not with Thee. Things held me far from Thee, which, unless they were in Thee, were not at all. Thou calledst, and shoutedst, and burstest, my deafness. Thou flashedst, shonest, and scatteredst my blindness. Thou breathedst odors, and *I drew in breath* and *pant for Thee*. I tasted, and *hunger and thirst*. Thou touchedst me, and I burned for Thy peace.

When I shall with my whole self cleave to Thee, I shall nowhere have sorrow, or labor; and my life shall wholly live, as wholly full of Thee. But now since whom Thou fillest, Thou liftest up, because I am not full of Thee I am a burden to myself. Lamentable joys strive with joyous sorrows: and on which side is the victory, I know not. Woe is me! Lord, have pity on me. My evil sorrows strive with my good joys; and on which side is the victory, I know not. Woe is me! Lord, have pity on me. Woe is me! lo! I hide not my wounds; Thou art the Physician, I the sick; Thou merciful, I miserable. *Is not the life of man upon earth all trial?* Who wishes for troubles and difficulties? Thou commandest them to be endured, not to be loved. No man loves what he endures, though he love to endure. For though he rejoices that he endures, he had rather there were nothing for him to endure. In adversity, I long for prosperity, in prosperity I fear adversity. What middle place is there between these two, where *the life of man is* not *all trial?* Woe to the prosperities of the world, once and again, through fear of adversity, and corruption of joy! Woe to the adversities of the world, once and again, and the third time, from the longing for prosperity, and because adversity itself is a hard thing, and lest it shatter endurance. Is not the *life of man upon earth all trial,* without any interval?

And all my hope is nowhere but in Thy exceeding great mercy. Give what Thou enjoinest, and enjoin what Thou wilt. Thou enjoinest us continency; and *when I knew,* saith one, *that no man can be*

333

continent, unless God give it, this also was a part of wisdom to know whose gift she is. By continency verily, are we bound up and brought back into One, whence we were dissipated into many. For too little doth he love Thee, who loves any thing with Thee, which he loveth not for Thee, O love, who ever burnest and never consumest! O charity, my God! kindle me. Thou enjoinest continency: give me what Thou enjoinest, and enjoin what Thou wilt.

Verily Thou enjoinest me continency from the *lust of the flesh, the lust of the eyes, and the ambition of the world.* Thou enjoinest continency from concubinage; and, for wedlock itself, Thou has counseled something better than what Thou hast permitted. And since Thou gavest it, it was done, even before I became a dispenser of Thy Sacrament. But there yet live in my memory (whereof I have much spoken) the images of such things, as my ill custom there fixed; which haunt me, strengthless when I am awake: but in sleep, not only so as to give pleasure, but even to obtain assent, and what is very like reality. Yea, so far prevails the illusion of the image, in my soul and in my flesh, that, when asleep, false visions persuade to that which when waking, the true cannot. Am I not then myself, O Lord my God? And yet there is so much difference betwixt myself and myself, within that moment wherein I pass from waking to sleeping, or return from sleeping to waking! Where is reason then, which, awake, resisteth such suggestions? And should the things themselves be urged on it, it remaineth unshaken. Is it clasped up with the eyes? is it lulled asleep with the senses of the body? And whence is it that often even in sleep we resist, and mindful of our purpose, and abiding most chastely in it, yield no assent to such enticements? And yet so much difference there is, that when it happeneth otherwise, upon waking we return to peace of conscience: and by this very difference discover that we did not, that yet we be sorry that in some way it was done in us.

Art Thou not mighty, God Almighty, so as to *heal all the diseases of my soul,* and by Thy more abundant grace to quench even the impure motions of my sleep? Thou wilt increase, Lord, Thy gifts more and more in me, that my soul may follow me to Thee, disentangled from the birdlime of concupiscence; that it rebel not against itself, and even in dreams not only not, through images of sense, commit those debasing corruptions, even to pollution of the flesh, but not even to consent unto them. For that nothing of this sort should have, over the pure affections even of a sleeper, the very least influence, not even such as a thought would restrain—to work this, not only during life, but even at my present age, is not hard for the Almighty, Who art *able to do above all that we ask or think*. But what I yet am in this kind of my evil, have I confessed unto my good Lord; *rejoicing with trembling,* in that which Thou hast given me, and bemoaning that wherein I am still imperfect; hoping, that Thou wilt perfect Thy mercies in me, even to perfect peace, which my outward and inward man shall have with Thee, when *death shall be swallowed up in victory*.

There is another *evil of the day,* which I would were *sufficient for it.* For by eating and drinking we repair the daily decays of our body, until Thou *destroy both belly and meat,* when Thou shalt slay my emptiness with a wonderful fullness, and *clothe this incorruptible with* an eternal *incorruption*. But now the necessity is sweet unto me, against which sweetness I fight, that I be not taken captive; and carry on a daily war by fastings; often *bringing my body into subjection,* and my pains are removed by pleasure. For hunger and thirst are in a manner pains; they burn and kill like a fever, unless the medicine of nourishments come to our aid. Which since it is at hand through the consolations of Thy gifts, with which land, and water, and air serve our weakness, our calamity is termed gratification.

This hast Thou taught me, that I should set myself to take food as physic. But while I am passing from the discomfort of emptiness to the content of replenishing, in the very passage the snare of concupiscence besets me. For that passing, is pleasure, nor is there any other way to pass thither, whither we needs must pass. And health being the cause of eating and drinking, there joineth itself as an attendant a dangerous pleasure, which mostly endeavors to go before it, so that I may for her sake do what I say I do, or wish to do, for health's sake. Nor have each the same measure; for what is enough for health, is too little for pleasure. And oft it is uncertain, whether it be the necessary care of the body which is yet asking for sustenance, or whether a voluptuous deceivableness of greediness is proffering its services. In this uncertainty the unhappy soul rejoiceth, and therein prepares an excuse to shield itself, glad that it appeareth not what sufficeth for the moderation of health, that under the cloak of health, it may disguise the matter of gratification. These temptations I daily endeavor to resist, and I call on Thy hand, and to Thee do I refer my perplexities; because I have as yet no settled counsel herein.

335

I hear the voice of my God commanding, *Let not your hearts be overcharged with surfeiting and drunkenness.* Drunkenness is far from me; Thou wilt have mercy that it come not near me. But fullfeeding sometimes creepeth upon Thy servant; Thou wilt have mercy, that it may be far from me. For *no one can be continent unless Thou give it.* Many things Thou givest us, praying for them; and what good soever we have received before we prayed, from Thee we received it; yea to the end we might afterward know this, did we before receive it. Drunkard was I never, but drunkards have I known made sober by Thee. From Thee then it was, that they who never were such, should not so be, as from Thee it was, that they who have been, should not ever so be; and from Thee it was, that both might know from Whom it was. I heard another voice of Thine, *Go not after thy lusts, and from thy pleasure turn away.* Yea by Thy favor have I heard that which I have much loved; *neither if we eat, shall we abound; neither if we eat not, shall we lack;* which is to say, neither shall the one make me plenteous, nor the other miserable. I heard also another, *for I have learned in whatsoever state I am, therewith to be content; I know how to abound, and how to suffer need. I can do all things through Christ that strengtheneth me.* Behold a soldier of the heavenly camp, not the dust which we are. But *remember,* Lord, *that we are dust,* and that of *dust thou hast made man;* and he *was lost and is found.* Nor could he of himself do this, because he whom I so loved, saying this through Thy inspiration, was of the same dust. *I can do all things* (saith he) *through Him that strengtheneth me.* Strengthen me, that *I can.* Give what Thou enjoinest, and enjoin what Thou wilt. He confesses to have received, and when *he glorieth, in the Lord he glorieth.* Another have I heard begging that he might receive, *Take from me* (saith he) *the desires of the belly;* whence it appeareth, O my holy God, that Thou givest, when that is done which Thou commandest to be done.

With the allurements of smells, I am not much concerned. When absent, I do not miss them; when present, I do not refuse them; yet ever ready to be without them. So I seem to myself; perchance I am deceived. For that also is a mournful darkness, whereby my abilities within me, are hidden from me; so that my mind making inquiry into herself of her own powers, ventures not readily to believe herself; because even what is in it, is mostly hidden, unless experience reveal it. And no one ought to be secure in that life, the whole whereof is called *a trial,* that he who hath been capable of worse to be made better, may not likewise of better be made worse. Our only hope, only confidence, only assured promise, is Thy mercy.

The delights of the ear had more firmly entangled and subdued me; but Thou didst loosen, and free me. Now, in those melodies which Thy words breathe soul into, when sung with a sweet and attuned voice, I do a little repose; yet not so as to be held thereby, but that I can disengage myself when I will. But with the words which are their life and whereby they find admission into me, themselves seek in my affections a place of some estimation, and I can scarcely assign them one suitable. For at one time I seem to myself to give them more honor than is seemly, feeling our minds to be more holily and fervently raised unto a flame of devotion, by the holy words themselves when thus sung, than when not; and that the several affections of our spirit, by a sweet variety, have their own proper measures in the voice and singing, by some hidden correspondence wherewith they are stirred up. But this contentment of the flesh, to which the soul must not be given over to be enervated, doth oft beguile me, the sense not so waiting upon reason, as patiently to follow her; but having been admitted merely for her sake, it strives even to run before her, and lead her. Thus in these things I unaware sin, but afterwards am aware of it.

At other times, shunning over-anxiously this very deception, I err in too great strictness; and sometimes to that degree, as to wish the whole melody of sweet music which is used to David's Psalter, banished from my ears, and the Church's too; and that mode seems to me safer, which I remember to have been often told me of Athanasius, Bishop of Alexandria, who made the reader of the psalm utter it with so slight inflection of voice, that it was nearer speaking than singing. Yet again, when I remember the tears I shed at the Psalmody of Thy Church, in the beginning of my recovered faith; and how at this time, I am moved, not with the singing, but with the things sung, when they are sung with a clear voice and modulation most suitable, I acknowledge the great use of this institution. Thus I fluctuate between peril of pleasure, and approved wholesomeness; inclined the rather (though not as pronouncing an irrevocable opinion) to approve of the usage of singing in the church; that so by the delight of the ears, the weaker minds may rise to the feeling of devotion. Yet when it befalls me to be more moved with the voice than the words sung, I confess to have sinned penally, and then had rather not hear music. Hear now my state; weep with me, and weep for me, ye, who so regulate your feelings within, as that good action ensues. For you who do not act, these things touch not you. But Thou, O Lord my God, hearken; behold, and see, and *have mercy, and heal me,* Thou, in whose presence I have become a problem to myself; and *that is my infirmity.*

There remains the pleasure of these eyes of my flesh, on which to make my confessions in the hearing of the ears of Thy temple, those brotherly and devout ears; and so to conclude the temptations of the *lust of the flesh,* which yet assail me, *groaning earnestly, and desiring to be clothed upon with my house from heaven.* The eyes love fair and varied forms, and bright and soft colors. Let not these occupy my soul; let God rather occupy it, *who made these* things, *very good* indeed, yet is He my good, not they. And these affect me, waking, the whole day, nor is any rest given me from them, as there is from musical, sometimes, in silence, from all voices. For this queen of colors, the light, bathing all which we behold, wherever I am through the day, gliding by me in varied forms, soothes me when engaged on other things, and not observing it. And so strongly doth it entwine itself, that if it be suddenly withdrawn, it is with longing sought for, and if absent long, saddeneth the mind.

O Thou Light, which Tobias saw, when, these eyes closed, he taught his son the way of life; and himself went before with the feet of charity, never swerving. Or which Isaac saw, when his fleshly *eyes being heavy* and closed by old age, it was vouchsafed him, not knowingly to bless his sons, but by blessing to know them. Or which Jacob saw, when he also, blind through great age, with illumined heart, in the persons of his sons shed light on the different races of the future people, in them foresignified; and laid his hands, mystically crossed, upon his grandchildren by Joseph, not as their father by his outward eye corrected them, but as himself inwardly discerned. This is the light, it is one, and all are one, who see and love it. But that corporeal light whereof I spoke, it seasoneth the life of this world for her blind lovers, with an enticing and dangerous sweetness. But they who know how to praise Thee for it, "O All-creating Lord," take it up in Thy hymns, and are not taken up with it in their sleep. Such would I be. These seductions of the eyes I resist, lest my feet wherewith I walk upon Thy way be ensnared; and I lift up mine invisible eyes to Thee, that Thou wouldest *pluck my feet out of the snare.* Thou dost ever and anon pluck them out, for they are ensnared. Thou ceasest not to pluck them out, while I often entangle myself in the snares on all sides laid; because *Thou that keepest Israel shalt neither slumber nor sleep.*

What innumerable toys, made by divers arts and manufactures, in our apparel, shoes, utensils and all sort of works, in pictures also and divers images, and these far exceeding all necessary and moderate use and all pious meaning, have men added to tempt their own eyes withal; outwardly following what themselves make, inwardly forsaking Him by whom themselves were made, and destroying that which themselves have been made! But I, my God and my Glory, do hence also sing a hymn to Thee, and do consecrate praise to Him who consecrateth me, because those beautiful patterns which through men's souls are conveyed into their cunning hands, come from that Beauty, Which is above our souls, Which my soul day and night sigheth after. But the framers and followers of the outward beauties, derive thence the rule of judging of them, but not of using them. And He is there, though they perceive Him not, that so they might not wander, but *keep their strength for Thee,* and not scatter it abroad upon pleasurable wearinesses. And I, though I speak and see this, entangle my steps with these outward beauties; but Thou pluckest me out, O Lord, Thou pluckest me out; *because Thy lovingkindness is before my eyes.* For I am taken miserably, and Thou pluckest me out mercifully; sometimes not perceiving it, when I had but lightly lighted upon them; otherwhiles with pain, because I had stuck fast in them.

To this is added, another form of temptation more manifoldly dangerous. For besides that concupiscence of the flesh which consisteth in the delight of all senses and pleasures, wherein its slaves, who *go far from Thee,* waste and *perish,* the soul hath, through the same senses of the body, a certain vain and curious desire, veiled under the title of knowledge and learning, not of delighting in the flesh, but of making experiments through the flesh. The seat whereof being in the appetite of knowledge, and sight being the sense chiefly used for attaining knowledge, it is in Divine language called, *The lust of the eyes.* For, to see belongeth properly to the eyes; yet we use this word of the other senses also, when we employ them in seeking knowledge. For we do not say, hark how it flashes, or smell how it glows, or taste how it shines, or feel how it gleams; for all these are said to be seen. And yet we say not only, see how it shineth, which the eyes alone can perceive; but also, see how it soundeth, see how it smelleth, see how it tasteth, see how hard it is. And so the general experience of the senses, as was said, is called *The lust of the eyes,* because the office of seeing, wherein the eyes hold the prerogative, the other senses by way

339

of similitude take to themselves, when they make search after any knowledge.

But by this may more evidently be discerned, wherein pleasure and wherein curiosity is the object of the senses; for pleasure seeketh objects beautiful, melodious, fragrant, savory, soft; but curiosity, for trial's sake, the contrary as well, not for the sake of suffering annoyance, but out of the lust of making trial and knowing them. For what pleasure hath it, to see in a mangled carcass what will make you shudder? and yet if it be lying near, they flock thither to be made sad and to turn pale. Even in sleep they are afraid to see it. As if when awake, any one forced them to see it, or any report of its beauty drew them thither! Thus also in the other senses, which it were long to go through. From this disease of curiosity, are all those strange sights exhibited in the theater. Hence men go on to search out the hidden powers of nature, (which is besides our end), which to know profits not, and wherein men desire nothing but to know. Hence also, if with that same end of perverted knowledge magical arts be inquired into. Hence also in religion itself, is God tempted, when signs and wonders are demanded of Him, not desired for any good end, but merely to make trial of.

In this so vast wilderness, full of snares and dangers, behold many of them I have cut off, and thrust out of my heart, as Thou hast given me, O God of my salvation. And yet when dare I say, since so many things of this kind buzz on all sides about our daily life—when dare I say, that nothing of this sort engages my attention, or causes in me an idle interest? True, the theaters do not now carry me away, nor care I to know the courses of the stars, nor did my soul ever consult ghosts departed; all sacrilegious mysteries I detest. From Thee, O Lord my God, to whom I owe humble and single-hearted service, by what artifices and suggestions doth the enemy deal with me to desire some sign! But I beseech thee by our King, and by our pure and holy country, Jerusalem, that as any consenting thereto is far from me, so may it ever be further and further. But when I pray Thee for the salvation of any, my end and intention is far different. Thou givest and wilt give me to *follow Thee* willingly, doing what Thou *wilt*.

Notwithstanding, in how many most petty and contemptible things is our curiosity daily tempted, and how often we give way, who can recount? How often do we begin, as if we were tolerating people telling vain stories, lest we offend the weak; then by degrees we take interest therein! I go not now to the circus to see a dog coursing a

340

hare; but in the field, if passing, that coursing peradventure will distract me even from some weighty thought, and draw me after it: not that I turn aside the body of my beast, yet still incline my mind thither. And unless Thou, having made me see my infirmity, didst speedily admonish me either through the sight itself, by some contemplation to rise towards Thee, or altogether to despise and pass it by, I dully stand fixed therein. What if, when sitting home, a lizard catching flies, or a spider entangling them rushing into her nets, ofttimes takes my attention? Is the thing different, because they are but small creatures? I go on from them to praise Thee the wonderful Creator and Orderer of all, but this does not first draw my attention. It is one thing to rise quickly, another not to fall. And of such things is my life full; and my one hope is Thy wonderful great mercy. For when our heart becomes the receptacle of such things, and is overcharged with throngs of this abundant vanity, then are our prayers also thereby often interrupted and distracted, and whilst in Thy presence we direct the voice of our heart to Thine ears, this so great concern is broken off, by the rushing in of I know not what idle thoughts. Shall we then account this also among things of slight concernment, or shall nought bring us back to hope, save Thy complete mercy, since Thou hast begun to change us?

And Thou knowest how far Thou hast already changed me, who first healedst me of the lust of vindicating myself, that so Thou mightest *forgive all* the rest of my *iniquities, and heal all my infirmities, and redeem my life from corruption, and crown me with mercy and pity, and satisfy my desire with good things:* who didst curb my pride with Thy fear, and tame my neck to Thy *yoke.* And now I bear it and it is *light* unto me, because so hast Thou promised, and hast made it; and verily so it was, and I knew it not, when I feared to take it.

But, O Lord, Thou alone Lord without pride, because Thou art the only true Lord, who hast no lord; hath this third kind of temptation also ceased from me, or can it cease through this whole life? To wish, namely, to be feared and loved of men, for no other end, but that we may have a joy therein which is no joy? A miserable life this, and a foul boastfulness! Hence especially it comes, that men do neither purely love, nor fear Thee. And therefore *dost Thou resist the proud, and givest grace to the humble:* yea, Thou thunderest down upon the ambitions of the world, and *the foundations of the mountains tremble.* Because now certain offices of human society make it necessary to be loved and feared of men, the adversary of our true blessedness layeth hard at us, everywhere spreading his snares of "well done, well done"; that greedily catching at them, we may be taken unawares, and sever our joy from Thy truth, and set it in the deceivingness of men; and be pleased at being loved and feared, not for Thy sake, but in Thy stead: and thus having been made like him, he may have them for his own, not in the bands of charity, but in the bonds of punishment: who purposed to *set his throne in the north,* that dark and chilled they might serve him, pervertedly and crookedly imitating Thee. But we, O Lord, behold we are *Thy little flock;* possess us as Thine, stretch Thy wings over us, and let us fly under them. Be Thou our glory; let us be loved for Thee, and Thy word feared in us. Who would be praised of men, when Thou blamest, will not be defended of men, when Thou judgest; nor delivered, when Thou condemnest. But when —not *the sinner is praised in the desires of his soul,* nor he *blessed who doth ungodly,* but—a man is praised for some gift which Thou hast given him, and he rejoices more at the praise for himself than that he hath the gift for which he is praised, he also is praised, while Thou dispraisest; and better is he who praised than he who is praised. For the one took pleasure in the gift of God in man; the other was better pleased with the gift of man, than of God.

By these temptations we are assailed daily, O Lord; without ceasing are we assailed. Our daily *furnace* is the tongue of men. And in this way also Thou commandest us continence. Give what Thou enjoinest, and enjoin what Thou wilt. Thou knowest on this matter the groans of my heart, and the floods of mine eyes. For I cannot learn how far I am more cleansed from this plague, and I much fear my *secret sins,* which Thine eyes know, mine do not. For in other kinds of temptations I have some sort of means of examining myself; in this, scarce any. For, in refraining my mind from the pleasures of the flesh, and idle curiosity, I see how much I have attained to, when I do without them; foregoing or not having them. For then I ask myself how much more or less troublesome it is to me, not to have them? Then, riches, which are desired, that they may serve to someone or two or all of the three concupiscences, if the soul cannot discern, whether, when it hath them, it despiseth them, they may be cast aside, that so it may prove itself. But to be without praise, and therein essay our powers, must we live ill, yea so abandonedly and atrociously, that no one should know without detesting us? What greater madness can be said, or thought of? But if praise useth and ought to accompany a good life

342

and good works, we ought as little to forego its company, as good life itself. Yet I know not, whether I can well or ill be without any thing, unless it be absent. . . .

How hast Thou loved us, good Father, who *sparedst not Thine only Son, but deliveredst Him up for us ungodly!* How hast Thou loved us, for whom, *He that thought it no robbery to be equal with Thee, was made subject even to the death of the cross,* He alone *free among the dead, having power to lay down His life, and power to take it again:* for us to Thee both Victor and Victim, and therefore Victor, because the Victim; for us to Thee Priest and Sacrifice, and therefore Priest because the Sacrifice; making us to Thee, of servants, sons, by being born of Thee, and serving us. Well then is my hope strong in Him, that Thou *wilt heal all my infirmities,* by Him Who *sitteth at Thy right hand and maketh intercession for us;* else should I despair. For many and great are my infirmities, many they are, and great; but Thy medicine is mightier. We might imagine that Thy Word was far from any union with man, and despair of ourselves, unless He had been *made flesh and dwelt among us.*

Affrighted with my sins and the burden of my misery, I had cast in my heart, and had purposed to *flee to the wilderness:* but Thou forbaddest me, and strengthenedst me, saying, *Therefore Christ died for all, that they which live may now no longer live unto themselves, but unto Him that died for them.* See, Lord, I *cast my care upon Thee,* that I may live, and *consider wondrous things out of Thy law.* Thou knowest my unskillfulness, and my infirmities; teach me, and heal me. He Thine only Son, *in Whom are hid all the treasures of wisdom and knowledge,* hath redeemed me with His blood. *Let not the proud speak evil of me;* because I meditate on my ransom, and eat and drink, and communicate it; and *poor,* desired to be *satisfied* from Him, among those that *eat and are satisfied, and they shall praise the Lord who seek Him.*

[*At this point Saint Augustine broke off the history of how God led him to Holy Orders, devoting the last three books of his* Confessions *to a discussion and interpretation of the Book of Genesis, with special emphasis on the errors of the Manichaeans.*]

Aaron Burr's

LETTER
CHALLENGING
ALEXANDER
HAMILTON
TO A DUEL

June 22, 1804

HOME COURSE APPRECIATION

GENERAL ALEXANDER HAMILTON (1757–1804) and Colonel Aaron Burr (1756–1836) had much in common. They were brave soldiers in the American Revolution, brilliant and ambitious lawyers, and New Yorkers by adoption. But in politics they parted company. Colonel Burr was a member of the Republican party (which became the present-day Democratic party) and General Hamilton was a Federalist.

Because of his shifting sentiments, Burr's adoption of Jefferson's kind of republicanism has been questioned. For Burr had an undue fondness for intrigue, and men quite naturally mistrusted him. He was too clever and his associates too wily to win confidence.

But no one doubted General Hamilton's conservative principles. "Your people, sir," said Hamilton, "your people is a great beast." He distrusted and feared democracy. His tastes were aristocratic and his friends were men of wealth. He believed in the privileges of property, in something like a hereditary peerage, and in life tenure for presidents. He stood for a strong central government and opposed Jefferson when he insisted on the rights of the individual states.

Thus from the very beginning these two brilliant men who shared the cream of New York's law business fought each other. When, in 1791, Burr defeated Hamilton's father-in-law, General Philip Schuyler, for the United States Senate, their disagreement became personal as well as political. Then in the election of 1800 Jefferson and Burr, both running on the same ticket, were tied for the presidency in the electoral college. Before the Twelfth Amendment was added to the Constitution in 1804, the man with the most electoral votes became President and the man with the next highest number became Vice-president. The election was thrown into the House of Representatives where the deadlock continued for thirty-five ballots, until Hamilton persuaded three Federalists who were voting for Burr to cast blank ballots. Jefferson was declared President and Burr had to be content with second place. Naturally he blamed Hamilton for his defeat.

When Burr decided to run for the governorship of New York in 1804, his campaign was marked by considerable intrigue and he lost again. Burr believed that Hamilton had much to do with this second defeat, for during the campaign, Hamilton had been quoted as calling Burr a "dangerous man" who was "not to be trusted with the reins of government."

Burr took advantage of the tricky gentleman's code of behavior to challenge Hamilton, who was reported to have cast contempt upon him in private conversation. An exchange of letters, each stiffer than the one before, culminated in the fatal challenge from Burr to Hamilton. Hamilton was opposed to dueling but he did not dare to refuse this challenge.

Three weeks later, early on the morning of July 11, 1804, the contestants met in Weehawken, New Jersey. Hamilton held his fire, but Burr shot to kill. Within little more than twenty-four hours, Alexander Hamilton was dead. His death on the "field of honor" was greeted with universal horror and Burr's reputation was blighted forever. Though he lived thirty-two years longer, Aaron Burr was never again in a position to seek office in the American government. Two great Americans had been sacrificed to the "code of honor" on the dueling grounds at Weehawken.

Sir

M R. V. NESS HAS THIS EVENING reported to me verbally that you refuse to answer my last letter, that you consider the course I have taken as intemperate and unnecessary and some other conversation which it is improper that I should notice.

My request to you was in the first instance prepared in a form the most simple in order that you might give to the affair that course to which you might be induced by your temper and your knowledge of facts. I relied with unsuspecting faith that from the frankness of a soldier and the candor of a gentleman I might expect an ingenuous declaration; that if, as I had reason to believe, you had used expressions derogatory to my honor, you would have had the spirit to maintain or the magnanimity to retract them, and, that if from your language injurious inferences had been improperly drawn, sincerity and decency would have pointed out to you the propriety of correcting errors which might then have been widely diffused.

With these impressions, I was greatly disappointed in receiving from you a letter which I could only consider as evasive and which in manner is not altogether decorous. In one expectation I find an intimation, that if I should dislike your refusal to acknowledge or deny the charge, you were ready to meet the consequences. This I deemed a sort of defiance, and I should have been justified if I had chosen to make it the basis of an immediate message: Yet, as you had also said something (though in any opinion unfounded) of the indefiniteness of my request; as I believed that your communication was the offspring, rather of false pride than of reflection, and, as I felt the utmost reluctance to proceed to extremities while any other hope remained, my request was repeated in terms more definite. To this you refuse all reply, reposing, as I am bound to presume on the tender of an alternative insinuated in your letter.

Thus, Sir, you have invited the course I am about to pursue, and now by your silence impose it upon me. If, therefore, your determinations are final, of which I am not permitted to doubt, Mr. Van Ness is authorized to communicate my further expectations either to yourself or to such friend as you may be pleased to indicate.

I have the honor to be

Yours respt

A. BURR

PARADISE
LOST

by

John Milton

A CONDENSATION

HOME COURSE APPRECIATION

JOHN MILTON'S "PARADISE LOST" might be likened to Saint Peter's Cathedral in Rome. It is a tremendous structure whose basic outlines are clear and simple, yet whose details are wonderfully elaborate. The central episode of the poem may be thought of as the eating of an apple. Yet the action that surrounds this single incident is so vast that the poem is often described as a history of the universe from the beginning of time to its very end. The poetic themes, from the fall of Satan to the resurrection of Christ, make it truly cosmic in scope. It is the greatest poem of austere Puritanism. It is the greatest example of baroque writing in the English language. And it is a personal work, which scrutiny of the man who wrote it and of his times will help make clear.

The eldest son of a successful lawyer, John Milton was born in London in 1608. Queen Elizabeth had been dead five years and Shakespeare, already in retirement, had eight years more of life. But many of the glorious figures of Elizabeth's period might still be seen on the streets of London during Milton's youth. Courtly Sir Walter Raleigh, bluff, red-faced Ben Jonson and calculating, cool Francis Bacon were but a few of the survivors from the confident reign of Elizabeth I. Milton was greatly influenced by Shakespeare and other writers of that preceding generation, but the problems of his own day cast an ever-darkening shadow across his life and thought. His character had a somber, almost gloomy touch that is foreign to the Elizabethan temper. For Milton's time was the time of Puritanism.

When, in the early sixteenth century, the English Church was "reformed" from Roman Catholicism by Henry VIII, not many changes were made in its internal structure. The lands belonging to the monks were confiscated, and the King took the place of the Pope as the head of the Church. But the government and discipline of the Church were left pretty much as they had been. There was a strong feeling, chiefly among the clergy, that Henry had not gone far enough, that the Church should be radically reformed according to the model laid down by John Calvin in his *Institutes of the Christian Religion* and exemplified in the Presbyterian Church of Geneva. This church was governed by a series of councils, democratically elected by the elders (or presbyters) of the entire Church, and convened in synods or councils for the government of the clergy and of the laity.

The "Puritans," as these critics of the Church were mockingly called, claimed that Calvin's system of Church government was described and prescribed in the Holy Scriptures; and they demanded that the English Church should be "purified" to conform with this model. Their demands sounded the more impressive as a widespread inflation, coupled with the loss of monastic lands, rendered the Church poor and somewhat ineffectual during the early seventeenth century.

Dissatisfaction over matters of taxation, monopolies, privileges of Parliament and economic reform led to widespread disaffection with the advisers and finally with the very character of King Charles I. Every attempt at reform was met by an act of government repression. By the time Milton was out of his twenties, his ambitious and self-confident middle class was engaged in a half-conspiratorial campaign for reform of both church and state. This campaign turned into the great Puritan revolution of 1640.

THE MOST LEARNED POET IN ENGLISH

MILTON SEEMS TO HAVE BEEN CAUGHT UP in the movement for reform while studying for holy orders at Cambridge in 1625. His intensive studies of Latin, Greek, Hebrew and Italian gave him an understanding of the literature, theology, mythology, geography and history of many cultures. No English poet has ever been more widely acquainted with books than John Milton, and his poetry is filled with his learning.

A preoccupation with books is often accompanied by an inability to get along with people, and Milton seems to have been a somewhat seclusive person. His friends were usually scholars, with whom he could discuss Greek texts or exchange playful Latin verses. He seems to have had few friendships with women during his youth.

In 1629 he received his B.A. degree at Cambridge, and in 1632 his M.A. But instead of entering the Church and taking orders, he retired to his father's estate in the little town of Horton, near London, where for six years he pursued his studies in solitude and isolation. Some of his neighbors at Horton were getting up a private party one day and they asked Milton to take part. He wrote a beautiful masque, called "Comus," on the virtues of chastity. Polished and clear in style, it represents Milton's first mature accomplishment in the art of poetry.

In 1637 Milton's former schoolmates produced a volume of memorial poems for a friend who had drowned. Milton's contribution, the only one written in English, was an elegy entitled "Lycidas." Far more important than mourning Edward King, whose name is never mentioned, "Lycidas" raises a number of questions about the vocation and reward of the poet. And, in passing, it utters a thunderous denunciation of the condition of the English clergy which makes perfectly clear why Milton felt himself unable to enter the Church. But more important than any of these things, "Lycidas" speaks in the genuine prophetic voice of the mature Milton. It has been called the most perfect lamentation for the dead in the English language.

TWENTY YEARS OF BITTER POLITICAL STRUGGLE

But "Lycidas" was also Milton's last poetic utterance for a long time. Shortly after writing it, he went abroad for a leisurely two-year tour through France and Italy to finish his education. While he was abroad, news reached him that civil war had broken out in England, and he returned home in 1639. For a while he was silent, meditating his plans and taking account of the national temper. Then in 1641, he issued his first prose tract, *Of Reformation in England*. For the next two decades his life was devoted almost entirely to prose and politics, public affairs and religious reform.

Milton, like the Puritan party as a whole, embarked on the business of reforming church and state with enthusiasm and confidence. The reformers swept bishops from the Church and certain unpopular agents of Charles I from the state without the least difficulty. But if the iron legions of Oliver Cromwell were clear about what they did not want in church and state, they were hard put to say what they did want. In the great debate over the forms to be taken, the voice of John Milton was heard. In *Areopagitica* (1644), he nobly defended the freedom of the press from all censorship; in *Eikonoklastes* (1649) he asserted the guilt of Charles Stuart and defended the right of the English people to try and to condemn him. In pamphlet after pam-

John Milton, totally blind, dictates *Paradise Lost* to his daughters.

phlet he tried to influence the English people toward the highest ideals of freedom and spiritual heroism.

MILTON'S MARRIAGES AND HIS DIVORCE TRACTS

Two of the tracts written between 1641–60 have a special interest because they reveal what was happening to Milton the man. These are the divorce tracts of 1644–45 and the two *Defences of the English People* of 1650–51. The divorce tracts appeared at a time of great public excitement and upheaval; and to conservatives, they seemed to condone the scandalous doctrine of "divorce at pleasure." Actually, they urged something much closer to the present concept of incompatibility as grounds for divorce. Behind their labored arguments were the painful circumstances of Milton's marriage in 1642.

Milton was almost thirty-five then, a man of stern religious temperament and little experience of women. His wife was a fun-loving girl of sixteen, from a large family of country gentry. She did not find her husband congenial and after a few months of married life she went home to her parents. Milton's divorce tracts were his typical response to this unhappy situation. They didn't change the divorce laws of England or do anything to change his legal status, but they did help to relieve his feelings. In the end, Mrs. Milton came back to her husband, and dutifully bore four children, before dying in childbed in 1652. Milton's second wife, whom he married in 1656, died a year later. In 1662 he married for the third time, to live contentedly with Elizabeth Minshull until his death.

TWO DEFENSES OF THE ENGLISH PEOPLE

MORE TRAGIC AND LESS PERSONAL are the circumstances surrounding Milton's two defenses of the English people. These Latin treatises, written in the violent personal style of the day, were inspired by the trial and execution of Charles Stuart in 1649. The execution of the king profoundly stirred all Europe. The divine rights of kings were at stake, and almost immediately the French scholar Claude Saumaise, better known by his Latin name Salmasius, published a book condemning the English people. Milton's reply, *A Defence of the English People,* appeared in 1650. Its Latin is excellent and its scorn for Salmasius incisive. Although it was not significant for its political reasoning, it made a deep impression on the Continent.

Some of Salmasius' friends issued a rejoinder, and Milton was about to crush them with a rebuttal of his own when he was warned that any further literary work would endanger his eyesight. Years of reading and writing by dim candlelight had taken their toll. Milton never hesitated. It was God's command that he assert the truth against Salmasius, and assert it he would, whatever the cost. He penned the *Second Defence* and so extinguished the last dim rays of his eyesight. His enemies were quick to assert, after the cruel fashion of the day, that his blindness was a divine punishment for defending hideous error. But Milton paid little heed; blindness was a small price to pay for the knowledge of a divine duty well performed.

MILTON'S INFLEXIBLE PRINCIPLES ARE PUT TO THE TEST

Loss of sight did not prevent Milton from accepting a post as Latin secretary to Oliver Cromwell. In those days much diplomatic correspondence was still conducted in Latin, and Milton could dictate Latin like a Roman. But things did not go well with the Puritan government. Though Milton might cling to his republican principles to the bitter end, the English people soon gave signs of being ready to recall Charles II from exile.

When the Restoration came, and the Puritan dream of a godly commonwealth tumbled forever to the earth, John Milton was a marked man. For a time his name was on the list of proscribed Puritans and he ran the risk of ending his life on the gallows. He actually went to jail for a while, but was released by the intervention of an influential friend. When he was finally liberated, it was only to find himself desolate, with all his political hopes ruined and his most sacred ideals become the object of ridicule in the merry, bawdy Restoration England of Charles II. It was under these circumstances that Milton showed the true heroism of his character. With every reason to despair or grow bitter, he set about rebuilding the career which fate had ruined. He returned to the poetic activity which twenty years before he had set aside, and began to compose *Paradise Lost*.

"PARADISE LOST" AND ITS EPIC QUALITIES

THE FULL GREATNESS OF "PARADISE LOST" can only be measured by the great epic poems of Homer, Vergil and Dante. The poem shows that Milton was capable of handling the most complex problems that face the epic poet. Milton adopted the epic style because he thought it alone worthy of the grandeur of his subject matter. This style does not attempt to be "natural"; it represents men and women not as they really are, but rather as they ought to be. The reader of *Paradise Lost* will note that many of the characters talk in much the same way. Satan sounds not too different from Adam; the angels sound much like Satan; even God does not talk very differently from the angels. This similarity is part of Milton's style, adopted to give his vast epic an interior unity.

Milton's language is so ornate and elaborate, so tangled with Latin grammar and Biblical references that it sometimes discourages the reader who approaches it for the first time. Many of these references are there largely to embellish the poem. The simplest way to approach the poem is to read over these names for their sounds and for the way they assemble the history and geography of many different cultures within the framework of Milton's own creation. The details of these allusions are often irrelevant; what they give us is a shadowy pageant of history:

> *And all who since, baptized or infidel,*
> *Jousted in Aspramont or Montalban*
> *Damasco, or Marocco, or Trebisond,*
> *Or whom Biserta sent from Afric shore*
> *When Charlemain with all his peerage fell*
> *By Fontarabbia. . . .*

WHO IS THE HERO OF THE POEM?

Because he adopted epic trappings, Milton has often been criticized for certain failures in comparison to such past epics as *The Divine Comedy* and *The Iliad*. One criticism is that the poem lacks a hero, or, that if it has one, the hero is Satan. While it is true that Satan dominates the first books of the poem in the grandest epic manner, his action ends with the temptation of Eve. Even when he builds his bridge to provide the passage for Sin and Death to the Earth, Satan is described as no longer a gigantic ruler of the underworld. He is compared to a bird or an insect. By the end of the poem, his mission is completed and his defeat through Christ's resurrection is assured. Satan is not the hero.

God the Father is not the hero in the sense that His appearances are too few for Him to be the central figure. Jesus the Son is often called the hero because it is He who will undergo the passion that will redeem the lost Paradise. If by 'hero' we mean the figure who embodies the ideals of the poem, then Jesus is surely this.

Adam and Eve can be considered the central figures of the poem in so far as their world is the concern of both Heaven and Hell. They are the only two human beings in the direct action of the poem, and they end it "taking their solitary way" from Eden into the world. If they lack the ideals we associate with heroes, they nevertheless gain perception at the end. Perhaps in terms of suffering and redemption, they are more tragic heroes than epic heroes. But the question of a hero is not crucial to an appreciation of the poem.

One of Milton's extraordinary achievements is his handling of time. His poem has its origins in a period before time as men know it, and it ends with a prophecy of man's destiny up to the end of time. The few centuries of man's life on earth—all that we have recorded as history—are but a small part of the poem, seen only in the angel Michael's prophecy. Yet we, who exist in this period, feel much a part of the poem, and when Adam and Eve leave Paradise, we realize that their burden has become ours. Milton would have us believe that we too have shared in this original sin and must work and pray for the redemption promised by Jesus. Part of Milton's genius is the way he shapes pagan traditions for Christian uses.

SHARP CRITICISM AND HIGH PRAISE

PARADISE LOST" IS ONE OF THE most highly praised and bitterly assailed poems in the English language. Critics have wrangled over the unconvincing war in Heaven, criticizing the highly ornate descriptions for a place that should be indescribable. Indeed, one thinks of Dante's inability to describe his vision of God. Milton, however, has his God speak and act, and so become liable to criticism as a dramatic character. Yet once he had elected his theme, Milton had to represent Heaven, and it is rather pointless to argue about the style in which he describes it, since this style is consistent throughout the poem.

Another criticism launched against the poem is that Satan and his Hell are more interesting than God and Heaven. The eminent critic C. S. Lewis has refuted this attack by showing that such an argument only reflects a certain temper that is more likely to accept a flaming presentation of evil than a more subtle presentation of divinity.

Other critics have attacked the poem on the grounds that everyone knows the story from the Bible, and therefore Milton cannot improve it or do anything new with it. Actually, the material Milton had to work with was much smaller than the body of his poem. One needs only to read the *Book of Genesis* to see how much he has added. Milton was not trying to improve on the Bible. By creating such images as Satan swimming through outer space or Adam discoursing with Eve, he was trying to make a well-known story relive in terms that would speak directly to his age. Adam and Eve speak not like primitive human beings nor like Biblical characters, but like seventeenth century people. In the same way, Shakespeare's Caesar or Hamlet speak and act like Elizabethans.

Nor is it true that Adam and Eve have no free will and are mere creatures whose lives are determined by the will of God. Michael destroys this argument within the structure of the poem. Milton himself mourns the fall of man but having accepted the reality of it, he regards it as a constant challenge to regain Paradise on Earth by following the ways of God. Once Adam and Eve have learned not remorse for their sins but hope, they gain "a paradise within them, happier far." Their innocence was glorious, but their God-given knowledge is even more divine. This pair decided the fate of the human race by their first sin, but they also passed on the hope of glory. And so they set off on a pilgrimage of which our own lives are but a part, and in which we, the readers, may all hope, through work and prayer, to share final glory.

Between the publication of *Paradise Lost* in 1667 and his death in 1674, Milton wrote two more poems: a short epic on Christ's temptation in the wilderness, *Paradise Regained,* and a tragedy in the classical style, *Samson Agonistes*. Though both are interesting creations, neither can approach *Paradise Lost* in scope. Doctor Johnson gave *Paradise Lost* its highest praise when he said, "With respect to design, this poem may claim the first place, and with respect to performance the second, among the productions of the human mind."

BOOK I

The Argument

This First Book proposes, first in brief, the whole subject—Man's disobedience, and the loss thereupon of Paradise, wherein he was placed; then touches the prime cause of his fall—the Serpent, or rather Satan in the Serpent; who, revolting from God, and drawing to his side many legions of Angels, was, by the command of God, driven out of Heaven, with all his crew, into the great Deep. Which action passed over, the Poem hastes into the midst of things; presenting Satan, with his Angels, now fallen into Hell—described here not in the center (for heaven and earth may be supposed as yet not made, certainly not yet accursed), but in a place of utter darkness, fitliest called Chaos. Here Satan, with his Angels lying on the burning lake, thunderstruck and astonished, after a certain space recovers, as from confusion; calls up him who, next in order and dignity, lay by him; they confer of their miserable fall. Satan awakens all his legions, who lay till then in the same manner confounded. They rise; their numbers, array of battle, their chief leaders named, according to the idols known afterwards in Canaan and the countries adjoining. To these Satan directs his speech; comforts them with hope yet of regaining Heaven; but tells them, lastly, of a new world and new kind of creature to be created, according to an ancient prophecy, or report, in Heaven—for that Angels were long before this visible creation was the opinion of many ancient Fathers. To find out the truth of this prophecy, and what to determine thereon, he refers to a full council. What his associates thence attempt. Pandemonium, the palace of Satan, rises, suddenly built out of the Deep: the infernal Peers there sit in council.

O F MAN'S FIRST disobedience, and the fruit
Of that forbidden tree, whose mortal taste
Brought death into the World, and all our woe,

With loss of Eden, till one greater Man
Restore us, and regain the blissful seat,
Sing, Heavenly Muse, that on the secret top
Of Oreb, or of Sinai, didst inspire
That shepherd who first taught the chosen seed,
In the beginning how the heavens and earth
Rose out of Chaos: or, if Sion hill
Delight thee more, and Siloa's brook that flowed
Fast by the oracle of God, I thence
Invoke thy aid to my adventurous song,
That with no middle flight intends to soar
Above th' Aonian mount, while it pursues
Things unattempted yet in prose or rhyme.
And chiefly thou, O Spirit, that dost prefer
Before all temples th' upright heart and pure,
Instruct me, for thou know'st; thou from the first
Wast present, and, with mighty wings outspread,
Dove-like sat'st brooding on the vast Abyss,
And mad'st it pregnant; what in me is dark
Illumine, what is low raise and support;
That, to the height of this great argument,
I may assert Eternal Providence,
And justify the ways of God to men.

   Say first—for Heaven hides nothing from thy view,
Nor the deep tract of Hell—say first what cause
Moved our grand parents, in that happy state,
Favored of Heaven so highly, to fall off
From their Creator, and transgress his will
For one restraint, lords of the World besides.
Who first seduced them to that foul revolt?

   Th' infernal Serpent; he it was whose guile,
Stirred up with envy and revenge, deceived
The mother of mankind, what time his pride
Had cast him out from Heaven, with all his host
Of rebel Angels, by whose aid, aspiring
To set himself in glory above his peers,
He trusted to have equaled the Most High,
If he opposed, and with ambitious aim
Against the throne and monarchy of God,
Raised impious war in Heaven and battle proud,

With vain attempt. Him the Almighty Power
Hurled headlong flaming from th' ethereal sky,
With hideous ruin and combustion, down
To bottomless perdition, there to dwell
In adamantine chains and penal fire,
Who durst defy th' Omnipotent to arms.
   Nine times the space that measures day and night
To mortal men, he, with his horrid crew,
Lay vanquished, rolling in the fiery gulf,
Confounded, though immortal. But his doom
Reserved him to more wrath; for now the thought
Both of lost happiness and lasting pain
Torments him: round he throws his baleful eyes,
That witnessed huge affliction and dismay,
Mixed with obdúrate pride and steadfast hate.
At once, as far as Angels ken, he views
The dismal situation waste and wild.
A dungeon horrible, on all sides round,
As one great furnace flamed; yet from those flames
No light; but rather darkness visible
Served only to discover sights of woe,
Regions of sorrow, doleful shades, where peace
And rest can never dwell, hope never comes
That comes to all, but torture without end
Still urges, and a fiery deluge, fed
With ever-burning sulphur unconsumed.
Such place Eternal Justice had prepared
For those rebellious; here their prison ordained
In outer darkness, and their portion set,
As far removed from God and light of Heaven
As from the center thrice to th' utmost pole.
Oh how unlike the place from whence they fell!
There the companions of his fall, o'erwhelmed
With floods and whirlwinds of tempestuous fire,
He soon discerns; and, weltering by his side,
One next himself in power, and next in crime,
Long after known in Palestine, and named
Beëlzebub. To whom th' Arch-Enemy,
And thence in Heaven called Satan, with bold words
Breaking the horrid silence, thus began:

353

"If thou beest he—but O how fallen! how changed
From him who, in the happy realms of light
Clothed with transcendent brightness, didst outshine
Myriads, though bright!—if he whom mutual league,
United thoughts and counsels, equal hope
And hazard in the glorious enterprise,
Joined with me once, now misery hath joined
In equal ruin; into what pit thou seest
From what height fallen: so much the stronger proved
He with his thunder: and till then who knew
The force of those dire arms? Yet not for those,
Nor what the potent Victor in his rage
Can else inflict, do I repent, or change,
Though changed in outward luster, that fixed mind,
And high disdain from sense of injured merit,
That with the Mightiest raised me to contend,
And to the fierce contentions brought along
Innumerable force of Spirits armed,
That durst dislike his reign, and, me preferring,
His utmost power with adverse power opposed
In dubious battle on the plains of Heaven,
And shook his throne. What though the field be lost?
All is not lost—the unconquerable will,
And study of revenge, immortal hate,
And courage never to submit or yield:
And what is else not to be overcome?
That glory never shall his wrath or might
Extort from me. To bow and sue for grace
With suppliant knee, and deify his power
Who, from the terror of his arm, so late
Doubted his empire—that were low indeed;
That were an ignominy and shame beneath
This downfall; since, by fate, the strength of Gods,
And this empyreal substance, cannot fail;
Since, through experience of this great event,
In arms not worse, in foresight much advanced,
We may with more successful hope resolve
To wage by force or guile eternal war,
Irreconcilable to our grand Foe,

354

Who triúmphs, and in th' excess of joy
Sole reigning holds the tyranny of Heaven."
   So spake th' apostate Angel, though in pain,
Vaunting aloud, but racked with deep despair;
And him thus answered soon his bold compeer:
   "O Prince, O Chief of many thronèd Powers
That led th' embattled Seraphim to war
Under thy conduct, and, in dreadful deeds
Fearless, endangered Heaven's perpetual King,
And put to proof his high supremacy,
Whether upheld by strength, or chance, or fate,
Too well I see and rue the dire event
That, with sad overthrow and foul defeat,
Hath lost us Heaven, and all this mighty host
In horrible destruction laid thus low,
As far as Gods and heavenly Essences
Can perish: for the mind and spirit remains
Invincible, and vigor soon returns,
Though all our glory extinct, and happy state
Here swallowed up in endless misery.
But what if he our Conqueror (whom I now
Of force believe almighty, since no less
Than such could have o'erpowered such force as ours)
Have left us this our spirit and strength entire,
Strongly to suffer and support our pains,
That we may so suffice his vengeful ire,
Or do him mightier service as his thralls
By right of war, whate'er his business be,
Here in the heart of Hell to work in fire,
Or do his errands in the gloomy Deep?
What can it then avail though yet we feel
Strength undiminished, or eternal being
To undergo eternal punishment?"
   Whereto with speedy words th' Arch-Fiend replied:
"Fallen Cherub, to be weak is miserable,
Doing or suffering: but of this be sure—
To do aught good never will be our task,
But ever to do ill our sole delight,
As being the contrary to his high will

Whom we resist. If then his providence
Out of our evil seek to bring forth good,
Our labor must be to pervert that end,
And out of good still to find means of evil;
Which ofttimes may succeed so as perhaps
Shall grieve him, if I fail not, and disturb
His inmost counsels from their destined aim.
But see! the angry Victor hath recalled
His ministers of vengeance and pursuit
Back to the gates of Heaven: the sulphurous hail,
Shot after us in storm, o'erblown hath laid
The fiery surge that from the precipice
Of Heaven received us falling; and the thunder,
Winged with red lightning and impetuous rage,
Perhaps hath spent his shafts, and ceases now
To bellow through the vast and boundless Deep.
Let us not slip th' occasion, whether scorn
Or satiate fury yield it from our Foe.
Seest thou yon dreary plain, forlorn and wild,
The seat of desolation, void of light,
Save what the glimmering of these livid flames
Casts pale and dreadful? Thither let us tend
From off the tossing of these fiery waves;
There rest, if any rest can harbor there;
And, re-assembling our afflicted powers,
Consult how we may henceforth most offend
Our enemy, our own loss how repair,
How overcome this dire calamity,
What reinforcement we may gain from hope,
If not, what resolution from despair."
    Thus Satan, talking to his nearest mate,
With head uplift above the wave, and eyes
That sparkling blazed; his other parts besides
Prone on the flood, extended long and large,
Lay floating many a rood, in bulk as huge
As whom the fables name of monstrous size,
Titanian or Earth-born, that warred on Jove,
Briareos or Typhon, whom the den
By ancient Tarsus held, or that sea-beast
Leviathan, which God of all his works

356

Created hugest that swim th' ocean-stream.
Him, haply slumbering on the Norway foam,
The pilot of some small night-foundered skiff,
Deeming some island, oft, as seamen tell,
With fixèd anchor in his scaly rind,
Moors by his side under the lee, while night
Invests the sea, and wishèd morn delays.
So stretched out huge in length the Arch-fiend lay,
Chained on the burning lake; nor ever thence
Had risen, or heaved his head, but that the will
And high permission of all-ruling Heaven
Left him at large to his own dark designs,
That with reiterated crimes he might
Heap on himself damnation, while he sought
Evil to others, and enraged might see
How all his malice served but to bring forth
Infinite goodness, grace, and mercy, shown
On Man by him seduced, but on himself
Treble confusion, wrath, and vengeance poured.
  Forthwith upright he rears from off the pool
His mighty stature; on each hand the flames
Driven backward slope their pointing spires, and, rolled
In billows, leave i' th' midst a horrid vale.
Then with expanded wings he steers his flight
Aloft, incumbent on the dusky air,
That felt unusual weight; till on dry land
He lights—if it were land that ever burned
With solid, as the lake with liquid fire,
And such appeared in hue as when the force
Of subterranean wind transports a hill
Torn from Pelorus, or the shattered side
Of thundering Etna, whose combustible
And fueled entrails, thence conceiving fire,
Sublimed with mineral fury, aid the winds,
And leave a singèd bottom all involved
With stench and smoke. Such resting found the sole
Of unblest feet. Him followed his next mate;
Both glorying to have scaped the Stygian flood
As gods, and by their own recovered strength,
Not by the sufferance of supernal Power.

357

"Is this the region, this the soil, the clime,"
Said then the lost Archangel, "this the seat
That we must change for Heaven?—this mournful gloom
For that celestial light? Be it so, since he
Who now is sovereign can dispose and bid
What shall be right: farthest from him is best,
Whom reason hath equaled, force hath made supreme
Above his equals. Farewell, happy fields,
Where joy for ever dwells! Hail, horrors! hail,
Infernal world! and thou, profoundest Hell,
Receive thy new possessor—one who brings
A mind not to be changed by place or time.
The mind is its own place, and in itself
Can make a Heaven of Hell, a Hell of Heaven.
What matter where, if I be still the same,
And what I should be, all but less than he
Whom thunder hath made greater? Here at least
We shall be free; th' Almighty hath not built
Here for his envy, will not drive us hence;
Here we may reign secure; and, in my choice,
To reign is worth ambition, though in Hell:
Better to reign in Hell than serve in Heaven.
But wherefore let we then our faithful friends,
Th' associates and co-partners of our loss,
Lie thus astonished on th' oblivious pool,
And call them not to share with us their part
In this unhappy mansion, or once more
With rallied arms to try what may be yet
Regained in Heaven, or what more lost in Hell?"
    So Satan spake; and him Beëlzebub
Thus answered: "Leader of those armies bright
Which, but th' Omnipotent, none could have foiled!
If once they hear that voice, their liveliest pledge
Of hopes in fears and dangers—heard so oft
In worst extremes, and on the perilous edge
Of battle, when it raged, in all assaults
Their surest signal—they will soon resume
New courage and revive, though now they lie
Groveling and prostrate on yon lake of fire,

As we erewhile, astounded and amazed;
No wonder, fallen such a pernicious height!"
   He scarce had ceased when the superior Fiend
Was moving toward the shore; his ponderous shield,
Ethereal temper, massy, large, and round,
Behind him cast. The broad circumference
Hung on his shoulders like the moon, whose orb
Through optic glass the Tuscan artist * views
At evening, from the top of Fesolè,
Or in Valdarno, to descry new lands,
Rivers, or mountains, in her spotty globe.
His spear—to equal which the tallest pine
Hewn on Norwegian hills, to be the mast
Of some great admiral, were but a wand—
He walked with, to support uneasy steps
Over the burning marl, not like those steps
On Heaven's azure; and the torrid clime
Smote on him sore besides, vaulted with fire.
Nathless he so endured, till on the beach
Of that inflamèd sea he stood, and called
His legions—Angel Forms, who lay entranced
Thick as autumnal leaves that strew the brooks
In Vallombrosa, where th' Etrurian shades
High over-arched embower; or scattered sedge
Afloat, when the fierce winds Orion armed
Hath vexed the Red-Sea coast, whose waves o'erthrew
Busiris and his Memphian chivalry,
While with perfidious hatred they pursued
The sojourners of Goshen, who beheld
From the safe shore their floating carcasses
And broken chariot-wheels. So thick bestrewn,
Abject and lost, lay these, covering the flood,
Under amazement of their hideous change.
He called so loud that all the hollow deep
Of Hell resounded: "Princes, Potentates,
Warriors, the Flower of Heaven—once yours; now lost,
If such astonishment as this can seize
Eternal Spirits! Or have ye chosen this place
* Galileo

After the toil of battle to repose
Your wearied virtue, for the ease you find
To slumber here, as in the vales of Heaven?
Or in this abject posture have ye sworn
To adore the Conqueror, who now beholds
Cherub and Seraph rolling in the flood
With scattered arms and ensigns, till anon
His swift pursuers from Heaven-gates discern
Th' advantage, and, descending, tread us down
Thus drooping, or with linkèd thunderbolts
Transfix us to the bottom of this gulf?
Awake, arise, or be for ever fallen!"
   They heard, and were abashed, and up they sprung
Upon the wing, as when men wont to watch
On duty, sleeping found by whom they dread,
Rouse and bestir themselves ere well awake.
Nor did they not perceive the evil plight
In which they were, or the fierce pains not feel;
Yet to their General's voice they soon obeyed
Innumerable. As when the potent rod
Of Amram's son,* in Egypt's evil day,
Waved round the coast, up-called a pitchy cloud
Of locusts, warping on the eastern wind,
That o'er the realm of impious Pharaoh hung
Like Night, and darkened all the land of Nile;
So numberless were those bad Angels seen
Hovering on wing under the cope of Hell,
'Twixt upper, nether, and surrounding fires;
Till, as a signal given, th' uplifted spear
Of their great Sultan waving to direct
Their course, in even balance down they light
On the firm brimstone, and fill all the plain:
A multitude like which the populous North
Poured never from her frozen loins to pass
Rhene or the Danaw, when her barbarous sons
Came like a deluge on the South, and spread
Beneath Gibraltar to the Libyan sands.
Forthwith, from every squadron and each band,
The heads and leaders thither haste where stood

* Moses

360

Their great Commander—godlike Shapes, and Forms
Excelling human; princely Dignities;
And Powers that erst in Heaven sat on thrones,
Though on their names in Heavenly records now
Be no memorial, blotted out and rased
By their rebellion from the Books of Life.
Nor had they yet among the sons of Eve
Got them new names, till, wandering o'er the earth,
Through God's high sufferance for the trial of man,
By falsities and lies the greatest part
Of mankind they corrupted to forsake
God their Creator, and th' invisible
Glory of him that made them to transform
Oft to the image of a brute, adorned
With gay religions full of pomp and gold,
And devils to adore for deities:
Then were they known to men by various names,
And various idols through the heathen world.
      Say, Muse, their names then known, who first, who last,
Roused from the slumber on that fiery couch,
At their great Emperor's call, as next in worth
Came singly where he stood on the bare strand,
While the promiscuous crowd stood yet aloof?
      The chief were those who, from the pit of Hell
Roaming to seek their prey on Earth, durst fix
Their seats, long after, next the seat of God,
Their altars by his altar, gods adored
Among the nations round, and durst abide
Jehovah thundering out of Sion, throned
Between the Cherubim; yea, often placed
Within his sanctuary itself their shrines,
Abominations; and with cursèd things
His holy rites and solemn feasts profaned,
And with their darkness durst affront his light.
First, Moloch, horrid king, besmeared with blood
Of human sacrifice, and parents' tears;
Though, for the noise of drums and timbrels loud,
Their children's cries unheard that passed through fire
To his grim idol. Him the Ammonite
Worshiped in Rabba and her watery plain,

361

In Argob and in Basan, to the stream
Of utmost Arnon. Nor content with such
Audacious neighborhood, the wisest heart
Of Solomon he led by fraud to build
His temple right against the temple of God
On that opprobrious hill,* and made his grove
The pleasant valley of Hinnom, Tophet thence
And black Gehenna called, the type of Hell.
Next Chemos, th' obscene dread of Moab's sons,
From Aroar to Nebo and the wild
Of southmost Abarim; in Hesebon
And Horonaim, Seon's realm, beyond
The flowery dale of Sibma clad with vines,
And Elealè to th' Asphaltic Pool:
Peor his other name, when he enticed
Israel in Sittim, on their march from Nile,
To do him wanton rites, which cost them woe.
Yet thence his lustful orgies he enlarged
Even to that hill of scandal, by the grove
Of Moloch homicide, lust hard by hate,
Till good Josiah drove them thence to Hell.
With these came they who, from the bordering flood
Of old Euphrates to the brook that parts
Egypt from Syrian ground, had general names
Of Baalim and Ashtaroth—those male,
These feminine. For Spirits, when they please,
Can either sex assume, or both; so soft
And uncompounded is their essence pure,
Not tied or manacled with joint or limb,
Nor founded on the brittle strength of bones,
Like cumbrous flesh; but, in what shape they choose,
Dilated or condensed, bright or obscure,
Can execute their airy purposes,
And works of love or enmity fulfill.
For those the race of Israel oft forsook
Their Living Strength, and unfrequented left
His righteous altar, bowing lowly down
To bestial gods; for which their heads as low
Bowed down in battle, sunk before the spear

* Mount of Olives

362

Of despicable foes. With these in troop
Came Astoreth, whom the Phoenicians called
Astartè, queen of heaven, with crescent horns;
To whose bright image nightly by the moon
Sidonian virgins paid their vows and songs;
In Sion also not unsung, where stood
Her temple on th' offensive mountain, built
By that uxorious king whose heart, though large,
Beguiled by fair idolatresses, fell
To idols foul. Thammuz came next behind,
Whose annual wound in Lebanon allured
The Syrian damsels to lament his fate
In amorous ditties all a summer's day,
While smooth Adonis from his native rock
Ran purple to the sea, supposed with blood
Of Thammuz yearly wounded: the love-tale
Infected Sion's daughters with like heat,
Whose wanton passions in the sacred porch
Ezekiel saw, when, by the vision led,
His eye surveyed the dark idolatries
Of alienated Judah. Next came one
Who mourned in earnest, when the captive ark
Maimed his brute image, head and hands lopt off,
In his own temple, on the grunsel-edge,*
Where he fell flat and shamed his worshipers:
Dagon his name, sea-monster, upward man
And downward fish; yet had his temple high
Reared in Azotus, dreaded through the coast
Of Palestine, in Gath and Ascalon,
And Accaron and Gaza's frontier bounds.
Him followed Rimmon, whose delightful seat
Was fair Damascus, on the fertile banks
Of Abbana and Pharphar, lucid streams.
He also against the house of God was bold:
A leper once he lost, and gained a king—
Ahaz, his sottish conqueror, whom he drew
God's altar to disparage and displace
For one of Syrian mode, whereon to burn
His odious offerings, and adore the gods
* Threshold

363

Whom he had vanquished. After these appeared
A crew who, under names of old renown—
Osiris, Isis, Orus, and their train—
With monstrous shapes and sorceries abused
Fanatic Egypt and her priests to seek
Their wandering gods disguised in brutish forms
Rather than human. Nor did Israel scape
Th' infection, when their borrowed gold composed
The calf in Oreb; and the rebel king
Doubled that sin in Bethel and in Dan,
Likening his Maker to the grazèd ox—
Jehovah, who, in one night, when he passed
From Egypt marching, equaled with one stroke
Both her first-born and all her bleating gods.
Belial came last; than whom a Spirit more lewd
Fell not from Heaven, or more gross to love
Vice for itself. To him no temple stood
Or altar smoked; yet who more oft than he
In temples and at altars, when the priest
Turns atheist, as did Eli's sons, who filled
With lust and violence the house of God?
In courts and palaces he also reigns,
And in luxurious cities, where the noise
Of riot ascends above their loftiest towers,
And injury and outrage; and, when night
Darkens the streets, then wander forth the sons
Of Belial, flown with insolence and wine.
Witness the streets of Sodom, and that night
In Gibeah, when the hospitable door
Exposed a matron, to avoid worse rape.
 These were the prime in order and in might:
The rest were long to tell; though far renowned
Th' Ionian gods—of Javan's issue held
Gods, yet confessed later than Heaven and Earth,
Their boasted parents;—Titan, Heaven's first-born,
With his enormous brood, and birthright seized
By younger Saturn: he from mightier Jove,
His own and Rhea's son, like measure found;
So Jove usurping reigned. These, first in Crete
And Ida known, thence on the snowy top

Of cold Olympus ruled the middle air,
Their highest heaven; or on the Delphian cliff,
Or in Dodona, and through all the bounds
Of Doric land; or who with Saturn old
Fled over Adria to th' Hesperian fields,
And o'er the Celtic roamed the utmost Isles.

All these and more came flocking; but with looks
Downcast and damp; yet such wherein appeared
Obscure some glimpse of joy to have found their Chief
Not in despair, to have found themselves not lost
In loss itself; which on his countenance cast
Like doubtful hue. But he, his wonted pride
Soon recollecting, with high words, that bore
Semblance of worth, not substance, gently raised
Their fainting courage, and dispelled their fears:
Then straight commands that, at the warlike sound
Of trumpets loud and clarions, be upreared
His mighty standard. That proud honor claimed
Azazel as his right, a Cherub tall:
Who forthwith from the glittering staff unfurled
Th' imperial ensign; which, full high advanced,
Shone like a meteor streaming to the wind,
With gems and golden luster rich emblazed,
Seraphic arms and trophies; all the while
Sonorous metal blowing martial sounds:
At which the universal host up-sent
A shout that tore Hell's concave, and beyond
Frighted the reign of Chaos and old Night.
All in a moment through the gloom were seen
Ten thousand banners rise into the air,
With orient colors waving: with them rose
A forest huge of spears; and thronging helms
Appeared, and serried shields in thick array
Of depth immeasurable. Anon they move
In perfect phalanx to the Dorian mood
Of flutes and soft recorders—such as raised
To height of noblest temper heroes old
Arming to battle, and instead of rage
Deliberate valor breathed, firm, and unmoved
With dread of death to flight or foul retreat;

365

Nor wanting power to mitigate and swage
With solemn touches troubled thoughts, and chase
Anguish and doubt and fear and sorrow and pain
From mortal or immortal minds. Thus they,
Breathing united force with fixèd thought,
Moved on in silence to soft pipes that charmed
Their painful steps o'er the burnt soil. And now
Advanced in view they stand—a horrid front
Of dreadful length and dazzling arms, in guise
Of warriors old, with ordered spear and shield,
Awaiting what command their mighty Chief
Had to impose. He through the armèd files
Darts his experienced eye, and soon traverse
The whole battalion views—their order due,
Their visages and stature as of gods;
Their number last he sums. And now his heart
Distends with pride, and, hardening in his strength,
Glories: for never, since created Man,
Met such embodied force as, named with these,
Could merit more than that small infantry
Warred on by cranes *—though all the giant brood
Of Phlegra with th' heroic race were joined
That fought at Thebes and Ilium, on each side
Mixed with auxiliar gods; and what resounds
In fable or romance of Uther's son,†
Begirt with British and Armoric knights;
And all who since, baptized or infidel,
Jousted in Aspramont, or Montalban,
Damasco, or Marocco, or Trebisond,
Or whom Biserta sent from Afric shore
When Charlemain with all his peerage fell
By Fontarabbia. Thus far these beyond
Compare of mortal prowess, yet observed
Their dread Commander. He, above the rest
In shape and gesture proudly eminent,
Stood like a tower. His form had yet not lost
All her original brightness, nor appeared

* Tradition placed a race of pygmies beyond the Himalayas. Mounted on goats,
they were supposedly at constant war with cranes.
† King Arthur

Less than Archangel ruined, and th' excess
Of glory obscured: as when the sun new-risen
Looks through the horizontal misty air
Shorn of his beams, or, from behind the moon,
In dim eclipse, disastrous twilight sheds
On half the nations, and with fear of change
Perplexes monarchs. Darkened so, yet shone
Above them all th' Archangel: but his face
Deep scars of thunder had entrenched, and care
Sat on his faded cheek, but under brows
Of dauntless courage, and considerate pride
Waiting revenge. Cruel his eye, but cast
Signs of remorse and passion, to behold
The fellows of his crime, the followers rather
(Far other once beheld in bliss), condemned
For ever now to have their lot in pain—
Millions of Spirits for his fault amerced
Of Heaven, and from eternal splendors flung
For his revolt—yet faithful how they stood,
Their glory withered; as, when heaven's fire
Hath scathed the forest oaks or mountain pines,
With singèd top their stately growth, though bare,
Stands on the blasted heath. He now prepared
To speak; whereat their doubled ranks they bend
From wing to wing, and half enclose him round
With all his peers: attention held them mute.
Thrice he assayed, and thrice, in spite of scorn,
Tears, such as Angels weep, burst forth: at last
Words interwove with sighs found out their way:
    "O myriads of immortal Spirits! O Powers
Matchless, but with th' Almighty!—and that strife
Was not inglorious, though th' event was dire,
As this place testifies, and this dire change,
Hateful to utter. But what power of mind,
Foreseeing or presaging, from the depth
Of knowledge past or present, could have feared
How such united force of gods, how such
As stood like these, could ever know repulse?
For who can yet believe, though after loss,
That all these puissant legions, whose exile

Hath emptied Heaven, shall fail to re-ascend,
Self-raised, and repossess their native seat?
For me, be witness all the host of Heaven,
If counsels different, or danger shunned
By me, have lost our hopes. But he who reigns
Monarch in Heaven till then as one secure
Sat on his throne, upheld by old repute,
Consent or custom, and his regal state
Put forth at full, but still his strength concealed—
Which tempted our attempt, and wrought our fall.
Henceforth his might we know, and know our own,
So as not either to provoke, or dread
New war provoked: our better part remains
To work in close design, by fraud or guile,
What force effected not; that he no less
At length from us may find, who overcomes
By force hath overcome but half his foe.
Space may produce new Worlds; whereof so rife
There went a fame in Heaven that he ere long
Intended to create, and therein plant
A generation whom his choice regard
Should favor equal to the Sons of Heaven.
Thither, if but to pry, shall be perhaps
Our first eruption—thither, or elsewhere;
For this infernal pit shall never hold
Celestial Spirits in bondage, nor th' Abyss
Long under darkness cover. But these thoughts
Full counsel must mature. Peace is despaired;
For who can think submission? War, then, war
Open or understood, must be resolved."
   He spake; and, to confirm his words, outflew
Millions of flaming swords, drawn from the thighs
Of mighty Cherubim; the sudden blaze
Far round illumined Hell. Highly they raged
Against the Highest, and fierce with graspèd arms
Clashed on their sounding shields the din of war,
Hurling defiance toward the vault of Heaven.
   There stood a hill not far, whose grisly top
Belched fire and rolling smoke; the rest entire
Shone with a glossy scurf—undoubted sign

That in his womb was hid metallic ore,
The work of sulphur. Thither, winged with speed,
A numerous brígade hastened: as when bands
Of pioneers, with spade and pickaxe armed,
Forerun the royal camp, to trench a field,
Or cast a rampart. Mammon led them on—
Mammon, the least erected Spirit that fell
From Heaven; for even in Heaven his looks and thoughts
Were always downward bent, admiring more
The riches of Heaven's pavement, trodden gold,
Than aught divine or holy else enjoyed
In vision beatific. By him first
Men also, and by his suggestion taught,
Ransacked the center, and with impious hands
Rifled the bowels of their mother Earth
For treasures better hid. Soon had his crew
Opened into the hill a spacious wound,
And digged out ribs of gold. Let none admire
That riches grow in Hell; that soil may best
Deserve the precious bane. And here let those
Who boast in mortal things, and wondering tell
Of Babel, and the works of Memphian kings,
Learn how their greatest monuments of fame
And strength, and art, are easily outdone
By Spirits reprobate, and in an hour
What in an age they, with incessant toil
And hands innumerable, scarce perform.
Night on the plain, in many cells prepared,
That underneath had veins of liquid fire
Sluiced from the lake, a second multitude
With wondrous art founded the massy ore,
Severing each kind, and scummed the bullion-dross.
A third as soon had formed within the ground
A various mold, and from the boiling cells
By strange conveyance filled each hollow nook;
As in an organ, from one blast of wind,
To many a row of pipes the sound-board breathes.
Anon out of the earth a fabric huge
Rose like an exhalation, with the sound
Of dulcet symphonies and voices sweet—

369

Built like a temple, where pilasters round
Were set, and Doric pillars overlaid
With golden architrave; nor did there want
Cornice or frieze, with bossy sculptures graven;
The roof was fretted gold. Not Babylon
Nor great Alcairo such magnificence
Equaled in all their glories, to enshrine
Belus or Serapis their gods, or seat
Their kings, when Egypt with Assyria strove
In wealth and luxury. Th' ascending pile
Stood fixed her stately height; and straight the doors,
Opening their brazen folds, discover, wide
Within, her ample spaces o'er the smooth
And level pavement: from the archèd roof,
Pendent by subtle magic, many a row
Of starry lamps and blazing cressets, fed
With naphtha and asphaltus, yielded light
As from a sky. The hasty multitude
Admiring entered; and the work some praise,
And some the architect. His hand was known
In Heaven by many a towered structure high,
Where sceptered Angels held their residence,
And sat as Princes, whom the supreme King
Exalted to such power, and gave to rule,
Each in his Hierarchy, the Orders bright.
Nor was his name unheard or unadored
In ancient Greece; and in Ausonian * land
Men called him Mulciber; † and how he fell
From Heaven they fabled, thrown by angry Jove
Sheer o'er the crystal battlements: from morn
To noon he fell, from noon to dewy eve,
A summer's day, and with the setting sun
Dropped from the zenith, like a falling star,
On Lemnos, th' Aegean isle. Thus they relate,
Erring; for he with this rebellious rout
Fell long before; nor aught availed him now
To have built in Heaven high towers; nor did he scape
By all his engines, but was headlong sent,

* Italy
† Vulcan, tossed out of heaven by Jupiter

370

With his industrious crew, to build in Hell.
   Meanwhile the wingèd Heralds, by command
Of sovereign power, with awful ceremony
And trumpet's sound, throughout the host proclaim
A solemn council forthwith to be held
At Pandemonium, the high capital
Of Satan and his peers. Their summons called
From every band and squarèd regiment
By place or choice the worthiest: they anon
With hundreds and with thousands trooping came
Attended. All access was thronged; the gates
And porches wide, but chief the spacious hall
(Though like a covered field, where champions bold
Wont ride in armed, and at the Soldan's chair
Defied the best of Paynim chivalry
To mortal combat, or career with lance),
Thick swarmed, both on the ground and in the air,
Brushed with the hiss of rustling wings. As bees
In spring-time, when the Sun with Taurus rides,
Pour forth their populous youth about the hive
In clusters; they among fresh dews and flowers
Fly to and fro, or on the smoothèd plank,
The suburb of their straw-built citadel,
New rubbed with balm, expatiate, and confer
Their state-affairs: so thick the airy crowd
Swarmed and were straitened; till, the signal given,
Behold a wonder! They but now who seemed
In bigness to surpass Earth's giant sons,
Now less than smallest dwarfs, in narrow room
Throng numberless—like that pygmean race
Beyond the Indian mount; or fairy elves,
Whose midnight revels, by a forest-side
Or fountain, some belated peasant sees,
Or dreams he sees, while overhead the Moon
Sits arbitress, and nearer to the Earth
Wheels her pale course: they, on their mirth and dance
Intent, with jocund music charm his ear;
At once with joy and fear his heart rebounds.
Thus incorporeal Spirits to smallest forms
Reduced their shapes immense, and were at large,

371

Though without number still, amidst the hall
Of that infernal court. But far within,
And in their own dimensions like themselves,
The great Seraphic Lords and Cherubim
In close recess and secret conclave sat,
A thousand demi-gods on golden seats,
Frequent and full. After short silence then,
And summons read, the great consult began.

BOOK II

The Argument

The consultation begun, Satan debates whether another battle be to be
hazarded for the recovery of Heaven: some advise it, others dissuade.
A third proposal is preferred, mentioned before by Satan—to search
the truth of that prophecy or tradition in Heaven concerning another
world, and another kind of Creature, equal, or not much inferior, to
themselves, about this time to be created. Their doubt who shall be
sent on this difficult search: Satan, their chief, undertakes alone the
voyage; is honored and applauded. The council thus ended, the rest
betake them several ways and to several employments, as their inclina-
tions lead them, to entertain the time till Satan return. He passes on
his journey to Hell-gates; finds them shut, and who sat there to guard
them; by whom at length they are opened, and discover to him the
great gulf between Hell and Heaven. With what difficulty he passes
through, directed by Chaos, the Power of that place, to the sight of
this new World which he sought.

H IGH ON A THRONE of royal state, which far
Outshone the wealth of Ormus and of Ind,
Or where the gorgeous East with richest hand
Showers on her kings barbaric pearl and gold,
Satan exalted sat, by merit raised
To that bad eminence; and, from despair
Thus high uplifted beyond hope, aspires
Beyond thus high, insatiate to pursue
Vain war with Heaven; and, by success untaught,
His proud imaginations thus displayed:

372

"Powers and Dominions, Deities of Heaven,
For since no deep within her gulf can hold
Immortal vigor, though oppressed and fallen,
I give not Heaven for lost; from this descent
Celestial Virtues * rising will appear
More glorious and more dread than from no fall,
And trust themselves to fear no second fate!
Me though just right, and the fixed laws of Heaven,
Did first create your leader—next, free choice,
With what besides in council or in fight
Hath been achieved of merit—yet this loss,
Thus far at least recovered, hath much more
Established in a safe, unenvied throne,
Yielded with full consent. The happier state
In Heaven, which follows dignity, might draw
Envy from each inferior; but who here
Will envy whom the highest place exposes
Foremost to stand against the Thunderer's aim
Your bulwark, and condemns to greatest share
Of endless pain? Where there is, then, no good
For which to strive, no strife can grow up there
From faction: for none sure will claim in Hell
Precedence; none whose portion is so small
Of present pain that with ambitious mind
Will covet more! With this advantage, then,
To union, and firm faith, and firm accord,
More than can be in Heaven, we now return
To claim our just inheritance of old,
Surer to prosper than prosperity
Could have assured us; and by what best way,
Whether of open war or covert guile,
We now debate. Who can advise may speak."

He ceased; and next him Moloch, sceptered king,
Stood up—the strongest and the fiercest Spirit
That fought in Heaven, now fiercer by despair.
His trust was with th' Eternal to be deemed
Equal in strength, and rather than be less
Cared not to be at all; with that care lost

* A rank in hell

Went all his fear: of God, or Hell, or worse,
He recked not, and these words thereafter spake:
   "My sentence is for open war. Of wiles,
More inexpert, I boast not: them let those
Contrive who need, or when they need; not now.
For, while they sit contriving, shall the rest—
Millions that stand in arms, and longing wait
The signal to ascend—sit lingering here,
Heaven's fugitives, and for their dwelling-place
Accept this dark opprobrious den of shame,
The prison of his tyranny who reigns
By our delay? No! let us rather choose,
Armed with Hell-flames and fury, all at once
O'er Heaven's high towers to force resistless way,
Turning our tortures into horrid arms
Against the Torturer; when, to meet the noise
Of his almighty engine, he shall hear
Infernal thunder, and, for lightning, see
Black fire and horror shot with equal rage
Among his Angels, and his throne itself
Mixed with Tartarean sulphur and strange fire,
His own invented torments. But perhaps
The way seems difficult, and steep to scale
With upright wing against a higher foe!
Let such bethink them, if the sleepy drench
Of that forgetful lake benumb not still,
That in our proper motion we ascend
Up to our native seat; descent and fall
To us is adverse. Who but felt of late,
When the fierce foe hung on our broken rear
Insulting, and pursued us through the Deep,
With what compulsion and laborious flight
We sunk thus low? Th' ascent is easy, then;
Th' event is feared! Should we again provoke
Our stronger, some worse way his wrath may find
To our destruction, if there be in Hell
Fear to be worse destroyed! What can be worse
Than to dwell here, driven out from bliss, condemned
In this abhorrèd deep to utter woe!
Where pain of inextinguishable fire

Must exercise us without hope of end
The vassals of his anger, when the scourge
Inexorably, and the torturing hour,
Calls us to penance? More destroyed than thus,
We should be quite abolished, and expire.
What fear we then? what doubt we to incense
His utmost ire? which, to the height enraged,
Will either quite consume us, and reduce
To nothing this essential—happier far
Than miserable to have eternal being—
Or, if our substance be indeed divine,
And cannot cease to be, we are at worst
On this side nothing; and by proof we feel
Our power sufficient to disturb his Heaven,
And with perpetual inroads to alarm,
Though inaccessible, his fatal throne:
Which, if not victory, is yet revenge."
  He ended frowning, and his look denounced
Desperate revenge, and battle dangerous
To less than gods. On th' other side up rose
Belial, in act more graceful and humane.
A fairer person lost not Heaven; he seemed
For dignity composed, and high exploit.
But all was false and hollow; though his tongue
Dropped manna, and could make the worse appear
The better reason, to perplex and dash
Maturest counsels: for his thoughts were low—
To vice industrious, but to nobler deeds
Timorous and slothful. Yet he pleased the ear,
And with persuasive accent thus began:
  "I should be much for open war, O Peers,
As not behind in hate, if what was urged
Main reason to persuade immediate war
Did not dissuade me most, and seem to cast
Ominous conjecture on the whole success;
When he who most excels in fact * of arms,
In what he counsels and in what excels
Mistrustful, grounds his courage on despair
And utter dissolution, as the scope
* Deeds

Of all his aim, after some dire revenge.
First, what revenge? The towers of Heaven are filled
With armèd watch, that render all access
Impregnable: oft on the bordering Deep
Encamp their legions, or with obscure wing
Scout far and wide into the realm of Night,
Scorning surprise. Or, could we break our way
By force, and at our heels all Hell should rise
With blackest insurrection to confound
Heaven's purest light, yet our great Enemy,
All incorruptible, would on his throne
Sit unpolluted, and th' ethereal mold,
Incapable of stain, would soon expel
Her mischief, and purge off the baser fire,
Victorious. Thus repulsed, our final hope
Is flat despair: we must exasperate
Th' Almighty Victor to spend all his rage;
And that must end us; that must be our cure—
To be no more. Sad cure! for who would lose,
Though full of pain, this intellectual being,
Those thoughts that wander through eternity,
To perish rather, swallowed up and lost
In the wide womb of uncreated Night,
Devoid of sense and motion? And who knows,
Let this be good, whether our angry Foe
Can give it, or will ever? How he can
Is doubtful; that he never will is sure.
Will he, so wise, let loose at once his ire,
Belike through impotence or unaware,
To give his enemies their wish, and end
Them in his anger whom his anger saves
To punish endless? 'Wherefore cease we, then?'
Say they who counsel war; 'we are decreed,
Reserved, and destined to eternal woe;
Whatever doing, what can we suffer more,
What can we suffer worse?' Is this, then, worst—
Thus sitting, thus consulting, thus in arms?
What when we fled amain, pursued and struck
With Heaven's afflicting thunder, and besought
The Deep to shelter us? This Hell then seemed

A refuge from those wounds. Or when we lay
Chained on the burning lake? That sure was worse.
What if the breath that kindled those grim fires,
Awaked, should blow them into sevenfold rage,
And plunge us in the flames; or from above
Should intermitted vengeance arm again
His red right hand to plague us? What if all
Her stores were opened, and this firmament
Of Hell should spout her cataracts of fire,
Impendent horrors, threatening hideous fall
One day upon our heads; while we perhaps,
Designing or exhorting glorious war,
Caught in a fiery tempest, shall be hurled,
Each on his rock transfixed, the sport and prey
Of racking whirlwinds, or for ever sunk
Under yon boiling ocean, wrapped in chains,
There to converse with everlasting groans,
Unrespited, unpitied, unreprieved,
Ages of hopeless end? This would be worse.
War, therefore, open or concealed, alike
My voice dissuades; for what can force or guile
With him, or who deceive his mind, whose eye
Views all things at one view? He from Heaven's height
All these our motions vain sees and derides,
Not more almighty to resist our might
Than wise to frustrate all our plots and wiles.
Shall we, then, live thus vile—the race of Heaven
Thus trampled, thus expelled, to suffer here
Chains and these torments? Better these than worse,
By my advice; since fate inevitable
Subdues us, and omnipotent decree,
The Victor's will. To suffer, as to do,
Our strength is equal; nor the law unjust
That so ordains. This was at first resolved,
If we were wise, against so great a foe
Contending, and so doubtful what might fall.
I laugh when those who at the spear are bold
And venturous, if that fail them, shrink, and fear
What yet they know must follow—to endure
Exile, or ignominy, or bonds, or pain,

The sentence of their Conqueror. This is now
Our doom; which if we can sustain and bear,
Our Supreme Foe in time may much remit
His anger, and perhaps, thus far removed,
Not mind us not offending, satisfied
With what is punished; whence these raging fires
Will slacken, if his breath stir not their flames.
Our purer essence then will overcome
Their noxious vapor; or, inured, not feel;
Or, changed at length, and to the place conformed
In temper and in nature, will receive
Familiar the fierce heat; and, void of pain,
This horror will grow mild, this darkness light;
Besides what hope the never-ending flight
Of future days may bring, what chance, what change
Worth waiting—since our present lot appears
For happy though but ill, for ill not worst,
If we procure not to ourselves more woe."
    Thus Belial, with words clothed in reason's garb,
Counseled ignoble ease and peaceful sloth,
Not peace; and after him thus Mammon spake:
    "Either to disenthrone the King of Heaven
We war, if war be best, or to regain
Our own right lost. Him to unthrone we then
May hope, when everlasting Fate shall yield
To fickle Chance, and Chaos judge the strife.
The former, vain to hope, argues as vain
The latter; for what place can be for us
Within Heaven's bound, unless Heaven's Lord supreme
We overpower? Suppose he should relent,
And publish grace to all, on promise made
Of new subjection; with what eyes could we
Stand in his presence humble, and receive
Strict laws imposed, to celebrate his throne
With warbled hymns, and to his Godhead sing
Forced hallelujahs, while he lordly sits
Our envied sovereign, and his altar breathes
Ambrosial odors and ambrosial flowers,
Our servile offerings? This must be our task
In Heaven, this our delight. How wearisome

Paradise Lost

Eternity so spent in worship paid
To whom we hate! Let us not then pursue,
By force impossible, by leave obtained
Unácceptable, though in Heaven, our state
Of splendid vassalage; but rather seek
Our own good from ourselves, and from our own
Live to ourselves, though in this vast recess,
Free and to none accountable, preferring
Hard liberty before the easy yoke
Of servile pomp. Our greatness will appear
Then most conspicuous when great things of small,
Useful of hurtful, prosperous of adverse,
We can create, and in what place soe'er
Thrive under evil, and work ease out of pain
Through labor and endurance. This deep world
Of darkness do we dread? How oft amidst
Thick clouds and dark doth Heaven's all-ruling Sire
Choose to reside, his glory unobscured,
And with the majesty of darkness round
Covers his throne, from whence deep thunders roar,
Mustering their rage, and Heaven resembles Hell!
As he our darkness, cannot we his light
Imitate when we please? This desert soil
Wants not her hidden luster, gems and gold;
Nor want we skill or art from whence to raise
Magnificence; and what can Heaven show more?
Our torments also may, in length of time,
Become our elements, these piercing fires
As soft as now severe, our temper changed
Into their temper; which must needs remove
The sensible * of pain. All things invite
To peaceful counsels, and the settled state
Of order, how in safety best we may
Compose our present evils, with regard
Of what we are and where, dismissing quite
All thoughts of war. Ye have what I advise."
　　He scarce had finished, when such murmur filled
Th' assembly as when hollow rocks retain
The sound of blustering winds, which all night long

* Sensation

Had roused the sea, now with hoarse cadence lull
Seafaring men o'erwatched, whose bark by chance,
Or pinnace, anchors in a craggy bay
After the tempest. Such applause was heard
As Mammon ended, and his sentence pleased,
Advising peace: for such another field
They dreaded worse than Hell; so much the fear
Of thunder and the sword of Michaël
Wrought still within them; and no less desire
To found this nether empire, which might rise,
By policy and long process of time,
In emulation opposite to Heaven.
Which when Beëlzebub perceived—than whom,
Satan except, none higher sat—with grave
Aspect he rose, and in his rising seemed
A pillar of state. Deep on his front engraven
Deliberation sat, and public care;
And princely counsel in his face yet shone,
Majestic, though in ruin. Sage he stood,
With Atlantean shoulders, fit to bear
The weight of mightiest monarchies; his look
Drew audience and attention still as night
Or summer's noontide air, while thus he spake:
   "Thrones and Imperial Powers, Offspring of Heaven,
Ethereal Virtues! or these titles now
Must we renounce, and, changing style, be called
Princes of Hell? for so the popular vote
Inclines—here to continue, and build up here
A growing empire; doubtless! while we dream,
And know not that the King of Heaven hath doomed
This place our dungeon, not our safe retreat
Beyond his potent arm, to live exempt
From Heaven's high jurisdiction, in new league
Banded against his throne, but to remain
In strictest bondage, though thus far removed,
Under th' inevitable curb, reserved
His captive multitude. For he, be sure,
In height or depth, still first and last will reign
Sole king, and of his kingdom lose no part
By our revolt, but over Hell extend

His empire, and with iron scepter rule
Us here, as with his golden those in Heaven.
What sit we then projecting peace and war?
War hath determined us and foiled with loss
Irreparable; terms of peace yet none
Vouchsafed or sought; for what peace will be given
To us enslaved, but custody severe,
And stripes and arbitrary punishment
Inflicted? and what peace can we return,
But, to our power, hostility and hate,
Untamed reluctance, and revenge, though slow,
Yet ever plotting how the Conqueror least
May reap his conquest, and may least rejoice
In doing what we most in suffering feel?
Nor will occasion want, nor shall we need
With dangerous expedition to invade
Heaven, whose high walls fear no assault or siege,
Or ambush from the Deep. What if we find
Some easier enterprise? There is a place
(If ancient and prophetic fame in Heaven
Err not)—another World, the happy seat
Of some new race, called Man, about this time
To be created like to us, though less
In power and excellence, but favored more
Of him who rules above; so was his will
Pronounced among the Gods, and by an oath
That shook Heaven's whole circumference confirmed.
Thither let us bend all our thoughts, to learn
What creatures there inhabit, of what mold
Or substance, how endued, and what their power
And where their weakness: how attempted best,
By force or subtlety. Though Heaven be shut,
And Heaven's high Arbitrator sit secure
In his own strength, this place may lie exposed,
The utmost border of his kingdom, left
To their defense who hold it: here, perhaps,
Some advantageous act may be achieved
By sudden onset—either with Hell-fire
To waste his whole creation, or possess
All as our own, and drive, as we were driven,

The puny habitants; or, if not drive,
Seduce them to our party, that their God
May prove their foe, and with repenting hand
Abolish his own works. This would surpass
Common revenge, and interrupt his joy
In our confusion, and our joy upraise
In his disturbance; when his darling sons,
Hurled headlong to partake with us, shall curse
Their frail original,* and faded bliss—
Faded so soon! Advise if this be worth
Attempting, or to sit in darkness here
Hatching vain empires." Thus Beëlzebub
Pleaded his devilish counsel—first devised
By Satan, and in part proposed: for whence,
But from the author of all ill, could spring
So deep a malice, to confound the race
Of mankind in one root, and Earth with Hell
To mingle and involve, done all to spite
The great Creator? But their spite still serves
His glory to augment. The bold design
Pleased highly those infernal States, and joy
Sparkled in all their eyes: with full assent
They vote: whereat his speech he thus renews:
"Well have ye judged, well ended long debate,
Synod of Gods, and, like to what ye are,
Great things resolved, which from the lowest deep
Will once more lift us up, in spite of fate,
Nearer our ancient seat—perhaps in view
Of those bright confines, whence, with neighboring arms,
And opportune excursion, we may chance
Re-enter Heaven; or else in some mild zone
Dwell, not unvisited of Heaven's fair light,
Secure, and at the brightening orient beam
Purge off this gloom: the soft delicious air,
To heal the scar of these corrosive fires,
Shall breathe her balm. But, first, whom shall we send
In search of this new World? whom shall we find
Sufficient? who shall tempt with wandering feet
The dark, unbottomed, infinite Abyss,

* Adam

And through the palpable obscure find out
His uncouth way, or spread his airy flight,
Upborne with indefatigable wings
Over the vast abrupt, ere he arrive
The happy Isle? What strength, what art, can then
Suffice, or what evasion bear him safe,
Through the strict senteries and stations thick
Of Angels watching round? Here he had need
All circumspection; and we now no less
Choice in our suffrage, for on whom we send
The weight of all, and our last hope, relies."
　　This said, he sat; and expectation held
His look suspense, awaiting who appeared
To second, or oppose, or undertake
The perilous attempt. But all sat mute,
Pondering the danger with deep thoughts; and each
In other's countenance read his own dismay,
Astonished. None among the choice and prime
Of those Heaven-warring champions could be found
So hardy as to proffer or accept,
Alone, the dreadful voyage; till, at last,
Satan, whom now transcendent glory raised
Above his fellows, with monarchal pride
Conscious of highest worth, unmoved thus spake:
　　"O Progeny of Heaven! Empyreal Thrones!
With reason hath deep silence and demur
Seized us, though undismayed. Long is the way
And hard, that out of Hell leads up to light.
Our prison strong, this huge convex of fire,
Outrageous to devour, immures us round
Ninefold; and gates of burning adamant,
Barred over us, prohibit all egress.
These passed, if any pass, the void profound
Of unessential * Night receives him next,
Wide-gaping, and with utter loss of being
Threatens him, plunged in that abortive gulf.
If thence he scape, into whatever world,
Or unknown region, what remains him less
Than unknown dangers, and as hard escape?
* Without substance

383

But I should ill become this throne, O Peers,
And this imperial sovereignty, adorned
With splendor, armed with power, if aught proposed
And judged of public moment in the shape
Of difficulty or danger, could deter
Me from attempting. Wherefore do I assume
These royalties, and not refuse to reign,
Refusing to accept as great a share
Of hazard as of honor, due alike
To him who reigns, and so much to him due
Of hazard more as he above the rest
High honored sits? Go, therefore, mighty Powers,
Terror of Heaven, though fallen; intend * at home,
While here shall be our home, what best may ease
The present misery, and render Hell
More tolerable, if there be cure or charm
To respite, or deceive, or slack the pain
Of this ill mansion; intermit no watch
Against a wakeful foe, while I abroad
Through all the coasts of dark destruction seek
Deliverance for us all. This enterprise
None shall partake with me." Thus saying, rose
The Monarch, and prevented all reply;
Prudent lest, from his resolution raised,
Others among the chief might offer now,
Certain to be refused, what erst they feared,
And, so refused, might in opinion stand
His rivals, winning cheap the high repute
Which he through hazard huge must earn. But they
Dreaded not more th' adventure than his voice
Forbidding; and at once with him they rose.
Their rising all at once was as the sound
Of thunder heard remote. Towards him they bend
With awful reverence prone, and as a God
Extol him equal to the Highest in Heaven.
Nor failed they to express how much they praised
That for the general safety he despised
His own: for neither do the Spirits damned
Lose all their virtue; lest bad men should boast

* Consider

384

Their specious deeds on earth, which glory excites,
Or close ambition varnished o'er with zeal.

[*Satan now sets off on his voyage to seek the world of Man. While
they await his return the other fallen angels pass their time in games
and philosophical discussions.*]

Meanwhile the Adversary of God and Man,
Satan, with thoughts inflamed of highest design,
Puts on swift wings, and toward the gates of Hell
Explores his solitary flight: sometimes
He scours the right hand coast, sometimes the left;
Now shaves with level wing the deep, then soars
Up to the fiery concave towering high.
As when far off at sea a fleet descried
Hangs in the clouds, by equinoctial winds
Close sailing from Bengala, or the isles
Of Ternate and Tidore, whence merchants bring
Their spicy drugs; they on the trading flood,
Through the wide Ethiopian to the Cape,
Ply stemming nightly toward the pole: so seemed
Far off the flying Fiend. At last appear
Hell-bounds, high reaching to the horrid roof,
And thrice threefold the gates; three folds were brass,
Three iron, three of adamantine rock,
Impenetrable, impaled with circling fire,
Yet unconsumed. Before the gates there sat
On either side a formidable Shape.
The one seemed woman to the waist, and fair,
But ended foul in many a scaly fold,
Voluminous and vast—a serpent armed
With mortal sting. About her middle round
A cry of Hell-hounds never-ceasing barked
With wide Cerberean mouths full loud, and rung
A hideous peal; yet, when they list, would creep,
If aught disturbed their noise, into her womb,
And kennel there; yet there still barked and howled
Within unseen. Far less abhorred than these
Vexed Scylla, bathing in the sea that parts
Calabria from the hoarse Trinacrian shore;

385

Nor uglier follow the night-hag, when, called
In secret, riding through the air she comes,
Lured with the smell of infant blood, to dance
With Lapland witches, while the laboring moon
Eclipses at their charms. The other Shape—
If shape it might be called that shape had none
Distinguishable in member, joint, or limb;
Or substance might be called that shadow seemed,
For each seemed either—black it stood as Night,
Fierce as ten Furies, terrible as Hell,
And shook a dreadful dart: what seemed his head
The likeness of a kingly crown had on.
Satan was now at hand, and from his seat
The monster moving onward came as fast
With horrid strides; Hell trembled as he strode.
Th' undaunted Fiend what this might be admired *—
Admired, not feared (God and his Son except,
Created thing naught valued he nor shunned),
And with disdainful look thus first began:
   "Whence and what art thou, execrable Shape,
That dar'st, though grim and terrible, advance
Thy miscreated front athwart my way
To yonder gates? Through them I mean to pass,
That be assured, without leave asked of thee.
Retire; or taste thy folly, and learn by proof,
Hell-born, not to contend with Spirits of Heaven."
   To whom the Goblin, full of wrath, replied:
"Art thou that traitor Angel? art thou he,
Who first broke peace in Heaven and faith, till then
Unbroken, and in proud rebellious arms
Drew after him the third part of Heaven's sons,
Conjured against the Highest—for which both thou
And they, outcast from God, are here condemned
To waste eternal days in woe and pain?
And reckon'st thou thyself with Spirits of Heaven,
Hell-doomed, and breath'st defiance here and scorn,
Where I reign king, and, to enrage thee more,
Thy king and lord? Back to thy punishment,
False fugitive; and to thy speed add wings,

* Wondered

386

Lest with a whip of scorpions I pursue
Thy lingering, or with one stroke of this dart
Strange horror seize thee, and pangs unfelt before."
    So spake the grisly Terror, and in shape,
So speaking and so threatening, grew tenfold,
More dreadful and deform. On th' other side,
Incensed with indignation, Satan stood
Unterrified, and like a comet burned,
That fires the length of Ophiuchus huge
In th' arctic sky, and from his horrid hair
Shakes pestilence and war. Each at the head
Leveled his deadly aim; their fatal hands
No second stroke intend; and such a frown
Each cast at th' other as when two black clouds,
With heaven's artillery fraught, come rattling on
Over the Caspian, then stand front to front
Hovering a space, till winds the signal blow
To join their dark encounter in mid-air.
So frowned the mighty combatants that Hell
Grew darker at their frown; so matched they stood;
For never but once more was either like
To meet so great a foe. And now great deeds
Had been achieved, whereof all Hell had rung,
Had not the snaky Sorceress, that sat
Fast by Hell-gate and kept the fatal key,
Risen, and with hideous outcry rushed between.
    "O father, what intends thy hand," she cried,
"Against thy only son? What fury, O son,
Possesses thee to bend that mortal dart
Against thy father's head? And know'st for whom?
For him who sits above, and laughs the while
At thee, ordained his drudge to execute
Whate'er his wrath, which he calls justice, bids—
His wrath, which one day will destroy ye both!"
    She spake, and at her words the hellish Pest
Forbore: then these to her Satan returned:
    "So strange thy outcry, and thy words so strange
Thou interposest, that my sudden hand,
Prevented, spares to tell thee yet by deeds
What it intends, till first I know of thee

387

What thing thou art, thus double-formed, and why,
In this infernal vale first met, thou call'st
Me father, and that phantasm call'st my son.
I know thee not, nor ever saw till now
Sight more detestable than him and thee."
   T' whom thus the Portress of Hell-gate replied:
"Hast thou forgot me, then; and do I seem
Now in thine eye so foul?—once deemed so fair
In Heaven, when at th' assembly, and in sight
Of all the Seraphim with thee combined
In bold conspiracy against Heaven's King,
All on a sudden miserable pain
Surprised thee, dim thine eyes and dizzy swum
In darkness, while thy head flames thick and fast
Threw forth, till on the left side opening wide,
Likest to thee in shape and countenance bright,
Then shining heavenly fair, a goddess armed,
Out of thy head I sprung. Amazement seized
All th' host of Heaven; back they recoiled afraid
At first, and called me *Sin,* and for a sign
Portentous held me; but, familiar grown,
I pleased, and with attractive graces won
The most averse—thee chiefly, who, full oft
Thyself in me thy perfect image viewing,
Becam'st enamored; and such joy thou took'st
With me in secret that my womb conceived
A growing burden. Meanwhile war arose,
And fields were fought in Heaven: wherein remained
(For what could else?) to our Almighty Foe
Clear victory; to our part loss and rout
Through all the Empyrean. Down they fell,
Driven headlong from the pitch of Heaven, down
Into this Deep; and in the general fall
I also: at which time this powerful key
Into my hands was given, with charge to keep
These gates forever shut, which none can pass
Without my opening. Pensive here I sat
Alone; but long I sat not, till my womb,
Pregnant by thee, and now excessive grown,
Prodigious motion felt and rueful throes.

388

At last this odious offspring whom thou seest,
Thine own begotten, breaking violent way,
Tore through my entrails, that, with fear and pain
Distorted, all my nether shape thus grew
Transformed: but he my inbred enemy
Forth issued, brandishing his fatal dart,
Made to destroy. I fled, and cried out *Death!*
Hell trembled at the hideous name, and sighed
From all her caves, and back resounded *Death!*
I fled; but he pursued (though more, it seems,
Inflamed with lust than rage), and, swifter far,
Me overtook, his mother, all dismayed,
And, in embraces forcible and foul
Engendering with me, of that rape begot
These yelling monsters, that with ceaseless cry
Surround me, as thou saw'st—hourly conceived
And hourly born, with sorrow infinite
To me; for, when they list, into the womb
That bred them they return, and howl, and gnaw
My bowels, their repast; then, bursting forth
Afresh, with conscious terrors vex me round,
That rest or intermission none I find.
Before mine eyes in opposition sits
Grim Death, my son and foe, who sets them on,
And me, his parent, would full soon devour
For want of other prey, but that he knows
His end with mine involved, and knows that I
Should prove a bitter morsel, and his bane,
Whenever that shall be: so Fate pronounced.
But thou, O father, I forewarn thee, shun
His deadly arrow; neither vainly hope
To be invulnerable in those bright arms,
Though tempered heavenly; for that mortal dint,
Save he who reigns above, none can resist."
    She finished; and the subtle Fiend his lore
Soon learned, now milder, and thus answered smooth:
    "Dear daughter—since thou claim'st me for thy sire,
And my fair son here show'st me, the dear pledge
Of dalliance had with thee in Heaven, and joys
Then sweet, now sad to mention, through dire change

Befallen us unforeseen, unthought-of—know,
I come no enemy, but to set free
From out this dark and dismal house of pain
Both him and thee, and all the heavenly host
Of Spirits that, in our just pretenses armed,
Fell with us from on high. From them I go
This uncouth errand sole, and one for all
Myself expose, with lonely steps to tread
Th' unfounded Deep, and through the void immense
To search, with wandering quest, a place foretold
Should be—and, by concurring signs, ere now
Created vast and round—a place of bliss
In the purlieus of Heaven; and therein placed
A race of upstart creatures, to supply
Perhaps our vacant room, though more removed,
Lest Heaven, surcharged with potent multitude,
Might hap to move new broils. Be this, or aught
Than this more secret, now designed, I haste
To know; and, this once known, shall soon return,
And bring ye to the place where thou and Death
Shall dwell at ease, and up and down unseen
Wing silently the buxom air, embalmed
With odors. There ye shall be fed and filled
Immeasurably; all things shall be your prey."
　　He ceased; for both seemed highly pleased, and Death
Grinned horrible a ghastly smile, to hear
His famine should be filled, and blessed his maw
Destined to that good hour. No less rejoiced
His mother bad, and thus bespake her sire:
　　"The key of this infernal Pit, by due
And by command of Heaven's all-powerful King,
I keep, by him forbidden to unlock
These adamantine gates; against all force
Death ready stands to interpose his dart,
Fearless to be o'ermatched by living might.
But what owe I to his commands above,
Who hates me, and hath hither thrust me down
Into this gloom of Tartarus profound,
To sit in hateful office here confined,
Inhabitant of Heaven and heavenly born—

Here in perpetual agony and pain,
With terrors and with clamors compassed round
Of mine own brood, that on my bowels feed?
Thou art my father, thou my author, thou
My being gav'st me; whom should I obey
But thee? whom follow? Thou wilt bring me soon
To that new world of light and bliss, among
The gods who live at ease, where I shall reign
At thy right hand voluptuous, as beseems
Thy daughter and thy darling, without end."
   Thus saying, from her side the fatal key,
Sad instrument of all our woe, she took;
And, towards the gate rolling her bestial train,
Forthwith the huge portcullis high up-drew,
Which, but herself, not all the Stygian Powers
Could once have moved; then in the key-hole turns
Th' intricate wards, and every bolt and bar
Of massy iron or solid rock with ease
Unfastens. On a sudden open fly,
With impetuous recoil and jarring sound,
Th' infernal doors, and on their hinges grate
Harsh thunder, that the lowest bottom shook
Of Erebus. She opened; but to shut
Excelled her power: the gates wide open stood,
That with extended wings a bannered host,
Under spread ensigns marching, might pass through
With horse and chariots ranked in loose array;
So wide they stood, and like a furnace-mouth
Cast forth redounding smoke and ruddy flame.
Before their eyes in sudden view appear
The secrets of the hoary Deep—a dark
Illimitable ocean, without bound,
Without dimension; where length, breadth, and height,
And time, and place, are lost; where eldest Night
And Chaos, ancestors of Nature, hold
Eternal anarchy, amidst the noise
Of endless wars, and by confusion stand.
For Hot, Cold, Moist, and Dry, four champions fierce,
Strive here for mastery, and to battle bring
Their embryon atoms: they around the flag

Of each his faction, in their several clans,
Light-armed or heavy, sharp, smooth, swift, or slow,
Swarm populous, unnumbered as the sands
Of Barca or Cyrenè's torrid soil,
Levied to side with warring winds, and poise
Their lighter wings. To whom these most adhere
He rules a moment: Chaos umpire sits,
And by decision more embroils the fray
By which he reigns: next him, high arbiter,
Chance governs all. Into this wild Abyss,
The womb of Nature, and perhaps her grave,
Of neither sea, nor shore, nor air, nor fire,
But all these in their pregnant causes mixed
Confusedly, and which thus must ever fight,
Unless th' Almighty Maker them ordain
His dark materials to create more worlds—
Into this wild Abyss the wary Fiend
Stood on the brink of Hell and looked a while,
Pondering his voyage; for no narrow frith
He had to cross. Nor was his ear less pealed *
With noises loud and ruinous (to compare
Great things with small) than when Bellona storms
With all her battering engines, bent to raze
Some capital city; or less than if this frame
Of Heaven were falling, and these elements
In mutiny had from her axle torn
The steadfast Earth. At last his sail-broad vans
He spread for flight, and, in the surging smoke
Uplifted, spurns the ground; thence many a league,
As in a cloudy chair, ascending rides
Audacious; but, that seat soon failing, meets
A vast vacuity. All unawares,
Fluttering his pennons vain, plumb-down he drops
Ten thousand fathom deep, and to this hour
Down had been falling, had not, by ill chance,
The strong rebuff of some tumultuous cloud,
Instinct with fire and niter, hurried him
As many miles aloft. That fury stayed—
Quenched in a boggy Syrtis, neither sea,

* Struck

Nor good dry land—nigh foundered, on he fares,
Treading the crude consistence, half on foot,
Half flying; behoves him now both oar and sail.
As when a griffin through the wilderness
With wingèd course, o'er hill or moory dale,
Pursues the Arimaspian,† who by stealth
Had from his wakeful custody purloined
The guarded gold; so eagerly the Fiend
O'er bog or steep, through strait, rough, dense, or rare,
With head, hands, wings, or feet, pursues his way,
And swims, or sinks, or wades, or creeps, or flies.
At length a universal hubbub wild
Of stunning sounds, and voices all confused,
Borne through the hollow dark, assaults his ear
With loudest vehemence. Thither he plies
Undaunted, to meet there whatever Power
Or Spirit of the nethermost Abyss
Might in that noise reside, of whom to ask
Which way the nearest coast of darkness lies
Bordering on light; when straight behold the throne
Of Chaos, and his dark pavilion spread
Wide on the wasteful Deep! With him enthroned
Sat sable-vested Night, eldest of things,
The consort of his reign; and by them stood
Orcus and Ades, and the dreaded name
Of Demogorgon; Rumor next, and Chance,
And Tumult, and Confusion, all embroiled,
And Discord with a thousand various mouths.
　　T' whom Satan, turning boldly, thus: "Ye Powers
And Spirits of this nethermost Abyss,
Chaos and ancient Night, I come no spy
With purpose to explore or to disturb
The secrets of your realm; but, by constraint
Wandering this darksome desert, as my way
Lies through your spacious empire up to light,
Alone and without guide, half lost, I seek,
What readiest path leads where your gloomy bounds
Confine * with Heaven; or, if some other place,

† One-eyed thieves of the griffons' gold
* Border

From your dominion won, th' Ethereal King
Possesses lately, thither to arrive
I travel this profound. Direct my course:
Directed, no mean recompense it brings
To your behoof, if I that region lost,
All usurpation thence expelled, reduce
To her original darkness and your sway
(Which is my present journey), and once more
Erect the standard there of ancient Night.
Yours be th' advantage all, mine the revenge!"

   Thus Satan; and him thus the Anarch old,
With faltering speech and visage incomposed,
Answered: "I know thee, stranger, who thou art—
That might leading Angel, who of late
Made head against Heaven's King, though overthrown.
I saw and heard; for such a numerous host
Fled not in silence through the frighted Deep,
With ruin upon ruin, rout on rout,
Confusion worse confounded; and Heaven-gates
Poured out by millions her victorious bands,
Pursuing. I upon my frontiers here
Keep residence; if all I can will serve
That little which is left so to defend,
Encroached on still through our intestine broils
Weakening the scepter of old Night: first, Hell,
Your dungeon, stretching far and wide beneath;
Now lately Heaven and Earth, another world
Hung o'er my realm, linked in a golden chain
To that side Heaven from whence your legions fell!
If that way be your walk, you have not far;
So much the nearer danger. Go, and speed;
Havoc, and spoil, and ruin, are my gain."

   He ceased; and Satan stayed not to reply,
But, glad that now his sea should find a shore,
With fresh alacrity and force renewed
Springs upward, like a pyramid of fire,
Into the wild expanse, and through the shock
Of fighting elements, on all sides round
Environed, wins his way; harder beset

394

And more endangered than when Argo passed
Through Bosporus betwixt the justling rocks,
Or when Ulysses on the larboard shunned
Charybdis, and by th' other whirlpool steered.
So he with difficulty and labor hard
Moved on, with difficulty and labor he;
But, he once passed, soon after, when Man fell,
Strange alteration! Sin and Death amain,
Following his track (such was the will of Heaven)
Paved after him a broad and beaten way
Over the dark Abyss, whose boiling gulf
Tamely endured a bridge of wondrous length,
From Hell continued, reaching th' utmost orb
Of this frail World; by which the Spirits perverse
With easy intercourse pass to and fro
To tempt or punish mortals, except whom
God and good Angels guard by special grace.
    But now at last the sacred influence
Of light appears, and from the walls of Heaven
Shoots far into the bosom of dim Night
A glimmering dawn. Here Nature first begins
Her farthest verge, and Chaos to retire,
As from her outmost works, a broken foe,
With tumult less and with less hostile din;
That Satan with less toil, and now with ease,
Wafts on the calmer wave by dubious light,
And, like a weather-beaten vessel, holds
Gladly the port, though shrouds and tackle torn;
Or in the emptier waste, resembling air,
Weighs his spread wings, at leisure to behold
Far off th' empyreal Heaven, extended wide
In circuit, undetermined square or round,
With opal towers and battlements adorned
Of living sapphire, once his native seat;
And, fast by, hanging in a golden chain,
This pendent World, in bigness as a star
Of smallest magnitude close by the moon.
Thither, full fraught with mischievous revenge,
Accursed, and in a cursèd hour, he hies.

BOOK III

The Argument

God, sitting on his throne, sees Satan flying towards this World, then newly created; shows him to the Son, who sat at his right hand; foretells the success of Satan in perverting mankind; clears his own justice and wisdom from all imputation, having created Man free, and able enough to have withstood his Tempter; yet declares his purpose of grace towards him, in regard he fell not of his own malice, as did Satan, but by him seduced. The Son of God renders praises to his Father for the manifestation of his gracious purpose towards Man: but God again declares that grace cannot be extended toward Man without the satisfaction of Divine Justice; Man hath offended the majesty of God by aspiring to Godhead, and therefore, with all his progeny, devoted to death, must die, unless someone can be found sufficient to answer for his offense, and undergo his punishment. The Son of God freely offers himself a ransom for Man: the Father accepts him, ordains his incarnation, pronounces his exaltation above all names in Heaven and Earth; commands all the Angels to adore him. They obey, and, hymning to their harps in full choir, celebrate the Father and the Son. Meanwhile Satan alights upon the bare convex of this World's outermost orb; where wandering he first finds a place since called the Limbo of Vanity; what persons and things fly up thither: thence comes to the gate of Heaven, described ascending by stairs, and the waters above the firmament that flow about it. His passage thence to the orb of the Sun: he finds there Uriel, the regent of that orb, but first changes himself into the shape of a meaner Angel, and, pretending a zealous desire to behold the new Creation, and Man whom God placed here, inquires of him the place of his habitation, and is directed: alights first on Mount Niphates.

HAIL, HOLY LIGHT, offspring of Heaven first-born!
Or of th' Eternal coeternal beam
May I express thee unblamed? since God is light,
And never but in unapproachèd light
Dwelt from eternity—dwelt then in thee,
Bright effluence of bright essence increate!
Or hear'st thou rather pure ethereal stream,
Whose fountain who shall tell? Before the Sun,
Before the heavens, thou wert, and at the voice
Of God, as with a mantle, didst invest

The rising world of waters dark and deep,
Won from the void and formless Infinite!
Thee I revisit now with bolder wing,
Escaped the Stygian Pool, though long detained
In that obscure sojourn, while in my flight,
Through utter and through middle Darkness * borne,
With other notes than to th' Orphean lyre
I sung of Chaos and eternal Night,
Taught by the Heavenly Muse to venture down
The dark descent, and up to re-ascend,
Though hard and rare. Thee I revisit safe,
And feel thy sovereign vital lamp; but thou
Revisit'st not these eyes, that roll in vain
To find thy piercing ray, and find no dawn;
So thick a drop serene hath quenched their orbs,
Or dim suffusion veiled. Yet not the more
Cease I to wander where the Muses haunt
Clear spring, or shady grove, or sunny hill,
Smit with the love of sacred song; but chief
Thee, Sion, and the flowery brooks beneath,
That wash thy hallowed feet, and warbling flow,
Nightly I visit: nor sometimes forget
Those other two equaled with me in fate,
So were I equaled with them in renown,
Blind Thamyris and blind Maeonides,
And Tiresias and Phineus, prophets old:
Then feed on thoughts that voluntary move
Harmonious numbers; as the wakeful bird
Sings darkling, and, in shadiest covert hid,
Tunes her nocturnal note. Thus with the year
Seasons return; but not to me returns
Day, or the sweet approach of even or morn,
Or sight of vernal bloom, or summer's rose,
Or flocks, or herds, or human face divine;
But cloud instead and ever-during dark
Surrounds me, from the cheerful ways of men
Cut off, and, for the book of knowledge fair,
Presented with a universal blank
Of Nature's works, to me expunged and razed,

* Hell and Chaos

And wisdom at one entrance quite shut out.
So much the rather thou, Celestial Light,
Shine inward, and the mind through all her powers
Irradiate; there plant eyes; all mist from thence
Purge and disperse, that I may see and tell
Of things invisible to mortal sight.

[*God foresees that Man, whose will is free, will succumb to the temptations of Satan and so deliver up the human race to eternal death. As atonement for Man's offense, the Son of God offers to assume human form and to suffer death. God accepts the offer and the angels sing their praise of Divine Wisdom.*]

Thus they in Heaven, above the starry sphere,
Their happy hours in joy and hymning spent.
Meanwhile, upon the firm opacous globe
Of this round World, whose first convex divides
The luminous inferior orbs, enclosed
From Chaos and th' inroad of Darkness old,
Satan alighted walks. A globe far off
It seemed; now seems a boundless continent,
Dark, waste, and wild, under the frown of Night
Starless exposed, and ever-threatening storms
Of Chaos blustering round, inclement sky,
Save on that side which from the wall of Heaven,
Though distant far, some small reflection gains
Of glimmering air less vexed with tempest loud.
Here walked the Fiend at large in spacious field.
As when a vulture, on Imaus bred,
Whose snowy ridge the roving Tartar bounds,
Dislodging from a region scarce of prey,
To gorge the flesh of lambs or yeanling kids
On hills where flocks are fed, flies toward the springs
Of Ganges or Hydaspes, Indian streams,
But in his way lights on the barren plains
Of Sericana, where Chineses drive
With sails and wind their cany wagons light;
So, on this windy sea of land, the Fiend
Walked up and down alone, bent on his prey:
Alone, for other creature in this place,

Living or lifeless, to be found was none;
None yet; but store hereafter from the Earth
Up hither like aerial vapors flew
Of all things transitory and vain, when sin
With vanity had filled the works of men—
Both all things vain, and all who in vain things
Built their fond hopes of glory or lasting fame,
Or happiness in this or th' other life.
All who have their reward on earth, the fruits
Of painful superstition and blind zeal,
Naught seeking but the praise of men, here find
Fit retribution, empty as their deeds;
All th' unaccomplished works of Nature's hand,
Abortive, monstrous, or unkindly mixed,
Dissolved on Earth, fleet hither, and in vain,
Till final dissolution, wander here—
Not in the neighboring moon, as some have dreamed:
Those argent fields more likely habitants,
Translated Saints, or middle Spirits hold,
Betwixt th' angelical and human kind.
Hither, of ill-joined sons and daughters born,
First from the ancient world those giants came,
With many a vain exploit, though then renowned:
The builders next of Babel on the plain
Of Sennaar, and still with vain design
New Babels, had they wherewithal, would build:
Others came single; he who, to be deemed
A god, leaped fondly into Etna flames,
Empedocles, and he who, to enjoy
Plato's Elysium, leaped into the sea,
Cleombrotus; and many more, too long,
Embryos and idiots, eremites * and friars,
White, black, and grey, with all their trumpery.
Here pilgrims roam, that strayed so far to seek
In Golgotha him dead who lives in Heaven;
And they who, to be sure of Paradise,
Dying put on the weeds of Dominic,
Or in Franciscan think to pass disguised.
They pass the planets seven, and pass the fixed,

* Hermits

399

And that crystalline sphere whose balance weighs
The trepidation talked, and that first moved;
And now Saint Peter at Heaven's wicket seems
To wait them with his keys, and now at foot
Of Heaven's ascent they lift their feet, when, lo!
A violent cross wind from either coast
Blows them transverse ten thousand leagues awry,
Into the devious air. Then might ye see
Cowls, hoods, and habits, with their wearers, tost
And fluttered into rags; then relics, beads,
Indulgences, dispenses, pardons, bulls,
The sport of winds: all these, upwhirled aloft,
Fly o'er the backside of the World far off
Into a Limbo large and broad, since called
The Paradise of Fools; to few unknown
Long after, now unpeopled and untrod.
　　All this dark globe the Fiend found as he passed;
And long he wandered, till at last a gleam
Of dawning light turned thitherward in haste
His traveled steps. Far distant he descries,
Ascending by degrees magnificent
Up to the wall of Heaven, a structure high;
At top whereof, but far more rich, appeared
The work as of a kingly palace-gate,
With frontispiece of diamond and gold
Embellished; thick with sparkling orient gems
The portal shone, inimitable on Earth
By model, or by shading pencil drawn.
The stairs were such as whereon Jacob saw
Angels ascending and descending, bands
Of guardians bright, when he from Esau fled
To Padan-Aram, in the field of Luz
Dreaming by night under the open sky,
And waking cried, *This is the gate of Heaven.*
Each stair mysteriously was meant, nor stood
There always, but drawn up to Heaven sometimes
Viewless; and underneath a bright sea flowed
Of jasper, or of liquid pearl, whereon
Who after came from Earth sailing arrived
Wafted by Angels, or flew o'er the lake

Rapt in a chariot drawn by fiery steeds.
The stairs were then let down, whether to dare
The Fiend by easy ascent, or aggravate
His sad exclusion from the doors of bliss:
Direct against which opened from beneath,
Just o'er the blissful seat of Paradise,
A passage down to th' Earth—a passage wide;
Wider by far than that of after-times
Over Mount Sion, and, though that were large,
Over the Promised Land to God so dear,
By which, to visit oft those happy tribes,
On high behests his Angels to and fro
Passed frequent, and his eye with choice regard
From Paneas, the fount of Jordan's flood,
To Beërsaba, where the Holy Land
Borders on Egypt and the Arabian shore.
So wide the opening seemed, where bounds were set
To darkness, such as bound the ocean wave.
Satan from hence, now on the lower stair,
That scaled by steps of gold to Heaven-gate,
Looks down with wonder at the sudden view
Of all this World at once. As when a scout,
Through dark and desert ways with peril gone
All night, at last by break of cheerful dawn
Obtains the brow of some high-climbing hill,
Which to his eye discovers unaware
The goodly prospect of some foreign land
First seen, or some renowned metropolis
With glistering spires and pinnacles adorned,
Which now the rising sun gilds with his beams;
Such wonder seized, though after Heaven seen,
The Spirit malign, but much more envy seized,
At sight of all this World beheld so fair.
Round he surveys (and well might, where he stood
So high above the circling canopy
Of Night's extended shade) from eastern point
Of Libra to the fleecy star that bears
Andromeda far off Atlantic seas
Beyond th' horizon; then from pole to pole
He views in breadth, and, without longer pause,

Down right into the World's first region throws
His flight precipitant, and winds with ease
Through the pure marble air his oblique way
Amongst innumerable stars, that shone
Stars distant, but nigh-hand seemed other worlds.
Or other worlds they seemed, or happy isles,
Like those Hesperian Gardens famed of old,
Fortunate fields, and groves, and flowery vales;
Thrice happy isles! But who dwelt happy there
He stayed not to inquire: above them all
The golden Sun, in splendor likest Heaven,
Allured his eye. Thither his course he bends,
Through the calm firmament (but up or down,
By center or eccentric, hard to tell,
Or longitude) where the great luminary,
Aloof the vulgar constellations thick,
That from his lordly eye keep distance due,
Dispenses light from far. They, as they move
Their starry dance in numbers that compute
Days, months, and years, towards his all-cheering lamp
Turn swift their various motions, or are turned
By his magnetic beam, that gently warms
The Universe, and to each inward part
With gentle penetration, though unseen,
Shoots invisible virtue even to the Deep;
So wondrously was set his station bright.
There lands the Fiend, a spot like which perhaps
Astronomer in the Sun's lucent orb
Through his glazed optic tube yet never saw.
The place he found beyond expression bright,
Compared with aught on Earth, metal or stone—
Not all parts like, but all alike informed
With radiant light, as glowing iron with fire.
If metal, part seemed gold, part silver clear;
If stone, carbuncle most or chrysolite,
Ruby or topaz, to the twelve that shone
In Aaron's breast-plate, and a stone besides,
Imagined rather oft than elsewhere seen—
That stone, or like to that, which here below
Philosophers in vain so long have sought;

402

In vain, though by their powerful art they bind
Volatile Hermes, and call up unbound
In various shapes old Proteus from the sea,
Drained through a limbec * to his native form.
What wonder then if fields and regions here
Breathe forth elixir pure, and rivers run
Potable gold, when, with one virtuous touch,
Th' arch-chemic Sun, so far from us remote,
Produces, with terrestrial humor mixed,
Here in the dark so many precious things
Of color glorious and effect so rare?
Here matter new to gaze the Devil met
Undazzled. Far and wide his eye commands;
For sight no obstacle found here, nor shade,
But all sunshine, as when his beams at noon
Culminate from th' equator, as they now
Shot upward still direct, whence no way round
Shadow from body opaque can fall; and the air,
Nowhere so clear, sharpened his visual ray
To objects distant far, whereby he soon
Saw within ken a glorious Angel stand,
The same whom John saw also in the Sun.
His back was turned, but not his brightness hid;
Of beaming sunny rays a golden tiar
Circled his head, nor less his locks behind
Illustrious on his shoulders fledge with wings
Lay waving round: on some great charge employed
He seemed, or fixed in cogitation deep.
Glad was the Spirit impure, as now in hope
To find who might direct his wandering flight
To Paradise, the happy seat of Man,
His journey's end, and our beginning woe.
But first he casts to change his proper shape,
Which else might work him danger or delay:
And now a stripling Cherub he appears,
Not of the prime, yet such as in his face
Youth smiled celestial, and to every limb
Suitable grace diffused; so well he feigned.
Under a coronet his flowing hair

* Alembic

In curls on either cheek played; wings he wore
Of many a colored plume sprinkled with gold,
His habit fit for speed succinct, and held
Before his decent steps a silver wand.
He drew not nigh unheard; the Angel bright,
Ere he drew nigh, his radiant visage turned,
Admonished by his ear, and straight was known
Th' Archangel Uriel—one of the seven
Who in God's presence, nearest to his throne,
Stand ready at command, and are his eyes
That run through all the Heavens, or down to th' Earth
Bear his swift errands over moist and dry,
O'er sea and land. Him Satan thus accosts:
   "Uriel! for thou of those seven Spirits that stand
In sight of God's high throne, gloriously bright,
The first art wont his great authentic will
Interpreter through highest heaven to bring,
Where all his Sons thy embassy attend,
And here art likeliest by supreme decree
Like honor to obtain, and as his eye
To visit oft this new Creation round—
Unspeakable desire to see and know
All these his wondrous works, but chiefly Man,
His chief delight and favor, him for whom
All these his works so wondrous he ordained,
Hath brought me from the choirs of Cherubim
Alone thus wandering. Brightest Seraph, tell
In which of all these shining orbs hath Man
His fixèd seat—or fixèd seat hath none,
But all these shining orbs his choice to dwell—
That I may find him, and with secret gaze
Or open admiration him behold
On whom the great Creator hath bestowed
Worlds, and on whom hath all these graces poured;
That both in him and all things, as is meet,
The Universal Maker we may praise;
Who justly hath driven out his rebel foes
To deepest Hell, and, to repair that loss,
Created this new happy race of Men
To serve him better: wise are all his ways!"

404

So spake the false dissembler unperceived;
For neither man nor angel can discern
Hypocrisy—the only evil that walks
Invisible, except to God alone,
By his permissive will, through Heaven and Earth;
And oft, though Wisdom wake, Suspicion sleeps
At Wisdom's gate, and to Simplicity
Resigns her charge, while Goodness thinks no ill
Where no ill seems: which now for once beguiled
Uriel, though Regent of the Sun, and held
The sharpest-sighted Spirit of all in Heaven;
Who to the fraudulent impostor foul,
In his uprightness, answer thus returned:
"Fair Angel, thy desire, which tends to know
The works of God, thereby to glorify
The great Work-master, leads to no excess
That reaches blame, but rather merits praise
The more it seems excess, that led thee hither
From thy empyreal mansion thus alone,
To witness with thine eyes what some perhaps,
Contented with report, hear only in Heaven:
For wonderful indeed are all his works,
Pleasant to know, and worthiest to be all
Had in remembrance always with delight!
But what created mind can comprehend
Their number, or the wisdom infinite
That brought them forth, but hid their causes deep?
I saw when, at his word, the formless mass,
This World's material mold, came to a heap:
Confusion heard his voice, and wild Uproar
Stood ruled, stood vast Infinitude confined;
Till, at his second bidding, Darkness fled,
Light shone, and order from disorder sprung.
Swift to their several quarters hasted then
The cumbrous elements—Earth, Flood, Air, Fire;
And this ethereal quintessence of Heaven
Flew upward, spirited with various forms,
That rolled orbicular, and turned to stars
Numberless, as thou seest, and how they move:
Each had his place appointed, each his course;

The rest in circuit walls this Universe.
Look downward on that globe, whose hither side
With light from hence, though but reflected, shines:
That place is Earth, the seat of Man; that light
His day, which else, as th' other hemisphere,
Night would invade; but there the neighboring Moon
(So call that opposite fair star) her aid
Timely interposes, and, her monthly round
Still ending, still renewing, through mid-heaven,
With borrowed light her countenance triform
Hence fills and empties, to enlighten th' Earth,
And in her pale dominion checks the night.
That spot to which I point is Paradise,
Adam's abode; those lofty shades his bower.
Thy way thou canst not miss; me mine requires."
    Thus said, he turned; and Satan, bowing low,
As to superior Spirits is wont in Heaven,
Where honor due and reverence none neglects,
Took leave, and toward the coast of Earth beneath,
Down from th' ecliptic, sped with hoped success,
Throws his steep flight in many an airy wheel,
Nor stayed, till on Niphates' top he lights.

BOOK IV

The Argument

Satan, now in prospect of Eden, and nigh the place where he must
now attempt the bold enterprise which he undertook alone against God
and Man, falls into many doubts with himself, and many passions—
fear, envy, and despair; but at length confirms himself in evil; journeys
on to Paradise, whose outward prospect and situation is described;
overleaps the bounds; sits, in the shape of a cormorant, on the Tree
of Life, as highest in the Garden, to look about him. The Garden described; Satan's first sight of Adam and Eve; his wonder at their excellent form and happy state, but with resolution to work their fall; over-
hears their discourse; thence gathers that the Tree of Knowledge was
forbidden them to eat of under penalty of death, and thereon intends
to found his temptation by seducing them to transgress; then leaves

406

them a while, to know further of their state by some other means.
Meanwhile Uriel, descending on a sunbeam, warns Gabriel, who had
in charge the gate of Paradise, that some evil Spirit had escaped the
Deep, and passed at noon by his Sphere, in the shape of a good Angel,
down to Paradise, discovered after by his furious gestures in the
mount. Gabriel promises to find him ere morning. Night coming on,
Adam and Eve discourse of going to their rest: their bower described;
their evening worship. Gabriel, drawing forth his bands of night-watch
to walk the rounds of Paradise, appoints two strong Angels to Adam's
bower, lest the evil Spirit should be there doing some harm to Adam
or Eve sleeping: there they find him at the ear of Eve, tempting her in
a dream, and bring him, though unwilling, to Gabriel; by whom questioned, he scornfully answers; prepares resistance; but, hindered by a
sign from Heaven, flies out of Paradise.

O FOR THAT warning voice, which he who saw
   Th' Apocalypse heard cry in Heaven aloud,
Then when the Dragon, put to second rout,
Came furious down to be revenged on men,
Woe to the inhabitants on Earth! that now,
While time was, our first parents had been warned
The coming of their secret foe, and scaped,
Haply so scaped, his mortal snare! For now
Satan, now first inflamed with rage, came down,
The tempter, ere th' accuser, of mankind,
To wreak on innocent frail Man his loss
Of that first battle, and his flight to Hell.
Yet not rejoicing in his speed, though bold
Far off and fearless, nor with cause to boast,
Begins his dire attempt; which, nigh the birth
Now rolling, boils in his tumultuous breast,
And like a devilish engine back recoils
Upon himself. Horror and doubt distract
His troubled thoughts, and from the bottom stir
The hell within him; for within him Hell
He brings, and round about him, nor from Hell
One step, no more than from himself, can fly
By change of place. Now Conscience wakes Despair
That slumbered; wakes the bitter memory
Of what he was, what is, and what must be
Worse; of worse deeds worse sufferings must ensue.
Sometimes toward Eden, which now in his view

Lay pleasant, his grieved look he fixes sad;
Sometimes toward Heaven and the full-blazing Sun,
Which now sat high in his meridian tower:
Then, much revolving, thus in sighs began:
  "O thou that, with surpassing glory crowned,
Look'st from thy sole dominion like the god
Of this new World—at whose sight all the stars
Hide their diminished heads—to thee I call,
But with no friendly voice, and add thy name,
O Sun, to tell thee how I hate thy beams,
That bring to my remembrance from what state
I fell, how glorious once above thy sphere,
Till pride and worse ambition threw me down,
Warring in Heaven against Heaven's matchless King!
Ah, wherefore? He deserved no such return
From me, whom he created what I was
In that bright eminence, and with his good
Upbraided none; nor was his service hard.
What could be less than to afford him praise,
The easiest recompense, and pay him thanks,
How due! Yet all his good proved ill in me,
And wrought but malice. Lifted up so high,
I 'sdained subjection, and thought one step higher
Would set me highest, and in a moment quit
The debt immense of endless gratitude,
So burdensome, still paying, still to owe;
Forgetful what from him I still received;
And understood not that a grateful mind
By owing owes not, but still pays, at once
Indebted and discharged—what burden then?
Oh, had his powerful destiny ordained
Me some inferior Angel, I had stood
Then happy; no unbounded hope had raised
Ambition. Yet why not? Some other Power
As great might have aspired, and me, though mean,
Drawn to his part. But other Powers as great
Fell not, but stand unshaken, from within
Or from without to all temptations armed!
Hadst thou the same free will and power to stand?
Thou hadst. Whom hast thou then, or what, to accuse,

But Heaven's free love dealt equally to all?
Be then his love accursed, since, love or hate,
To me alike it deals eternal woe.
Nay, cursed be thou; since against his thy will
Chose freely what it now so justly rues.
Me miserable! which way shall I fly
Infinite wrath and infinite despair?
Which way I fly is Hell; myself am Hell;
And, in the lowest deep, a lower deep
Still threatening to devour me opens wide,
To which the Hell I suffer seems a Heaven.
O, then, at last relent! Is there no place
Left for repentance, none for pardon left?
None left but by submission; and that word
Disdain forbids me, and my dread of shame
Among the Spirits beneath, whom I seduced
With other promises and other vaunts
Than to submit, boasting I could subdue
Th' Omnipotent. Ay me! they little know
How dearly I abide that boast so vain,
Under what torments inwardly I groan.
While they adore me on the throne of Hell,
With diadem and scepter high advanced,
The lower still I fall, only supreme
In misery: such joy ambition finds!
But say I could repent, and could obtain,
By act of grace, my former state, how soon
Would height recall high thoughts, how soon unsay
What feigned submission swore! Ease would recant
Vows made in pain, as violent and void
(For never can true reconcilement grow
Where wounds of deadly hate have pierced so deep);
Which would but lead me to a worse relapse
And heavier fall: so should I purchase dear
Short intermission, bought with double smart.
This knows my Punisher; therefore as far
From granting he, as I from begging, peace.
All hope excluded thus, behold, instead
Of us, outcast, exiled, his new delight,
Mankind, created, and for him this World!

409

So farewell hope, and, with hope, farewell fear,
Farewell remorse! All good to me is lost;
Evil, be thou my good: by thee at least
Divided empire with Heaven's King I hold,
By thee, and more than half perhaps will reign;
As Man ere long, and this new World, shall know."
    Thus while he spake, each passion dimmed his face,
Thrice changed with pale—ire, envy, and despair;
Which marred his borrowed visage, and betrayed
Him counterfeit, if any eye beheld:
For heavenly minds from such distempers foul
Are ever clear. Whereof he soon aware
Each perturbation smoothed with outward calm,
Artificer of fraud; and was the first
That practiced falsehood under saintly show,
Deep malice to conceal, couched with revenge:
Yet not enough had practiced to deceive
Uriel, once warned; whose eye pursued him down
The way he went, and on th' Assyrian mount
Saw him disfigured, more than could befall
Spirit of happy sort: his gestures fierce
He marked and mad demeanor, then alone,
As he supposed, all unobserved, unseen.
    So on he fares, and to the border comes
Of Eden, where delicious Paradise,
Now nearer, crowns with her enclosure green,
As with a rural mound, the champaign head *
Of a steep wilderness, whose hairy sides
With thicket overgrown, grotesque and wild,
Access denied; and overhead up-grew
Insuperable height of loftiest shade,
Cedar, and pine, and fir, and branching palm,
A sylvan scene, and, as the ranks ascend
Shade above shade, a woody theater
Of stateliest view. Yet higher than their tops
The verdurous wall of Paradise up-sprung;
Which to our general sire gave prospect large
Into his nether empire neighboring round.
And higher than that wall a circling row

* In medieval legend, a plateau high above the waters of Noah's flood

410

Of goodliest trees, loaden with fairest fruit,
Blossoms and fruits at once of golden hue,
Appeared, with gay enameled colors mixed;
On which the sun more glad impressed his beams
Than in fair evening cloud, or humid bow,†
When God hath showered the earth: so lovely seemed
That landscape. And of pure now purer air
Meets his approach, and to the heart inspires
Vernal delight and joy, able to drive
All sadness but despair. Now gentle gales,
Fanning their odoriferous wings, dispense
Native perfumes, and whisper whence they stole
Those balmy spoils. As, when to them who sail
Beyond the Cape of Hope, and now are past
Mozambic, off at sea north-east winds blow
Sabean odors from the spicy shore
Of Araby the Blest, with such delay
Well pleased they slack their course, and many a league
Cheered with the grateful smell old Ocean smiles;
So entertained those odorous sweets the Fiend
Who came their bane, though with them better pleased
Than Asmodeus with the fishy fume
That drove him, though enamored, from the spouse
Of Tobit's son, and with a vengeance sent
From Media post to Egypt, there fast bound.
    Now to th' ascent of that steep savage hill
Satan had journeyed on, pensive and slow;
But further way found none; so thick entwined,
As one continued brake, the undergrowth
Of shrubs and tangling bushes had perplexed
All path of man or beast that passed that way.
One gate there only was, and that looked east
On th' other side. Which when th' Arch-Felon saw,
Due entrance he disdained, and, in contempt,
At one slight bound high overleaped all bound
Of hill or highest wall, and sheer within
Lights on his feet. As when a prowling wolf,
Whom hunger drives to seek new haunt for prey,
Watching where shepherds pen their flocks at eve,

† Rainbow

In hurdled cotes amid the field secure,
Leaps o'er the fence with ease into the fold;
Or as a thief, bent to unhoard the cash
Of some rich burgher, whose substantial doors,
Cross-barred and bolted fast, fear no assault,
In at the window climbs, or o'er the tiles;
So climbed this first grand Thief into God's fold:
So since into his Church lewd hirelings climb.
Thence up he flew, and on the Tree of Life,
The middle tree and highest there that grew,
Sat like a cormorant; yet not true life
Thereby regained, but sat devising death
To them who lived; nor on the virtue thought
Of that life-giving plant, but only used
For prospect, what well used had been the pledge
Of immortality. So little knows
Any, but God alone, to value right
The good before him, but perverts best things
To worst abuse, or to their meanest use.
Beneath him, with new wonder, now he views,
To all delight of human sense exposed,
In narrow room Nature's whole wealth; yea, more,
A Heaven on Earth: for blissful Paradise
Of God the garden was, by him in the east
Of Eden planted. Eden stretched her line
From Auran eastward to the royal towers
Of great Seleucia, built by Grecian kings,
Or where the sons of Eden long before
Dwelt in Telassar. In this pleasant soil
His far more pleasant garden God ordained.
Out of the fertile ground he caused to grow
All trees of noblest kind for sight, smell, taste,
And all amid them stood the Tree of Life,
High eminent, blooming ambrosial fruit
Of vegetable gold; and next to life,
Our death, the Tree of Knowledge, grew fast by—
Knowledge of good, bought dear by knowing ill.
Southward through Eden went a river large,
Nor changed his course, but through the shaggy hill
Passed underneath engulfed; for God had thrown

That mountain, as his garden-mold, high raised
Upon the rapid current, which, through veins
Of porous earth with kindly * thirst up-drawn,
Rose a fresh fountain, and with many a rill
Watered the garden; thence united fell
Down the steep glade, and met the nether flood,
Which from his darksome passage now appears,
And now, divided into four main streams,
Runs diverse, wandering many a famous realm
And country whereof here needs no account;
But rather to tell how, if Art could tell
How, from that sapphire fount the crispèd † brooks,
Rolling on orient pearl and sands of gold,
With mazy error under pendent shades
Ran nectar, visiting each plant, and fed
Flowers worthy of Paradise, which not nice Art
In beds and curious knots, but Nature boon ‡
Poured forth profuse on hill, and dale, and plain,
Both where the morning sun first warmly smote
The open field, and where the unpierced shade
Embrowned the noontide bowers. Thus was this place,
A happy rural seat of various view:
Groves whose rich trees wept odorous gums and balm;
Others whose fruit, burnished with golden rind,
Hung amiable—Hesperian fables true,
If true, here only—and of delicious taste.
Betwixt them lawns, or level downs, and flocks
Grazing the tender herb, were interposed,
Or palmy hillock; or the flowery lap
Of some irriguous valley spread her store,
Flowers of all hue, and without thorn the rose.
Another side, umbrageous grots and caves
Of cool recess, o'er which the mantling vine
Lays forth her purple grape, and gently creeps
Luxuriant; meanwhile murmuring waters fall
Down the slope hills dispersed, or in a lake,
That to the fringèd bank with myrtle crowned

* Natural
† Rippling
‡ Bountiful

Her crystal mirror holds, unite their streams.
The birds their choir apply; airs, vernal airs,
Breathing the smell of field and grove, attune
The trembling leaves, while universal Pan,
Knit with the Graces and the Hours in dance,
Led on th' eternal Spring. Not that fair field
Of Enna, where Proserpin gathering flowers,
Herself a fairer flower, by gloomy Dis
Was gathered—which cost Ceres all that pain
To seek her through the world—nor that sweet grove
Of Daphne, by Orontes and th' inspired
Castalian spring, might with this Paradise
Of Eden strive; nor that Nyseian isle,
Girt with the river Triton, where old Cham,
Whom Gentiles Ammon call and Libyan Jove,
Hid Amalthea, and her florid son,
Young Bacchus, from his stepdame Rhea's eye;
Nor, where Abassin kings their issue guard,
Mount Amara (though this by some supposed
True Paradise) under the Ethiop line *
By Nilus' head, enclosed with shining rock,
A whole day's journey high, but wide remote
From this Assyrian garden, where the Fiend
Saw undelighted all delight, all kind
Of living creatures, new to sight and strange.
Two of far nobler shape, erect and tall,
God-like erect, with native honor clad
In naked majesty, seemed lords of all,
And worthy seemed; for in their looks divine
The image of their glorious Maker shone,
Truth, wisdom, sanctitude severe and pure—
Severe, but in true filial freedom placed,
Whence true authority in men: though both
Not equal, as their sex not equal seemed;
For contemplation he and valor formed,
For softness she and sweet attractive grace;
He for God only, she for God in him.
His fair large front and eye sublime declared
Absolute rule; and hyacinthine locks

* The equator

414

Round from his parted forelock manly hung
Clustering, but not beneath his shoulders broad:
She, as a veil down to the slender waist,
Her unadornèd golden tresses wore
Disheveled, but in wanton ringlets waved
As the vine curls her tendrils, which implied
Subjection, but required with gentle sway,
And by her yielded, by him best received
Yielded, with coy † submission, modest pride,
And sweet, reluctant, amorous delay.
Nor those mysterious parts were then concealed;
Then was not guilty shame. Dishonest shame
Of Nature's works, honor dishonorable,
Sin-bred, how have ye troubled all mankind
With shows instead, mere shows of seeming pure,
And banished from man's life his happiest life,
Simplicity and spotless innocence!
So passed they naked on, nor shunned the sight
Of God or Angel; for they thought no ill:
So hand in hand they passed, the loveliest pair
That ever since in love's embraces met—
Adam the goodliest man of men since born
His sons; the fairest of her daughters Eve.
Under a tuft of shade that on a green
Stood whispering soft, by a fresh fountain-side,
They sat them down; and, after no more toil
Of their sweet gardening labor than sufficed
To recommend cool Zephyr, and make ease
More easy, wholesome thirst and appetite
More grateful, to their supper-fruits they fell—
Nectarine fruits, which the compliant boughs
Yielded them, sidelong as they sat recline
On the soft downy bank damasked with flowers.
The savory pulp they chew, and in the rind,
Still as they thirsted, scoop the brimming stream;
Nor gentle purpose, nor endearing smiles
Wanted, nor youthful dalliance, as beseems
Fair couple linked in happy nuptial league,
Alone as they. About them frisking played

† Shy

All beasts of th' earth, since wild, and of all chase
In wood or wilderness, forest or den.
Sporting the lion ramped, and in his paw
Dandled the kid; bears, tigers, ounces, pards,
Gamboled before them; th' unwieldy elephant,
To make them mirth, used all his might, and wreathed
His lithe proboscis; close the serpent sly,
Insinuating, wove with Gordian twine
His braided train, and of his fatal guile
Gave proof unheeded. Others on the grass
Couched, and, now filled with pasture, gazing sat,
Or bedward ruminating; for the sun,
Declined, was hasting now with prone career
To th' ocean isles, and in th' ascending scale
Of Heaven the stars that usher evening rose. . . .

*[Satan, overwhelmed with shame and grief at the sight of the perfect
innocence of Adam and Eve, seeks a way by which he may ruin
them. Peeping and skulking about, he learns that they are forbidden to eat the fruit of one special Tree. When the angels Uriel and
Gabriel search Paradise, they discover Satan squatting like a toad
in the bower of Adam and Eve, and whispering in Eve's ear. But
when they threaten to load Satan with chains and return him to
Hell, he escapes.]*

BOOK V

The Argument

Morning approached, Eve relates to Adam her troublesome dream; he
likes it not, yet comforts her: they come forth to their day labors: their
morning hymn at the door of their bower. God, to render Man inexcus-
able, sends Raphael to admonish him of his obedience, of his free
estate, of his enemy near at hand, who he is, and why his enemy, and
whatever else may avail Adam to know. Raphael comes down to Paradise; his appearance described; his coming discerned by Adam afar off,
sitting at the door of his bower; he goes out to meet him, brings him
to his lodge, entertains him with the choicest fruits of Paradise, got
together by Eve; their discourse at table. Raphael performs his mes-

416

sage, minds Adam of his state and of his enemy; relates, at Adam's
request, who that enemy is, and how he came to be so, beginning from
his first revolt in Heaven, and the occasion thereof; how he drew his
legions after him to the parts of the North, and there incited them to
rebel with him, persuading all but only Abdiel, a Seraph, who in argument dissuades and opposes him, then forsakes him.

[*While they are at work in the garden, Raphael tells Adam and
Eve that if they are obedient to God's will they may some day
achieve the rank and power of angels, but only if they are obedient.*]

To whom the Patriarch of Mankind replied:
  "O favorable Spirit, propitious guest,
Well hast thou taught the way that might direct
Our knowledge, and the scale of Nature set
From center to circumference, whereon,
In contemplation of created things,
By steps we may ascend to God. But say,
What meant that caution joined, *If ye be found
Obedient?* Can we want obedience, then,
To him, or possibly his love desert,
Who formed us from the dust, and placed us here
Full to the utmost measure of what bliss
Human desires can seek or apprehend?"
  To whom the Angel: "Son of Heaven and Earth,
Attend! That thou art happy, owe to God;
That thou continuest such, owe to thyself,
That is, to thy obedience; therein stand.
This was that caution given thee; be advised.
God made thee perfect, not immutable;
And good he made thee; but to persevere
He left it in thy power—ordained thy will
By nature free, not overruled by fate
Inextricable, or strict necessity.
Our voluntary service he requires,
Not our necessitated. Such with him
Finds no acceptance, nor can find; for how
Can hearts not free be tried whether they serve
Willing or no, who will but what they must
By destiny, and can no other choose?
Myself, and all th' angelic host, that stand

In sight of God enthroned, our happy state
Hold, as you yours, while our obedience holds.
On other surety none: freely we serve,
Because we freely love, as in our will
To love or not; in this we stand or fall.
And some are fallen, to disobedience fallen,
And so from Heaven to deepest Hell. O fall
From what high state of bliss into what woe!"

    To whom our great progenitor: "Thy words
Attentive, and with more delighted ear,
Divine instructor, I have heard, than when
Cherubic songs by night from neighboring hills
Aërial music send. Nor knew I not
To be, both will and deed, created free.
Yet that we never shall forget to love
Our Maker, and obey him whose command
Single is yet so just, my constant thoughts
Assured me, and still assure; though what thou tell'st
Hath passed in Heaven some doubt within me move,
But more desire to hear, if thou consent,
The full relation, which must needs be strange,
Worthy of sacred silence to be heard.
And we have yet large day, for scarce the Sun
Hath finished half his journey, and scarce begins
His other half in the great zone of heaven."

    Thus Adam made request; and Raphael,
After short pause assenting, thus began:

    "High matter thou enjoin'st me, O prime of Men—
Sad task and hard; for how shall I relate
To human sense th' invisible exploits
Of warring Spirits? how, without remorse,
The ruin of so many, glorious once
And perfect while they stood? how, last, unfold
The secrets of another world, perhaps
Not lawful to reveal? Yet for thy good
This is dispensed; and what surmounts the reach
Of human sense I shall delineate so,
By likening spiritual to corporal forms,
As may express them best—though what if Earth
Be but the shadow of Heaven, and things therein

Each to other like, more than on Earth is thought?
   "As yet this World was not, and Chaos wild
Reigned where these heavens now roll, where Earth now rests
Upon her center poised, when on a day
(For Time, though in Eternity, applied
To motion, measures all things durable
By present, past, and future), on such day
As Heaven's great year brings forth, th' empyreal host
Of Angels, by imperial summons called,
Innumerable before th' Almighty's throne
Forthwith from all the ends of Heaven appeared
Under their Hierarchs in Orders bright.
Ten thousand thousand ensigns high advanced,
Standards and gonfalons, 'twixt van and rear
Stream in the air, and for distinction serve
Of hierarchies, orders, and degrees;
Or in their glittering tissues bear emblazed
Holy memorials, acts of zeal and love
Recorded eminent. Thus when in orbs
Or circuit inexpressible they stood,
Orb within orb, the Father Infinite,
By whom in bliss embosomed sat the Son,
Amidst, as from a flaming mount, whose top
Brightness had made invisible, thus spake:
   " 'Hear, all ye Angels, Progeny of Light,
Thrones, Dominations, Princedoms, Virtues, Powers,
Hear my decree, which unrevoked shall stand!
This day I have begot whom I declare
My only Son, and on this holy hill
Him have anointed, whom ye now behold
At my right hand. Your head I him appoint.
And by myself have sworn to him shall bow
All knees in Heaven, and shall confess him Lord.
Under his great vicegerent reign abide,
United as one individual soul,
For ever happy. Him who disobeys
Me disobeys, breaks union, and, that day,
Cast out from God and blessèd vision, falls
Into utter darkness, deep engulfed, his place
Ordained without redemption, without end.'

"So spake th' Omnipotent, and with his words
All seemed well pleased; all seemed, but were not all.
That day, as other solemn days, they spent
In song and dance about the sacred hill—
Mystical dance, which yonder starry sphere
Of planets, and of fixed, in all her wheels
Resembles nearest; mazes intricate,
Eccentric, intervolved, yet regular
Then most when most irregular they seem;
And in their motions harmony divine
So smooths her charming tones that God's own ear
Listens delighted. Evening now approached
(For we have also our evening and our morn—
We ours for change delectable, not need),
Forthwith from dance to sweet repast they turn
Desirous: all in circles as they stood,
Tables are set, and on a sudden piled
With Angels' food; and rubied nectar flows
In pearl, in diamond, and massy gold,
Fruit of delicious vines, the growth of Heaven.
On flowers reposed, and with fresh flowerets crowned,
They eat, they drink, and in communion sweet
Quaff immortality and joy, secure
Of surfeit where full measure only bounds
Excess, before th' all-bounteous King, who showered
With copious hand, rejoicing in their joy.
Now when ambrosial Night, with clouds exhaled
From that high mount of God, whence light and shade
Spring both, the face of brightest Heaven had changed
To grateful twilight (for Night comes not there
In darker veil), and roseate dews disposed
All but the unsleeping eyes of God to rest,
Wide over all the plain, and wider far
Than all his globous Earth in plain outspread
(Such are the courts of God), th' angelic throng,
Dispersed in bands and files, their camp extend
By living streams among the trees of life—
Pavilions numberless and sudden reared,
Celestial tabernacles, where they slept,
Fanned with cool winds; save those who, in their course,

420

Melodious hymns about the sovereign throne
Alternate all night long. But not so waked
Satan—so call him now; his former name
Is heard no more in Heaven. He, of the first,
If not the first Archangel, great in power,
In favor, and pre-eminence, yet fraught
With envy against the Son of God, that day
Honored by his great Father, and proclaimed
Messiah, King Anointed, could not bear,
Through pride, that sight, and thought himself impaired.
Deep malice thence conceiving and disdain,
Soon as midnight brought on the dusky hour
Friendliest to sleep and silence, he resolved
With all his legions to dislodge, and leave
Unworshiped, unobeyed, the Throne supreme,
Contemptuous, and, his next subordinate *
Awakening, thus to him in secret spake:
    " 'Sleep'st thou, companion dear? what sleep can close
Thy eyelids? and rememb'rest what decree,
Of yesterday, so late hath passed the lips
Of Heaven's Almighty? Thou to me thy thoughts
Wast wont, I mine to thee was wont to impart;
Both waking we were one; how then can now
Thy sleep dissent? New laws thou seest imposed;
New laws from him who reigns new minds may raise
In us who serve—new counsels, to debate
What doubtful may ensue. More in this place
To utter is not safe. Assemble thou
Of all those myriads which we lead the chief;
Tell them that, by command, ere yet dim Night
Her shadowy cloud withdraws, I am to haste,
And all who under me their banners wave,
Homeward with flying march where we possess
The quarters of the North, there to prepare
Fit entertainment to receive our King,
The great Messiah, and his new commands,
Who speedily through all the Hierarchies
Intends to pass triumphant, and give laws.'
    "So spake the false Archangel, and infused

* Beëlzebub

421

Bad influence into th' unwary breast
Of his associate. He together calls,
Or several one by one, the regent Powers,
Under him regent; tells, as he was taught,
That, the Most High commanding, now ere Night,
Now ere dim Night had disencumbered Heaven,
The great hierarchal standard was to move;
Tells the suggested cause, and casts between
Ambiguous words and jealousies, to sound
Or taint integrity. But all obeyed
The wonted signal and superior voice
Of their great Potentate; for great indeed
His name, and high was his degree in Heaven:
His countenance, as the morning-star that guides
The starry flock, allured them, and with lies
Drew after him the third part of Heaven's host.
Meanwhile, th' Eternal Eye, whose sight discerns
Abstrusest thoughts, from forth his holy Mount,
And from within the golden lamps that burn
Nightly before him, saw without their light
Rebellion rising—saw in whom, how spread
Among the Sons of Morn, what multitudes
Were banded to oppose his high decree;
And, smiling, to his only Son thus said:
  " 'Son, thou in whom my glory I behold
In full resplendence, Heir of all my might,
Nearly it now concerns us to be sure
Of our omnipotence, and with what arms
We mean to hold what anciently we claim
Of deity or empire: such a foe
Is rising, who intends to erect his throne
Equal to ours, throughout the spacious North;
Nor so content, hath in his thought to try
In battle what our power is or our right.
Let us advise, and to this hazard draw
With speed what force is left, and all employ
In our defense, lest unawares we lose
This our high place, our sanctuary, our hill.'
  "To whom the Son, with calm aspéct and clear
Lightening divine, ineffable, serene,

Made answer: 'Mighty Father, thou thy foes
Justly hast in derision, and secure
Laugh'st at their vain designs and tumults vain—
Matter to me of glory, whom their hate
Illustrates, when they see all regal power
Given me to quell their pride, and in event
Know whether I be dextrous to subdue
Thy rebels, or be found the worst in Heaven.'
    "So spake the Son; but Satan with his Powers
Far was advanced on wingèd speed, an host
Innumerable as the stars of night,
Or stars of morning, dew-drops which the sun
Impearls on every leaf and every flower.
Regions they passed, the mighty regencies
Of Seraphim and Potentates and Thrones
In their triple degrees—regions to which
All thy dominion, Adam, is no more
Than what this garden is to all the earth
And all the sea, from one entire globose
Stretched into longitude; which having passed,
At length into the limits of the North
They came, and Satan to his royal seat
High on a hill, far blazing, as a mount
Raised on a mount, with pyramids and towers
From diamond quarries hewn and rocks of gold—
The palace of great Lucifer (so call
That structure, in the dialect of men
Interpreted) which, not long after, he,
Affecting all equality with God,
In imitation of that mount whereon
Messiah was declared in sight of Heaven,
The Mountain of the Congregation called;
For thither he assembled all his train,
Pretending so commanded to consult
About the great reception of their King
Thither to come, and with calumnious art
Of counterfeited truth thus held their ears:
    " 'Thrones, Dominations, Princedoms, Virtues, Powers—
If these magnific titles yet remain
Not merely titular, since by decree

Another now hath to himself engrossed
All power, and us eclipsed under the name
Of King Anointed; for whom all this haste
Of midnight march, and hurried meeting here,
This only to consult, how we may best,
With what may be devised of honors new,
Receive him coming to receive from us
Knee-tribute yet unpaid, prostration vile!
Too much to one! but double, how endured—
To one and to his image now proclaimed?
But what if better counsels might erect
Our minds, and teach us to cast off this yoke?
Will ye submit your necks, and choose to bend
The supple knee? Ye will not, if I trust
To know ye right, or if ye know yourselves
Natives and Sons of Heaven possessed before
By none, and, if not equal all, yet free,
Equally free; for orders and degrees
Jar not with liberty, but well consist.
Who can in reason, then, or right, assume
Monarchy over such as live by right
His equals—if in power and splendor less,
In freedom equal? or can introduce
Law and edict on us, who without law
Err not? much less for this to be our Lord,
And look for adoration, to th' abuse
Of those imperial titles which assert
Our being ordained to govern, not to serve!'
    "Thus far his bold discourse without control
Had audience, when, among the Seraphim,
Abdiel, than whom none with more zeal adored
The Deity, and divine commands obeyed,
Stood up, and in a flame of zeal severe
The current of his fury thus opposed:
    " 'O argument blasphémous, false, and proud—
Words which no ear ever to hear in Heaven
Expected; least of all from thee, ingrate,
In place thyself so high above thy peers!
Canst thou with impious obloquy condemn
The just decree of God, pronounced and sworn,

424

That to his only Son, by right endued
With regal scepter, every soul in Heaven
Shall bend the knee, and in that honor due
Confess him rightful King? Unjust, thou say'st,
Flatly unjust, to bind with laws the free,
And equal over equals to let reign,
One over all with unsucceeded power!
Shalt thou give law to God? shalt thou dispute
With him the points of liberty, who made
Thee what thou art, and formed the Powers of Heaven
Such as he pleased, and circumscribed their being?
Yet, by experience taught, we know how good,
And of our good and of our dignity
How provident, he is—how far from thought
To make us less; bent rather to exalt
Our happy state, under one head more near
United. But—to grant it thee unjust
That equal over equals monarch reign—
Thyself, though great and glorious, dost thou count,
Or all angelic nature joined in one,
Equal to him, begotten Son, by whom,
As by his Word, the mighty Father made
All things, even thee, and all the Spirits of Heaven
By him created in their bright degrees,
Crowned them with glory and to their glory named
Thrones, Dominations, Princedoms, Virtues, Powers?—
Essential Powers; nor by his reign obscured,
But more illustrious made since he, the head,
One of our number thus reduced becomes;
His laws our laws; all honor to him done
Returns our own. Cease, then, this impious rage,
And tempt not these; but hasten to appease
Th' incensèd Father and th'incensèd Son
While pardon may be found, in time besought.'
   "So spake the fervent Angel; but his zeal
None seconded, as out of season judged,
Or singular and rash. Whereat rejoiced
Th' Apostate, and, more haughty, thus replied:
   " 'That we were formed, then, say'st thou? and the work
Of secondary hands, by task transferred

425

From Father to his Son? Strange point and new!
Doctrine which we would know whence learned! Who saw
When this creation was? Remember'st thou
Thy making, while the Maker gave thee being?
We know no time when we were not as now;
Know none before us, self-begot, self-raised
By our own quickening power when fatal course
Had circled his full orb, the birth mature
Of this our native Heaven, ethereal Sons.
Our puissance is our own; our own right hand
Shall teach us highest deeds, by proof to try
Who is our equal. Then thou shalt behold
Whether by supplication we intend
Address, and to begirt th' Almighty Throne
Beseeching or besieging. This report,
These tidings, carry to th' Anointed King;
And fly, ere evil intercept thy flight.'
    "He said; and, as the sound of waters deep,
Hoarse murmur echoed to his words applause
Through the infinite host. Nor less for that
The flaming Seraph, fearless, though alone,
Encompassed round with foes, thus answered bold:
    " 'O alienate from God, O Spirit accursed,
Forsaken of all good! I see thy fall
Determined, and thy hapless crew involved
In this perfidious fraud, contagion spread
Both of thy crime and punishment. Henceforth
No more be troubled how to quit the yoke
Of God's Messiah. Those indulgent laws
Will not be now vouchsafed; other decrees
Against thee are gone forth without recall;
That golden scepter which thou didst reject
Is now an iron rod to bruise and break
Thy disobedience. Well thou didst advise;
Yet not for thy advice or threats I fly
These wicked tents devoted,* lest the wrath
Impendent, raging into sudden flame,
Distinguish not: for soon expect to feel
His thunder on thy head, devouring fire.
* Doomed

426

Then who created thee lamenting learn,
When who can uncreate thee thou shalt know.'
    "So spake the Seraph Abdiel, faithful found;
Among the faithless faithful only he;
Among innumerable false unmoved,
Unshaken, unseduced, unterrified,
His loyalty he kept, his love, his zeal;
Nor number nor example with him wrought
To swerve from truth, or change his constant mind,
Though single. From amidst them forth he passed,
Long way through hostile scorn, which he sustained
Superior, nor of violence feared aught;
And with retorted scorn his back he turned
On those proud towers, to swift destruction doomed."

BOOK VI

The Argument

Raphael continues to relate how Michael and Gabriel were sent forth
to battle against Satan and his Angels. The first fight described: Satan
and his Powers retire under night. He calls a council; invents devilish
engines, which, in the second day's fight, put Michael and his Angels
to some disorder; but they at length, pulling up mountains, overwhelmed both the force and machines of Satan. Yet, the tumult not so
ending, God, on the third day, sends Messiah his Son, for whom he
had reserved the glory of that victory. He, in the power of his Father,
coming to the place, and causing all his legions to stand still on either
side, with his chariot and thunder driving into the midst of his enemies,
pursues them, unable to resist, towards the wall of Heaven; which
opening, they leap down with horror and confusion into the place of
punishment prepared for them in the Deep. Messiah returns with triumph to his Father.

ALL NIGHT the dreadless Angel, unpursued,
    Through Heaven's wide champaign held his way, till **Morn**,
Waked by the circling Hours, with rosy hand
Unbarred the gates of Light. There is a cave
Within the Mount of God, fast by his throne,

Where Light and Darkness in perpetual round
Lodge and dislodge by turns—which makes through Heaven
Grateful vicissitude, like day and night;
Light issues forth, and at the other door
Obsequious Darkness enters, till her hour
To veil the heaven, though darkness there might well
Seem twilight here. And now went forth the Morn
Such as in highest heaven, arrayed in gold
Empyreal; from before her vanished Night,
Shot through with orient beams; when all the plain
Covered with thick embattled squadrons bright,
Chariots, and flaming arms, and fiery steeds,
Reflecting blaze on blaze, first met his view.
War he perceived, war in procinct,* and found
Already known what he for news had thought
To have reported. Gladly then he mixed
Among those friendly Powers, who him received
With joy and acclamations loud, that one,
That of so many myriads fallen yet one,
Returned not lost. On to the sacred hill
They led him, high applauded, and present
Before the seat supreme; from whence a voice,
From midst a golden cloud, thus mild was heard:
   " 'Servant of God, well done! Well hast thou fought
The better fight, who single hast maintained
Against revolted multitudes the cause
Of truth, in word mightier than they in arms,
And for the testimony of truth hast borne
Universal reproach, far worse to bear
Than violence; for this was all thy care—
To stand approved in sight of God, though worlds
Judged thee perverse. The easier conquest now
Remains thee—aided by this host of friends,
Back on thy foes more glorious to return
Than scorned thou didst depart; and to subdue
By force who reason for their law refuse—
Right reason for their law, and for their King
Messiah, who by right of merit reigns.
   Go, Michael, of celestial armies prince,

* Readiness

And thou, in military prowess next,
Gabriel; lead forth to battle these my sons
Invincible; lead forth my armèd Saints,
By thousands and by millions ranged for fight,
Equal in number to that godless crew
Rebellious. Them with fire and hostile arms
Fearless assault; and, to the brow of Heaven
Pursuing, drive them out from God and bliss
Into their place of punishment, the gulf
Of Tartarus, which ready opens wide
His fiery chaos to receive their fall.'
   "So spake the sovereign voice; and clouds began
To darken all the hill, and smoke to roll
In dusky wreaths reluctant flames, the sign
Of wrath awaked; nor with less dread the loud
Ethereal trumpet from on high gan blow.
At which command the Powers militant
That stood for Heaven, in mighty quadrate joined
Of union irresistible, moved on
In silence their bright legions to the sound
Of instrumental harmony, that breathed
Heroic ardor to adventurous deeds
Under their godlike leaders, in the cause
Of God and his Messiah. On they move,
Indissolubly firm; nor obvious * hill,
Nor straitening vale, nor wood, nor stream, divides
Their perfect ranks; for high above the ground
Their march was, and the passive air upbore
Their nimble tread. As when the total kind
Of birds, in orderly array on wing,
Came summoned over Eden to receive
Their names of thee; so over many a tract
Of Heaven they marched, and many a province wide,
Tenfold the length of this terrene. At last,
Far in th' horizon, to the north, appeared
From skirt to skirt a fiery region, stretched
In battailous aspéct; and, nearer view,
Bristled with upright beams innumerable
Of rigid spears, and helmets thronged, and shields

* Intervening

Various, with boastful argument portrayed,
The banded Powers of Satan hasting on
With furious expedition; for they weened
That self-same day, by fight or by surprise,
To win the Mount of God, and on his throne
To set the envier of his state, the proud
Aspirer. But their thoughts proved fond and vain
In the mid-way; though strange to us it seemed
At first that Angel should with Angel war,
And in fierce hosting meet, who wont to meet
So oft in festivals of joy and love
Unanimous, as sons of one great Sire,
Hymning th' Eternal Father. But the shout
Of battle now began, and rushing sound
Of onset ended soon each milder thought.
High in the midst, exalted as a God,
Th' Apostate in his sun-bright chariot sat,
Idol of majesty divine, enclosed
With flaming Cherubim and golden shields;
Then lighted from his gorgeous throne—for now
'Twixt host and host but narrow space was left,
A dreadful interval, and front to front
Presented stood, in terrible array
Of hideous length. Before the cloudy van,
On the rough edge of battle ere it joined,
Satan, with vast and haughty strides advanced,
Came towering, armed in adamant and gold.
Abdiel that sight endured not, where he stood
Among the mightiest, bent on highest deeds,
And thus his own undaunted heart explores:
    " 'O Heaven! that such resemblance of the Highest
Should yet remain, where faith and realty
Remain not! Wherefore should not strength and might
There fail where virtue fails, or weakest prove
Where boldest, though to sight unconquerable?
His puissance, trusting in th' Almighty's aid,
I mean to try, whose reason I have tried
Unsound and false; nor is it aught but just
That he who in debate of truth hath won
Should win in arms, in both disputes alike

430

Victor. Though brutish that contést and foul,
When reason hath to deal with force, yet so
Most reason is that reason overcome.'
   "So pondering, and from his armèd peers
Forth-stepping opposite, half-way he met
His daring foe, at this prevention more
Incensed, and thus securely him defied:
   " 'Proud, art thou met? Thy hope was to have reached
The height of thy aspiring unopposed—
The throne of God unguarded, and his side
Abandoned at the terror of thy power
Or potent tongue. Fool! not to think how vain
Against th' Omnipotent to rise in arms;
Who, out of smallest things, could without end
Have raised incessant armies to defeat
Thy folly; or with solitary hand,
Reaching beyond all limit, at one blow,
Unaided could have finished thee, and whelmed
Thy legions under darkness! But thou seest
All are not of thy train; there be who faith
Prefer, and piety to God, though then
To thee not visible when I alone
Seemed in thy world erroneous to dissent
From all: my sect thou seest; now learn too late
How few sometimes may know when thousands err.'
   "Whom the grand Foe, with scornful eye askance,
Thus answered: 'Ill for thee, but in wished hour
Of my revenge, first sought for, thou return'st
From flight, seditious Angel, to receive
Thy merited reward, the first assay
Of this right hand provoked, since first that tongue,
Inspired with contradiction, durst oppose
A third part of the gods, in synod met
Their deities to assert: who, while they feel
Vigor divine within them, can allow
Omnipotence to none. But well thou com'st
Before thy fellows, ambitious to win
From me some plume, that thy success may show
Destruction to the rest. This pause between
(Unanswered lest thou boast) to let thee know.

At first I thought that liberty and Heaven
To heavenly souls had been all one; but now
I see that most through sloth had rather serve,
Ministering Spirits, trained up in feast and song:
Such hast thou armed, the ministrelsy of heaven—
Servility with freedom to contend,
As both their deeds compared this day shall prove.'
 "To whom, in brief, thus Abdiel stern replied:
'Apostate! still thou err'st, nor end wilt find
Of erring, from the path of truth remote.
Unjustly thou deprav'st it with the name
Of servitude, to serve whom God ordains,
Or Nature: God and Nature bid the same,
When he who rules is worthiest, and excels
Them whom he governs. This is servitude—
To serve th' unwise, or him who hath rebelled
Against his worthier, as thine now serve thee,
Thyself not free, but to thyself enthralled;
Yet lewdly dar'st our ministering upbraid.
Reign thou in Hell, thy kingdom; let me serve
In Heaven God ever blest, and his divine
Behests obey, worthiest to be obeyed.
Yet chains in Hell, not realms, expect: meanwhile,
From me returned, as erst thou saidst, from flight,
This greeting on thy impious crest receive.'
 "So saying, a noble stroke he lifted high,
Which hung not, but so swift with tempest fell
On the proud crest of Satan that no sight,
Nor motion of swift thought, less could his shield,
Such ruin intercept. Ten paces huge
He back recoiled; the tenth on bended knee
His massy spear upstayed: as if, on earth,
Winds under ground, or waters forcing way,
Sidelong had pushed a mountain from his seat,
Half-sunk with all his pines. Amazement seized
The rebel Thrones, but greater rage, to see
Thus foiled their mightiest; ours joy filled, and shout,
Presage of victory, and fierce desire
Of battle: whereat Michaël bid sound
Th' Archangel trumpet. Through the vast of Heaven

432

It sounded, and the faithful armies rung
Hosanna to the Highest; nor stood at gaze
The adverse legions, nor less hideous joined
The horrid shock. Now storming fury rose,
And clamor such as heard in Heaven till now
Was never; arms on armor clashing brayed
Horrible discord, and the madding wheels
Of brazen chariots raged; dire was the noise
Of conflict; overhead the dismal hiss
Of fiery darts in flaming volleys flew,
And, flying, vaulted either host with fire.
So under fiery cope together rushed
Both battles main with ruinous assault
And inextinguishable rage. All Heaven
Resounded; and, had Earth been then, all Earth
Had to her center shook. What wonder, when
Millions of fierce encountering Angels fought
On either side, the least of whom could wield
These elements, and arm him with the force
Of all their regions? How much more of power
Army against army numberless to raise
Dreadful combustion warring, and disturb,
Though not destroy, their happy native seat;
Had not th' Eternal King Omnipotent
From his strong hold of Heaven high overruled
And limited their might, though numbered such
As each divided legion might have seemed
A numerous host, in strength each armèd hand
A legion; led in fight, yet leader seemed
Each warrior single as in chief; expert
When to advance, or stand, or turn the sway
Of battle, open when, and when to close
The ridges of grim war. No thought of flight,
None of retreat, no unbecoming deed
That argued fear; each on himself relied
As only in his arm the moment lay
Of victory. Deeds of eternal fame
Were done, but infinite; for wide was spread
That war, and various: sometimes on firm ground
A standing fight; then, soaring on main wing,

433

Tormented all the air; all air seemed then
Conflicting fire. Long time in even scale
The battle hung; till Satan, who that day
Prodigious power had shown, and met in arms
No equal, ranging through the dire attack
Of fighting Seraphim confused, at length
Saw where the sword of Michael smote, and felled
Squadrons at once: with huge two-handed sway
Brandished aloft, the horrid edge came down
Wide-wasting. Such destruction to withstand
He hasted, and opposed the rocky orb
Of tenfold adamant, his ample shield,
A vast circumference. At his approach
The great Archangel from his warlike toil
Surceased, and, glad, as hoping here to end
Intestine war in Heaven, the Arch-foe subdued,
Or captive dragged in chains, with hostile frown
And visage all inflamed, first thus began:
  " 'Author of evil, unknown till thy revolt,
Unnamed in Heaven, now plenteous as thou seest
These acts of hateful strife—hateful to all,
Though heaviest, by just measure, on thyself
And thy adherents—how hast thou disturbed
Heaven's blessed peace, and into Nature brought
Misery, uncreated till the crime
Of thy rebellion! how hast thou instilled
Thy malice into thousands, once upright
And faithful, now proved false! But think not here
To trouble holy rest; Heaven casts thee out
From all her confines; Heaven, the seat of bliss,
Brooks not the works of violence and war.
Hence, then, and Evil go with thee along,
Thy offspring, to the place of evil, Hell—
Thou and thy wicked crew! there mingle broils!
Ere this avenging sword begin thy doom,
Or some more sudden vengeance, winged from God,
Precipitate thee with augmented pain.'
  "So spake the Prince of Angels; to whom thus
The Adversary: 'Nor think thou with wind
Of airy threats to awe whom yet with deeds

434

Thou canst not. Hast thou turned the least of these
To flight—or, if to fall, but that they rise
Unvanquished—easier to transact with me
That thou shouldst hope, imperious, and with threats
To chase me hence? Err not that so shall end
The strife which thou call'st evil, but we style
The strife of glory; which we mean to win,
Or turn this Heaven itself into the Hell
Thou fablest; here, however, to dwell free,
If not to reign. Meanwhile, thy utmost force—
And join him named Almighty to thy aid—
I fly not, but have sought thee far and nigh.'
   "They ended parle,* and both addressed for fight
Unspeakable; for who, though with the tongue
Of Angels, can relate, or to what things
Liken on Earth conspicuous, that may lift
Human imagination to such height
Of godlike power? for likest gods they seemed,
Stood they or moved, in stature, motion, arms,
Fit to decide the empire of great Heaven.
Now waved their fiery swords, and in the air
Made horrid circles; two broad suns their shields
Blazed opposite, while Expectation stood
In horror; from each hand with speed retired,
Where erst was thickest fight, th' angelic throng,
And left large field, unsafe within the wind
Of such commotion: such as (to set forth
Great things by small) if, Nature's concord broke,
Among the constellations war were sprung,
Two planets, rushing from aspéct malign
Of fiercest opposition in mid sky,
Should combat, and their jarring spheres confound.
Together both, with next to almighty arm
Uplifted imminent, one stroke they aimed
That might determine, and not need repeat
As not of power, at once; nor odds appeared
In might or swift prevention. But the sword
Of Michael from the armory of God
Was given him tempered so, that neither keen

* Speech

Nor solid might resist that edge: it met
The sword of Satan, with steep force to smite
Descending, and in half cut sheer; nor stayed,
But, with swift wheel reverse, deep entering, shared *
All his right side. Then Satan first knew pain,
And writhed him to and fro convolved; so sore
The griding sword with discontinuous wound
Passed through him. But th' ethereal substance closed,
Not long divisible; and from the gash
A stream of nectarous humor issuing flowed
Sanguine, such as celestial Spirits may bleed,
And all his armor stained, erewhile so bright.
Forthwith, on all sides, to his aid was run
By Angels many and strong, who interposed
Defense, while others bore him on their shields
Back to his chariot where it stood retired
From off the files of war: there they him laid
Gnashing for anguish, and despite, and shame
To find himself not matchless, and his pride
Humbled by such rebuke, so far beneath
His confidence to equal God in power.
Yet soon he healed; for Spirits, that live throughout
Vital in every part—not, as frail Man,
In entrails, heart or head, liver or reins—
Cannot but by annihilating die;
Nor in their liquid texture mortal wound
Receive, no more than can the fluid air:
All heart they live, all head, all eye, all ear,
All intellect, all sense; and as they please
They limb themselves, and color, shape, or size
Assume, as likes them best, condense or rare.
  "Meanwhile, in other parts, like deeds deserved
Memorial, where the might of Gabriel fought,
And with fierce ensigns pierced the deep array
Of Moloch, furious king, who him defied,
And at his chariot-wheels to drag him bound
Threatened, nor from the Holy One of Heaven
Refrained his tongue blasphémous, but anon,
Down cloven to the waist, with shattered arms

* Cut

436

And uncouth pain fled bellowing. On each wing
Uriel and Raphaël his vaunting foe,
Though huge and in a rock of diamond armed,
Vanquished Adramelech and Asmadai,
Two potent Thrones, that to be less than Gods
Disdained, but meaner thoughts learned in their flight,
Mangled with ghastly wounds through plate and mail.
Nor stood unmindful Abdiel to annoy
The atheist crew, but with redoubled blow
Ariel, and Arioch, and the violence
Of Ramiel, scorched and blasted, overthrew.
I might relate of thousands, and their names
Eternize here on Earth; but those elect
Angels, contented with their fame in Heaven,
Seek not the praise of men: the other sort,
In might though wondrous and in acts of war,
Nor of renown less eager, yet by doom
Canceled from Heaven and sacred memory,
Nameless in dark oblivion let them dwell.
For strength from truth divided, and from just,
Illaudable, nought merits but dispraise
And ignominy, yet to glory aspires,
Vain-glorious, and through infamy seeks fame:
Therefore eternal silence be their doom.
    "And now, their mightiest quelled, the battle swerved,
With many an inroad gored; deformèd rout
Entered, and foul disorder; all the ground
With shivered armor strewn, and on a heap
Chariot and charioteer lay overturned,
And fiery foaming steeds; what stood recoiled,
O'er-wearied, through the faint Satanic host,
Defensive scarce, or with pale fear surprised—
Then first with fear surprised and sense of pain—
Fled ignominious, to such evil brought
By sin of disobedience, till that hour
Not liable to fear, or flight, or pain.
Far otherwise th' inviolable Saints
In cubic phalanx firm advanced entire,
Invulnerable, impenetrably armed;
Such high advantages their innocence

437

Gave them above their foes—not to have sinned,
Not to have disobeyed; in fight they stood
Unwearied, unobnoxious to be pained
By wound, though from their place by violence moved."

[*Having lost the first day's battle, Satan proposes that his forces use gunpowder and cannon, which he has just invented. They do so, wreak tremendous havoc on the good angels, and rejoice over their success.*]

"So they among themselves in pleasant vein
Stood scoffing, heightened in their thoughts beyond
All doubt of victory; Eternal Might
To match with their inventions they presumed
So easy, and of his thunder made a scorn,
And all his host derided, while they stood
A while in trouble. But they stood not long;
Rage prompted them at length, and found them arms
Against such hellish mischief fit to oppose.
Forthwith (behold the excellence, the power,
Which God hath in his mighty Angels placed!)
Their arms away they threw, and to the hills
(For Earth hath this variety from Heaven
Of pleasure situate in hill and dale)
Light as the lightning-glimpse they ran, they flew;
From their foundations, loosening to and fro,
They plucked the seated hills, with all their load,
Rocks, waters, woods, and, by the shaggy tops
Uplifting, bore them in their hands. Amaze,
Be sure, and terror, seized the rebel host,
When coming towards them so dread they saw
The bottom of the mountains upward turned,
Till on those cursèd engines' triple row
They saw them whelmed, and all their confidence
Under the weight of mountains buried deep;
Themselves invaded next, and on their heads
Main promontories flung, which in the air
Came shadowing, and oppressed whole legions armed.
Their armor helped their harm, crushed in and bruised,
Into their substance pent—which wrought them pain

Implacable, and many a dolorous groan,
Long struggling underneath, ere they could wind
Out of such prison, though Spirits of purest light,
Purest at first, now gross by sinning grown.
The rest, in imitation, to like arms
Betook them, and the neighboring hills uptore;
So hills amid the air encountered hills,
Hurled to and fro with jaculation dire,
That underground they fought in dismal shade:
Infernal noise! war seemed a civil game
To this uproar; horrid confusion heaped
Upon confusion rose. And now all Heaven
Had gone to wrack, with ruin overspread,
Had not th' Almighty Father, where he sits
Shrined in his sanctuary of Heaven secure,
Consulting on the sum of things, foreseen
This tumult, and permitted all, advised,
That his great purpose he might so fulfil,
To honor his anointed Son, avenged
Upon his enemies, and to declare
All power on him transferred."

[*The Son of God, riding in a mystic chariot and armed with the glorious majesty of almighty wrath, crushes the army of rebellious angels and drives it over the ramparts of Heaven.*]

BOOK VII

The Argument

Raphael, at the request of Adam, relates how and wherefore this World was first created: that God, after the expelling of Satan and his Angels out of Heaven, declared his pleasure to create another World, and other creatures to dwell therein; sends his Son with glory, and attendance of Angels, to perform the work of creation in six days: the Angels celebrate with hymns the performance thereof, and his reascension into Heaven.

John Milton

BOOK VIII

The Argument

Adam inquires concerning celestial motions; is doubtfully answered, and exhorted to search rather things more worthy of knowledge. Adam assents, and, still desirous to detain Raphael, relates to him what he remembered since his own creation—his placing in Paradise; his talk with God concerning solitude and fit society; his first meeting and nuptials with Eve. His discourse with the Angel thereupon; who, after admonitions repeated, departs.

BOOK IX

The Argument

Satan, having compassed the Earth, with meditated guile returns as a mist by night into Paradise; enters into the Serpent sleeping. Adam and Eve in the morning go forth to their labors, which Eve proposes to divide in several places, each laboring apart: Adam consents not, alleging the danger lest that enemy of whom they were forewarned should attempt her found alone. Eve, loath to be thought not circumspect or firm enough, urges her going apart, the rather desirous to make trial of her strength; Adam at last yields. The Serpent finds her alone: his subtle approach, first gazing, then speaking, with much flattery extoling Eve above all other creatures. Eve, wondering to hear the Serpent speak, asks how he attained to human speech and such understanding not till now; the Serpent answers that by tasting of a certain tree in the garden he attained both to speech and reason, till then void of both. Eve requires him to bring her to that tree, and finds it to be the Tree of Knowledge forbidden: the Serpent, now grown bolder, with many wiles and arguments induces her at length to eat. She, pleased with the taste, deliberates a while whether to impart thereof to Adam or not; at last brings him of the fruit; relates what persuaded her to eat thereof. Adam, at first amazed, but perceiving her lost, resolves, through vehemence of love, to perish with her, and, extenuating the trespass, eats also of the fruit. The effects thereof in them both; they seek to cover their nakedness; then fall to variance and accusation of one another.

440

N<small>O MORE OF</small> talk where God or Angel Guest
With Man, as with his friend, familiar used
To sit indulgent, and with him partake
Rural repast, permitting him the while
Venial discourse unblamed. I now must change
Those notes to tragic—foul distrust, and breach
Disloyal, on the part of man, revolt
And disobedience; on the part of Heaven,
Now alienated, distance and distaste,
Anger and just rebuke, and judgment given,
That brought into this World a world of woe,
Sin and her shadow Death, and Misery,
Death's harbinger. Sad task! yet argument
Not less but more heroic than the wrath
Of stern Achilles on his foe pursued
Thrice fugitive about Troy wall; or rage
Of Turnus for Lavinia disespoused;
Or Neptune's ire, or Juno's, that so long
Perplexed the Greek, and Cytherea's son:
If answerable style I can obtain
Of my celestial Patroness, who deigns
Her nightly visitation unimplored,
And dictates to me slumbering, or inspires
Easy my unpremeditated verse,
Since first this subject for heroic song
Pleased me, long choosing and beginning late,
Not sedulous by nature to indite
Wars, hitherto the only argument
Heroic deemed, chief mastery to dissect
With long and tedious havoc fabled knights
In battles feigned (the better fortitude
Of patience and heroic martyrdom
Unsung), or to describe races and games,
Or tilting furniture,* emblazoned shields,
Impreses † quaint, caparisons and steeds,
Bases ‡ and tinsel trappings, gorgeous knights
At joust and tournament; then marshaled feast

* A knight's equipment
† Devices
‡ Coverings for chargers

Served up in hall with sewers and seneschals:
The skill of artifice or office mean;
Not that which justly gives heroic name
To person or to poem. Me, of these
Nor skilled nor studious, higher argument
Remains, sufficient of itself to raise
That name, unless an age too late, or cold
Climate, or years, damp my intended wing
Depressed; and much they may if all be mine,
Not hers who brings it nightly to my ear.
　　The Sun was sunk, and after him the Star
Of Hesperus, whose office is to bring
Twilight upon the Earth, short arbiter
'Twixt day and night, and now from end to end
Night's hemisphere had veiled the horizon round,
When Satan, who late fled before the threats
Of Gabriel out of Eden, now improved
In meditated fraud and malice, bent
On Man's destruction, maugre what might hap
Of heavier on himself, fearless returned.
By night he fled, and at midnight returned
From compassing the Earth—cautious of day
Since Uriel, Regent of the Sun, descried
His entrance, and forewarned the Cherubim
That kept their watch. Thence, full of anguish, driven,
The space of seven continued nights he rode
With darkness—thrice the equinoctial line
He circled, four times crossed the car of Night
From pole to pole, traversing each colure—
On the eighth returned, and on the coast averse
From entrance or cherubic watch by stealth
Found unsuspected way. There was a place
(Now not, though Sin, not Time, first wrought the change)
Where Tigris, at the foot of Paradise,
Into a gulf shot under ground, till part
Rose up a fountain by the Tree of Life.
In with the river sunk, and with it rose,
Satan, involved in rising mist; then sought
Where to lie hid. Sea he had searched and land
From Eden over Pontus, and the Pool

Maeotis, up beyond the river Ob;
Downward as far antarctic; and, in length,
West from Orontes to the ocean barred
At Darien, thence to the land where flows
Ganges and Indus. Thus the orb he roamed
With narrow search, and with inspection deep
Considered every creature, which of all
Most opportune might serve his wiles, and found
The Serpent subtlest beast of all the field.
Him, after long debate, irresolute
Of thoughts revolved, his final sentence chose
Fit vessel, fittest imp of fraud, in whom
To enter, and his dark suggestions hide
From sharpest sight; for in the wily snake
Whatever sleights none would suspicious mark,
As from his wit and native subtlety
Proceeding, which, in other beasts observed,
Doubt might beget of diabolic power
Active within beyond the sense of brute.
Thus he resolved, but first from inward grief
His bursting passion into plaints thus poured. . . .

[*After declaring his open hatred of God and Man in a long soliloquy, Satan finds the serpent and enters into his spirit. The next morning Eve decides that for this one day she will work at a distance from Adam. He tries to discourage her, but she insists and he allows her to follow her own desire.*]

Thus saying, from her husband's hand her hand
Soft she withdrew, and, like a wood-nymph light,
Oread or Dryad, or of Delia's train,
Betook her to the groves, but Delia's self
In gait surpassed and goddess-like deport,
Though not as she with bow and quiver armed,
But with such gardening tools as Art, yet rude,
Guiltless of fire had formed, or Angels brought.
To Pales, or Pomona, thus adorned,
Likest she seemed—Pomona when she fled
Vertumnus—or to Ceres in her prime,
Yet virgin of Proserpina from Jove.

443

Her long with ardent look his eye pursued
Delighted, but desiring more her stay.
Oft he to her his charge of quick return
Repeated; she to him as oft engaged
To be returned by noon amid the bower,
And all things in best order to invite
Noontide repast, or afternoon's repose.
O much deceived, much failing, hapless Eve,
Of thy presumed return! event perverse!
Thou never from that hour in Paradise
Found'st either sweet repast or sound repose:
Such ambush, hid among sweet flowers and shades,
Waited, with hellish rancor imminent,
To intercept thy way, or send thee back
Despoiled of innocence, of faith, of bliss.
For now, and since first break of dawn, the Fiend,
Mere serpent in appearance, forth was come,
And on his quest where likeliest he might find
The only two of mankind, but in them
The whole included race, his purposed prey.
In bower and field he sought, where any tuft
Of grove or garden-plot more pleasant lay,
Their tendance or plantation for delight;
By fountain or by shady rivulet
He sought them both, but wished his hap might find
Eve separate; he wished, but not with hope
Of what so seldom chanced, when to his wish,
Beyond his hope, Eve separate he spies,
Veiled in a cloud of fragrance, where she stood,
Half-spied, so thick the roses bushing round
About her glowed, oft stooping to support
Each flower of tender stalk, whose head, though gay
Carnation, purple, azure, or specked with gold,
Hung drooping unsustained. Them she upstays
Gently with myrtle band, mindless the while
Herself, though fairest unsupported flower,
From her best prop so far, and storm so nigh.
Nearer he drew, and many a walk traversed
Of stateliest covert, cedar, pine, or palm;
Then voluble and bold, now hid, now seen

Among thick-woven arborets, and flowers
Embordered on each bank, the hand of Eve:
Spot more delicious than those gardens feigned
Or of revived Adonis, or renowned
Alcinoüs, host of old Laertes' son,
Or that, not mystic, where the sapient king
Held dalliance with his fair Egyptian spouse.
Much he the place admired, the person more.
As one who, long in populous city pent,
Where houses thick and sewers annoy the air,
Forth issuing on a summer's morn, to breathe
Among the pleasant villages and farms
Adjoined, from each thing met conceives delight—
The smell of grain, or tedded grass, or kine,
Or dairy, each rural sight, each rural sound—
If chance with nymph-like step fair virgin pass,
What pleasing seemed, for her now pleases more,
She most, and in her look sums all delight:
Such pleasure took the Serpent to behold
This flowery plat, the sweet recess of Eve
Thus early, thus alone. Her heavenly form
Angelic, but more soft and feminine,
Her graceful innocence, her every air
Of gesture or least action, overawed
His malice, and with rapine sweet bereaved
His fierceness of the fierce intent it brought.
That space the Evil One abstracted stood
From his own evil, and for the time remained
Stupidly good, of enmity disarmed,
Of guile, of hate, of envy, of revenge.
But the hot hell that always in him burns,
Though in mid Heaven, soon ended his delight
And tortures him now more, the more he sees
Of pleasure not for him ordained. Then soon
Fierce hate he recollects, and all his thoughts
Of mischief, gratulating, thus excites:
    "Thoughts, whither have ye led me? with what sweet
Compulsion thus transported to forget
What hither brought us? hate, not love, nor hope
Of Paradise for Hell, hope her to taste

Of pleasure, but all pleasure to destroy,
Save what is in destroying; other joy
To me is lost. Then let me not let pass
Occasion which now smiles. Behold alone
The Woman, opportune to all attempts;
Her husband, for I view far round, not nigh,
Whose higher intellectual more I shun,
And strength, of courage haughty, and of limb
Heroic built, though of terrestrial mold;
Foe not informidable, exempt from wound—
I not; so much hath Hell debased, and pain
Enfeebled me, to what I was in Heaven.
She fair, divinely fair, fit love for Gods,
Not terrible, though terror be in love,
And beauty, not approached by stronger hate,
Hate stronger under show of love well feigned,
The way which to her ruin now I tend."
    So spake the Enemy of Mankind, enclosed
In serpent, inmate bad, and toward Eve
Addressed his way—not with indented wave,
Prone on the ground, as since, but on his rear,
Circular base of rising folds, that towered
Fold above fold, a surging maze; his head
Crested aloft, and carbuncle his eyes;
With burnished neck of verdant gold, erect
Amidst his circling spires, that on the grass
Floated redundant. Pleasing was his shape
And lovely; never since of serpent kind
Lovelier—not those that in Illyria changed
Hermione and Cadmus, or the god
In Epidaurus: nor to which transformed
Ammonian Jove, or Capitoline, was seen,
He with Olympias, this with her who bore
Scipio, the height of Rome. With tract oblique
At first, as one, who sought access but feared
To interrupt, sidelong he works his way.
As when a ship, by skillful steersman wrought
Nigh river's mouth, or foreland, where the wind
Veers oft, as oft so steers, and shifts her sail,
So varied he, and of his tortuous train

446

Curled many a wanton wreath in sight of Eve,
To lure her eye. She, busied, heard the sound
Of rustling leaves, but minded not, as used
To such disport before her through the field
From every beast, more duteous at her call
Than at Circean call the herd disguised.
He, bolder now, uncalled before her stood,
But as in gaze admiring. Oft he bowed
His turret crest and sleek enameled neck,
Fawning, and licked the ground whereon she trod.
His gentle dumb expression turned at length
The eye of Eve to mark his play; he, glad
Of her attention gained, with serpent-tongue
Organic, or impulse of vocal air,
His fraudulent temptation thus began:
    "Wonder not, sovereign mistress (if perhaps
Thou canst who art sole wonder), much less arm
Thy looks, the heaven of mildness, with disdain,
Displeased that I approach thee thus, and gaze
Insatiate, I thus single, nor have feared
Thy awful brow, more awful thus retired.
Fairest resemblance of thy Maker fair,
Thee all things living gaze on, all things thine
By gift, and thy celestial beauty adore,
With ravishment beheld—there best beheld
Where universally admired. But here,
In this enclosure wild, these beasts among,
Beholders rude, and shallow to discern
Half what in thee is fair, one man except,
Who sees thee (and what is one?) who shouldst be seen
A Goddess among Gods, adored and served
By Angels numberless, thy daily train?"
So glozed the Tempter, and his proem tuned.
Into the heart of Eve his words made way,
Though at the voice much marveling; at length,
Not unamazed, she thus in answer spake:
    "What may this mean? Language of Man pronounced
By tongue of brute, and human sense expressed!
The first at least of these I thought denied
To beasts, whom God on their creation-day

447

Created mute to all articulate sound;
The latter I demur, for in their looks
Much reason, and in their actions, oft appears.
Thee, Serpent, subtlest beast of all the field
I knew, but not with human voice endued;
Redouble then this miracle, and say,
How cam'st thou speakable of mute, and how
To me so friendly grown above the rest
Of brutal kind that daily are in sight:
Say, for such wonder claims attention due."
    To whom the guileful Tempter thus replied:
"Empress of this fair World, resplendent Eve!
Easy to me it is to tell thee all
What thou command'st, and right thou shouldst be obeyed.
I was at first as other beasts that graze
The trodden herb, of abject thoughts and low,
As was my food, nor aught but food discerned
Or sex, and apprehended nothing high:
Till on a day, roving the field, I chanced
A goodly tree far distant to behold,
Loaden with fruit of fairest colors mixed,
Ruddy and gold. I nearer drew to gaze;
When from the boughs a savory odor blown,
Grateful to appetite, more pleased my sense
Than smell of sweetest fennel, or the teats
Of ewe or goat dropping with milk at even,
Unsucked of lamb or kid, that tend their play.
To satisfy the sharp desire I had
Of tasting those fair apples, I resolved
Not to defer; hunger and thirst at once,
Powerful persuaders, quickened at the scent
Of that alluring fruit, urged me so keen.
About the mossy trunk I wound me soon;
For, high from ground, the branches would require
Thy utmost reach, or Adam's: round the tree
All other beasts that saw, with like desire
Longing and envying stood, but could not reach.
Amid the tree now got, where plenty hung
Tempting so nigh, to pluck and eat my fill
I spared not; for such pleasure till that hour

At feed or fountain never had I found.
Sated at length, ere long I might perceive
Strange alteration in me, to degree
Of reason in my inward powers, and speech
Wanted not long, though to this shape retained.
Thenceforth to speculations high or deep
I turned my thoughts, and with capacious mind
Considered all things visible in Heaven,
Or Earth, or Middle, all things fair and good.
But all that fair and good in thy divine
Semblance and in thy beauty's heavenly ray,
United I beheld—no fair to thine
Equivalent or second; which compelled
Me thus, though importune perhaps, to come
And gaze, and worship thee of right declared
Sovereign of creatures, universal Dame!"
   So talked the spirited sly Snake; and Eve,
Yet more amazed, unwary thus replied:
   "Serpent, thy overpraising leaves in doubt
The virtue of that fruit, in thee first proved.
But say, where grows the tree? from hence how far?
For many are the trees of God that grow
In Paradise, and various, yet unknown
To us; in such abundance lies our choice
As leaves a greater store of fruit untouched,
Still hanging incorruptible, till men
Grow up to their provision, and more hands
Help to disburden Nature of her bearth."
   To whom the wily Adder, blithe and glad:
"Empress, the way is ready, and not long—
Beyond a row of myrtles, on a flat,
Fast by a fountain, one small thicket past
Of blowing myrrh and balm. If thou accept
My conduct, I can bring thee thither soon."
   "Lead, then," said Eve. He, leading, swiftly rolled
In tangles, and made intricate seem straight,
To mischief swift. Hope elevates, and joy
Brightens his crest. As when a wandering fire,
Compact of unctuous vapor, which the night
Condenses, and the cold environs round,

Kindled through agitation to a flame
(Which oft, they say, some evil spirit attends),
Hovering and blazing with delusive light,
Misleads th' amazed night-wanderer from his way
To bogs and mires, and oft through pond or pool,
There swallowed up and lost, from succor far:
So glistered the dire Snake, and into fraud
Led Eve, our credulous mother, to the Tree
Of Prohibition, root of all our woe;
Which when she saw, thus to her guide she spake:
   "Serpent, we might have spared our coming hither,
Fruitless to me, though fruit be here to excess,
The credit of whose virtue rest with thee—
Wondrous indeed, if cause of such effects!
But of this tree we may not taste or touch;
God so commanded, and left that command
Sole daughter of his voice: for rest, we live
Law to ourselves; our reason is our law."
   To whom the Tempter guilefully replied:
   "Indeed! Hath God then said that of the fruit
Of all these garden-trees ye shall not eat,
Yet lords declared of all in earth or air?"
   To whom thus Eve, yet sinless: "Of the fruit
Of each tree in the garden we may eat;
But of the fruit of this fair tree, amidst
The garden, God hath said, 'Ye shall not eat
Thereof, nor shall ye touch it, lest ye die.' "
She scarce had said, though brief, when now more bold
The Tempter, but with show of zeal and love
To Man, and indignation at his wrong,
New part puts on, and, as to passion moved,
Fluctuates disturbed, yet comely, and in act
Raised, as of some great matter to begin.
As when of old some orator renowned
In Athens or free Rome, where eloquence
Flourished, since mute, to some great cause addressed,
Stood in himself collected, while each part,
Motion, each act, won audience ere the tongue
Sometimes in height began, as no delay
Of preface brooking through his zeal of right:

So standing, moving, or to height upgrown,
The Tempter, all impassioned, thus began:
   "O sacred, wise, and wisdom-giving Plant,
Mother of science! now I feel thy power
Within me clear, not only to discern
Things in their causes, but to trace the ways
Of highest agents, deemed however wise.
Queen of this Universe! do not believe
Those rigid threats of death. Ye shall not die.
How should ye? By the fruit? it gives you life
To knowledge. By the Threatener? look on me,
Me who have touched and tasted, yet both live,
And life more perfect have attained than Fate
Meant me, by venturing higher than my lot.
Shall that be shut to Man which to the beast
Is open? or will God incense his ire
For such a petty trespass, and not praise
Rather your dauntless virtue, whom the pain
Of death denounced, whatever thing Death be,
Deterred not from achieving what might lead
To happier life, knowledge of good and evil?
Of good, how just? of evil—if what is evil
Be real, why not known, since easier shunned?
God therefore cannot hurt ye, and be just;
Not just, not God; not feared then, nor obeyed;
Your fear itself of death removes the fear.
Why, then, was this forbid? Why but to awe,
Why but to keep ye low and ignorant,
His worshipers? He knows that in the day
Ye eat thereof your eyes, that seem so clear,
Yet are but dim, shall perfectly be then
Opened and cleared, and ye shall be as Gods,
Knowing both good and evil, as they know.
That ye should be as Gods, since I as Man,
Internal Man, is but proportion meet—
I, of brute, human; ye, of human, Gods.
So ye shall die perhaps, by putting off
Human, to put on Gods—death to be wished,
Though threatened, which no worse than this can bring!
And what are Gods, that Man may not become

As they, participating godlike food?
The Gods are first, and that advantage use
On our belief, that all from them proceeds.
I question it; for this fair Earth I see,
Warmed by the Sun, producing every kind;
Them nothing. If they all things, who enclosed
Knowledge of good and evil in this tree,
That whoso eats thereof forthwith attains
Wisdom without their leave? and wherein lies
Th' offense, that Man should thus attain to know?
What can your knowledge hurt him, or this tree
Impart against his will, if all be his?
Or is it envy? and can envy dwell
In heavenly breasts? These, these and many more
Causes import * your need of this fair fruit.
Goddess humane, reach, then, and freely taste!"
 He ended; and his words, replete with guile,
Into her heart too easy entrance won.
Fixed on the fruit she gazed, which to behold
Might tempt alone; and in her ears the sound
Yet rung of his persuasive words, impregned †
With reason, to her seeming, and with truth.
Meanwhile the hour of noon drew on, and waked
An eager appetite, raised by the smell
So savory of that fruit, which with desire,
Inclinable now grown to touch or taste,
Solicited her longing eye; yet first,
Pausing a while, thus to herself she mused:
 "Great are thy virtues, doubtless, best of fruits,
Though kept from Man, and worthy to be admired,
Whose taste, too long forborne, at first assay
Gave elocution to the mute, and taught
The tongue not made for speech to speak thy praise.
Thy praise he also who forbids thy use
Conceals not from us, naming thee the Tree
Of Knowledge, knowledge both of good and evil;
Forbids us then to taste. But his forbidding
Commends thee more, while it infers the good

* Prove
† Filled

452

By thee communicated, and our want;
For good unknown sure is not had, or, had
And yet unknown, is as not had at all.
In plain, then, what forbids he but to know?
Forbids us good, forbids us to be wise!
Such prohibitions bind not. But, if Death
Bind us with after-bands, what profits then
Our inward freedom? In the day we eat
Of this fair fruit, our doom is we shall die!
How dies the Serpent? He hath eaten, and lives,
And knows, and speaks, and reasons, and discerns,
Irrational till then. For us alone
Was death invented? or to us denied
This intellectual food, for beasts reserved?
For beasts it seems; yet that one beast which first
Hath tasted envies not, but brings with joy
The good befallen him, author unsuspect,
Friendly to Man, far from deceit or guile.
What fear I, then? rather, what know to fear
Under this ignorance of good and evil,
Of God or Death, of law or penalty?
Here grows the cure of all, this fruit divine,
Fair to the eye, inviting to the taste,
Of virtue to make wise. What hinders, then,
To reach, and feed at once both body and mind?"
  So saying, her rash hand in evil hour
Forth-reaching to the fruit, she plucked, she eat.
Earth felt the wound, and Nature from her seat,
Sighing through all her works, gave signs of woe
That all was lost. Back to the thicket slunk
The guilty Serpent, and well might, for Eve,
Intent now wholly on her taste, naught else
Regarded; such delight till then, as seemed,
In fruit she never tasted, whether true,
Or fancied so through expectation high
Of knowledge; nor was Godhead from her thought.
Greedily she ingorged without restraint,
And knew not eating death. Satiate at length,
And heightened as with wine, jocund and boon,*

* Jolly

Thus to herself she pleasingly began:
   "O sovereign, virtuous, precious of all trees
In Paradise! of operation blest
To sapience, hitherto obscured, infamed,
And thy fair fruit let hang, as to no end
Created! but henceforth my early care,
Not without song, each morning, and due praise,
Shall tend thee, and the fertile burden ease
Of thy full branches, offered free to all;
Till, dieted by thee, I grow mature
In knowledge, as the Gods who all things know.
Though others envy what they cannot give—
For, had the gift been theirs, it had not here
Thus grown! Experience, next to thee I owe,
Best guide: not following thee, I had remained
In ignorance; thou open'st Wisdom's way,
And giv'st access, though secret she retire.
And I perhaps am secret: Heaven is high—
High, and remote to see from thence distinct
Each thing on Earth; and other care perhaps
May have diverted from continual watch
Our great Forbidder, safe with all his spies
About him. But to Adam in what sort
Shall I appear? Shall I to him make known
As yet my change, and give him to partake
Full happiness with me, or rather not,
But keep the odds of knowledge in my power
Without copartner? so to add what wants
In female sex, the more to draw his love,
And render me more equal, and perhaps—
A thing not undesirable—sometime
Superior; for, inferior, who is free?
This may be well; but what if God have seen,
And death ensue? Then I shall be no more;
And Adam, wedded to another Eve,
Shall live with her enjoying, I extinct!
A death to think! Confirmed, then, I resolve
Adam shall share with me in bliss or woe.
So dear I love him that with him all deaths
I could endure, without him live no life."

454

So saying, from the tree her step she turned,
But first low reverence done, as to the Power
That dwelt within, whose presence had infused
Into the plant sciential sap, derived
From nectar, drink of Gods.

[*Having paid a reverence to the fatal tree, and so added the sin of idolatry to her other misdeeds, Eve hastens to pick another apple, to present to Adam. He has already started out to find her, carrying a garland of flowers, and she tells him immediately of the wonderful discovery she has made.*]

Thus Eve with countenance blithe her story told;
But in her cheek distemper flushing glowed.
On th' other side, Adam, soon as he heard
The fatal trespass done by Eve, amazed,
Astonied stood and blank, while horror chill
Ran through his veins, and all his joints relaxed.
From his slack hand the garland wreathed for Eve
Down dropped, and all the faded roses shed.
Speechless he stood and pale, till thus at length
First to himself he inward silence broke:
"O fairest of creation, last and best
Of all God's works, creature in whom excelled
Whatever can to sight or thought be formed,
Holy, divine, good, amiable, or sweet!
How art thou lost! how on a sudden lost,
Defaced, deflowered, and now to death devote!
Rather, how hast thou yielded to transgress
The strict forbiddance, how to violate
The sacred fruit forbidden? Some cursèd fraud
Of enemy hath beguiled thee, yet unknown,
And me with thee hath ruined; for with thee
Certain my resolution is to die.
How can I live without thee; how forego
Thy sweet converse, and love so dearly joined,
To live again in these wild woods forlorn?
Should God create another Eve, and I
Another rib afford, yet loss of thee
Would never from my heart. No, no! I feel

455

The link of nature draw me: flesh of flesh,
Bone of my bone thou art, and from thy state
Mine never shall be parted, bliss or woe."
   So having said, as one from sad dismay
Recomforted, and, after thoughts disturbed,
Submitting to what seemed remediless,
Thus in calm mood his words to Eve he turned:
   "Bold deed thou hast presumed, adventurous Eve,
And peril great provoked, who thus hast dared
Had it been only coveting to eye
That sacred food, sacred to abstinence;
Much more to taste it, under ban to touch.
But past who can recall, or done undo?
Not God Omnipotent, nor Fate! Yet so
Perhaps thou shalt not die; perhaps the fact
Is not so heinous now—foretasted fruit,
Profaned first by the Serpent, by him first
Made common and unhallowed ere your taste,
Nor yet on him found deadly. He yet lives—
Lives, as thou saidst, and gains to live, as Man,
Higher degree of life: inducement strong
To us, as likely, tasting, to attain
Proportional ascent; which cannot be
But to be Gods, or Angels, demigods.
Nor can I think that God, Creator wise,
Though threatening, will in earnest so destroy
Us, his prime creatures, dignified so high,
Set over all his works; which, in our fall,
For us created, needs with us must fail,
Dependent made. So God shall uncreate,
Be frustrate, do, undo, and labor lose—
Not well conceived of God; who, though his power
Creation could repeat, yet would be loath
Us to abolish, lest the Adversary
Triumph and say: 'Fickle their state whom God
Most favors; who can please him long? Me first
He ruined, now Mankind; whom will he next?'—
Matter of scorn not to be given the Foe.
However, I with thee have fixed my lot,
Certain to undergo like doom. If death

Consort with thee, death is to me as life;
So forcible within my heart I feel
The bond of Nature draw me to my own—
My own in thee; for what thou art is mine.
Our state cannot be severed; we are one,
One flesh; to lose thee were to lose myself."
    So Adam; and thus Eve to him replied:
"O glorious trial of exceeding love,
Illustrious evidence, example high!
Engaging me to emulate; but, short
Of thy perfection, how shall I attain,
Adam? from whose dear side I boast me sprung,
And gladly of our union hear thee speak,
One heart, one soul in both; whereof good proof
This day affords, declaring thee resolved,
Rather than death, or aught than death more dread,
Shall separate us, linked in love so dear,
To undergo with me one guilt, one crime,
If any be, of tasting this fair fruit;
Whose virtue (for of good still good proceeds,
Direct, or by occasion) hath presented
This happy trial of thy love, which else
So eminently never had been known.
Were it I thought death menaced would ensue
This my attempt, I would sustain alone
The worst, and not persuade thee—rather die
Deserted than oblige thee with a fact
Pernicious to thy peace, chiefly assured
Remarkably so late of thy so true,
So faithful, love unequaled. But I feel
Far otherwise th' event—not death, but life
Augmented, opened eyes, new hopes, new joys,
Taste so divine that what of sweet before
Hath touched my sense flat seems to this and harsh.
On my experience, Adam, freely taste,
And fear of death deliver to the winds."
    So saying, she embraced him, and for joy
Tenderly wept, much won that he his love
Had so ennobled, as of choice to incur
Divine displeasure for her sake, or death.

457

In recompense (for such compliance bad
Such recompense best merits), from the bough
She gave him of that fair enticing fruit
With liberal hand. He scrupled not to eat,
Against his better knowledge, not deceived,
But fondly overcome with female charm.
Earth trembled from her entrails, as again
In pangs, and Nature gave a second groan;
Sky loured, and, muttering thunder, some sad drops
Wept at completing of the mortal sin
Original; while Adam took no thought,
Eating his fill, nor Eve to iterate
Her former trespass feared, the more to soothe
Him with her loved society; that now.
As with new wine intoxicated both,
They swim in mirth, and fancy that they feel
Divinity within them breeding wings
Wherewith to scorn the Earth. But that false fruit
Far other operation first displayed,
Carnal desire inflaming. He on Eve
Began to cast lascivious eyes; she him
As wantonly repaid; in lust they burn,
Till Adam thus 'gan Eve to dalliance move:
　　"Eve, now I see thou art exact of taste
And elegant—of sapience no small part;
Since to each meaning savor we apply,
And palate call judicious. I the praise
Yield thee; so well this day thou hast purveyed.
Much pleasure we have lost, while we abstained
From this delightful fruit, nor known till now
True relish, tasting. If such pleasure be
In things to us forbidden, it might be wished
For this one tree had been forbidden ten.
But come; so well refreshed, now let us play,
As meet is, after such delicious fare;
For never did thy beauty, since the day
I saw thee first and wedded thee, adorned
With all perfections, so inflame my sense
With ardor to enjoy thee, fairer now
Than ever—bounty of this virtuous tree!"

458

So said he, and forbore not glance or toy
Of amorous intent, well understood
Of Eve, whose eye darted contagious fire.
Her hand he seized, and to a shady bank,
Thick overhead with verdant roof embowered,
He led her, nothing loath; flowers were the couch,
Pansies, and violets, and asphodel,
And hyacinth—Earth's freshest, softest lap.
There they their fill of love and love's disport
Took largely, of their mutual guilt the seal,
The solace of their sin, till dewy sleep
Oppressed them, wearied with their amorous play.

[*Rising from a troubled sleep, Adam and Eve know the evil they have done and the good they have lost, and for the first time their hearts are prey to unruly passions. Because they are ashamed, they make clothing from the leaves of trees to cover their nakedness, and, for the same reason, begin to quarrel, each blaming the other for their present plight.*]

BOOK X

The Argument

Man's transgression known, the guardian Angels forsake Paradise, and return up to Heaven to approve their vigilance, and are approved; God declaring that the entrance of Satan could not be by them prevented. He sends his Son to judge the transgressors; who descends, and gives sentence accordingly; then, in pity, clothes them both, and reascends. Sin and Death sitting till then at the gates of Hell, by wondrous sympathy feeling the success of Satan in this new World, and the sin by Man there committed, resolve to sit no longer confined in Hell, but to follow Satan, their sire, up to the place of Man: to make the way easier from Hell to this World to and fro, they pave a broad highway or bridge over Chaos, according to the track that Satan first made; then, preparing for Earth, they meet him, proud of his success, returning to Hell; their mutual gratulation. Satan arrives at Pandemonium; in full assembly relates, with boasting, his success against Man; instead of applause is entertained with a general hiss by all his audience, transformed, with himself also, suddenly into Serpents, according to his doom given in Paradise; then, deluded with a show of the Forbidden Tree springing up before them, they, greedily reaching to take of the fruit, chew dust and bitter ashes. The proceedings of Sin and Death: God foretells the final victory of his Son over them, and the renewing of all things; but, for the present, commands his Angels to make several alterations in the Heavens and Elements. Adam, more and more perceiving his fallen condition, heavily bewails, rejects the condolement of Eve; she persists, and at length appeases him: then, to evade the curse likely to fall on their offspring, proposes to Adam violent ways; which he approves not, but, conceiving better hope, puts her in mind of the late promise made them, that her seed should be revenged on the Serpent, and exhorts her, with him, to seek peace of the offended Deity by repentance and supplication.

[*God foretells the ultimate triumph of his Son; and the angels celebrate it with a song of jubilee.*]

S UCH WAS THEIR song,
     While the Creator, calling forth by name
His mighty Angels, gave them several charge,
As sorted best with present things. The Sun
Had first his precept so to move, so shine,
As might affect the Earth with cold and heat
Scarce tolerable, and from the north to call
Decrepit winter, from the south to bring
Solstitial summer's heat. To the blanc * Moon
Her office they prescribed; to th' other five
Their planetary motions and aspécts,
In sextile, square, and trine, and opposite,
Of noxious efficacy, and when to join
In synod unbenign; and taught the fixed
Their influence malignant when to shower—
Which of them, rising with the Sun or falling,
Should prove tempestuous. To the winds they set
Their corners, when with bluster to confound
Sea, air, and shore; the thunder when to roll
With terror through the dark aerial hall.
Some say he bid his Angels turn askance
The poles of Earth twice ten degrees and more
From the Sun's axle; they with labor pushed

* Pale

460

Oblique the centric Globe: some say the Sun
Was bid turn reins from th' equinoctial road
Like distant breadth to Taurus with the seven
Atlantic Sisters, and the Spartan Twins,
Up to the Tropic Crab; thence down amain
By Leo, and the Virgin, and the Scales,
As deep as Capricorn; to bring in change
Of seasons to each clime. Else had the spring
Perpetual smiled on Earth with verdant flowers,
Equal in days and nights, except to those
Beyond the polar circles; to them day
Had unbenighted shone, while the low Sun,
To recompense his distance, in their sight
Had rounded still th' horizon, and not known
Or east or west—which had forbid the snow
From cold Estotiland, and south as far
Beneath Magellan. At that tasted fruit,
The Sun, as from Thyestean banquet, turned
His course intended; else how had the world
Inhabited, though sinless, more than now
Avoided pinching cold and scorching heat?
These changes in the heavens, though slow, produced
Like change on sea and land—sideral blast,
Vapor, and mist, and exhalation hot,
Corrupt and pestilent. Now from the north
Of Norumbega, and the Samoed shore,
Bursting their brazen dungeon, armed with ice,
And snow, and hail, and stormy gust and flaw,
Boreas and Caecias and Argestes loud
And Thrascias rend the woods, and seas upturn;
With adverse blasts upturns them from the south
Notus and Afer, black with thunderous clouds
From Serraliona; thwart of these, as fierce
Forth rush the Levant and the Ponent winds,
Eurus and Zephyr, with their lateral noise,
Sirocco and Libecchio. Thus began
Outrage from lifeless things; but Discord first,
Daughter of Sin, among th' irrational
Death introduced through fierce antipathy.

461

Beast now with beast 'gan war, and fowl with fowl,
And fish with fish. To graze the herb all leaving
Devoured each other; nor stood much in awe
Of Man, but fled him, or with countenance grim
Glared on him passing. These were from without
The growing miseries; which Adam saw
Already in part, though hid in gloomiest shade,
To sorrow abandoned, but worse felt within,
And, in a troubled sea of passion tost,
Thus to disburden sought with sad complaint:

[*Adam complains of his harsh fate; he tries to fix the blame on God,
only to acknowledge, after many vain evasions, that he himself has
been at fault.*]

Whom thus afflicted when sad Eve beheld,
Desolate where she sat, approaching nigh,
Soft words to his fierce passion she assayed;
But her, with stern regard, he thus repelled:
    "Out of my sight, thou serpent! That name best
Befits thee, with him leagued, thyself as false
And hateful: nothing wants, but that thy shape
Like his, and color serpentine, may show
Thy inward fraud, to warn all creatures from thee
Henceforth, lest that too heavenly form, pretended
To hellish falsehood, snare them. But for thee
I had persisted happy, had not thy pride
And wandering vanity when least was safe,
Rejected my forewarning, and disdained
Not to be trusted—longing to be seen,
Though by the Devil himself; him overweening
To overreach; but, with the Serpent meeting,
Fooled and beguiled; by him thou, I by thee,
To trust thee from my side, imagined wise,
Constant, mature, proof against all assaults,
And understood not all was but a show,
Rather than solid virtue, all but a rib
Crooked by nature—bent, as now appears,
More to the part siníster—from me drawn;

462

Well if thrown out, as supernumerary
To my just number found! Oh, why did God,
Creator wise, that peopled highest Heaven
With Spirits masculine, create at last
This novelty on Earth, this fair defect
Of Nature, and not fill the World at once
With men as Angels, without feminine;
Or find some other way to generate
Mankind? This mischief had not then befallen,
And more that shall befall—innumerable
Disturbances on Earth through female snares,
And strait conjunction with this sex. For either
He never shall find out fit mate, but such
As some misfortune brings him, or mistake;
Or whom he wishes most shall seldom gain,
Through her perverseness, but shall see her gained
By a far worse, or, if she love, withheld
By parents; or his happiest choice too late
Shall meet, already linked and wedlock-bound
To a fell adversary, his hate or shame:
Which infinite calamity shall cause
To human life, and household peace confound."
    He added not, and from her turned; but Eve,
Not so repulsed, with tears that ceased not flowing,
And tresses all disordered, at his feet
Fell humble, and, embracing them, besought
His peace, and thus proceeded in her plaint:
    "Forsake me not thus, Adam! witness Heaven
What love sincere and reverence in my heart
I bear thee, and unweeting have offended,
Unhappily deceived! Thy suppliant
I beg, and clasp thy knees; bereave me not
Whereon I live, thy gentle looks, thy aid,
Thy counsel in this uttermost distress,
My only strength and stay. Forlorn of thee,
Whither shall I betake me, where subsist?
While yet we live, scarce one short hour perhaps,
Between us two let there be peace; both joining,
As joined in injuries, one enmity

Against a foe by doom express assigned us,
That cruel Serpent. On me exercise not
Thy hatred for this misery befallen—
On me already lost, me than thyself
More miserable. Both have sinned; but thou
Against God only; I against God and thee,
And to the place of judgment will return,
There with my cries importune Heaven, that all
The sentence, from thy head removed, may light
On me, sole cause to thee of all this woe,
Me, me only, just object of his ire."

    She ended, weeping; and her lowly plight,
Immovable till peace obtained from fault
Acknowledged and deplored, in Adam wrought
Commiseration. Soon his heart relented
Towards her, his life so late, and sole delight,
Now at his feet submissive in distress—
Creature so fair his reconcilement seeking,
His counsel whom she had displeased, his aid.
As one disarmed, his anger all he lost,
And thus with peaceful words upraised her soon:

    "Unwary, and too desirous, as before
So now, of what thou know'st not, who desir'st
The punishment all on thyself! Alas!
Bear thine own first, ill able to sustain
His full wrath whose thou feel'st as yet least part,
And my displeasure bear'st so ill. If prayers
Could alter high decrees, I to that place
Would speed before thee, and be louder heard,
That on my head all might be visited,
Thy frailty and infirmer sex forgiven,
To me committed, and by me exposed.
But rise; let us no more contend, nor blame
Each other, blamed enough elsewhere, but strive
In offices of love how we may lighten
Each other's burden in our share of woe;
Since this day's death denounced, if aught I see,
Will prove no sudden, but a slow-paced evil,
A long day's dying, to augment our pain,
And to our seed (O hapless seed!) derived."

Paradise Lost

[Eve suggests that she and Adam commit suicide to cut short the miseries of the human race; but Adam urges that they still have ground for hope.]

Remember with what mild
And gracious temper he both heard and judged,
Without wrath or reviling. We expected
Immediate dissolution, which we thought
Was meant by death that day; when, lo! to thee
Pains only in child-bearing were foretold,
And bringing forth, soon recompensed with joy,
Fruit of thy womb. On me the curse aslope
Glanced on the ground. With labor I must earn
My bread; what harm? Idleness had been worse;
My labor will sustain me; and, lest cold
Or heat should injure us, his timely care
Hath, unbesought, provided, and his hands
Clothed us unworthy, pitying while he judged.
How much more, if we pray him, will his ear
Be open, and his heart to pity incline,
And teach us further by what means to shun
Th' inclement seasons, rain, ice, hail, and snow!
Which now the sky, with various face, begins
To show us in this mountain, while the winds
Blow moist and keen, shattering the graceful locks
Of these fair spreading trees; which bids us seek
Some better shroud, some better warmth to cherish
Our limbs benumbed—ere this diurnal star
Leave cold the night, how we his gathered beams
Reflected may with matter sere foment,
Or by collision of two bodies grind
The air attrite * to fire; as late the clouds,
Justling, or pushed with winds, rude in their shock,
Tine † the slant lightning, whose thwart flame, driven down,
Kindles the gummy bark of fir or pine,
And sends a comfortable heat from far,
Which might supply the sun. Such fire to use,
And what may else be remedy or cure

* Rubbed
† Kindle

To evils which our own misdeeds have wrought,
He will instruct us praying, and of grace
Beseeching him; so as we need not fear
To pass commodiously this life, sustained
By him with many comforts, till we end
In dust, our final rest and native home.
What better can we do than, to the place
Repairing where he judged us, prostrate fall
Before him reverent, and there confess
Humbly our faults, and pardon beg, with tears
Watering the ground, and with our sighs the air
Frequenting, sent from hearts contrite, in sign
Of sorrow unfeigned and humiliation meek?
Undoubtedly he will relent, and turn
From his displeasure, in whose look serene,
When angry most he seemed and most severe,
What else but favor, grace, and mercy shone?"
    So spake our Father penitent; nor Eve
Felt less remorse. They, forthwith to the place
Repairing where he judged them, prostrate fell
Before him reverent, and both confessed
Humbly their faults, and pardon begged, with tears
Watering the ground, and with their sighs the air
Frequenting, sent from hearts contrite, in sign
Of sorrow unfeigned and humiliation meek.

BOOK XI

The Argument

The Son of God presents to his Father the prayers of our first parents
now repenting, and intercedes for them. God accepts them, but declares that they must no longer abide in Paradise; sends Michael with
a band of Cherubim to dispossess them, but first to reveal to Adam
future things: Michael's coming down. Adam shows to Eve certain
ominous signs: he discerns Michael's approach; goes out to meet him:
the Angel denounces their departure. Eve's lamentation. Adam pleads,
but submits; the Angel leads him up to a high hill; sets before him in
vision what shall happen till the Flood.

466

BOOK XII

The Argument

The Angel Michael continues, from the Flood, to relate what shall succeed; then, in the mention of Abraham, comes by degrees to explain who that Seed of Woman shall be which was promised Adam and Eve in the Fall: his incarnation, death, resurrection, and ascension: the state of the Church till his second coming. Adam, greatly satisfied and recomforted by these relations and promises, descends the hill with Michael; wakens Eve, who all this while had slept, but with gentle dreams composed to quietness of mind and submission. Michael in either hand leads them out of Paradise, the fiery sword waving behind them, and the Cherubim taking their stations to guard the place.

[*Continuing his prediction of the future, Michael relates to Adam the story of Abraham and the history of the Jews till the coming of Christ, concluding his narrative with a short account of the Last Judgment and the Second Coming. Eve now tells Adam that she is ready to go with him wherever he leads.*]

SO SPAKE our mother Eve; and Adam heard
  Well pleased, but answered not; for now too nigh
Th' Archangel stood, and from the other hill
To their fixed station, all in bright array,
The Cherubim descended, on the ground
Gliding meteorous, as evening mist
Risen from a river o'er the marish * glides,
And gathers ground fast at the laborer's heel
Homeward returning. High in front advanced,
The brandished sword of God before them blazed,
Fierce as a comet; which with torrid heat,
And vapor as the Libyan air adust,
Began to parch that temperate clime; whereat
In either hand the hastening Angel caught
Our lingering parents, and to th' eastern gate
Led them direct, and down the cliff as fast
To the subjected plain, then disappeared.
They, looking back, all th' eastern side beheld

* Marsh

Of Paradise, so late their happy seat,
Waved over by that flaming brand; the gate
With dreadful faces thronged and fiery arms.
Some natural tears they dropped, but wiped them soon,
The world was all before them, where to choose
Their place of rest, and Providence their guide.
They, hand in hand, with wandering steps and slow,
Through Eden took their solitary way.

Further Reading

CRIME AND PUNISHMENT by Fyodor Dostoevski

DOSTOEVSKI, F. *The Diary of a Writer*. Translated and annotated by B. Brasol. New York: C. SCRIBNER'S SONS, 1949.

LAVRIN, J. *Dostoevsky*. New York: THE MACMILLAN COMPANY, 1947.

LLOYD, J. A. T. *Fyodor Dostoevsky*. New York: C. SCRIBNER'S SONS, 1947.

SIMMONS, E. J. *Dostoevski: The Making of a Novelist*. London and New York: OXFORD UNIVERSITY PRESS, 1940.

YARMOLINSKY, A. *Dostoevsky: A Life*. New York: HARCOURT, BRACE AND COMPANY, 1934.

THE DIARY OF SAMUEL PEPYS

BRYANT, A. W. M. *Samuel Pepys*. 3 vols., New York: THE MACMILLAN COMPANY, 1933–39.

CHAPPELL, E. (ed.) *Shorthand Letters of Samuel Pepys*. London: CAMBRIDGE UNIVERSITY PRESS, 1933.

DRINKWATER, J. *Pepys, His Life and Character*. Garden City, N.Y.: DOUBLEDAY, DORAN & COMPANY, INC., 1930.

LUBBOCK, P. *Samuel Pepys* (Literary Lives). New York: C. SCRIBNER'S SONS, 1909.

TANNER, J. R. (ed.) *Further Correspondence of Samuel Pepys*. London: G. BELL AND SONS, LTD., 1929.

THE CONFESSIONS OF SAINT AUGUSTINE

A Monument to Saint Augustine. Essays on some aspects of his thought written in commemoration of his 15th centenary. New York: L. MACVEAGH, 1930.

LESAAR, H. H. *Saint Augustine*. Translated by T. P. Arkell. London: BURNS, OATES & WASHBOURNE, LTD., 1931.

SIMPSON, W. J. S. *St. Augustine's Conversion*. New York: THE MACMILLAN COMPANY, 1930.

West, R. *St. Augustine*. New York: APPLETON-CENTURY CO., 1933.

Willis, G. G. *St. Augustine and the Donatist Controversy*. New York: THE MACMILLAN COMPANY, 1951.

Paradise Lost by John Milton

Hanford, J. H. *Milton Handbook*. New York: CROFTS & CO., 1939.

Lewis, C. S. *A Preface to Paradise Lost*. London: OXFORD UNIVERSITY PRESS, 1940.

Raleigh, W. A. *Milton*. New York & London: G. P. PUTNAM'S SONS, 1900.

Tillyard, E. M. W. *Milton*. New York: THE MACMILLAN COMPANY, 1947.

Waldock, A. J. A. *Paradise Lost and Its Critics*. London: CAMBRIDGE UNIVERSITY PRESS, 1947.

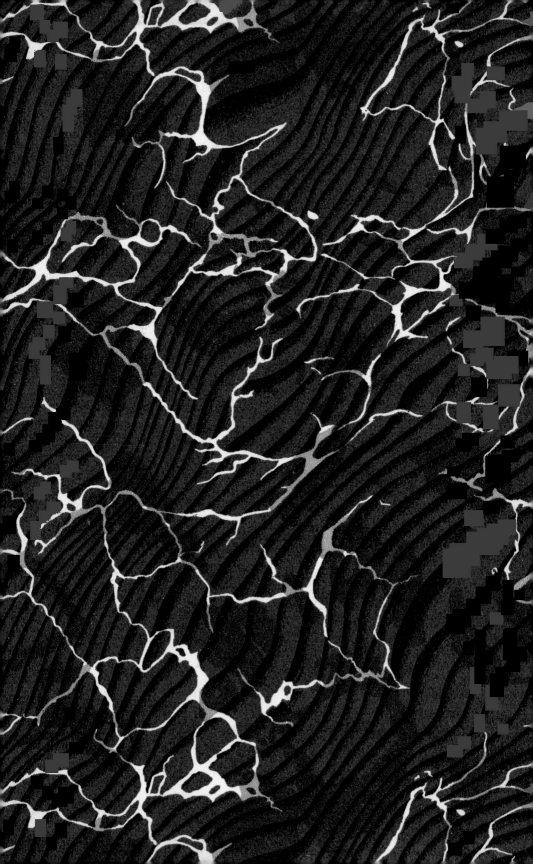